SUPERLIVING

How to Make the Most of Life

The Essential Guide to Successful Living!

PETER COX AND PEGGY BRUSSEAU

VERMILION
LONDON

For Louis

Acknowledgements

We would like to thank everyone who has helped us to bring the *Superliving!* project into being, especially our contributors Jolyon Barker, Paul Beardmore, Angela Buhl-Nielsen, Jane Egginton, Christine Ingham, Lawrence Joffe, Dinah Murray, Karen Ross, James Russell, Mary Senechal, Lucy Stubbs, Alan Tutt and Richard Witcombe.

A Free Update For Our Readers!

As a service to our readers, we have produced a free update to the information contained in this book. If you would like to receive it, together with information about *The Superliving! Report*, please send a stamped self-addressed envelope to: Superliving! Update, PO Box 1612, London NW3 1TD.

Published in 1992 by Vermilion
an imprint of Ebury Press
Random Century House
20 Vauxhall Bridge Road
London SW1V 2SA

A catalogue record for this book is available from the British Library.

ISBN 0-85223-925-4

Printed and bound in Great Britain by Clays Ltd, St Ives plc.

Peter Cox & Peggy Brusseau

Welcome To Superliving!

'Superliving' is a word which we've created to describe an approach to life. 'Living' is not a subject which is taught in schools or colleges, although maybe it should be. It's not even something which most of us are comfortable talking about. When was the last time someone asked you: "How's your life going?" Probably, never.

Now let's scare you a little. Look at the table below, and find the age group which most closely matches your own age. Then read across to either the male or female column. The figure you see is the number of weeks you have left to live.

AGE	MALE	FEMALE
20	1822	2011
30	1493	1675
40	1167	1342
50	855	1023
60	577	728
70	360	470
80	206	268

So if you're female and 30, you have 1675 weeks left. If you're male and 40, you have 1167 weeks remaining. And so on. What we've done in this table is to take the official figures of life expectancy, subtract the amount of time (about 8 hours) which people spend asleep in bed, and express the period remaining in weeks. Most people we've shown this to find the result rather shocking. After all, a life expectancy of just over 1000 weeks doesn't sound very generous, does it?

Our aim in presenting this information to you in rather an unusual way is not to depress you – heaven forbid! – but to make you think seriously about the way you choose to spend the rest of your life – *and what you expect from it.*

No one ever teaches us about the skills and rewards involved in the act of living. Most of us have to teach ourselves, sometimes well, other times not so well. Probably the very first lesson we ever learn is that life can be dreadfully painful. Very quickly, we learn to avoid doing things which could bring hurt. Almost from day one, we accept that there are whole areas of living which it is safest never to explore.

Then there is the 'no' word. Every parent knows that they have to restrain their child from danger. The way this is usually done is by issuing negative commands: "Don't put you hand near the fire", "Don't touch those sharp scissors", "Don't put your fingers in the electric socket", and so on. All done in the best interests of the child, of course, but all reinforcing one central negative theme – that life is dangerous, and the safest thing is *not* to explore it.

Well, *Superliving!* takes the opposite point of view. We recognize that life certainly is dangerous (more so every day), but we don't believe that the best way of avoiding danger is to withdraw from living. Having watched the lifestyles and living patterns of friends, business associates, the famous and those whom society regards as being successful, we believe there are five basic attitudes towards living which characterize the sort of person who gets maximum value for every day spent alive. We call them the Five Golden Rules Of Superliving!

One: Live Defensively

Here's a parable. Once upon a time, there were three honey-loving bears who lived beside a deep, fast-flowing river. On the other side of the river was a hive full of the most delectable wild honey it is possible to imagine. The first bear gazed wistfully towards the hive and said: "Our parents taught us never to go into the dark, deep water because the strong current will sweep us away. So I'm staying put right here." The second bear said: "I know we were taught never to swim in the dark, deep water. But that honey looks mighty good to me, and I'm going to risk it just this once." He dived in, and sure enough, the strong current swept him away. Now, the third bear said: "That dark, deep water looks far too cold to risk just for a mouthful of honey. I'll take a walk upriver and see if there isn't another way of getting across." After a pleasant walk of a mile or so, he came upon a beaver's dam which allowed him to traverse the river with ease, where he lived in honey-heaven for years and years, until the Inland Revenue got to hear about him. Moral: No doubt about it, the world *is* a risky kind of place. But that's no reason to stay at home all your life, nor to go to the other extreme and run headlong into danger. Living defensively means understanding risk, and taking creative steps to minimize its impact on your life.

Two: Be Your Own Expert

The world is full of 'experts'. Switch on the television or radio and they'll bombard you with unsolicited advice. Often, one expert will directly contradict the opinion of another. An example: when the meat industry recently wanted to discredit the views of health authorities who warned that the consumption of animal fats was linked to heart disease, they hired their own expert, a 'world authority on nutrition and diet'. Suddenly, The Expert was everywhere – press, magazines, newspapers, television – attacking the idea that meat consumption could be linked to heart disease. Strangely, no one mentioned that he was being *paid* by the meat industry to promote their viewpoint – and without this knowledge, most viewers would have assumed that he was simply an impartial scientist, giving independent advice. This sort of sleazy arrangement goes on all the time, and the net result is to disseminate widespread confusion about what we should or shouldn't be eating- which is, no doubt, precisely what some organizations want.

The antidote to this kind of media manipulation is to take steps to become *your own* expert, particularly when dealing with vital matters. When we were working on a previous book with Paul and Linda McCartney – perhaps two of the most successful people in the world – we were struck with the way that they always took pains to inform themselves about the matters they were dealing with. They only take decisions of consequence – whether about music, business, their farm or their lives – after absorbing as much information as possible from many sources. This, in itself, is an antidote to 'expertitis'. But how do you go about becoming your own expert? Well you can start right here – *Superliving!* is packed full of the essential knowledge that you need about today's foremost issues – information which is often difficult or impossible to obtain from any other place. But the single most important piece of advice is this: *ask questions.* Keep on asking questions until you get to the original source – and then check that for yourself. In this book, we've listed as many important sources as we could, because we consider this piece of advice to be so vitally important.

Of course, in today's complex world, few of us have the time or resources to become an expert in every conceivable area of human activity. At certain times – when we need medical treatment, for example – we have to rely on the expertise of others. So how should we decide whom to trust? As our chapter on doctors shows (How To Avoid Being Cured To Death) medical advice is sometimes inconsistent, and sometimes downright incorrect. Our 'test' for finding a dependable expert is this: no genuine specialist will ever object to being intelligently questioned, or to revealing how and why they have reached the conclusions or advice offered. Also, they will admit to areas of uncertainty or doubt, and be tolerant of conclusions other than their own. But beware when you encounter an expert whose underlying attitude is "Do this because I tell you to". Such a person is bigoted and, therefore, dangerous. Always remember that, in the final analysis, experts are only as good as the advice they offer. It is up to you to decide whether to accept it, to reject it, or to seek further information.

Three: Never Work Just For The Money

We're all wage slaves today, aren't we? Well, no. Not all of us. A few people seem to be able to have interesting and worthwhile occupations, be well paid, and feel a sense of accomplishment in their work. What is their secret? Actually, it's quite simple: *Do what you like doing!* Once again, this is something that never seems to be taught in schools, where most of us are dragooned into believing that there are only a certain number of career paths open to us. What rubbish! There are an infinity of careers out there, most of them waiting to be invented. A few years ago, a friend of ours created a burger suitable for vegetarians. The received wisdom at the time was that there was no market for such products – vegetarians didn't eat burgers, and besides, no one had ever done it before. How wrong they were! Five years later, the Vegeburger® is now on the shelves of every supermarket and health food store in the country, and our friend is a millionaire several times over! So don't listen to the 'you-can't-do-it-because-it-hasn't-been-done-before' school of thought. Back your own judgement. It is so easy to fall into the trap of working solely for money. And what do you use the money for, in any case? Why, to pay the bills, to pay the mortgage, to buy the food, all of which enables you to have a job...

No. Life is simply too short to sell your precious time in return for a few pounds in your bank account. You can always get money. But you'll never be able to retrieve wasted years spent working in a job which saps your spirit.

Four: Leave The World Better Than You Found It

Doesn't this make sense to you? Of course, it's easier said than done. All of us want to improve the world a little bit, but knowing where to start is so difficult. However, you'll find that this book will provide you with some interesting areas to think about, such as What You Can Do About World Hunger and How To Be A Caring Consumer. The biggest enemy of advancement is the attitude that 'we' don't count. When faced with wars, famine, pestilence and pollution on a global scale, the temptation is sometimes to feel overwhelmed. After all, what can one person do in the face of such overpowering misery? Well, perhaps that's how they *want* you to feel – disenfranchised. Certainly, a docile, uncomplaining electorate is much easier for politicians to dominate (and no, we *don't* have a political axe to grind – we distrust them all equally!). But consider this. You are the centre of your universe. If you want to change it, you can. The journey of a thousand leagues begins with a single step, and living with love and compassion for the planet and its inhabitants is the first step towards planetary healing. Isaac Asimov once observed: "Things do change. The only question is that since things are deteriorating so quickly, will society and man's habits change quickly enough?" The answer lies squarely in your hands.

Five: Conventional Wisdom Is Usually Wrong

Does this sound excessively cynical? We don't mean it to be. But when you consider just how many of yesterday's orthodox attitudes were so terribly wrong, it strongly suggests that we should be very cautious about taking too much for granted.

Just a generation ago, psychiatrists all over the world regularly prescribed electroconvulsive therapy (ECT) for patients with schizophrenia. There was *no evidence* that ECT worked, and yet orthodox opinion deemed that the correct treatment for this condition was to strap the patient onto a bench and pass a current through their brain (large enough to cause such violent convulsions that bones would break if the patient was not tranquillized). There is no telling how many thousands of people have been permanently hurt by this unscientific procedure.

For three decades (from the 1940s until the 1970s) the artificial hormone diethylstilboestrol (DES) was widely prescribed to prevent miscarriages, despite the fact that there was *no evidence* that it was effective. What it did do, however, was to inflict a highly unusual tumour (clear cell adenocarcinoma of the vagina) on hundreds of daughters of the women who originally took the drug. Today, it seems that even the grandchildren of the original patients may also be cursed with this disease.[1]

There are, of course, thousands of other examples like these, in which innocent people have been damaged or killed by accepting advice which they mistakenly trusted was correct. It is all very well for the experts in the field to shrug their shoulders and say, apologetically, "we didn't know", but that doesn't undo the damage, nor does it prevent it from happening again under different circumstances.

We propose that, ultimately, our only defence against disasters such as these is to question each and every piece of received orthodox wisdom as it affects us. Too often, a treatment, drug, regulation or foodstuff is presumed to be harmless unless proved otherwise. We suggest that it is infinitely more prudent to assume precisely the opposite. Anything labelled 'new' necessarily means 'untested' (new drugs are laboratory-tested on animals, but the real reason for this is to protect the manufacturers from a lawsuit for negligence, not to protect consumers).

No one else is looking after your interests but yourself. Bearing in mind the past record, you have every reason to be distrustful of those who seek to convince you that something is good purely because it is new, particularly when the only evidence that can be offered is no more than opinion.

Superliving! is based on these five golden rules. But in addition, we wanted to make it practical, positive and pioneering as well. **Practical**, because *Superliving!* is down-to-earth and can help you to face many of the most important issues in your life today. **Positive**, because you have a basic right to feel great! Today, we all know what the problems are. But what are the solutions? Well, we hope you'll find at least some of them in here. And **Pioneering** because we wanted to stimulate and provoke you with new frontiers to cross, to challenge you to keep one step ahead in today's dynamic world.

In a nutshell, *Superliving!*" is all about being the best you can be!

As always, we would welcome and value your thoughts and comments.

Peter Cox & Peggy Brusseau
London

Contents

~

Book One

SUPERFOOD!

Book Two

SUPERHEALTH!

Book Three

SUPERHOME!

Finding your Superhome

CHAPTER

Making your Superhome

Defending your Superhome

Book Four
SUPERYOU!

When things Go Wrong: Coping with Adversity

Making things Go Better: Tools for Success

BOOK ONE

SUPERFOOD!

Chapter 1
What contaminates your drinking water – and what to do about it

~

Aluminium

"For years, we thought that aluminium was one of the least toxic of metals," says Ann Prescott, a lecturer in chemistry who has made a study of the effects of aluminium on people with chronic kidney failure. "The situation regarding the toxicity of aluminium is similar to that for lead a few years ago. Although we knew that lead was poisonous, we did not know the detailed biochemistry."[2]

There are more pollutants in your water than you think. Here's how to reduce your exposure to the most dangerous substances.

Aluminium is one of the commonest elements in the earth's crust. Despite that, our bodies have absolutely no dietary requirement for it. Today, there are strong suggestions that aluminium intake is linked to Alzheimer's disease – a form of senile dementia now becoming increasingly common. Aluminium gets into our water in two ways. In some areas, it is deliberately added to the water supply in order to make discoloured tapwater appear clear. And in addition, there is growing evidence that acid rain, caused by emissions from power stations and motor vehicles, can slowly leach environmental aluminium deposits into the water table. Apart from pressing the authorities to take action on both of these important issues, here are some steps you can take immediately to limit your exposure to aluminium.

How to reduce your aluminium intake

~ Throw out any aluminium cooking utensils.
~ Avoid using aluminium-containing medicines, such as antacids.
~ Check food labels for the addition of aluminium salts used as emulsifying, anti-caking, bleaching and raising agents. If they're present, don't use the product.
~ Cut down on tea consumption (tea contains significant amounts of aluminium).
~ Use fresh food rather than choosing products in aluminium tins. Don't buy fruit juices which are sold in cartons lined with aluminium foil, because the citric acid contained in the juice can dissolve aluminium and increase the amount absorbed by the body
~ Increase your consumption of calcium-containing food, because aluminium may cause the body to lose calcium.
~ Install a reverse osmosis water treatment system for your drinking water – it will remove much more aluminium than an activated-carbon filter (see below).

Lead

Lead is a highly toxic element for which there is no safe level of exposure. In the first century BC, the great Roman civil engineer Vitruvius wrote, "water ought by no means to be conducted in lead pipes, if we want to have it wholesome". Some experts even believe that lead poisoning was at the root of the fall of the Roman Empire. In Roman times water was collected from lead-covered roofs by lead gutters which ran into lead-lined storage containers. Grapes were boiled in lead pots to make wine. Many cosmetics, ointments and medicines contained significant amounts of lead. Such high exposure would have affected mental abilities and caused falling birth rates among the Roman ruling classes.

Tragically, it's taken us a long time to learn our lesson. Even in very small amounts, lead can affect the developing nervous systems of children. This leads to lower performance in IQ tests, hyperactivity and behavioural difficulties. Older water pipes and tanks made of lead are still in use in some cities, and lead-containing pigment, plumbing, solder and bearings all slowly discharge this dangerous substance into our water supply. The risk of significant lead intake is particularly high in places where the water is very soft (that is, with a low mineral content), where it is mildly acidic, and where the water stands in the pipes for some time.

While the only real solution to the lead hazard is to replace all lead-containing piping, here are some additional steps you can take to reduce your risks.

How to reduce your lead intake

~ Run the tap for a few minutes at the start of the day to flush out the water that has stood in the pipes overnight.

~ Don't use water from the hot tap for *anything* that you're going to consume – particularly things that babies might eat – because lead dissolves more easily in hot water.

~ It has been shown that taking a small amount of algin every day may help to purge free lead from your body. Available from some health food shops, it's made from Pacific kelp seaweed and is sometimes used as a food thickening agent.

~ Research carried out by the Association of London Chief Environmental Health Officers has revealed that you are at risk from lead poisoning if you grow your own vegetables within a six-mile radius of Marble Arch in central London.[3] A report in *The Times* confirmed that the lead contamination of vegetation and dust along the M25 was "near a level that mining companies would consider a worthwhile deposit for recovering metal".[4] This research would presumably apply to other urban areas with very heavy traffic. If you can, avoid eating vegetables grown near these areas.

~ Another less direct way that lead may enter your body is through certain kitchen pottery. Lead in glazes can be released if acidic foods (such as fruit juices and vinegar) are stored in pottery which has been inadequately glazed or fired. Those quaint mugs or jars from your recent holiday abroad may not be quite as innocuous as you assumed. Lead-crystal glass can also release significant quantities of lead, particularly if liquid is allowed to stand in contact with it for any period.

~ A reverse osmosis treatment system can effectively reduce lead levels.

Cadmium

Cadmium is a trace mineral which is similar to zinc, and whose toxic effects are kept under control in our bodies by the presence of zinc. However, unlike zinc, it has no useful function to perform in the human system. It has been linked to high blood pressure, cancer, birth deformities, liver and kidney damage, and it acts as a neurotoxin.

It contaminates the water supply when the electroplating and PVC industries discharge effluent into the ground water. Landfill sites used to dump industrial waste can also slowly leach out their cadmium into the surrounding ground water. Galvanized metal pipes can also be a significant source of cadmium pollution, particularly in soft water areas.

How to reduce your cadmium intake

~ Run the tap for a few minutes at the start of the day and never use water from the hot tap for consumption.

~ Don't smoke – cigarettes can contain significant amounts of it.

~ Cut out tea and coffee – drinking five cups of either per day can double your daily intake of cadmium.

~ Ensure your diet contains a good source of zinc, to counter the effects of cadmium toxicity.

~ A reverse osmosis water treatment system will reduce cadmium levels.

Nitrates

The newspapers are full of stories about nitrate pollution, but what are the facts about nitrates in our water supply? Let's examine the evidence.

To start with, nitrates occur in many parts of our diet – in foods such as leafy vegetables, meat and milk. Our increasing reliance on intensive agricultural systems means that nitrogen-containing fertilizers continually drain off the land to contaminate the water supply.

Nitrates are not in themselves very toxic. The problem begins when they are transformed by bacteria into another form of nitrogen, known as nitrites. These substances can interfere with the oxygen-carrying capacity of the blood and can produce the 'blue baby' syndrome in young children. Unfortunately, that's not all the bad news, because nitrites can go on to react with other substances to produce nitrosamines – which are known to cause cancer.

The scientific evidence shows that those areas which have a high level of nitrates in the water supply also have a greater number of certain types of cancers – particularly stomach cancer. The problem is likely to get worse before it gets better because of the long time it takes for nitrogen fertilizers to leach off the land and contaminate ground water. Today's tap water often reflects nitrate levels of some years ago. What can be done to reduce our risk?

How to reduce your nitrate intake

~ People who smoke produce chemicals in their bodies which can interact with nitrates in the water supply to produce cancer-causing nitrosamines.

~ Avoid processed meat products because they may contain a high level of nitrites which will add to your total intake.

~ When you buy leafy vegetables such as spinach, cabbage and cauliflower, try to choose those grown using natural organic methods. Many commercially-farmed vegetables have high nitrate levels because of the enormous amounts of fertilizer used on them.

~ Select vegetables which naturally contain less nitrates such as beans, peas, wheat products, and rice.

~ Foods high in vitamins C and E may prevent or reduce the formation of nitrosamines in your stomach, so make sure your diet contains good sources of these.

~ The reverse osmosis treatment system can reduce nitrate levels appreciably.

Chlorine

As we all know, chlorine is routinely added to tap water in order to disinfect it. But you may be surprised to learn that chlorination does not kill all disease-causing organisms. Chlorine is not effective against many viruses and protozoa – two classes of micro-organisms which can be just as lethal as bacteria. And even worse, there is evidence that certain types of bacteria, which were once killed by chlorine, may now be acquiring resistance to it. This could well become an important public health problem because more and more of our water supplies are being re-used. The water you flush away in the toilet today may appear in someone else's cup of tea tomorrow, together with an unhealthy dose of pathogens.

Organisms which are resistant to chlorination include enteric viruses such as polio; the viruses that cause hepatitis; rotavirus which causes infantile diarrhoea; giardia which causes chronic diarrhoea, weight loss and cramps. Perhaps the most resistant of all are those intestinal parasites called helminths, otherwise known as worms. All these disease-causing organisms can survive the process of water chlorination, and serve to remind us that chlorinated water is not necessarily pure water.

However, there is a further problem with the chlorination of water, which occurs when chlorine comes into contact with natural organic compounds formed from decaying vegetation. Surface water – such as rivers and streams – often contains considerable amounts of decaying vegetation. When chlorine reacts with these substances, it produces compounds known as trihalomethanes (THMs) which could threaten our health. One such THM is chloroform, which is known to be capable of causing cancer. Although research is still under way at the moment, other THMs may ultimately prove to be equally dangerous. It does at least seem prudent to try to reduce our exposure to these compounds.

How to reduce your chlorine intake

~ A combined activated-carbon/reverse osmosis water treatment system can significantly reduce THM levels. Reverse osmosis can also reduce micro-organism levels significantly.
~ The best form of protection against chlorine-resistant organisms is for the water authorities to install more comprehensive filtration, coagulation and sedimentation procedures.

Organic contaminants

Organic chemicals are potentially dangerous to us because, just like the chemistry of life itself, they are based on carbon. As a result, they can easily enter into human tissues and seriously disrupt the body's complex chemical reactions, perhaps leading to cancerous changes.

Organic chemicals can pollute your water if you live near a toxic waste landfill, or in an agricultural area where herbicides and pesticides are heavily used. Some industries also discharge their organic wastes directly into river water which is used as a source for tap water.

There are millions of organic chemicals but some of the better-known ones include benzene, carbon tetrachloride and chloroform. Many of these water-polluting substances can be vaporized in a hot shower and researchers have found that you could actually absorb up to one hundred times more pollutants simply by breathing the air around a shower than you could by drinking all the water that passes through the shower. Taking a long, hot shower is therefore much more of a health risk than taking a bath.

How to reduce your intake of organic contaminants

~ Take cold showers or warm baths.
~ Many organic chemicals in drinking water can be reduced by using a combined activated-carbon/reverse osmosis water treatment system.

Testing your water

Because of increasing public concern about the quality of their drinking water, some private laboratories now offer a full water testing service. You may find local ones now listed in your phone book. You can also contact your water authority and ask them to do an analysis of your own house supply. Also, at least one company markets simple and cheap do-it-yourself water testing kits for nitrates and aluminium: you'll find the address in the Help section.

Choosing a water treatment system

There are four main types of domestic water treatment systems.

~ Filtration. Water filtration systems can be used to remove small particles such as dirt or sediment, and sometimes even bacteria, from your water supply. However, simply filtering your water will not remove any chemical contamination which may be present. If you happen to obtain your water supply from a stream or borehole, a good water filter makes an important first stage in the purification process. Otherwise – don't bother buying expensive filtration equipment because all domestic tapwater is pre-filtered by the time it reaches your home.

~ Activated carbon filter. Activated-carbon filters have become very popular recently and can be seen in many homes in the form of a plastic jug with a centrally-mounted carbon filter through which water is allowed to trickle.

Carbon is 'activated' by steam-heating charcoal to a high temperature without oxygen. The resulting granules are honeycombed with a labyrinth of tiny channels which greatly increase the available surface area. As water flows through this network of tiny tunnels, molecules of contaminating chemicals are trapped in this honeycomb, and the water is purified. Since the contaminants build up inside the filter, the cartridge obviously needs to be changed quite frequently. Activated carbon filters can remove many objectionable tastes and odours, including chlorine, and will also reduce many of the organic contaminants in water. They are not so effective in removing dissolved metals such as iron, lead, or copper, nor for removing nitrates.

~ Reverse osmosis. Reverse osmosis is a process by which impure water is forced through a very fine membrane. The extremely tiny pores in the membrane can filter out very small bacteria, and will also remove many kinds of chemical molecules as well, including lead and nitrates. Small molecules such as the trihalomethanes, the group that includes chloroform, are not removed very effectively. Reverse osmosis filters are usually self-cleaning and therefore have a greater life span than activated-charcoal filters, although initially, they are much more expensive to install.

~ Distillation. Contrary to popular belief, distilled water isn't totally pure water. Here's how it works. As the water boils in the still, it produces water vapour which is collected and condensed in another container, thus leaving behind many of the contaminants. However, those substances which have a boiling point very close to that of water, like some of the trihalomethanes, cannot be removed. Like kettles, stills accumulate scale, a build-up of magnesium and calcium, and need to be cleaned periodically. Distilled water should not be stored for long periods since bacteria can breed very easily in it. Distillation is a slow process which doesn't produce water in large quantity.

Which to choose

The best all-round water treatment system is not cheap. Because each method is good for some types of contaminants, but not for others, it is best to install a system which combines reverse osmosis and activated carbon. A number of companies now install these combined units, from about £300 upwards. The system should be properly installed under the sink. The carbon filter will need to be changed quite frequently to preserve its effectiveness.

Bottled water

Don't buy bottled water thinking it's bacteriologically purer than tap water. In independent tests, some brands of still bottled water were shown to have some

10,000 bacteria per millilitre, which exceeds the EC regulations for tap water.[5]

Bottled water's advertising plays heavily on its chic, healthy image, and sometimes talks about 'minerals'. In actual fact, the mineral content provided by bottled water is relatively insignificant, especially if you are already eating a varied diet. Some do specify a low sodium content which may be of use if your doctor has prescribed this for you.

CHAPTER 2
VITAMINS AND YOUR CHILD'S INTELLIGENCE

~

Can you boost your child's IQ by using vitamin supplements? So far, it looks as if the answer is yes . . .

Health-crazy parents are wasting their money trying to improve children's brainpower with vitamins! screamed the newspaper headline. 'Chemist and health food shop shelves were left bare after a TV documentary claimed vitamin tablets improve children's performance in class.'[6] The queston is: were those parents victims of vitamin hysteria? Or were they acting prudently? In reality, it's extremely difficult to decide, largely because of the way that news such as this is reported. One day you'll read one thing, the next day another report is published, and the headlines will be entirely different. It's not the newspapers' fault – after all, they have to report the latest news – but it does make it almost impossible to understand the context of what's being reported. So here is the story behind the headlines. This is what happened to create such an uproar.

Your child's diet on trial

That was the title of a BBC TV programme which came to the startling conclusion that vitamin supplements can make your child more intelligent. The programme documented two trials carried out at the Darland School in Wales. The whole thing started when Gwilym Roberts, Head of Science at the school, became aware of changes in his pupils over a period of several years. His current pupils seemed to have less concentration and higher levels of irritability than pupils he taught seven or eight years previously. This he attributed to poor diet, possibly brought about by changes in the school meal system which had changed from planned, balanced meals to offer cafeteria-style food which the children could select themselves. Initially, ninety children aged twelve and thirteen years were asked to keep a 'food diary' for three days, logging absolutely all the food they consumed during that period. When the diaries were collected and analysed, it was found that in most cases the average intake of vitamins was close to the officially recommended daily allowance (RDA). The intake of minerals, however, was rather lower than the RDA. The most common deficiencies were in Zinc, Folic acid, vitamin B_6 and Calcium.

So could vitamin or mineral deficiency be responsible for poor academic ability – and could it be rectified by vitamin supplementation? An experiment set out to discover the answer.

The children were given tests which measured two types of intelligence, verbal and non-verbal. Verbal intelligence is intended to be a measure of an individual's acquired or learned intelligence, while non-verbal intelligence is considered to be innate (the answers do not require general information and vocabulary).

The children were then divided into three randomly-chosen groups. Thirty pupils were given a combined multi-vitamin and mineral tablet, thirty were given an identical looking placebo, and the rest no tablets at all. It was run as a 'double blind' trial: neither the pupils nor the scientists knew which group each pupil belonged to until the experiment had finished.

The magic formula

This is what the supplement contained:

bioflavonoids 50mg
choline bitartrate 70mg
inositol 30mg
pantothenic acid 50mg
pyridoxine (B_6) 12mg
riboflavin (B_2) 5mg
vitamin B_{12} 10mcg
vitamin D 3mcg
vitamin K 100mcg
chromium 0.2mg
manganese 1.5mg
iodine 50mcg
zinc 10mg.
biotin 100mcg
folic acid 100mcg
niacin 50mg
para-aminobenzoic acid 10mg
thiamine (B_1) 3.9mg
vitamin A 375mcg
vitamin C 500mg
vitamin E 70 IU
calcium gluconate 100mg
magnesium 7.6mg
molybdenum 0.1mg
iron 1.3mg

The results

After eight months the pupils were given intelligence tests again.

The researchers found that there was no significant difference between the groups on verbal intelligence scores.[7]. However, when it came to non-verbal intelligence scores, it was found that *only* the group taking the supplements had increased their average score – from 111 to 120. The children taking the placebo remained unchanged at 109.

It was also found that the IQs of the two children on the poorest diet shot up by fifteen points after taking the supplements. Overall, the results clearly suggested that all children might benefit from regular vitamin and mineral supplements – and that's when the brawling began; because to most nutritionists, the results were seen much as a bull might view a red rag.

The controversy erupts

Conventional nutritionists were amazed – and suspicious. Many eminent specialists wrote to *The Lancet* (which had published the original research), to voice their criticisms.[8]

"Parents who buy these tablets as a supplement to a healthy diet are literally throwing their money down the drain," warned John Dickerson, Professor of Human Nutrition at Surrey University. "All your daily needs are in your food and the extra in tablets is excreted, so it is all passed down the loo." Vitamins that don't pass through the system can cause harm, he warned.[9]

Some attempts were made to duplicate the results. In one, 154 eleven- and twelve-year-old school children were given the same formula, with the addition of copper and selenium. But in this study, no increase in intelligence was found.[10] However, this study only lasted four weeks, as opposed to eight months for the earlier trial.

Another study, this time conducted by researchers at King's College, London, gave a vitamin-mineral supplement to 227 children, aged seven to twelve years. The children were also requested to take tests of verbal and non-verbal intelligence before and after the trial. This time, there were no significant differences between the supplement and placebo groups in intelligence test performance. The scientists concluded that their results "show clearly that no improvement in intelligence can be expected from the administration of vitamin-mineral supplements".

But once again, the trial was only conducted over a twenty-eight-day period – not for the full eight months of the first study.

Next, some Scottish researchers tried to duplicate the results of the first startling experiment, in a trial which this time lasted for seven months. The results were disappointing. "Vitamin and mineral supplementation does not improve the performance of schoolchildren in tests of reasoning," the researchers concluded.[11]

But in answer to this work, one of the two original Welsh researchers and a colleague from Brussels wrote to *The Lancet* with the results of yet a further study, this time carried out in Belgium. When they attempted to repeat their original findings, they found that the effects of supplements on the intelligence of thirteen-year-old Belgian schoolchildren were modified by the quality of diet the children were eating in the first place. In boys whose diet was poor, there was a beneficial effect of supplementation on non-verbal intelligence, but not among those who ate a better diet to begin with. The researchers concluded that "a diet low in vitamins and minerals is related to poorer attitude and lack of attention. Thus the supplements are not increasing scores but rather preventing a dietary-induced decrement."[12]

What to believe?

If you're a parent, you want to do the best for your child. So should you be giving him or her regular vitamin supplements?

It will be years yet before the medical and scientific worlds arrive at a consensus. More fuel was thrown on to the fire early in 1991, when news of a further group of experiments was announced which seemed to provide more evidence that vitamin supplementation and intelligence are clearly linked. This time, some extremely distinguished people lent their names to the work – such as two-times Nobel prizewinner and scourge of the medical 'establishment' Linus Pauling (see chapter 85 for more information about him), and Professor John Yudkin, whose pioneering book *Pure, White and Deadly* exposed the health hazards of sugar.[13] The research – which was not all published at the time this book went to press – was carried out amongst 600 children split between California, England and Israel. Said Professor Yudkin: "The results are very exciting. We believe we have stopped the arguments because we have used a large number of children, providing different doses of all the known vitamins and minerals and a wide variety of intelligence tests."[14]

But, of course, the arguments haven't stopped. Prominent amongst the critics was campaigning journalist Duncan Campbell, who in a half page article in a Sunday newspaper criticized the work on a number of grounds.[15] For instance, he pointed out that the trial results were as yet incomplete, and those which had been published had only appeared in a very small, rather obscure journal, and had not been made available to other independent experts for scrutiny. He also focused attention on the questionable connection between a second BBC QED programme (broadcast on 27 February 1991) and sales promotion for 'Vitachieve', a vitamin pill for children.

The entire issue is, in fact, a classic illustration of the huge gulf which exists between conventional scientists and nutritionists on the one hand, and on the other, those who are more towards the perimeters of orthodox science. Attitudes harden, emotions are aroused, but very little gets resolved. In the meantime, what should we do?

The evidence is not conclusive, but it *is* suggestive. Bear in mind that the studies which failed to show a link between vitamin intake and intelligence do not disprove the theory. "Absence of proof is not proof of absence." Although the jury is still out, a prudent parent might wish to add a suitable supplement to their child's diet. Certainly, there are very few risks involved, and the potential benefits greatly outweigh them. But what exactly constitutes a 'suitable supplement'? That's not so easy to answer, at least until more work has been done to identify precisely which vitamins or minerals seem to have the most effect. As Professor Yudkin said, "Now people will be kept busy for years determining which one of the twenty-three ingredients is the active one."[16] The fact is, not all nutritional supplements are equal: some contain appreciably fewer ingredients than others. Particular nutrients to watch out for are folic acid, magnesium and zinc, all of them essential for growing children, but not all present in all multi-vitamin pills by any means. So keep taking the pills – and watch this space.

Chapter 3
What you should know about food irradiation

~

Food irradiation is here to stay, so now you must decide whether you want to buy irradiated food.

The solid concrete walls are two metres thick. Inside, a large pool of water emits an eerie blue light – it's called the Cerenkov glow – and it's coming from submerged racks of radioactive cobalt-60. Pull the cobalt out of the water for just one minute, and the radiation would kill you.

So why on earth do they want to expose our food to this stuff?

What it is

"Food irradiation works for the same reason radiation therapy works on humans," explains Dr. John Cox, scientist-founder of Citrex Inc, a research and development firm in Florida. "Cells that are metabolizing faster are affected more – like cancer cells in humans, insects in a grapefruit, the eyes of a potato and bacteria in meat."

The benefits of irradiating food have been quite widely publicised. It destroys harmful bacteria, like salmonella; it delays the ripening of fruit and the sprouting of some vegetables; it destroys insects which can infest grain and other products in storage. It also kills *trichinae*, the worm in pork that causes trichinosis. These benefits are certainly welcome since they can help prevent food poisoning. On a more global level, they can help conserve the world's food resources, since it's estimated that between 25 and 30 per cent is lost each year whilst it is in storage.

Even the lowest levels of radiation used on foods are quite high. For example, a chest X-ray exposes you to less than one rad (a 'rad' is a measure of radiation that stands for 'radiation absorbed dose'). But it takes 10,000 to 50,000 rads to kill insects or sterilize them so they don't reproduce. Controlling the bugs in pork takes up to 100,000 rads, and 1,000,000 rads is needed to kill most bacteria and moulds.

Food irradiation has been illegal in Britain since the 1960s. In 1982 a Government Advisory Committee was set up to look into the whole issue of irradiation again. Its findings were presented in 1986 and recommended that the ban be lifted. However, controversy erupted when it emerged that the committee had very close links with the food irradiation industry, and allegations were made that it was not as impartial as it should have been.

Another controversial element of the report was that both the Committee and Government refused to produce the references to the primary sources of the scientific studies which they used in reaching its conclusions. More doubts were cast on the report's recommendations.

Despite these problems the report was accepted by the Government and paved the way for an amendment to the Food Bill which gave the Government the power to lift the ban on irradiating food, despite a call for its postponement by the British Medical Association after a report by the BMA's Board of Science. The report voiced concern over the long-term effects of consuming irradiated food after human and rat experiments showed that it could cause potentially malignant changes in blood cells.

What's wrong with irradiation?

~ Irradiation can't make bad food good.

Because irradiating food kills off the microbes which make food smell bad when it is no longer edible, the danger is that an 'off' smell – which is nature's way of warning us not to eat it – simply won't be there any more. Just smelling a piece of meat won't tell you anything.

~ Irradiation cannot remove the harmful toxins which have been produced by bacteria prior to the food being treated. Neither can irradiation prevent re-contamination after food has been treated.

~ Although irradiation can kill off many harmful bacteria it cannot deal with all of them. Unfortunately the ones which are not affected are the more dangerous ones: and no one yet knows whether the microbes which are left can mutate into more dangerous forms.

~ There are limits to the process.

It is not a cure-all for the problems of food safety. Foods such as chicken, for example, will be routinely irradiated because most chicken is contaminated with salmonella, the bacteria that causes food poisoning. Surely it would be more sensible – but no doubt more expensive for the farmers – to increase hygiene so that chickens aren't so heavily contaminated in the first place.

~ Perhaps the main area of concern is over the chemical changes which occur in the food after it has been irradiated. One of the changes produces free radicals. These have been associated with many serious diseases including cancer (see chapter 9). No one knows much about other chemical changes which occur and neither has research considered the effect of irradiation on either pesticide residues in food, or on the other chemicals which are already added to food. The effect on packaging materials which are present when food is treated is also unknown.

~ Besides these unknown changes there are others which have not been brought to the public's eye. The effect of irradiation on the cellulose in plant cell walls makes some vegetables lose their texture and become soft and mushy. With proteins some amino acids are destroyed whilst others lose particular chemical properties, reducing food values.

Beef also loses its texture and its taste is affected; the taste and smell of eggs change and few dairy products are suitable for treatment. How vitamins in food are affected by irradiation is still open to some difference in opinion. Some say they are not affected very much, whilst others say they are reduced by up to 30 per cent. Vitamin A is one which does appear to be destroyed. This vitamin has been associated with cancer prevention – the less vitamin A you consume, the more likely you are to develop cancer.

~ Children in India who were fed freshly-irradiated cereal were later found to have chromosome defects. Fortunately the effect was reversible but it underlines another area of concern, that of the long-term effects of eating irradiated food.

Who wants it?

The people who are directly involved in the food irradiation business want to see the public eating irradiated food. But others, too, would like to see the process accepted.

The nuclear industry, of which irradiation is an offshoot, would like to present itself in a more favourable light (glow?) and sell themselves as people who only have the safety of your food at heart. Some sections of the food industry, too, support irradiation since they stand to gain financially by being able to extend the shelf life of products. And obviously the Government wants it. Out of all the people who will benefit from its introduction, the consumer has least to gain when one weighs the possibility of many new problems which might emerge.

Those who don't want it are, perhaps, more important. They include many of the major food retailers, as well as the general public.

Now that irradiated food is on the menu, the irradiation industry is gearing up to fight its next battle. So far, the Government has decided that all irradiated food should be clearly labelled as such. This, at least, will allow you to choose whether you want to buy 'nuked' food or not. But this might change. The managing director of Britain's leading irradiation company has said that full labelling of products treated with gamma rays (one type of radiation) wouldn't be possible.[17] That would mean the consumer would have no way of knowing what had been irradiated, and which food hadn't. And no mention has yet been made of controls over restaurants and other catering outlets where the public could unknowingly be served irradiated food.

There are still many areas of concern about irradiated food which could affect you. The long-term effects are perhaps the most serious and need to be investigated. Until that has been done – and it will take many years to prove conclusive safety – avoid buying irradiated food.

If you are concerned, write to your supermarkets to voice your support for those who have decided not to stock irradiated food. And if you decide not to shop at stores which sell irradiated food, write to tell them about your decision and why.

CHAPTER 4

WHAT TO LOOK FOR WHEN YOU READ A FOOD LABEL

~

Don't judge a food by its label – it doesn't always give you the full story.

Suppose you're out shopping. You've a choice of two products which appear to be identical, except for the packaging. Chances are, you'll choose the one which is prominently labelled 'low in fat'.

All well and good. But what doeslow in fat' actually mean? At best, the claim is meaningless. At worst, it is potentially misleading – because one manufacturer's idea of low in fat may be very different from another's. That's why it's essential to study the small print and take a careful look at the label.

Food labelling laws are there to protect you. You're entitled to know what's in the food you buy. But the laws are by no means perfect. Manufacturers look to design and marketing experts to tempt you towards their particular product, simply because it looks the most appetizing. They expect you to fall into their trap. Here's how to read a food label.

Ingredients

The list of ingredients shows, in order of the amount contained, what the manufacturer has used to produce the food. So the ingredient which comes first is the one used in the greatest amount and the last one is used in the smallest amount.

It can be instructive to pick up a can of soup: on the front, a photograph or illustration of a nourishing meal; and at the top of the ingredients list the word 'water', which has to be included if it accounts for more than five per cent of the total weight.

You'll notice that manufacturers are obliged to name all the additives they use. Often, this makes for a long list! Food manufacturers can choose from over 3,500 additives. They're described either by their serial number or by their chemical name.

You can also see the extent to which flavourings and preservatives have been used. Very often, highly processed food will mostly consist of only these ingredients. For example, one label on a can of oxtail soup reveals that oxtail comes eleventh in the list of ingredients – behind processed starch, glucose syrup and sodium compounds.

Nutritional values

Here's where labelling directives are not as stringent as they ought to be. At present all we have are voluntary guidelines. And yet nutritional labelling is essential when it comes to choosing food which contains all the ingredients you need to be sure of a healthy diet. Surely, when manufacturers choose to make a nutritional claim – such as 'low in fat' – they should be forced to explain just what they mean.

To be fair, many of them do. You'll see labelling information is often given under four standard headings: energy, protein, carbohydrate and fat. But even this doesn't always give the full nutritional story. You might be told the fat content; but without revealing whether additional amounts of saturated fat have been included. Ignorance is certainly not bliss where sugar, saturates, dietary fibre and sodium are concerned.

The fatal flaw of any voluntary system is that it can be cheerfully ignored by producers who wish to draw a veil over the nutritional content of their products. So what can you do? It's simple. Read the labels. Then choose the foods which do give adequate nutritional information. Leave the others on the shelves. Until nutritional labelling becomes mandatory, consumer power will remain your most effective weapon.

Names – and how they might mislead you

No one expects a swiss roll to have been manufactured in Switzerland. But how do you interpret the words 'apricot flavour'? It would be a mistake to assume the roll contains any apricots at all! If it did, the label would say 'apricot flavoured'. Note the subtle difference! And what about 'home-baked'? In whose home?

What the label doesn't tell you

If any particular ingredient accounts for less than five per cent of the total, it needn't be mentioned. Thus it is impossible to know whether hormones, pesticides, antibiotics or tenderizers have been used. Often, they have. The way to be certain that your food hasn't been interfered with in this way is to buy organic produce from a specialist retailer. One you can trust.

In fact, the European Commission has announced plans to introduce a green labelling scheme. Predictably – and depressingly – the British government responded by commenting: "It would be very hard to enforce on food and drink."

Symbols for selling

An increasing number of symbols and logos adorn our packaged food. Look out for the circular identification of the Organic Farmers and Growers, which represents "a group of environmentally minded producers" who aim to ensure "that the living organisms with which they work become allies rather than enemies or slaves".

A green V symbol is the widely recognized emblem of vegetarianism, which you will also see applied to goods which are entirely free of slaughterhouse products – such as toiletries, clothes and 'beauty without cruelty' cosmetics.

It is encouraging to see the symbol for recyclable materials on food packaging. Usually, it is the secondary layers which you can save and take to a collection point.

Finally, choose the Tidyman symbol. It may have little to do with influencing your shopping choices, but at least it's an attempt to show greater consideration for the environment; and initiatives like these should of course be encouraged.

Coming soon – labelling that can keep you out of the doctor's surgery

It's not only food labels that can help protect your health.

What about the ingredients contained in shampoos, cosmetics, toothpaste, deodorants and skin care products? You might be allergic to them and end up suffering from sore eyes, painfully sensitive skin, allergies or eczema.

At present, manufacturers of toiletries are under no obligation to publish the equivalent of the list of ingredients which are compulsory for food labels. The result is that doctors are forced to write to manufacturers to ask whether particular products contain suspect preservatives.

In contrast, American manufacturers have been forced to label their products since 1977, and this requirement has aided medical understanding of rare sensitivities.

To give praise where praise is due, the Body Shop leads the way with manuals which list ingredients of all products, and which you, as a customer, are welcome to consult. What's more, the company has announced plans to introduce full ingredient labelling.

Elida Gibbs says it plans to follow suit, while Marks & Spencer is considering full ingredient labels. The Co-op must be congratulated for its decision to label all non-food products with their source, ingredients, usage and safety instructions – which include advice in braille on bleach products.

What you can do about inadequate labelling

Any complaint you have about a particular product should be made to the shop it came from or be directed to the manufacturers – you'll find the address on the label. If their response is inadequate, contact your local authority's trading standards department, which is responsible for enforcing the law on food labelling.

And finally, remember it's a buyers' market. So reject the products that provide you with insufficient information to make an informed decision. That way, you hit the manufacturers where it hurts most – at the checkouts.

Chapter 5
Food poisoning – protect and survive!

~

Chicken, eggs, baby food, beef, cheese, chilled foods, even yoghurt and drinking water have all been at the centre of recent food scares, leaving many of us confused about what we can – and cannot – eat. Here's what you should do to reduce your risks of food poisoning.

Today, food production is mass production. The trouble is, one small mistake along the line can affect thousands of people. Sometimes it seems that hardly a week goes by without some kind of food scare. The Ministry of Agriculture Fisheries and Food (MAFF) admits that most cases go unreported, but it estimates that about 1.5 million people suffer food poisoning every year. What's more, it says that every year, about one hundred deaths are directly attributable to contaminated food. During the first nine months of 1989, 34,000 cases of food poisoning were reported – a 50 per cent increase on the same period in the previous year.

So just what's going on? Who should be blamed? What can you do to make sure your next meal isn't your last?

Know the enemy

There are three distinct types of food poisoning bacteria: listeria, salmonella and botulism.

These food bugs are present in the soil, water and air around us. They can get into your food at any stage from production to sale – and from purchase to eating.

~ Listeria hit the headlines in 1989. Chilled foods and soft cheeses were found to be contaminated. Pregnant women were warned to change their diet or risk damage to their unborn child, as well as their own health.

~ Salmonella – the most common cause of food poisoning – usually infects poultry and red meat, unpasteurized milk and eggs. Junior health minister Edwina Currie paid with her job when she was the victim of a furious backlash from the poultry industry.

~ Botulism is the most dangerous bacterium of all – a single teaspoonful of the pure substance could kill hundreds of thousands of people. It is far less common in the United Kingdom than in France or the USA. But in 1989, twenty-six people in England were taken seriously ill when a batch of yoghurt was infected. A major incident could be just around the corner.

Food producers are coming under increasing pressure to clean up their act – literally. Intensive farming practices, contaminated animal feeds and sheer disregard for hygiene can all put you in hospital.

So what are the symptoms of food poisoning? It is sensible to get yourself to a doctor if you unexpectedly go down with cramps, nausea, shivering, diarrhoea, double vision, a severe headache or overwhelming fatigue.

What you must do

Prevention is obviously better than cure. So here's what you can do to protect yourself against the risk of food poisoning.

~ Take chilled or frozen food home as quickly as possible, particularly in the summer. Bacteria thrive in the heat. So putting supermarket food into the back of a car on a hot day is like putting it into a greenhouse. It's well worth investing in a cool-bag.

~ Buy a thermometer for your fridge. It's been estimated that the temperature of 80 per cent of fridges in the UK are set too high. The recommended temperature is no more than 5°C.

~ Although it may seem to be the safest thing to keep eggs in the refrigerator, it isn't. Condensation can unplug tiny, porous holes in the shell, allowing dangerous

bacteria to penetrate. And the lowered temperature of the yolk means it needs even longer cooking.
~ Never eat raw eggs in any form (e.g. mayonnaise). Always make sure they're thoroughly cooked.
~ Cook everything thoroughly. If you still eat meat, it's worth investing in a meat thermometer, too. Beef should be cooked to an internal temperature of 60°C or above for rare, 70°C for medium and 77°C for well done. Lamb and pork need to be cooked to an internal temperature of 77°C.
~ Don't stuff poultry – cook the stuffing separately.
~ Refrigerate cooked meat quickly – don't leave it at room temperature for more than 90 minutes.
~ Be particularly careful if you use a microwave oven. The evidence suggests that you shouldn't rely on them to kill off bacteria in your food. Always follow the recommended standing times.
~ Discard the packaging from chilled foods – whether you're heating them in a microwave or a conventional oven. You don't want to take a chance on poisonous chemicals melting and finding their way into your food. Styrene, which is used in polystyrene, is a suspected carcinogen.
~ Store raw and cooked foods separately. Never leave leftover canned food in its tin. Try to buy salads and vegetables that are unprepared and unprocessed. One of the most devastating listeria epidemics, in 1981, was traced back to ready-made coleslaw.
~ Wash food before you eat it – even if you've grown it yourself. Vegetables and fruit can harbour bacteria from the soil. And it is possible to wash away salmonella which is living in meat and poultry.
~ Never reheat food more than once. Make sure it's not underheated.
~ Don't take chances. If your food smells off, throw it away.
~ Be certain that frozen food is thoroughly defrosted before cooking.
~ Be sure all kitchen towels, sponges, surfaces, food equipment and cutting boards are kept clean. When you're preparing a meal, it's also prudent to wash utensils and worktops between stages: don't use the same knife or chopping board for raw meat, cooked food and fresh vegetables without washing them between times. The ideal system is to keep one chopping board for meat and another for vegetables.
~ Put all rubbish and scraps of food straight into the waste bin – and always keep the lid securely down, so that flies can't get in and germs can't get out.
~ Cut down on the quantity of food you cook. This reduces the amount of leftovers in your diet, which are a major source of food poisoning.

It's better to be careful than to be sick. So by incorporating these precautions into your daily routine, you will minimize the risk of food poisoning.

What they must do

Here are some basic suggestions which, if adopted, would mean we can eat without fear.
~ An end to the intensive rearing of animals and birds.
~ Stricter temperature controls should be introduced in shops. All shop refrigerators should display thermometers, so we can be sure the food we're buying has been correctly stored.
~ All food should be labelled with recommended storage temperatures.
~ Compulsory training of food handlers, leading to a certificate of competence, should be introduced.

~ All new domestic fridges should be fitted with thermometers.
The whole question of food safety is too important to be simply a matter of personal responsibility. The fact is that food producers must change their habits. If you are concerned about food poisoning, write to your supermarket and Member of Parliament to ask when they intend to implement these simple measures.

CHAPTER 6

HOW TO SAFEGUARD THE NUTRIENTS IN YOUR FOOD

~

There's no point in eating the right food if you don't store and cook it properly. Here are the golden rules.

The level of nutrition you receive from your diet depends not only on what food you choose to eat but also on how you store and cook it, three opportunities for loss of vital nutrients. If you lead a hectic, demanding life, you need these nutrients even more and therefore need to know how you can safeguard them.

Choice of food

~ The more a foodstuff is processed, the greater the loss of natural nutrients. So buy only unprocessed wholefoods.
~ If possible, buy organic food, preferably from local producers. Organic foods are more likely to have their nutrients intact and, if they are from local producers, they will not have been in long storage during transit. Nutrients decay with time, so eat close to the soil!
~ Do check the use-by date. Old produce will have suffered severe nutritional decay. Shopkeepers always put older stock at the front of the display – so disarrange their display, and buy from the back.
~ Canning and bottling reduces the levels of vitamin C, thiamine and folic acid. Vitamin C loss continues during storage. If you have to buy canned food, do not keep it overlong. Although it may be safe to eat, its nutrients may be severely depleted.
~ Foods which contain sulphur dioxide as a preservative will have almost entirely lost their thiamine (vitamin B_1) content.
~ Freeze-dried foods are relatively good since there is no heating to deplete nutrients.
~ Frozen foods suffer some thiamine and vitamin C loss. However the loss is less than in fresh food which has been kept for a number of days (see Storage, below). If shopping for fresh food is a problem for you, frozen foods are probably the next best alternative, but be extra careful not to overcook them (see Cooking, below).
~ Choose unrefined monounsaturated oils, like olive oil, for cooking. Pure, refined polyunsaturated oils turn rancid more easily.
~ Don't buy tinned goods which are damaged – no matter how much of a bargain they appear to be. Small cracks in the lining inside the cans affect the contents which will certainly affect the delicate vitamins and other nutrients and may even cause the food itself to turn bad.

Storage

~ Store oils, fats and oily foods like cheeses and shelled nuts in the refrigerator. This will help to slow down the process of oxidation which turns them rancid.
~ Vitamin C, thiamine, riboflavin and folic acid all decay quickly in air. Once vegetables are harvested, the damaged tissues release an enzyme which starts to

destroy the vitamin C. Blanching inhibits the enzyme, which is why freezing fresh vegetables is much better than keeping them unfrozen and eating them many days later.

~ Vegetables lose around 70 per cent of their folic acid content within three days if they are stored in daylight. Store vegetables in the refrigerator until you are ready to use them, or freeze them straight away.

~ Store grains and cereals whole and in a dry, cool place.

~ Milk supplies the best source of riboflavin, but up to 50 per cent is destroyed within two hours in sunlight! That pinta left on the doorstep will still lose 20 per cent even if the weather's cloudy.

Cooking

~ Cooking is generally harmful to the nutrients in food. However it also changes starches, proteins and some vitamins into accessible forms for us as well as releasing nutrients in some foods which are otherwise bound in, like the amino acid tryptophan in cornmeal. Cooking is necessary for other foods to destroy toxic substances such as those found in soya beans and kidney beans. Cooking also makes some foods, like meat, palatable to eat. However, there are ways in which you can reduce the nutrient loss in foods during the cooking process.

~ Pressure cooking is perhaps the best way to reduce nutrient loss. Invest in a non-aluminium pressure cooker which, because of the reduced cooking times, will also reduce energy consumption and therefore the size of your fuel bills.

~ After pressure cooking, steaming and microwave cooking are the next healthiest options. Buying a steamer is obviously a lot cheaper than a microwave oven! Further down the list are:

boiling
grilling
stir frying (at high temperature where the fat seals in the nutrients)
sautéing
deep frying

~ If you cook with fat don't let it become so hot that it starts to smoke. At this temperature the essential fatty acid linoleic acid is destroyed immediately.

~ Fats which have been used for cooking once must be discarded since the linoleic acid and vitamins A and C will have been lost.

~ If you boil food, do so for the minimum amount of time and then use the water for stock afterwards. The fragile water-soluble vitamins as well as some minerals leach into cooking water, which is why soups are so nutritious.

~ Don't add bicarbonate of soda to cooking water, even if you see it recommended in cooking pulses. It destroys valuable B vitamins.

~ Prepare food immediately before cooking – remember that vitamin C is destroyed once cells are damaged in vegetables – and for the same reason try not to chop them too finely. Scrubbing vegetables is better than peeling them.

~ Once prepared, immerse the vegetables in ready boiling water straight away.

~ Use pans with close-fitting lids and avoid using copper pans which encourage oxidation and vitamin C loss.

~ Once food is cooked, eat it straight away. Keeping it warm will only result in further nutrient loss, which is why eating out too frequently may be less than healthy for you.

If you lead a hectic lifestyle, and consider that you don't have time for some of the advice given above, think again. The life you lead is totally dependent on a good nutritional support system – without which, you're just running on empty. And you can only do that for so long. Shopping regularly for fresh foods can appear to present a problem – if you don't attach a very high priority to it. But just think – no sensible person buys a Rolls Royce then tries to fuel it on two star petrol! It's the same with your body – the better the fuel, the better the performance you'll receive.

CHAPTER 7

HOW TO AVOID CHEMICAL RESIDUE IN YOUR FOOD

~

Most people are now aware of the harm certain food additives can cause, but did you know some residues found in food may lead to mental illness and even cancer?

Pesticides are poisons. Their basic purpose is to kill pests. In an ideal world, pesticides are not supposed to leave any residue on food by the time it's ready for us to eat. But a huge amount of evidence clearly shows that the food we eat *can* be tainted with pesticide residue, even if it's been washed many times. The question is – what should we do about it?

Insecticides

Used to kill bugs and beetles which threaten a farmer's crops, some insecticides are chemically very similar to nerve gases, and work by attacking the central nervous system of the animals they are intended to kill. Another type of insecticide – the organochlorines – includes DDT, which biologist Rachel Carson first warned the world about in 1962 in her book *Silent Spring.* Carson believed that the use of DDT was causing a dramatic decrease in the numbers of many species of birds, hence the title of her book. But we now know it isn't only birds that suffer from the effects of DDT and similar substances. This group of chemicals is classified as 'persistent' – they are not easily destroyed or degraded, so they persist for years. The organochlorines are also attracted to fatty substances, so they can be found in greater concentrations in milk, cheese, meat, and human breast milk. Although DDT itself has now been banned, other organochlorines are still used, despite animal and bacterial studies having linked them to cancer, birth defects and genetic mutations.

There is no question that these substances can be just as fatal to humans (as they can be to other animals) if we're accidentally dosed with them – as in an industrial accident, for example. But what isn't so clear is what the long-term effects of eating food containing insecticide residue might be.

Herbicides

Farmers spend twice as much on herbicides as they do on insecticides and fungicides put together. They are used to kill off weeds by either preventing their growth, or sometimes by causing unnaturally rapid growth. Many of these herbicides are designed to be absorbed directly into the system of the plant itself, so that it is impossible to get rid of them simply by washing.

One such systemic herbicide is 2,4,5-T (short for 2,4,5-trichlorophenoxy acetic acid) which was an ingredient in Agent Orange, the herbicide used by the U.S. Army in Vietnam. The army had used Agent Orange in 1963 to destroy the food supply of the Vietcong, and strip them of cover in dense mountainous regions. Certainly, at the time it was first used, there was no evidence that it brought immediate illness and death in its wake. But years later, the effects started to be noticed. Vietnamese people exposed to it showed an unusually high level of clinical abnormalities such as miscarriages, birth defects and sterility. The exposure of American soldiers led to their suffering from cancer and to deformities in their children.

The probable cause of these devastating problems was another substance present in the herbicide called dioxin, which is formed during the 2,4,5-T manufacturing process. Tests on animals have shown dioxin to be one of the deadliest synthetic substances known to man. The manufacturer of Agent Orange has always publicly stated that trace levels of dioxin in the environment are not harmful. But a confidential report which they commissioned years before the product was withdrawn from sale showed the opposite – that dioxin causes a long-term breakdown in the human immune system.[18] Exposure to dioxin can disrupt your white blood cells, and so reduce your body's ability to fight off disease.

Another connection between the use of herbicides and human illness was revealed when a scientist exposed a statistical connection between the use of herbicides and Parkinson's Disease, which affects the central nervous system in humans.[19] It is suspected that a certain group of herbicides (chemically very similar to MPTP, a designer drug known to produce an irreversible Parkinsonian-like syndrome in humans), is capable of bringing about the slow destruction of a specific group of brain cells, thus causing Parkinson's Disease. Again, this effect can take many years to happen, making it very difficult for scientists to prove that there's a health problem – until it's too late.

Fungicides

These substances limit or kill fungal infections in food products. One class of fungicides, which contains ethylene bisdithiocarbamate (EBDC) is estimated by a manufacturer to be used on up to 70 per cent of potatoes, 40 per cent of apples and 10 per cent of wheat in the UK.[20] But studies show that, both on food and in the body, EBDC can gradually break down into a chemical called ethylenethiourea (ETU) which causes tumours and birth defects in laboratory animals.[21] Although fungicides containing these substances have been banned or restricted in other countries, including America, Canada and the USSR, the British government's advisory committee on pesticides reached "a clear conclusion that there is no risk to consumers from their use", according to David Maclean, the food minister, when he spoke in February 1990.[22] Yet five months previously in America, the four major manufacturers of EBDCs agreed to suspend their use on more than sixty fruits and vegetables because of what was termed 'theoretical' cancer risks.[23] According to the Natural Resources Defence Council "the cancer risk from the continued food uses of the EBDCs is dangerously high".[24]

Safety tests

Consumers are surely entitled to know that the substances used on their foodstuffs are safe. But in this area, as in many others, safety information is consistently denied to the public, usually on the grounds of "commercial confidentiality". The government and its bureaucracy apparently believe that it is more important to protect the commercial secrets of the pesticide manufacturers than the health of the public.

In fact, governments do not generally test pesticides themselves – they rely on manufacturers to submit safety tests. And therefore, they rely on the manufacturers' scientists to be honest. But they're not, always.

A company called International Bio Test was, in the late 1970s, responsible for about a third of all the animal safety tests on pesticides in the world. As a result of evidence provided by their tests, many pesticides were passed as 'safe'. But many of the tests were faked. Animals which had died in their cages while being fed pesticides were simply thrown away, and fresh animals were substituted just before the experiments concluded. The results, of course, showed that the chemicals were safe.[25] So much for animal testing.

The answer's in the soil

Thankfully, many supermarket chains have now started to stock organic produce. So what is organic food? The Soil Association says: "Organic food is produced responsibly, taking account of the needs of consumers, farm animals and the environment. Organic farmers produce food which:

~ Is grown without artificial pesticides and fertilizers.
~ Tastes good rather than just looks good.
~ Is never irradiated.
~ Contains no artificial hormones, genetically manipulated organisms or unnecessary medication.
~ Is not over-processed to remove the goodness.
~ Does not contain flavourings, dyes and other additives.
~ Is nutritious, living food which promotes positive health and well being."

At the moment then, the standards which organic farmers and producers work to are not controlled by government. Instead it has been left up to independent bodies, namely the Soil Association and the UK Register of Organic Food Standards to work things out. Between them these two bodies have established working standards and have developed a symbol system so that organic produce can be easily identified by the consumer. This well-known symbol provides assurance that the produce has reached certain standards. The symbol system's standards reach further than addressing just the food and aims to make sure that the farming practices are environmentally friendly. Farmers, growers, food processors, distributors and industrial manufacturers (who make farm products) can all apply to use the Soil Association's symbol.

Until the symbol scheme becomes a statutory requirement it does mean that not all food which you see labelled as 'organic' is of the same guaranteed standard. Food without any 'official' indication of it being organic is obviously to be treated with caution. Should you always believe the hand-written scrawl saying 'organic apples'? Probably not. And imported produce, which is labelled 'organic', may originate from countries who have very different regulations, although the Soil Association does work internationally and imported foods can apply to carry their symbol.

Of course, organic food needs to be safe for the environment as well as for us. In America, the National Academy of Sciences reported that agriculture there was responsible for about 50 per cent of all water pollution. In many areas of Britain, nitrate pollution of the water supply is a major health problem (see chapter 1). It has been clearly established that modern biological-organic farming methods lead both to lower leaching of nitrates into the water supply, and to lower nitrate content in vegetables.[26] So going organic is good for the environment, too.

Children at risk

Children are much more vulnerable than adults to the toxic effects of chemical residue. "Children's systems can retain a greater portion of a given toxin because their gastrointestinal tract is more easily penetrated," says Steven Markowitz, MD, assistant professor in the division of environmental and occupational medicine at Mount Sinai School of Medicine in New York City. "And kids eat more per unit weight than adults do, so the tissues in their bodies may be more exposed to these substances." On top of this, children are dramatically more susceptible to carcinogens than adults are, because infancy and childhood are periods of rapid cell division. "The cells of many different tissues in the body are proliferating, and that increases the chances that a genetic change leading to cancer will result," says Steven Markowitz.[27] So if you can't afford to provide organic food for all the family, do try giving it to just the youngest – they are the most at risk from the long-term health effects of pesticides.

Organic meat

Recently, organic meat has become popular with some consumers, who regard it as a kinder and healthier way of producing meat than the conventional intensively-reared livestock system. The Soil Association encourages naturopathic medical treatment of organically-reared animals, but they are still allowed to be treated with conventional medicines and all cattle are injected for warble fly. Free-range chickens are still allowed to have their beaks trimmed and have their forward vision restricted. Meat bearing the 'organic' label may have been reared more humanely but there is no absolute guarantee that it is totally free from any unwelcome inorganic residues. Nor is it, by any stretch of the imagination, cruelty-free, as some would have us believe. The slaughterhouse is still an ugly place, organic or not.

Controlling the cost

The organic symbol scheme goes a long way to ensure consistently high standards of food production, and should be supported whenever possible. However, the cost of buying organic can sometimes be very offputting. Lowering the price of organic food – and thus making it available to many more people – must be the next goal for the producers. In fact, organic agriculture is not necessarily any more expensive for the farmer. In 1983, the first well-documented scientific study was published which showed that an organic farm can achieve crop yields comparable to conventional farms at less cost, and with half the pollution and soil erosion produced by orthodox farming methods. The study, undertaken by the independent Rodale Research Center of Emmaus, Pennsylvania, demonstrated that farming costs were slashed by between 10 and 30 per cent, because organic farming doesn't use expensive chemical fertilizers. At the same time, crop yields equalled or exceeded state averages. For example, corn yields averaged 108 bushels per acre, compared to 85.3 bushels produced by conventional chemical farming.[28]

The high prices you are expected to pay for organic goods in the shops may have more to do with the premium which retailers believe they can get away with. Certainly, with prices at their current levels you must make sure that you are indeed getting the very highest quality. Those sad lettuces in the little health food shop around the corner may have all the right signs and symbols, but their wilting leaves won't provide you with many nutrients! Because supermarkets do have better distribution networks and a higher turnover, they may yet be the better bet for the long-term future of organic food for all. Let's insist that they sell it – cheaply!

CHAPTER 8
THE TRUTH ABOUT CAFFEINE, THE MIND DRUG

~

You may not think of caffeine as a drug at all, but try kicking it, and you'll soon find just how powerfully addictive it is!

Caffeine is probably the most widely used stimulant in the world. It can be found in a huge range of products and substances, including tea, coffee, cocoa, colas and many other soft drinks, and also diuretics, tonics, headache tablets, and a galaxy of other pills and potions. But today, more and more people are choosing to eliminate it from their lifestyles.

To understand why people are going caffeine-free – and to help you decide whether you, too, should consider kicking the caffeine habit – here are some key facts for you to consider.

~ Caffeine gives you a short-term lift by releasing energy that has been stored in your liver. This sudden burst of energy may, however, place quite a strain on your body's endocrine system.

~ Caffeine stimulates the heart and respiratory system, dilates the coronary arteries, increases your circulation, constricts the blood vessels in your brain, raises your blood pressure and increases the output of the stress hormones. It also has a diuretic (urine-producing) effect. Not all of these changes are beneficial, especially, for example, in people who suffer from heart ailments. Since caffeine can cross the placenta, pregnant women should avoid it, as no drug can be proved to be safe beyond all doubt if taken during pregnancy.

~ A disorder called caffeinism can be produced in regular caffeine users – symptoms include anxiety, headaches, depression and listlessness. As they get older, tea or coffee drinkers may unexpectedly start to experience symptoms such as insomnia, irregular heartbeats, nervousness, irritability, or restlessness. Some symptoms can even be mistaken for psychiatric illnesses! Dependence on caffeine often makes withdrawal difficult to achieve.

~ Because caffeine increases secretions from the stomach, it may be implicated in the development of stomach ulcers, and people who suffer from this complaint should consider reducing their consumption.

~ Caffeine can raise cholesterol levels, reduce the amount of thiamine (vitamin B_1), vitamin C, zinc and potassium in your body, and may impair iron absorption. It has also been linked to the development of osteoporosis, and there have been suggestions that caffeine consumption may increase the risk of developing certain forms of cancer.

How to kick caffeine

If you are a serious coffee-drinker and you want to cut it out, you're going to find it more difficult than you might suppose. Here are some hints:

~ Read the labels. Caffeine is all around you. For example, caffeine is often found as an ingredient in painkillers sold in chemists' shops, and many brands of soft drinks include quite a dose. Avoid them!

~ Try replacing caffeine-containing beverages with grain-based beverages such as Barley Cup and Yannoh, herbal teas, or fruit juices.

~ If you really need the lift that caffeine can give you, consider using, on an occasional basis only, either ginseng preparations or alternatively guarana, which is obtained from the bark of a Brazilian tree. It can be bought in capsule form in health food shops and can give you a longer and more sustained energy boost.

~ Decaffeinated coffee can be a useful substitute. There are three commonly-used methods for taking the kick out of coffee. One of them uses methylene chloride, which dissolves the caffeine out of the coffee beans. All traces of methylene chloride are then supposed to be removed from the coffee by evaporation and steam treatment. However, methylene chloride is capable of producing cancer and for this reason, the two other methods are probably safer choices. One involves using a solvent called ethyl acetate, which is naturally found in coffee beans and fruits such as bananas and pineapples, and dissolves caffeine in a similar manner to methylene chloride. The other method is called the Swiss Water Process, and simply uses pure water, carbon filters and no chemicals at all.

~ If you need a strong black coffee to kick you into gear in the mornings, try going for a jog or brisk walk instead. Provided you don't overdo it, it will have exactly the same effect, except that you won't have produced it by using a drug! You'll feel more alert and mentally active, and ready for the day. You'll also be calmer, which is guaranteed to get your day off to a better start. Do the same again later in the day: ten minutes is all it takes!

~ If you visit people where you're routinely offered a tea or coffee, get into the habit of carrying a couple of your favourite herbal tea bags with you. It removes the temptation to say 'Yes' to the inevitable offer of coffee; and it also provides a conversation point too!

Chapter 9
Round up all free radicals!

~

Free radicals are highly reactive molecules of oxygen which roam your body in search of a missing electron. They may sound harmless enough, but they damage healthy tissues badly, in a process called oxidation. This has been linked not only to the onset of premature ageing, but also to many other diseases including cancer, heart disease and immune system deficiency.

Oxygen in the air rusts your car, and oxygen in your body wears it out: so get rustproofed now!

How it happens

Oxygen is, of course, essential to life. We'd quickly die without it. So how can oxygen in your body be bad for you? The answer is that oxygen molecules are turned into free radicals inside your body by the continual process of metabolism. During this process oxygen molecules are generated which have an electron missing – a free radical. These free radical molecules immediately start to scavenge for electrons to kidnap from other molecules. This sets in motion a continuing chain reaction which produces yet more free radicals, damaging cell membranes, proteins, carbohydrates and deoxyribonucleic acid (DNA), the genetic material of the cell and of life itself.

Up to now, some sixty diseases have been associated with free radical activity, including Alzheimer's disease, arthritis, multiple sclerosis and cataracts. Even the small signs of ageing, the liver spots – areas of brown spots which appear on hands and arms later in life – and wrinkles are related to free radical attack.

What you can do

You would be forgiven for thinking at this stage that there is no hope of successfully stopping the destruction caused by free radicals. After all, the very activities needed to stay alive seem to generate them. But in fact, your body has what are called 'free radical quenchers' which react with – and control – free radicals as they arise. Under ideal conditions, the free radicals and the quenchers stay in balance. But if there's an excess of free radical activity in the body, and not enough quenchers to control it, then, obviously, your body will be overwhelmed by this extra barrage of free radical production, and it will become diseased. Here's a list of the substances and activities which are known to increase free radical activity – avoid them!

~ Tobacco smoke
~ Environmental pollutants
~ Some food additives
~ Heavy metals
~ Sunlight
~ Irradiated foodstuffs
~ Radiation
~ Rancid fats and oils
~ Herbicides
~ Burnt food
~ Emotional distress
~ Physical trauma
~ Excessive exercise
~ Alcohol

Research has shown that the following vitamins and minerals can help the body to defend itself against free radical attack:

Take vitamin C

Vitamin C is a very effective antioxidant and free radical quencher. You can even see it at work for yourself. Cut an apple in half. Pour lemon juice, which is high in vitamin C, on one half, leaving the other untouched. The half without the lemon juice will go brown through oxidation much faster than the half which is protected by the antioxidant vitamin C.

In a recent study conducted at the University of California at Berkeley, scientists isolated plasma from human blood, incubated it at body temperature and added a chemical that is known to produce free radicals as it decomposes. When vitamin C was added, it neutralized 100 per cent of the free radicals generated.[29]

The official British recommended daily allowance of vitamin C (a meagre 60 milligrams a day) is calculated on the basis of the vitamin's ability to prevent symptoms of deficiency (such as scurvy), and not on its antioxidant powers. Various researchers have suggested an optimal intake of between 250 and 5,000 milligrams daily. Twice Nobel prizewinner and distinguished scientist Linus Pauling, a long-time advocate of vitamin C, goes further, and has proposed 6 grams (6,000 milligrams) and up to 18 grams (18,000 milligrams) orally every day for most adults[30] (see chapter 85 for more information about vitamin C).

Take vitamin E

Natural vitamin E, d-alpha tocopherol, is also an effective free radical scavenger. We know that pollutants in the air we breathe – in particular nitrogen dioxide and ozone – attack our lungs, partially burning the fats naturally present in our lung cells. This produces free radicals which then do tremendous damage – lung cancer may be one result. Researchers at Duke University, the University of California at Los Angeles, the University of California at Davis and the University of Kentucky have found that vitamin E can protect lung tissue from nitrogen dioxide and ozone in smoggy areas.[31]

Vitamin E is a fat-soluble vitamin, and is stored mainly in the liver and fatty tissues of the body. The suggested daily allowance for adults in many countries is in the region of 10 milligrams. However, many biochemists believe that the daily intake of a vitamin E supplement should be no lower than 100 milligrams. Vitamin E is usually non-toxic. Rarely, large doses, over 300 milligrams a day, have caused nausea, diarrhoea, cramps, fatigue, weakness, headache, blurred vision, rash, or increased cholesterol and triglycerides. It is a good idea to start on a low intake and gradually increase it, because vitamin E has a tendency to raise blood pressure when given in large doses to someone who is not accustomed to it. Consult your doctor first if you have iron-deficient anaemia, bleeding or clotting problems, cystic fibrosis, rheumatic heart disease, intestinal problems, liver disease or an overactive thyroid, or if you're taking other medication.

Take beta carotene

Beta carotene is a natural substance found in plants which is turned into vitamin A in the wall of the small intestine during digestion. Vitamin A helps fight cancer, perhaps by nipping tumour development in the bud by quenching free radicals. Beta carotene is abundant in the plant kingdom and there should be no need to take supplements. Eat plenty of foods such as broccoli, tomatoes, carrots, sweet potatoes, parsnips, squash, beets, spinach, and fruits like cantaloupes and papayas. Other rich sources of beta carotene are easy to spot: bright green, orange or yellow fruits or vegetables almost always contain useful amounts.

Vitamins C and E and beta carotene can directly scavenge free radicals. In addition, recent work suggests that trace elements have an important part to play in this process, too.

Take selenium

Even though selenium is only needed by the body in the minutest quantities, it is an essential trace mineral and vital to life. It can increase the quenching activity of vitamin E in the body, and so helps protect cell membranes from free radical attack.[32] It has also been shown to have considerable anti-cancer properties.[33] In America, the National Research Council has recommended a daily intake of 50-200 micrograms of selenium for adults (a microgram is one thousandth of a milligram, so 200 micrograms equal 0.2 milligrams). However, one authority – Gerhard Schrauzer, PhD, of the University of California – says that 250-300 micrograms can protect against most cancers, and that most people consume only about 100 micrograms daily.[34] At higher doses, selenium can be toxic to the human body. Although it is not certain at precisely what level selenium begins to cause adverse effects, it has been found that doses of 900 micrograms (0.9 milligrams) per day can make hair and nails fall out and can affect the nervous system.[35] You'd be unlikely to get this from your diet, and supplements are clearly marked with the dosage they contain.

What else to do

Besides taking good vitamin supplements and eating foods already rich in these vitamins and minerals, there are other steps you can take to help minimize free radical production in your own body.

~ Use only olive oil – both saturated and polyunsaturated fats may contribute to free radical activity.

~ Avoid grilling, barbecuing or deep-frying food – steam or poach instead.
~ Filter your drinking water.
~ Avoid alcohol – this is one of the most prolific producers of free radicals.
~ Give up smoking and avoid smoky atmospheres.
~ Eat only wholefoods rather than processed foods.

Whilst medical research spends millions trying to find cures for our modern day illnesses, it makes more sense to prevent trouble before it starts. So begin your preventive health care now. Don't let those free radicals get a hold on you!

CHAPTER 10

WHAT YOU REALLY NEED TO KNOW ABOUT OILS AND FATS

~

Confused about oils and fats? Here's what you need to know.

We all eat too much fat. That's about the simplest thing you can say about this bewildering and rapidly changing field of research. In fact, we all need some fat as part of our daily diet. Fats supply energy and help to conserve body heat, while stored fats help to protect the body from physical injury. But most of us carry around far too much. An overweight person, for example, can have as much as 100 kilograms (220lb) of excess fat on their body – enough to supply their energy needs for a whole year!

Most people are confused about the type and amount of fat they should be eating. We seem to get one message one week, and the opposite the next. This is partly due to the fact that certain food producers – those who have most to lose if we reduce our consumption of their products – have sometimes deliberately set out to confuse consumers about what they should or shouldn't be eating. This makes it very difficult for anyone to understand what to do any more. So let's start with the basics.

What is fat?

Fats are solid at room temperature, oils are liquid. But scientists now use the term 'fat' to include all oils and fats, whether or not they're solid or liquid. So we will, too.

Chemically, fats are made up of three molecules of fatty acids and one of an alcohol called glycerol. What's a fatty acid? We'll come to that in a moment. You'll also hear the word 'triglycerides' used to describe fat – it means three fatty acid molecules (tri) plus glycerol . . . tri-glyceride.

What's a fatty acid?

Acids found in fats are called fatty acids. There are four major fatty acids: palmitic, stearic, oleic and linoleic. Remember, each molecule of fat contains three of these four fatty acids. Now it's the combination of these acids in the fat molecule that determines whether the fat is saturated, unsaturated, or polyunsaturated.

All fats are long chains of carbon and hydrogen atoms. When all the available sites on the carbon atoms are filled with hydrogen atoms, the fat is saturated. If there are unfilled spaces, the fat is unsaturated. The more empty spaces, the more unsaturated the fat is.

Saturated

Palmitic fatty acid has sixteen carbon atoms and no unsaturated carbon bonds. So it's called 'saturated'.

Stearic fatty acid has eighteen carbon atoms and no unsaturated carbon bonds. So it's also called 'saturated'.

Saturated fat is known to raise the level of cholesterol in your blood. The more you eat, the higher your cholesterol level, and the greater your chances of suffering a stroke or heart attack. As a guide, saturated fat is usually solid at room temperature. Animal fat contains lots of saturated fat – lard, meat, butter and so on. A few plant fats also contain significant amounts – principally coconut and palm oil.

Monounsaturated

Oleic fatty acid has eighteen carbon atoms and one unsaturated carbon bond. So it's called 'mono-unsaturated'.

Composition of Selected Fats per 100 grams

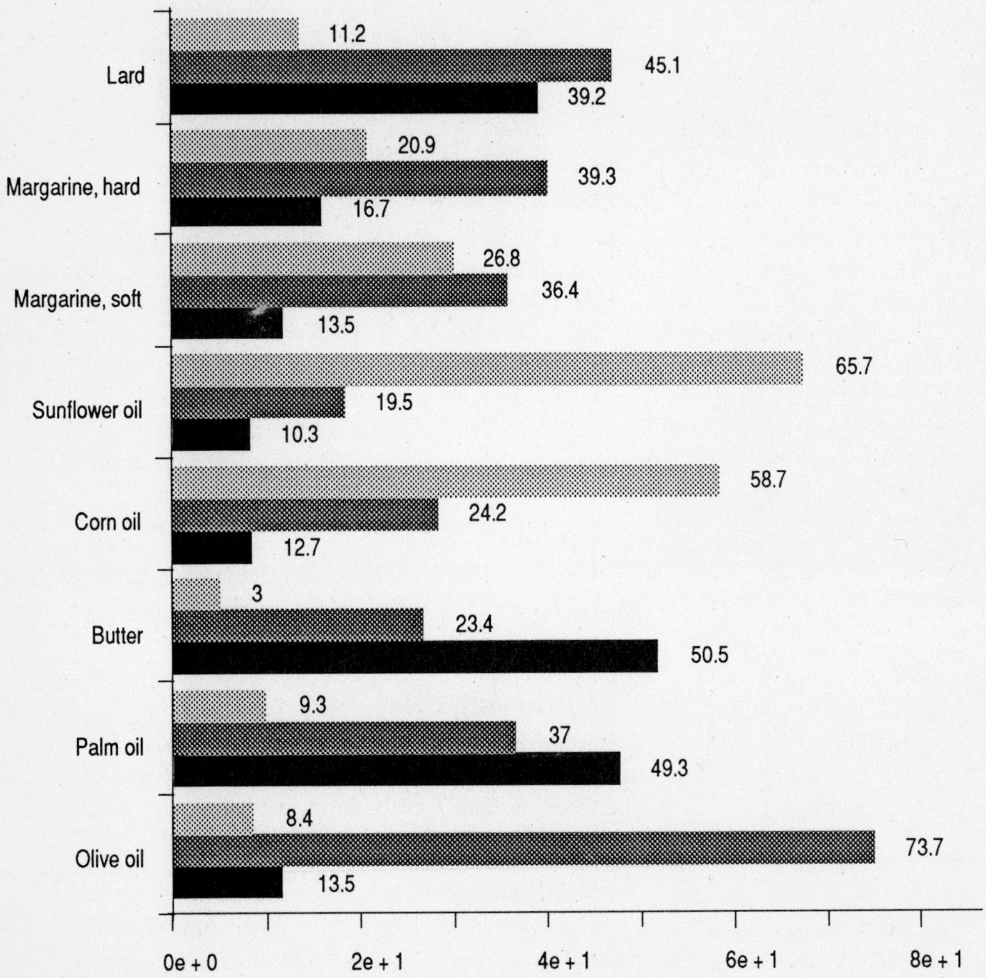

[Black = saturated, shaded = monounsaturated, grey = polyunsaturated. Units are grams of fat per 100 grams of oil]
margarine, soft = soyabean (hydrogenated)
margarines, hard = soyabean (hydrogenated)
Source: USDA Agricultural Handbook no. 84

Ongoing research suggests that monounsaturated fat is much healthier than saturated fat. A major source is olive oil. Experiments on humans show that switching to monounsaturated fat from the saturated kind can not only decrease the risk of heart disease, but it may also be able to lower your blood pressure. It is also less prone to go rancid than other types of fat, and rancidity is believed by some scientists to promote cancer.

Polyunsaturated

Linoleic fatty acid has eighteen carbon atoms and two unsaturated carbon bonds. So it's called 'poly-unsaturated'.

Early research indicated that polyunsaturated fats lowered total and LDL cholesterol more than did monounsaturated fats. The latest research, however, finds no difference in their cholesterol-lowering ability. The more polyunsaturated an oil is, the more it can be damaged by excess heat, air and light. Most polyunsaturated oils should only be used raw, because once damaged, they form free radicals (see chapter 9). Good sources of polyunsaturated fats include sunflower and corn oil. We all need a little linoleic acid in our diets every day, because of the four major fatty acids, this is the only one we can't synthesize for ourselves internally.

You can see from the table exactly how much monounsaturated, polyunsaturated and saturated fat there is in some common types of fats.

Butter or margarine?

For a long time, heart specialists have been calling for people to cut out saturated fats contained in red meat, full cream milk and butter, advising them instead to turn to low fat milks, vegetable margarines, wholemeal foods and more vegetables. Fierce advertising wars have tried to persuade us over the years that one or other is healthier. In fact, some margarines can contain as much total as butter, although their saturated fat content would be less. Advertising has also tried to persuade us to increase the amount of polyunsaturated margarine we eat which, if we didn't reduce our other fat consumption, would simply result in us eating more fat than ever. So what should you do?

No more than 30 per cent of our calorie intake a day should consist of fats but the average is more like 40 per cent and in some cases much higher. So the first step is to reduce our fat intake by a quarter. Just switching from butter to ordinary margarine isn't going to do this, but choosing one of the new very low fat margarine spreads will certainly help.

Choosing oils

Also, consider whether you really need to eat margarine or butter in any case. If you want something to put on your toast in the morning, why not try lightly brushing a little olive oil on to it? Similarly, when cooking, replace butter with olive oil. The way oils are produced is important, too. There are three methods of extraction:

Cold pressing

This is the traditional hydraulic pressing process where the temperature is kept low throughout, thereby preserving temperature-sensitive vitamins. The end product is expensive, mainly because there is a high percentage of waste in the discarded pulp, but the oil is nutritious and tastes and smells good. Buy it – so what if it's more expensive – you use less! Which is what we all need to do, in any case!

Screw or expeller

This process involves high pressure pressing which generates high temperatures. Vitamins are destroyed during this process although it enables more oil to be extracted. It is dark, strong smelling and needs further refining and deodorizing.

Solvent extraction

This is the most common process because it produces the highest yields. The grains or seeds are ground, steamed and then mixed with solvents. The solvents used are either the petroleum-based benzene, hexane or heptane. The mixture is then heated to remove the solvents and then washed with caustic soda. This has the effect of destroying its valuable lecithin content. After this it is bleached and filtered which removes precious minerals as well as any coloured substances. Finally it is heated to a high temperature to deodorize it.

Although manufacturers insist that any chemical residues are minimal, they are of substances which are known to be carcinogenic. Ironically the manufacturers call this end product 'pure' but it must be pointed out that this refers to its chemical purity only.

One other aspect of vegetable oils produced by solvent extraction is that they have lost their vitamin E. This vitamin helps stop the oil from going rancid. Rancid oils are dangerous because they provide the raw material for producing free radicals in our bodies. Sometimes chemical retardants are added to stop the oil from turning rancid, but it would seem to be much more sensible to stick with the cold pressed oils which keep well for up to six months.

Hydrogenated oils

You sometimes see this term on labels. Manufacturers hydrogenate oils to increase the shelf life of the product but it also has the effect of increasing its saturated fat content.

The process of hydrogenation fills some unsaturated bonds of the fat molecule with hydrogen atoms, making it more similar to a saturated fat. For example, soyabean oil in its natural state is only 15 per cent saturated. But when it's partially hydrogenated it is closer to 25 per cent saturated, similar to vegetable shortenings.

Hydrogenation produces 'transformed unsaturated fats', usually called 'trans fatty acids', which may be just as bad for your heart as saturated fats are. So avoid hydrogenated fats where you can.

Non-fat substitutes

Non-fat fats are being hailed as the dieter's dream. Just as sweeteners like saccharine were introduced to give people with a sweet tooth the taste of sugar without the calories, so non-fat fats are appearing in response to public concern about the level of fat in their diet. Although they taste and behave like fats, they are very low in 'real' fats and therefore low in calories.

Once such product, Simplesse, has been developed and manufactured by the NutraSweet Co., a subsidiary of Monsanto Co. Simplesse is made by cooking and blending egg-white and milk protein into a creamy, rich fluid that has the texture and taste of fat, but fewer calories and less cholesterol. Another such product, Olestra, is made by Procter & Gamble, and consists of a sucrose polyester made by chemically linking several fatty acid molecules to a molecule of sugar. Because of its structure, it is not metabolized by the body and, therefore, adds no fat, calories or cholesterol to the diet.

Whilst these new products are to be welcomed, there is some concern that they may encourage poor eating habits since it will mean you can eat twice as much of a previously too-fattening product – perhaps at the expense of more nutritious food. These new products need to be treated with caution until they have proved themselves.

How to count your fat and cholesterol

When nutritionists tell us that we've got to cut our fat consumption by 25 per cent, it can be very difficult indeed to translate that into action. Which 25 per cent? What foods should you cut out? And what should you replace them with?

Until recently, no one could really say for sure how 'good' or 'bad' different foods were likely to be for your long-suffering arteries. Then some clever university researchers in Portland, Oregon confronted this problem and, after much medical and mathematical work, they produced a scoring system that would allow anyone quickly and simply to compare different types of food for their ability to raise your cholesterol level and block-up your blood vessels.[36] Using this formula, we've calculated 'Cholesterol Quotients' (CQs) for a number of common foodstuffs. It'll let you start to count your fat and cholesterol intake, in the same way as you can count calories. So what should your maximum CQ intake be each day? Different people will have different limits. See which of the following groups is the most appropriate for you:

CQ Limit One: For the general population

In general, no one (whether or not they have a cholesterol problem) should exceed this limit, which is 40 CQs per day.

CQ Limit Two: For those with some risk factors

If your present cholesterol level is 6.2 mmols/litre or above *or* if your cholesterol level is 5.2 mmols/litre or above *and* you suffer from coronary heart disease *or* have associated risk factors, then use this limit. The recommendations of an Expert Committee of the World Health Organization on the prevention of heart disease also suggest that a great many other people, too, should keep within the intakes represented by Limit Two, which is 30 CQs per day.

CQ Limit Three: For those with greater need to lower cholesterol

If you have tried CQ Limit Two for about three months but cholesterol-lowering is insufficient, you may then wish to further reduce your saturated fat and cholesterol intake to this level, which is 20 CQs a day.

These limits are, of course, generalizations, and should be modified on the advice of your doctor or dietician.

Note – almost all fruits and vegetables have a CQ of zero, and are therefore not included in the list that follows. A complete list of CQs for 2,000 foods appears in *The Quick Cholesterol and Fat Counter*, by Peter Cox and Peggy Brusseau (Century Publishing) from which this list is taken.

		CQ
Baked Potato	1 Medium	0
	1 Medium with 1/2 Tin (220g) Baked Beans	0
	1 Medium with 1 Pat Butter	3
	1 Medium with 1/2 Cup Low fat Cottage Cheese	2
	1 Medium with 1 Pat Butter and 55g Cheddar	18
Roast Beef	Frozen Dinner with Potatoes, Peas and Corn, 3.5oz (100g)	5
	Home Recipe, 1 Portion	14
	Tinned, 3.5oz (100g)	9
Shepherd's Pie	With Mince, Home Recipe, 1 Portion	13

Steak and Kidney Pie	Home Recipe, 1 Portion	41
Biscuits – Butter	Thin, Rich, 4 Biscuits (50g)	6
Biscuits – Cheese	10 Round Biscuits (34.4g)	3
Biscuits – Chocolate	4 Biscuits (50g)	3
Biscuits – Digestive	Chocolate Coated, 1 Biscuit (13g)	1
	Chocolate Coated, 4 Biscuits (50g)	4
	Plain, 1 Biscuit (14.2g)	0
	Plain, 4 Biscuits (56.8g)	1
	Plain, 1 Cup Crumbs (85g)	2
Biscuits – Ginger	4 Biscuits (28g)	1
Butter	Hard, 1 Pat (5g)	3
	4oz (113.4g)	70
	Whipped, 1 Pat (3.8g)	2
	4oz (75.6g)	47
Cheese – Blue	1oz (28g)	6
Cheese – Brie	1oz (28g)	6
Cheese – Camembert	1oz (28g)	5
Cheese – Cheddar	1oz (28g)	7
	1 Cup, Shredded (113g)	30
Cheese – Cheshire	1oz (28g)	7
Cheese – Cottage	Creamed, 1 Cup (210g)	8
	Creamed, with Fruit, 1 Cup (226g)	6
	Low fat, 1 per cent Fat, 1 Cup (226g)	2
	Low fat, 2 per cent Fat, 1 Cup (226g)	4
Cheese – Cream	1oz (28g)	8
Cheese – Edam	1oz (28g)	6
Cheese – Parmesan	Grated, 1 Tbsp (5g)	1
	1oz (28g)	6
Cheese – Processed	Pasteurized, 1oz (28g)	7
	Pasteurized, Swiss, 1oz (28g)	6
Cheese and Tomato Sandwich	1 Sandwich (100g)	19
Cheeseburger	1 Regular	9
	1 Double-decker	19
Cheese Cake	With Fruit Topping, 1 Portion (1/6 of Cake)	15
Chicken Casserole	1 Cup (245g)	22
Chicken Salad	1 Portion (218g)	4
Chicken Sandwich	Plain, 1 Sandwich (182g)	12
	With Cheese, 1 Sandwich (228g)	16
Chicken – Fried	Breast or Wing, 2 Pieces (163g)	15
	Drumstick or Thigh, 2 Pieces (148g)	15
	Dinner, Frozen with Mixed Vegetables, 1 Serving (100g)	5
Chips	Fried in Animal Fat, 1 Regular Portion (76g)	6
	1 Large Portion (115g)	10
	Fried in Animal Fat and Vegetable Oil, 1 Regular Portion (76g)	6
	1 Large Portion (115g)	9
	Fried in Vegetable Oil, 1 Regular Portion (76g)	4

	1 Large Portion (115g)	6
Doughnuts	Cake Type, 1 Doughnut (58g)	4
	Yeast, Glazed, 1 Doughnut (42g)	3
	Yeast, Plain, 1 Doughnut (42g)	3
Egg and Cheese Sandwich	1 Sandwich (156g)	21
Egg Salad Sandwich	1 Sandwich (153g)	21
Egg – Fried	1 Large Egg (46g)	15
Egg – Hard-boiled	1 Large Egg (50g)	15
	1 Cup, chopped (136g)	42
Egg – Omelette	Home Recipe, 1-Egg Omelette (64g)	23
Egg – Poached	1 Large Egg (50g)	15
Fish and Chips	1 Portion (167g)	10
Fish – Cod	Braised or Baked, 3oz (85g)	2
Gravy	Dehydrated, Prepared with Water, 1 Cup (246.1g)	0
	Tinned, 1 Cup (238.4g)	0
Ham Sandwich	1 Sandwich (140g)	7
Hamburger	Plain, 1 Regular Patty (90g)	6
	1 Large Patty (113g)	12
	With Condiments and Vegetables, 1 Regular Patty (110g)	5
	1 Large Patty (218g)	15
	Double-decker with Condiments, 2 Regular Patties (215g)	17
	2 Large Patties (259g)	23
Ice Cream	French Vanilla, Soft Serve, 1 Cup (173g)	21
	Vanilla, Approximately 10 per cent Fat, 1 Cup (133g)	12
	Vanilla, Approximately 16 per cent Fat, 1 Cup (148g)	19
	Sundae, Caramel, 1 Sundae (155g)	6
	Sundae, Hot Fudge, 1 Sundae (158g)	6
	Sundae, Strawberry, 1 Sundae (153g)	5
Macaroni Cheese	Made with Butter, 1 Cup (200g)	15
	Made with Margarine, 1 Cup (200g)	11
	Tinned, 1 Cup (240g)	5
	1 Tin (430g)	10
Margarine – Diet Spreads:	(40 per cent Fat)	
Corn (Hydrogenated and Regular)	1 Tsp (4.8g)	0
	1 Cup (232g)	15
Soyabean (Hydrogenated)	1 Tsp (4.8g)	0
	1 Cup (232g)	15
Margarine – Hard Block: (80 per cent Fat)		
Coconut (Hydrogenated and Regular) and Safflower and Palm (Hydrogenated)		
	1 Tsp (4.7g)	3
	1 Block (113.4g)	65
Corn and Soyabean (Hydrogenated) and Cottonseed (Hydrogenated)		
	1 Tsp (4.7g)	1
	1 Block (113.4g)	17
Corn (Hydrogenated and Regular)	1 Tsp (4.7g)	1

	1 Block (113.4g)	16
Milk – Low fat	1 per cent Fat, 1 Cup (244g)	2
	2 per cent Fat, 1 Cup (244g)	4
Milk – Skimmed	1 Cup (245g)	0
Milk – Whole	1 Cup (244g)	7
Milk – Soya	1 Cup (240g)	1
Peanut Butter	1 Tbsp (16g)	2
	1 Cup (258g)	25
Nuts – Almonds	Dried, Blanched, 1oz (26 Kernels) (28.4g)	1
	1 Cup Kernels (145g)	7
	Dried, Unblanched, 1oz (24 Kernels) (28.4g)	1
	1 Cup Kernels (142g)	7
	Dry Roasted, 1oz (28.4g)	1
	1 Cup Kernels (138g)	7
Nuts – Brazils	1oz (6–8 Kernels) (28.4g)	5
	1 Cup (32 Kernels) (140g)	23
Nuts – Cashews	Dry Roasted, 1oz (28.4g)	3
	1 Cup Whole and Halves (137g)	13
	1 Cup Whole and Halves (130g)	13
Nuts – Chestnuts	Boiled and Steamed, 1oz (28.4g)	0
	1 Cup (145g)	0
	Dried, Unpeeled, 1oz (28.4g)	0
	1 Cup (100g)	1
	Fresh, Unpeeled, 1oz (28.4g)	0
	1 Cup (145g)	1
	Roasted, 1oz (28.4g)	0
	1 Cup (143g)	1
Nuts – Coconuts	Cream, Tinned, 1 Tbsp (19g)	3
	1 Cup (296g)	47
	Meat, Dried (Desiccated), 1oz (28.4g)	16
	3.5oz (100g)	58
Nuts – Hazels	Dried, 1oz (28.4g)	1
	1 Cup Chopped Kernels (115g)	5
	Dry Roasted, 1oz (28.4g)	1
	1 Cup Kernels (115g)	5
	Oil Roasted, 1oz (28.4g)	1
	1 Cup Kernels (115g)	5
Nuts – Mixed	Dry Roasted, 1oz (28.4g)	2
	1 Cup (137g)	10
	Oil Roasted, 1oz (28.4g)	3
	1 Cup (142g)	13
Nuts – Peanuts	1oz (28.4g)	2
	1 Cup (146g)	10
	Oil Roasted, 1oz (28.4g)	2
	1 Cup (144g)	10
Nuts – Walnuts	1oz (14 Halves) (28.4g)	2
	1 Cup Pieces (120g)	7
Oil – Olive	1 Tbsp (13.5g)	2
	1 Cup (216g)	29
Oil – Sunflower	Linoleic (60 per cent and over), 1 Tbsp (13.6g)	1
	1 Cup (218g)	23
	Linoleic (Hydrogenated), 1 Tbsp (13.6g)	2

	1 Cup (218g)	29
Pizza	Cheese Topping, Frozen, Baked, 1 Slice (57g)	2
	Cheese Topping, Frozen, Baked, 1 Pizza (425g)	13
	Cheese, Ham and Vegetable Topping, Baked, 1 Slice (65g)	2
	Pepperoni and Cheese Topping, Baked, 1 Slice (53g)	2
Plantain	Boiled or Stewed, 1 Cup Slices (154g)	0
	Fresh, 1 Cup Slices (148g)	0
Ploughman's Lunch	With Cheddar, French Bread, Butter and Pickle made with 4oz (115g) Cheddar, 3 Pats Butter	40
Potato Crisps	1oz Packet (28.4g)	3
Salad – Mixed	Without Dressing, 1.5 Cups (207g)	0
	With Cheese and Egg, without Dressing 1.5 Cups (217g)	8
	With Chicken, without Dressing 1.5 Cups (218g)	4
	With Pasta and Seafood, without Dressing 1.5 Cups (417g)	5
	With Shrimp, without Dressing 1.5 Cups (236g)	10
Sausage – Pork and Beef	1 Link (27g)	4
Sausage – Vegetarian	Meatless, 1 Link (25g)	1
	1 Patty (38g)	1
Soup – Tomato	Dry Mix made with Water, 1 Cup (265g)	1
	Tinned, Condensed, 1 Cup (251g)	1
	1 Tin (305g)	1
	Tinned, Prepared with Equal Volume Milk, 1 Cup (248g)	4
	1 Tin (602g)	9
	Tinned, Prepared with Equal Volume Water, 1 Cup (244g)	0
	1 Tin (593g)	1
Spaghetti	In Tomato Sauce with Cheese, Home Recipe, 1 Cup (250g)	2
	In Tomato Sauce with Cheese, Tinned, 1 Cup (250g)	0
	1 Tin (432g)	1
Yoghurt	Fruit, Low fat, 1 Small Container (113g)	1
	1 Medium Container (227g)	3
	Plain, Low fat, 1 Small Container (113g)	1
	1 Medium Container (227g)	3
	Plain, Skimmed Milk, 1 Small Container (113g)	0
	1 Medium Container (227g)	0
	Plain, Whole Milk, 1 Small Container (113g)	3
	1 Medium Container (227g)	6
	Vanilla, Low fat, 1 Small Container (113g)	1
	1 Medium Container (227g)	2
Yorkshire Pudding	2 Puddings (55g)	4

Chapter 11
Eating green – how and why you should go vegetarian

~

Are you a meat eater who would love to go vegetarian? You don't have to wait any longer, it's never been easier.

Millions of people are vegetarian these days, and there are many millions more who would like to be, but don't know how to go about it. The fact is that we would all be healthier – and the world would have more food – if Western countries were to decrease their meat consumption. So here are some answers to the most common concerns raised by people who are on the brink of 'eating green'.

How natural is it?

Meat has assumed such a central part in our culture that some people today feel worried that their bodies are biologically 'programmed' to eat it, and if they don't get it, they'll be unhealthy. In fact, the exact opposite is closer to the truth. We can scientifically prove that human genes have changed very, very little for several tens of thousands of years. In other words, our bodies are still in the Stone Age, and expect the sort of nutrition they were getting then. But in the last couple of hundred years, our diet has changed more radically than in all the 10,000 years previously. The fact is that there is nothing at all natural about the quantity or quality of meat that is consumed in the average Western diet these days.

Today, meat is available in unlimited quantity everywhere. If you want to eat it, you just have to step into the nearest burger bar. However, research shows that if our ancestors wanted to eat meat, they'd have to endure four strenuous days of hunting before they could be likely to make a kill.[37] No wonder meat was a scarce foodstuff!

Another major difference between our ancestors' diet and the food we eat today is not just in the quantity of meat consumed, but also its quality. Modern meat animals are bred to be fat: the carcass of a slaughtered animal can easily be 30 per cent fat or more. But the sort of animal that primitive people hunted was a wild animal – it had, on average, only 3.9 per cent fat on its carcass. So today, even if we cut our meat consumption back to the greatly reduced amount that our ancestors consumed, we will still be taking in seven times more fat than they did! But even this isn't the end of the story. The type of fat on the carcass of the animal that our ancestors ate was different, as well. Primitive meat had five times more polyunsaturated fat in it than today's meat does, which is high in saturated fat, but much lower in polyunsaturated. You can begin to see how very different the two diets are. In evolutionary terms, the meat we eat today is a new food for us. This means that we're actually conducting a huge experiment on our own bodies. And judging by the epidemic of cancers, heart disease, high blood pressure, diabetes and other modern killer diseases which meat-eaters are extremely likely to suffer from, the results don't look good.

Is it healthier?

Here, the facts are very clear. Many scientific studies show that vegetarians are much healthier than meat eaters. Vegetarians have much less risk of developing coronary heart disease,[38] and a vegetarian diet has even been successfully used to stop heart disease from progressing in people suffering from it.[39] A vegetarian diet also cuts the risk of suffering from many kinds of cancer,[40] reduces the risk of developing diabetes,[41] lowers the risk of osteoporosis[42] and vegetarians have significantly lower mean blood pressures than omnivores.[43]

Feeding the world

If you are an average meat-eating Westerner, you may be shocked to learn that, every year, you munch your way through one ton (about 1,000 kg) of grain.[44] Ninety-three per cent of this is eaten indirectly, in the form of meat and meat products. A meat animal is nothing more or less than a machine – a machine which is used to convert vegetable protein into animal protein. But as a machine, it is deplorably inefficient. For every kilo of meat protein that is produced as steak, *twenty kilos* of vegetable protein have to be put into the cow, in the form of high-quality grain. The twenty kilos *could* have gone to make vital human food. Quite clearly, we need to do something about using our global food resources in a more sane way.

This system of food production is so outrageously inefficient, because the meat producers are trying to flout one of the most fundamental laws of nature. This is the law that explains, amongst other things, why large, fierce animals are comparatively rare, but smaller, vegetable-feeding ones are much more numerous.

In the wild, food chains exist whereby one 'level' of the chain consumes something on a lower level of the chain. At the bottom of the chain, there are lots and lots of animals feeding on a profusion of plentiful foodstuff (for example, rabbits feeding on grass). At the top of the chain, there are just a few fierce animals who feed on the lower levels (for example, foxes feeding on rabbits). Thus, the foxes are indirectly eating the lowest level of the chain – grass. Now if things get out of balance, and the fox population suddenly expands, there won't be enough rabbits to go round. So the foxes starve until things get back into balance again.

By rights, therefore, if humans were designed to be predominantly carnivores, and exist on flesh foods, there would be relatively few of us, living at a good distance from each other. But it's quite obvious, however, that we're *not* like that. Humans are not carnivorous creatures, and there are far too many of us to live at such a precariously high position in the food chain. But that's where the meat industry ignores nature, because in attempting to provide all of us with as much meat as we can eat, the industry has to feed the cows truly vast quantities of vegetable protein. The result is that, globally, cows compete with humans for food. And the cows win. The consequence of this perversion of nature is continual enforced starvation for hundreds of millions of our fellow humans. It has been estimated that if the Western world was to cut its meat consumption by just 50 per cent, each person doing so would release enough grain to keep two more people alive, who otherwise would starve.

What about protein?

The good news is that, having grown used to the taste and texture of meat, you don't have to give it all up for the sake of your conscience and exist on a diet of bean sprouts and nut cutlets. Many years ago, people started to experiment with the idea of turning vegetable protein directly into meat – bypassing the animal on the way, and therefore making the process far more efficient.

In the 1890s Dr. John Harvey Kellogg, the health foods innovator, developed a method to make vegetable substances into meat-like products. There are two traditional methods used to make meat substitutes. The first involves extruding dissolved protein through spinnerets and making them into groups of fibres. Flavours, colours, binders and other substances are then added. In the second method, vegetable protein along with flavours, colours and other additives are made into one mass with the use of a cooker-extruder. This mass is then made into meat-like shapes.

Most of these foods – called textured vegetable protein, or TVP – are made from soya beans, which are incredibly high in good-quality protein. You can buy TVP in two forms – either loose (for example, chunks or mince) for you to use in your own recipes, or already made into burgers, sausages, etc. They are cheap, will store well, tasty and, most important, allow you to continue using the recipes you've got used to. Hint – you'll find TVP chunks will taste their best if they're lightly sautéd in oil *before* being further cooked or re-hydrated. Sautéing them with chopped onions or mushrooms also gives them a delicious flavour. For a list of stockists of other vegetarian products, see the Help section.

Introducing Quorn

Quorn was developed in the 1960s during the search for a new source of protein. It is now available both in ready meals and for home cooking from supermarkets everywhere.

Quorn is a distant relative of the mushroom, and is grown in a fermenter. Vegetable flavours, colours and a small amount of egg white are added before the product is cut into appropriate shapes.

Ounce for ounce, Quorn contains as much protein as egg. Unlike other sources of protein, though, it contains 4.8 per cent dietary fibre (meat, cheese and eggs contain none). The total fat content of Quorn is 3.5 per cent compared to the 34.4 per cent found in cheese and it is completely cholesterol- and gluten-free. Although Quorn is low in calories, its high levels of dietary fibre help to leave you feeling full.

Currently, you can buy Quorn in a range of 40 ready-made meals, including pies, curries and stir-frys. Or it can be bought in 250g packs for your own home cooking, where it can be microwaved, grilled (if marinated first), baked or sautéd. Of course the great thing is that there is no bone or gristle and therefore no preparation! Also, unlike meat, it does not shrink during cooking and can be ready to eat after five minutes' heating.

Because Quorn absorbs other flavours very quickly you have to be careful about the use of other strong ingredients. If you are using garlic, lemon or wine, for example, use about half the normal quantities. This ability to pick up other flavour sources makes Quorn ideal for marinating. And, unlike meat, which takes about 24 hours to marinate properly, it only needs between 30 minutes and an hour before it is ready for cooking.

Food technology is often accused of providing nutritionally worthless food at great expense. In the case of Quorn and other new meats, the opposite is true. We're on the verge of the greatest food revolution since humans discovered fire and the art of cooking itself. And in this, it's a revolution which can benefit each person on earth.

What about fish?

Over recent years we've been led to believe that we should all increase our consumption of fish. Three key reasons have been given:

~ Unlike farmed animals, fish are free from drugs or other undesirable substances.
~ Fish is the only source of the essential Omega 3 fatty acids.
~ Eating fish is more morally acceptable than eating the meat of animals which have been intensively reared and farmed.

These arguments have appealed to many. But each one of them is wrong.

Most people think of fish as being in the 'free-range' category. This is of course true for those in the open seas. Increasingly, however, the fish on your dinner table is likely to have come not from the wilds of the Atlantic but from an intensive fish farm. Fish farming is turning into big business, especially in Scotland, where companies can take advantage of the financial assistance provided by the Highlands and Islands Development Board. The fish raised in these farms are no different from their intensively reared red-meat cousins. They are caged in just the same way, with their movement restricted. They are control-fed.

Take fish-farmed salmon. Because they are not able to find their own natural food, their flesh turns grey instead of the lovely pink which they become when they feed naturally on crustaceans in the ocean. To cure this 'cosmetic' problem, farmed salmon are fed a dye so that they *do* look the correct colour. The dye – called canthaxantin – was formerly used to produce a fake tan in humans, but was banned when it emerged that it could cause blindness in high doses. But this is by no means the end of the story.

~ Intensive fish farming uses antibiotics, just like its land-based equivalent. Rainbow trout, for instance, are extremely susceptible to disease when crowded unnaturally into enclosed tanks – so out come the drugs.

~ Fish farmers use a highly toxic compound called Dichlorvos to eradicate sea lice infestation in salmon. Despite being on the government's 'red list' of the most dangerous chemicals that can enter waterways, and being classified as a potential human carcinogen by the US Environmental Protection Agency, the Ministry of Agriculture has agreed to permit its use, at least until mid-1992. What about the 'purity' of other fish meat? In 1986 the Dutch government put out a warning in Holland for people not to eat flat fish which had been caught in shallow North Sea waters. They did this after finding that the fish were too diseased and contaminated. Their report corroborated a previous one from the German government (the British government did not accept either country's findings). Attention has been focused over recent years on the pollution of our rivers and coastlines. Fish which live in a polluted environment are obviously going to suffer the effects and can become contaminated with:

~ Pesticides
~ Heavy metals
~ PCBs
~ Radionuclides

Older, larger fish become most contaminated, especially those which are bottom-feeders like carp. The toxins are stored in the fish's fat cells, so the fat which is *supposed* to be beneficial to you may also contain other elements which are not quite so welcome!

It doesn't take much common sense to realize that if we treat our rivers and seas as huge open sewers, sooner or later infection is going to occur. This is precisely what happened in the North Sea recently, when an overwhelmingly sudden viral outbreak decimated the seal population. But sadly, we have short memories – or perhaps we just don't like to think that the fish we eat also happen to live in that same open sewer.

Omega 3 fatty acids

There's no disputing that fish oil can make you very healthy – if you happen to make fish oil capsules! For several years, they've been the fastest-moving items in health food shops. According to the manufacturers, fish oil can treat asthma, prevent cancer, lower your cholesterol level and banish arthritis. But what is the evidence?

~ Fish oil is indeed a source of the omega 3 essential fatty acids. But, contrary to popular opinion, it's not the only source. Flaxseed (linseed) oil actually contains about twice as much omega 3 essential fatty acids as is found in fish oil.
~ Fish oil has been touted as the ultimate cure for heart disease. It's not. Some studies have indeed shown that large doses of fish oil can lower triglycerides (blood fats). But when continued over a longer period of time – six months or so – the initial triglyceride-lowering effect of fish oil in patients with high levels almost disappears.[45]
~ Another study casts doubt on the benefits of fish oil for heart patients who have had angioplasty, a medical treatment for narrowed arteries. Because fish oil makes your blood thinner, it was thought that it could help keep clogged arteries open. And three small studies first hinted that it could. However, a larger study from Harvard Medical School and Beth Israel Hospital shows that people taking fish oil actually had a higher rate of recurrent narrowing of the arteries and more heart attacks than people taking olive oil![46]
~ It has now passed into folklore that the Inuit or Eskimos, as they are popularly known, have much less heart disease than other Westerners, and that this reduction in heart disease is due to the fish oil they consume. Actually, if you study almost any native population, you'll find they have much less heart disease than we do. In March 1990, *The American Journal of Public Health* published a review of previous scientific work on this subject. The author of the review wrote:

> "Several studies have reported that arctic populations, which typically consume large amounts of fatty fish, have a low rate of atherosclerosis and cardiovascular disease. But a thorough examination of the methods used in these projects reveals that the evidence may not have been reliable. Two studies that reported causes of death used data from a modest number of autopsies that were performed without standard procedures by inadequately trained personnel."[47]

So it seems that the 'Eskimo connection' is far less certain than we've been led to believe.
~ The same research which was supposed to demonstrate that fish oil lowers heart disease also shows that Eskimos were dying in greater numbers from cerebrovascular haemorrhages – strokes. Since fish oil is known to thin the blood, this is a perfectly possible consequence. But this finding has received very little publicity.
A recent study conducted to assess the benefits of fish oil on young people with raised levels of fats in their blood ended up proving just how dramatic this blood-thinning effect can be. Of eleven patients, eight of them had nosebleeds while taking the oil. "It is concluded", wrote the scientists, "that the dose of fish oil necessary to reduce blood lipid levels may be associated with an extremely high risk of bleeding problems in adolescents."[48]
~ Can fish oil help in arthritis? Again, the evidence is far less conclusive than the publicity indicates. A 1985 study found that people who took one specific omega 3 (known as EPA) reported less morning stiffness when compared to another group of people who didn't take the oil.[49] But there were no improvements in other areas, such as grip strength, exercise ability, fatigue or swelling. Note – the people on fish oil didn't actually get any better, it was just that the people *not* taking fish oil got worse. This is hardly conclusive proof.
~ As far as cholesterol is concerned, the results are very mixed indeed. Some studies have shown that large doses of fish oil can lower cholesterol levels dramatically. But other studies have shown just the opposite – that it can, in fact, raise them, and in particular raise the level of 'bad' LDL cholesterol.

So are there any health benefits at all in eating fish? Apart from the questions of contamination and pollution raised above, scientific work does indicate that eating two or three fish meals a week can indeed help prevent heart attack deaths. But it is far from clear whether this is due to an ingredient in the fish itself, or whether this is simply because the subjects were eating a more nearly vegetarian diet.

Some hints for the fish-eater:

~ Ask your fishmonger where the fish was caught and buy only fish from the ocean, not from near the shores of the British Isles. Tell your fishmonger why you are asking. (Remember they are in business to sell fish so they may try to tell you otherwise. There is no need to argue about it, but neither is there any need for you to feel pressurized into buying fish which you now know you should avoid.)
~ If you eat fish you have caught yourself consider having some sample catches checked by your local environmental health officer first. Your town hall can put you in contact with them.
~ Join a pressure group like Greenpeace or Friends of the Earth, who are pushing for our waterways to become pollution-free.
Ultimately, going vegetarian is about adopting a kinder, more harmonious way of living with the other creatures who share our planet. If we don't exploit them quite so ruthlessly, perhaps we'll all lead more contented lives.

Chapter 12
The facts about ginseng

~

Ginseng is big business for the exporting countries – but do we really know what we're doing when we self-prescribe this powerful herb?

Go into any health food shop and you are more than likely to find ginseng products in abundance. They are all derived from the herb of that name which can come from either China, Korea, America, the Himalayas, Japan or Siberia, although strictly speaking ginseng from the last is not from the same plant family.

Originally used in ancient China, it was initially brought to the West by early Dutch traders. In the 18th century a Jesuit priest in Quebec heard about ginseng and subsequently found it growing wild in eastern Canada. Since the beginning of this century it has also been commercially grown in some American states.

In Chinese medicine ginseng is used by doctors in combination with other herbs to target specific problem areas of the body. It is reputed to have tonic and stimulant properties and claims to be able to treat a host of other medical complaints including:
~ Cancer
~ Rheumatism
~ Diabetes
~ Sexual debility
~ Ageing
~ Mental disorders
Few of these claims have been well verified in the West. Most experiments are carried out by the countries which produce and sell it. Perhaps not surprisingly, their tests have shown some remarkable results:
~ Inhibiting cancer
~ Increasing resistance to stress
~ Improving the effect of anti-cancer drugs whilst reducing their side-effects

~ Increasing resistance to irradiation and toxic gases
~ Extending survival time during food deprivation

Side-effects

Like all drugs, ginseng is capable of producing adverse reactions in some people. In the rush to market it as the latest miracle cure, very little attention has been focused on its side-effects. Perhaps the most spectacular one to be reported is its ability to make men grow breasts. Ginseng contains oestrogen-like compounds, which means that, occasionally, it can have a strange effect on males. Also, some women who have taken it orally or as a cream have experienced vaginal bleeding.[50] Other adverse effects from taking ginseng have been known to include:
~ Hypertension (high blood pressure)
~ Nervousness
~ Sleeplessness
~ Skin eruptions
~ Morning diarrhoea
~ Nausea and vomiting
~ Palpitations
~ Decrease in sexual potency

Today, you can buy ginseng in many different forms: tea (made from its leaves), capsules, tablets, extracts, cigarettes, lozenges of dried root, soaps, creams, ointments and even sweets, chewing gum and fizzy drinks. Perhaps its very profusion in the health food shops encourages us to treat it with rather less than respect.

In traditional Chinese medicine, ginseng can be a powerful and effective herb. But many Chinese doctors maintain that it should only be used by old people – to rejuvenate old bones, and to give extra vigour and long life to the weary. Younger people who take it risk 'burning up' their vigour; it is said ginseng has the power to make the old young, and the young old. Don't use ginseng unless it is prescribed for you by a practitioner who knows what he's doing.

CHAPTER 13
'GREEN BLOOD' – THE SECRET OF WHEATGRASS JUICE

~

Unless you were a cow in a previous life, you probably don't know that a special kind of grass – wheatgrass – can help you regain control of your health and give you extra energy and strength!

Chlorophyll, the pigment in grass, has been used as a folk remedy since ancient times. If you leave a brick on your lawn, it takes about a week for the grass under the brick to go yellow. Without exposure to sunlight, plants are unable to manufacture the chlorophyll that turns them green – so you might say that chlorophyll is a kind of condensed sunlight.

Wheatgrass is the fastest and easiest grass to grow and it has one of the highest concentrations of nutrients. The easiest way to absorb this goodness is by extracting the juice – the green 'blood' of the plant.

Wheatgrass juice works to improve your health in two ways:
~ By filling the nutritional gaps in your diet
~ By cleansing your blood

What's in it and what it does

~ Wheatgrass juice is high in vitamins. It contains the same amount of vitamin C as oranges. You need vitamin C for healthy skin, teeth, eyes, muscles and joints. Wheatgrass juice is as high in vitamin A as carrots and apricots, and contains three times as much as iceberg lettuce. Vitamin A is essential for normal growth, good eyesight, reproduction and calcium absorption. Without it, you run the risk of brittle bones and have lowered resistance to infection and illness. It is also an excellent source of essential B vitamins which are necessary for normal brain and body development and to maintain your digestive system. What's more 'green blood' is high in vitamin E, without which your muscles waste away and your body becomes unable to heal itself.

~ Wheatgrass juice also contains many essential minerals: calcium, magnesium, potassium, iron, sodium and trace minerals, needed to help your bones, teeth, hair and skin stay healthy.

~ In addition to being rich in vitamins and minerals, wheatgrass helps your body rid itself of the toxins accumulated by eating processed foods, breathing polluted air, and drinking impure water.

~ Your body has natural, internal defences for protecting itself from external poisons. But it is not designed to cope with the huge quantities you are exposed to by living in a modern, contaminated environment. Wheatgrass juice contains natural enzymes which help your natural defences by strengthening cells and removing the poisons from your blood stream.

~ Wheatgrass juice also has a dilating effect upon your blood vessels, expanding them so the blood flows through more easily. Improved circulation makes it easier for your body to distribute valuable nutrients to your cells, and for you to get rid of any waste products

~ There is also evidence that it can increase the number of red blood cells, and a corresponding boost in the iron content of the blood. Blood rich in iron helps the distribution of oxygen and nutrients to your cells.[51]

How to grow it

Wheatgrass is easy to grow at home, and a juicer is the only expensive item you'll need.

The first step is setting up an indoor garden. You'll need topsoil to grow the grass in, and some plastic trays. You can grow the grass in automatic sprouters, but it isn't so good because it won't contain any of the nutrients found in healthy soil.

Because most soil in Britain is tired or polluted, you might like to use peat moss, which you can buy cheaply from your local garden centre.

Lay the soil in trays a couple of inches deep. Cafeteria trays are ideal: you should be able to get some from a restaurant supply store. You'll need two trays for each crop of wheatgrass, one to hold the soil and another to cover it for the first three days of growth.

The seeds, or wheatberries, are small, oval shaped and coloured a rich brown. They are very cheap, and are available at most health food shops. About one cup of dry seeds should be sufficient for a 25 by 35cm tray. Wash the wheatberries, and soak for 24 hours, rinsing after twelve hours. Spread the seeds over the tray – each seed should touch another, but they shouldn't be piled on top of each other.

Sprinkle water on the soil – enough to make it damp, but not so as the seeds are swimming. Then cover the seeds with a second tray – this will protect the germinating seeds from light and keep them warm. Leave for three days, or only two in the middle of summer.

Harvesting

At the end of this time, take the top tray off. The grass should be a little over two centimetres high. Put the tray out in the sun, and water daily. When the grass is 20cm tall it will be ready to harvest. This takes about five to ten days.

When the wheatgrass is ready to harvest, cut it as close to the soil as you can – most of the nutrients are stored near the root and you don't want to waste any. The grass will keep, unwashed, in a plastic bag in your fridge, for up to seven days; but the sooner you use it the better it is for you.

Preparation

To juice the grass, you can use either a manual or electric juice extractor. But select one that uses a squeezing action – some work by spinning a fine metal filter at high speed against the food to be juiced, and this type will very quickly become blocked by the fibrous leaves and produce little juice. Each tray will give you 200-300 grams of juice depending on how long the grass was. Once you have juiced it, it won't keep at all, so drink it straight away.

Take three times a week for maximum benefit. You can also use the juice as a breath freshener, or to ease sore throats. Most people find the taste refreshing and invigorating, but if it disagrees with you, mix with other juices – carrot and tomato are especially good.

Wheatgrass is a storehouse of essential vitamins and minerals. It stimulates enzyme activity and will help cleanse your body of chemicals and pollution. Regular doses of liquid sunshine will bring a bounce to your step and a twinkle to your eye!

Chapter 14
Spirulina – the Prehistoric Prescription

~

Spirulina is being hailed as the ultimate miracle food supplement. It's natural, it's concentrated, and there are few side effects. But it's not a newly manufactured product of scientific research – it has actually been around for millions of years.

Spirulina is a bluey green microscopic algae, which first appeared in the primeval soup, acting as the catalyst for the production of oxygen on Earth. Today it lives in the fresh waters of ponds and lakes, and it is creating a lot of excitement because of its incredible properties.

Spirulina is currently cultivated in Japan, Thailand, southern California and Mexico, because their warm climates are ideally suited to it. Prototype spirulina cultivation systems are under development in India, Togo and Peru in an attempt to use this wonderful substance to treat malnutrition in Third World countries. Because it is such a simple food, babies can digest it very easily, and so may respond to it better than to other emergency foodstuffs.

Spirulina appears to strengthen the body's immune system and therefore assists the body to fight off disease. Specifically, spirulina contains a balanced spectrum of vitamins, minerals and important nutrients.

What's in it for you

~ It contains over 100 nutrients.
~ It has the correct balance of all eight essential amino acids and ten of the twelve non-essential amino acids.
~ It can be regarded as a complete protein as it consists of about 65 per cent protein (the same amount as eggs).

~ It is rich in vitamin B complex, with high levels of B_1 (thiamine), B_2 (riboflavin), B_3 (niacin), B_5 and B_6 and is the richest plant source of vitamin B_{12} (just one teaspoon contains over twice the US recommended daily intake).
~ It is high in fatty acids.
~ It may be useful for controlling cholesterol and blood pressure.
~ It is rich in vitamin E, iron, phosphorus, magnesium and beta carotene.
~ It is a tremendously efficient producer of protein – 25 times more efficient than maize, 300 times more efficient than beef.
~ It can be used as a tonic and an energy booster.
~ It contains arginine, an amino acid which promotes the release of the body's growth hormone, and helps build muscle.
~ It can be used in the treatment of obesity and diabetes mellitus.
~ Dieters find it useful, because it contains significant amounts of phenylalanine, a natural appetite suppressant.

Many ancient cultures have appreciated the nutritional properties of spirulina. The Aztecs used to eat 'tecuitlatl' – tiny cakes made from the plant. Today, it is used in Israel to purify water, and in India as a cheap and plentiful animal food. In America and France blue food colouring as well as health foods and cosmetics contain the algae. Studies are now being carried out to see if it can be used as a means of producing oxygen in submarines and spaceships.

How to take it

You can buy spirulina in tablet form to take as you would any other supplement. It is also sold as a powder which you can use in cooking or mix with water to make a paste. It is normally only available in health food shops and so can be rather expensive. The usual adult dose is about six 500mg tablets per day.

As research into all the many properties of spirulina is still in its early stages, the toxicity levels are not yet known. So, some standard warnings apply: it is best not to take it if you are either pregnant, planning to get pregnant, or breastfeeding. If you are taking any sort of medication, including aspirins, laxatives, cold and cough medicines or other vitamin supplements, consult your doctor first. Do not give to any child under two years old. If you do start taking spirulina and notice diarrhoea, nausea or vomiting, discontinue use and consult a doctor; such symptoms could be an indication of overdose or side effects.

If you're thinking about taking a nutritional supplement, spirulina is such a complete yet natural substance that it's hard to better. A course of three or four weeks will almost certainly persuade you of its value.

Chapter 15
The Seeds of the Future

~

Whether you are bored with rice, have an allergy to wheat, or just want to try something new, these newly rediscovered seeds are the answer!

Today, an increasing number of people suffer from complaints such as acid stomach, intermittent diarrhoea, headaches and vitamin deficiencies. These can often be signs of digestive problems, possibly caused by an allergy to gluten, which is found in many grains, especially wheat.

The answer to this growing problem lies outside the normal Western diet. Gluten-free seeds such as quinoa, amaranth and teff have either been completely ignored by the West, or simply shrugged off as Third World foodstuffs, a second-class substitute for those who are too poor to be able to buy wheat. How wrong can you be! Now, these extraordinary seeds are being welcomed as the exotic, trendy new food of the future.

All three seeds contain high amounts of fibre and very little fat. They also have the correct balance of amino acids for the body, which makes them particularly easy to digest. They are especially recommended for children, the elderly, pregnant women and people with protein deficiencies. Such individuals may have problems eating large amounts of food normally needed to gain their required nutritional intake. Quinoa, amaranth and teff, with their highly concentrated protein and vitamin content, are therefore ideal.

Quinoa: the mother grain

Pronounced 'keen-wah', this seed has been cultivated since 3000 BC. The Incas called it 'The Mother Grain' and it is now grown by the Indians of the Andes. It contains an extraordinarily-high 20 per cent protein, twice the amount normally found in wheat grains, and more amino acids too. Quinoa is a high-fibre food, often used as a meat substitute because of its high levels of protein. It is a tiny golden-coloured grain with a delicate, slightly nutty flavour. It can look very attractive as part of a meal because, during cooking, the germ separates, giving a spiral effect. Quinoa is cooked just like rice, but does not stick. For every one cup of quinoa, use four cups of boiling water and simmer for 25 minutes. Eat instead of rice or potatoes or with warm milk as a cereal or rice pudding. As a seed it costs around 70p for a 125 gram packet containing enough for two portions. Since it will be some time before cookery books catch up and include quinoa in their recipes, here are some serving ideas for you:

~ Add quinoa to soups and cook for a further 15 minutes for a thick, nourishing food.

~ Use cooked, cooled quinoa tossed with other vegetables in salads.

~ When making stuffed peppers, use quinoa instead of rice.

~ To make quinoa pudding, wash and drain two or three ounces of the grain and bring to the boil in one pint of milk. Simmer for five minutes then remove from the heat and add one ounce of castor sugar. Pour the mixture into a two pint, ovenproof dish, adding a little butter and nutmeg. Put in a preheated oven at Gas Mark 4/180°C/350°F for about an hour, or until a golden coloured skin appears.

Amaranth for the gods

A stunningly attractive plant with purple, red or gold flowers, amaranth is grown by the Aztecs. It was actually banned for a long time because of a tradition with Aztec women which involved the use of the grain in religious ceremonies. They would grind the Amaranth seed, mix it with honey or blood, and make shapes of snakes, birds, deer and gods as part of sacrificial rituals.

It is now used for other purposes! Amaranth is especially valuable because of its tremendous nutritional profile, being high in phosphorus, iron, potassium, zinc, vitamin E, calcium and vitamin B complex. It also contains about 16 per cent protein, compared to the 10 per cent normally found in corn and other major cereals. The red variety is sometimes used to make a red, non-toxic food colouring.

As a food, it is very versatile; the seeds, leaves and even the flowers can be eaten. It has great potential as a vegetable crop – the leaves taste a little like artichoke, and can be cooked in the same way as spinach, or stir-fried in a little soy sauce. The chewy seeds can be eaten as a breakfast cereal or as a snack. They can also be used to make flour for baking flat breads or, when mixed with other grains, will make leavened bread. As part of a meal, cook and sprinkle the grain on salads, vegetables and casseroles, or toast and use as seasoning. It is possible to buy amaranth popcorn which is light and rather nutty, and even amaranth chocolate! Some ideas for you to experiment with:

~ Boil amaranth seeds in two or three times their volume of water and chill. The mixture will become gelatinous and can be used as a thickener in jams and preserves.

~ To make a hypoallergenic wheat flour substitute, sift one cup of cornstarch, one cup of rye, potato or rice flour and one cup of amaranth flour several times. The mixture can then be used for certain flat breads, pancakes and biscuits.

~ For a tasty porridge, bring to the boil half a cup of water or fruit juice and gradually add one quarter of a cup of amaranth seed grain. Lower the heat and parboil for about 30 minutes. Eat with nuts, fruit or honey. Or, for a savoury dish, add soya sauce, salt and ginger.

~ You can even grow amaranth at home, in the same way as you would sprout any other seed: 1. Buy organically grown seeds and remove any damaged or mouldy ones. 2. Wash a quarter of a cup in a strainer, put in one cup of cold water and leave overnight. 3. The next day, drain off the water and moisten the inside of a jam jar with water. 4. Put the seeds in the jar, moving it around so the seeds stick to the sides and put a piece of muslin over the top, held with a rubber band. 5. Put the jar lying on its side in a warm dark place, rinsing it out two or three times every day (make sure you turn the jar upside down when finished to drain out all the water). 6. After one day the sprout should have grown to the same length as the seed. It is then ready for cooking. If you want to eat the sprouts raw, wait another day before using.

Teff

Teff is the dark brown seed of an Ethiopian grass. The name comes from the Ethiopian word for 'lost' because the seeds are so tiny. Ethiopians use it to make 'Ingera', a flat, spongy bread. It can also be used in cakes and biscuits. To cook, put one cup of teff in three cups of boiling water. Stir and cover, and simmer for 20 minutes or until all the water has evaporated. When cooked, it actually looks like a thick chocolate pudding, but is not at all stodgy and can be eaten in place of rice.

At the moment these grains can be bought in health food shops. As more and more people become aware of these wonder grains, the price will rapidly drop, and they may become available in supermarkets.

Chapter 16
New food from the deep – seaweed and sea vegetables

~

These plants are one of the most ancient of life forms; they are also undiscovered sea treasure having almost magical nutritional properties.

Seaweeds are used in ice cream, processed meats and cosmetics as a binding agent, but are sadly neglected as a general food product. But manufacturers are catching on fast. Currently under test are seaweed burgers and algae-flavoured crisps – hoped to be the new low-calorie convenience foods.

More protein than meat and more calcium than milk, sea vegetables are the single most nutritious food you can eat! And they're in your health food shop now!

What's in a seaweed?

The composition of the sea and our blood is chemically very similar. Seaweeds actually assimilate minerals from the sea, making them rich in trace elements and vitamins.

The list of the medicinal properties of sea vegetables is almost endless. They have an alkalizing effect on the blood, and have been used as a blood cleanser, ridding it of metallic and radioactive elements. Seaweeds have been used as beauty aids, too – they are thought to give the hair and skin a beautiful appearance and help prevent ageing. Slimmers take note: because we don't absorb much of the carbohydrate element of these plants, they are also extremely low in calories. It should be mentioned that all these plants contain a high level of iodine – this gives some varieties a strong flavour which can be an acquired taste.

The healing power of seaweed is actually used by Britain's National Health Service. One variety – Kaltostat – is used as a wound dressing in hospitals nationwide. Its particular characteristics make it an ideal healing agent; it keeps wounds moist and will then combine with them to form a protective layer. Because it is a natural haemostat, this seaweed actually reduces bleeding. Research is being carried out at the moment to produce a seaweed-based burn treatment.

Seaweed is normally sold in a dry form which can be stored for some considerable time – several years in a cool, dry place. This means you can have a supply of as-good-as-fresh vegetables permanently in your kitchen. Oriental food shops and health food outlets normally sell the dried form, although it can be expensive. There are numerous varieties, often very different, so it is worth discovering your own favourite.

Agar

This seaweed grows worldwide, but is most commonly found in this country and America. In Japan, their freeze-dried version is called 'kanten'. Agar is rich in iodine, calcium, iron, phosphorus and vitamins A, B complex, C, D and K and also works as a gentle laxative. It is normally used for its unusual gelling quality and, as gelatins contain animal bones and ligaments, is popular as a vegetarian alternative. To make a healthy jelly with no chemicals, simmer some agar with fruit juice and some pieces of fresh fruit for a few minutes. Then, just pour into a mould and leave to set at room temperature. It will set best with citrus fruits and apples – for flans with chocolate, rhubarb or spinach, use Irish Moss. Agar is also good as a thickener in soups and other dishes.

Arame

One of the most beautiful seaweeds, found only in Japan, arame comes in fine, almost lacy strands. This makes it good for dinner parties as an unusual and attractive vegetable. Arame is popular because it has quite a sweet taste and a crunchy texture. Its medicinal properties, in addition to those of seaweed generally, include treatment of female disorders and high blood pressure. In terms of its health value, it contains a high level of protein, iodine, calcium and iron. To use, wash, then soak in cold water for about 15 minutes. Squeeze out the water (which you should try and use in your cooking as it will have absorbed many of the plant's minerals) and steam gently for use in salads. Or you can sauté it with other vegetables for a side dish.

Dulse

Red in colour, dulse can be found on the west coast of Britain, in Ireland and Iceland. It is the highest food source of iron and provides significant amounts of phosphorus, potassium, magnesium and protein. Its rather nutty taste means it is sometimes chewed as tobacco. Dulse can also be used in soup and salads, although it does take five hours to cook.

Hijiki

This seaweed is extremely rich in minerals, calcium (containing ten times the amount in a glass of milk) and iron. This makes it a good food for pregnant women. As it expands to four times its size when soaked, hijiki is also ideal for dieters – providing numerous vitamins and minerals, and bulk with few of the calories. So remember to only use a small quantity when cooking.

Irish Moss

This red seaweed is used as a gel in ice cream and salad dressings or as a vegetable in casseroles and soups. High in vitamin A and iodine, Irish Moss also contains sulphur, so rinse thoroughly before eating. To make an Irish Moss blancmange, rinse the seaweed until straight and add one cup to three of milk, along with some sugar and flavouring. Simmer the mixture and stir. Strain and put into a mould to set. Irish Moss is good for sore throats, coughs and digestive disorders. For a child's cold, put a teaspoon in hot milk with some honey.

Kelps

One of the most incredible of plants, kelp has been used all over the world for hundreds of years. The Tibetan people eat it because they believe it gives them god-like power. Kombu, wakame and arame, along with about 900 other varieties, are all included in the kelp family, although they are normally sold under their individual names. Kelp can be bought as a powder to use instead of salt, but you only need half the amount you would normally use. It is also sold in tablet form and used medicinally for a variety of ailments, such as weight loss, kidney problems and circulatory illnesses.

Kombu

Normally sold in strands or sheets, there are several varieties available. Dashi kombu can be used as a soup stock; ne-kombu is a root which is good for treating specific ailments, and tororo kombu serves as a sauce when mixed with rice vinegar. If the label does not specify, it usually means the seaweed is the type used as an addition to casseroles or soups, or to wrap vegetables for sushi. Kombu is the original form of that staple of Chinese and fast food restaurants, monosodium glutamate (MSG), and so is a wonderful yet natural flavour enhancer (it doesn't have the unpleasant effects which MSG has). To use in cooking, just break a piece off and add as a thickener or a flavoursome alternative to salt.

Laver

Laver grows in the UK and Ireland – especially on the west coast. Translucent purple, it can be found quite easily on rocks and stones. To cook, wash and then boil until mushy. Laver will keep like this for several days. When you are ready to eat it, just beat in some butter and lemon and use as a sauce. Laver is a delicacy in South west Wales where it can be bought in this puréed state under the name of laverbread – which is fried in cakes and eaten at breakfast. To make a bread, liquidize 25 grams of the seaweed in $^3/_4$ pint of water. Add one teaspoon of gomasio (available from oriental grocers), one teaspoon of cold pressed sunflower oil, 400 grams of flour and 25 grams of fresh yeast and mix together. Put the mixture in two 1lb oiled bread tins and into an oven at Gas Mark 7/210°C/425°F for 20 minutes.

Nori

Nori is the only seaweed that is cultivated. It contains 35 per cent protein – more than meat, fish or chicken – and more vitamin A than carrots. Sold in lasagne-like sheets, this seaweed can be toasted over a flame until crisp and is utterly delicious when crumbled into salads or soups (don't try to grill as it will burn). Nori is particularly good as a garnish because its rich dark green colour contrasts with so many more common vegetables.

Sloke

This sea spinach is found on the coast of Wales. To prepare, wash well, shake dry and then squash into a saucepan. Cook over a gentle heat for several hours. You can tell it's ready when it begins to look like over-cooked spinach. Eat it cold in a salad, or add butter, salt and pepper and eat as a vegetable.

Wakame

A rich source of calcium, wakame actually tastes quite sweet. As it is a feathery plant which looks quite pretty, it is good for salads. It can also be roasted and crumbled into soups or simply used as a vegetable. To cook, soak for ten minutes in cold water, chop and boil in the soaking water.

For those of you who may be tempted to collect your own seaweed, be sure to check that the area is pollution free. Some of our coasts still suffer from being municipal dustbins!

CHAPTER 17

THE POSTAGE-STAMP GARDEN – NUTRITIOUS FOODS TO GROW AT HOME

~

You may not have a garden, but you don't have to miss out on the delights of your very own home-grown fresh food. The tiniest square of land or your narrowest window ledge is a potential hotbed of home-produced vegetables, herbs and even edible flowers!

Home-grown vegetables taste quite unlike shop-bought ones and stay fresh – right up to the time of eating. As well as having the luxury of an instant supply of completely fresh produce, growing your own vegetables means you can be certain they are 100 per cent organic. And, of course, there is the all-important question of cost. Don't you begrudge paying over the odds for produce that is chemically treated and probably less than fresh?

Sprouts

You can have a year-round supply of highly nutritious sprouts for little effort and not much cost. Don't dismiss them as exotic and rather tasteless salads. The term sprouts covers much more than just Chinese mung bean sprouts. Any seed will sprout, but the best are legumes like peas, beans, fenugreek, alfalfa and clover, and vegetables such as parsley, celery and lettuce. Mustard and cress are, in fact, sprouts, and you probably know how easy they are to grow. An incredible source of concentrated nutrition, high in protein, amino acids, vitamins A, E, K, and especially B and C, sprouts do not need soil or sunshine. All that is required is air, moisture and a jar. So there is no reason why you should not soon have your own crop of this invigoratingly healthy and versatile food.

How to grow them

1. Use a container with some sort of drainage, such as a colander, strainer, mesh tray, or even a flower pot with a net over the hole. A jar with a piece of cheesecloth or muslin held in place around the top with a rubber band is perhaps the simplest and most effective. The size of the jar depends on how many seeds you are sprouting, but it should be at least half a litre.
2. Seeds can be bought from health food stores and some supermarkets. Pick out all the clean, whole ones and throw out the rest.
3. For every decilitre the jar holds, use between two and three tablespoons of seeds. First, they must be soaked in four times their own volume of water, ideally mineral water, until their bulk is doubled. This normally takes about eight hours, or overnight. After this time, pour off the water. It contains a lot of the seeds' goodness and so should be used in cooking if possible.
4. The sprout container should be kept in darkness – just throw a tea-towel over the jar. The seeds must be rinsed two or three times a day through the mesh of the jar. Make sure you drain them thoroughly each time by turning the container upside down, or the sprouts will rot.
5. Throw away any seeds that have not sprouted after two days. The rest will be ready to eat after four or five days. On the last day they can be put into the light, but only for a few hours or they will become bitter.
6. Most sprouts will need a final rinsing and draining before being put in the fridge in a covered container for storage. Some varieties, however, have loose husks which need to be removed. Place them in a large bowl of water and agitate until the husks float to the top and you can skim them off.

Cooking sprouts

Any grain or vegetable sprouts will not require cooking, but these beans or peas may be simmered quickly to make them easier to digest.

Mung bean sprouts: 1 to 3 minutes.
Lentil bean sprouts: 1 to 5 minutes.
Peas: 1 to 5 minutes.
Chickpeas: 3 minutes.
Fenugreek: 1 to3 minutes.
Soya beans: 1 to 5 minutes.

Vegetable sprouts are good in salads and sandwiches, or as a garnish for any dish. Grain sprouts can be used in bread – just mix into the dough before baking. Bean sprouts can be steamed with other vegetables or stir fried for a couple of minutes.

Yoghurt

Do you like the idea of having a continuous, cheap supply of delicious protein? Then make your own yoghurt. For every one cup of yoghurt you want, you need the same amount of milk, a culture to set it and a warm place. You must sterilize all equipment first by putting one tablespoon of five per cent chlorine bleach into two gallons of warm, but not hot, water and soak for at least 30 seconds.

1. Fill four one-and-a-half decilitre (quarter pint) jars (with lids) with water at a temperature of about 38°C to within five centimetres from the top in order to sterilize them.
2. Put a heating pad (such as those used for arthritic pain) on a moderate heat in a warm place and cover with a towel.
3. Pour one cup of warm water from one of the jars into an electric blender. Turn the blender on low and add one cup of non-instant dried skimmed milk and one quarter of a cup of 'starter' yoghurt (simply commercial yoghurt, but make sure it does not contain any stabilizers).
4. As soon as the mixture becomes smooth, turn off the blender and put it back into the jar. Do the same with the other jars and put them all on the heating pad with a towel over the top.
5. Just leave the jars for about three hours, and then check them. When the yoghurt is set, put it in the fridge, making sure it does not get moved or knocked. It is ready to eat when it slightly resists a gentle finger touch.

Trouble-shooting

~ The yoghurt does not set. In this case the milk powder probably was not fresh enough. Make sure you buy it from a shop with a fast turnover and smell it to check it has no odour. It could also mean that the temperature was too high; at 49°C the bacteria cannot live, so check with a thermometer. If the starter yoghurt contained stabilizers, the bacteria would be inactivated, so buy a different make. It is also possible some liquid was left in the container during sterilization which would kill the bacteria.

~ The yoghurt does not taste right. If it tastes cheesy, the cause may be some leftover bacteria, so sterilize all containers and change the culture. If it is chalky, the powdered milk was probably too concentrated. If foam builds up, just skim it off. If the yoghurt separates and tastes sour, it may have been exposed to too much heat, so do not leave it on the pad for so long next time. Alternatively, it may not have been exposed to enough cold air – ensure there is space around the container in the fridge.

Herbs

You can grow herbs almost anywhere as they are so hardy and thrive with constant picking. In a garden, their best position is in a border, all planted together. Paving slabs laid corner to corner on the earth make a super chequerboard herb garden. Each square of bare earth gives good breathing space and root room for a single herb species. And with the paving stones, you can get to the most remote plant without having to put on your wellies! Start them in the spring, in a sunny spot. If you do not have a garden, make up the right soil using an equal quantity of sand, leaf-mould and soil. Put in containers, such as troughs or flower pots, on a sunny windowsill and keep well watered. It is even possible to grow taller varieties as they will conveniently become dwarfed in a confined space. Mint may be a little more difficult as it has spreading roots, so plant it in a separate pot.

Do not rule out indoor space – you can grow a bay tree in your sitting room, for example. Make use of patios, balconies and walls with hanging pots. It is a good idea to use strawberry pots with a small herb planted in each pocket and a bigger one in the middle. Do not forget to put stones or pieces of slate in the bottom for drainage.

Drying herbs

Pick just before the buds open into flowers as they will be more flavoursome. Make sure not to do this when the weather is damp or the plants are wet from dew. Put them in bundles and hang them upside down, either in an airy, but fairly dark place, or in a cupboard. They will be ready in from twelve days to three weeks, depending on how much moisture there is in the atmosphere. When your herbs are fully dried, take the leaves off the stalks and put them in jars which are both clean and dry, making sure they are airtight. It is a good idea to label the contents of each container. When using dried herbs in cooking you will only need about one third the amount you would use of fresh herbs.

Flowers

Flowers are a neglected food! Fun, flavoursome and attractive, they well deserve any growing space you may have. Use them in vegetable dishes, salads or preserved in pickles. Just cook as you would vegetables. In this country, we originally cultivated flowers for use in cooking and medicine, the idea to grow them as beautiful plants came from abroad.

Nasturtiums

Sometimes called Indian cress, the name of these flowers comes from the Latin for 'twisted nose' because of their pungent smell. They are, in fact, very peppery and so can be used in salads and sandwiches for added flavour. The pods, especially the orange and red ones, can be used instead of capers, or for flavouring vinegar. Grow them indoors in a sunny window or in pots trailing down. Just make sure the compost is moist and then forget about them.

Carnations

Use them crystallized or pickled in conserves or sauces.

Pansies

Great for decorations of any sort, especially on cakes when crystallized.

Roses

Use old-fashioned perfumed roses, such as Queen of Denmark (white), Cardinal Richelieu (red) or Madame Hardy (damask). The leaves of rose-geranium, either fresh or dried can be used to give a subtle flavour to sweets, jams and jellies.

Elders

The young shoots or blossoms can be used in pickles and the berries in chutney or wine.

Marigolds

Good for seasoning generally, marigold can also be used in place of saffron. The fresh or dried petals can be put in salads and soups.

Honey

Anyone can keep bees. All you need is a little patience and a sense of danger! A big garden is not necessary, as long as you ensure the hives are a suitable distance from neighbours and animals. To look after one hive, expect to spend about an hour a week. Although honey yields vary considerably, an average is about 18kg from each hive. Bear in mind the initial outlay to buy the necessary equipment and be careful in choosing a position that is away from both wind and sun. You can have great fun watching the incredible activities of your bees as well as the satisfaction of producing this miracle food in your own back garden. To store your honey, use screw-top jam jars, labelled with the date and put in a cool, dark place.

Chapter 18

Your home dairy – unlimited protein for pennies a week

~

In Japan it's called The Great Treasure and Bringer of Happiness. Now it's time for us in the West to discover the soya bean.

Soya beans were first cultivated in the eastern half of North China over 3,000 years ago. We don't know exactly when, because it was before written records were kept. But it is said that they were a gift to all generations of mankind from the sages and wise rulers of China.

Originally, soya beans were hard and tiny – indigestible unless carefully prepared – and they grew on a vine that crawled along the ground. But by 1100 BC the soya bean had been taught to stand up straight and bear bigger, more palatable seeds.

Since then they have become a staple of the Eastern diet.

The protein bean

In countries where overpopulation is a problem, the soya bean is prized for its protein efficiency. It produces 33 per cent more protein per acre than rice, its nearest rival, and *twenty times* more than beef. That China is able to feed a quarter of the world's population with only a tenth of its arable land, owes much to the soya bean.

When soya beans were first brought to France in 1880, nutritionists were amazed to discover that, unlike other beans, the soya bean contains virtually no starch – which the body uses to make sugar – and recommended that they be used as part of a diet for diabetics.

Experts began to examine the soya bean more thoroughly. Each time a new health issue arose, the soya bean would be tested to see how it rated. They explored digestibility, amino acids, vitamin and mineral levels, acid-alkaline balance, allergenicity, salt, fat and cholesterol – all of which were found to be ideal.

In fact, soya beans are such an ideal food, the real puzzle is why we in the West have never valued them as highly as our neighbours in the East do. But perhaps we're catching on now.

At the moment soya beans are used to produce soya bean oil, to feed meat animals, to make margarine, cardboard, paint, glue, to brew beer . . . and Henry Ford even made a car body out of soya beans . . . but almost never for what soya beans are most suited: *eating!*

The number of foods you can make from soya beans is limited only by your imagination.

Soymilk

Soymilk is low in calories, contains no cholesterol, and can be used in place of dairy milk in almost every way. It makes excellent milkshakes and is the ideal substitute for dairy milk if you are allergic to lactose or if you simply want to reap the health benefits of a diet free of animal products. Of the commercial brands, Bonsoy is an excellent example of the second generation of soymilks adapted for Western palates. Based on a Japanese recipe, it is particularly creamy and has a lovely coconut aftertaste. Even if you've tried soymilk in the past and not liked it, then give Bonsoy a try. Alternatively, you could try making your own!

Tofu

Tofu has a higher percentage of protein than any other natural food in existence, is very low in saturated fats and is entirely cholesterol free. It's used in East Asia in the same way as you would use eggs or meat.

Tofu plays a tasty supporting role to almost anything in pies, dips, fritters and sauces, complementing the main ingredients. Or you can use tofu as your star – in a tofu burger, tofu salad, tofu fried rice, chilli con tofu. It is also extremely good barbecued. Next time you make a stew or a soup, try substituting tofu for meat.

How to make soymilk and tofu

Making soymilk and tofu is like making bread. It's relaxing and therapeutic, tastes good and costs far less than a psychiatrist. Have a go!

~ Rinse a cup of soya beans and leave them to soak in three cups of water overnight – about eight to ten hours. Or, if you're in a hurry, pour the same amount of boiling water over the soya beans and soak until the beans double in size and are free of wrinkles (usually two to four hours).

~ When they've finished soaking, drain them and put them in a blender with 2½ cups of boiling water for every cup of beans. Grind them to a fine slurry then pour the mixture into a pot.

~ Cook over a medium high flame in the biggest pot you have (about 1½ to 2 gallons), stirring occasionally. As soon as the mixture starts to boil, turn the heat right down and leave it on a slow simmer for 20 minutes. Keep an eye on it though – it can boil up and foam over very quickly.

~ After 20 minutes, put a colander in the second biggest pot you've got and line it with cheese cloth. Then, pour or ladle your mixture into the colander, catching the pulp in the cloth, and the milk in the pot. Twist the cheese cloth tightly closed, and press on the pulp to extract whatever milk is left. At this stage, you have the milk! You can cool it, bottle it, perhaps flavour it with a drop of almond essence and a little cane sugar, and drink it! Or you can continue and make tofu.

~ When you've extracted the milk, prepare a solidifier. You can use different ingredients, depending on what kind of tofu you want. For subtle, sweet tofu, use two teaspoons magnesium chloride or calcium chloride (both of which you can get from your chemist). If you want mild soft tofu, use two teaspoons Epsom salts. And if you want tart or sour tofu use four tablespoons lemon juice, or three tablespoons cider vinegar.

Stir half the solidifier into your mixture with a wooden spoon, wait until it has stopped swirling then pour a little more over the top. Put the lid on your second biggest pot to retain the heat for curdling and leave for five minutes. The tofu should start to form big, white curds. If it still looks milky, then poke the top few inches to activate curdling, and gently stir a little more solidifier in. Cover the pot and leave it for a couple of minutes.

~ After two minutes you should have large white curds, floating in clear, yellow whey.

If you have milky liquid left, add a bit more solidifier and give it another slow stir. Always stir gently so as not to break up the curds, and only stir the top few inches of the pot.

When all the soymilk is formed into curds and clear whey, then the tofu is ready for pressing. If you find you have very few curds, then either you added the solidifier too fast or the soya beans weren't ground fine enough, leaving you with a thin milk and low yield.

~ Now you're ready to press the tofu. And you need a tofu press. You can buy one, or make one yourself. All you need is a small box, about the size of a bread tin, with holes in it to let the whey drain out. You can make one out of wood, or simply drill small holes in your bread tin.

~ Line the colander with the cheese cloth, and ladle the curds into the colander. Pack the cheese cloth and curds into your tofu press. Put a weight – a jar of water, a clean rock or a brick will do – on top of the cheese cloth to press down on the curds. After about 20 minutes, longer if you want really firm tofu, remove the weight. The cheese cloth should be firm to the touch; gently peel the cloth away from the curds. This is your tofu.

It tastes best fresh, but it will last for up to a week if you store it in water in the refrigerator, making sure to change the water every day.

When you strained the slurry through the cheese cloth, you separated it into soymilk, and a soya bean pulp which looks a little like sawdust. The pulp is high in dietary fibre, and absorbs flavours well. It improves soups, sautés and stews, or you can add it to your breakfast cereal. The Japanese use it to cure diarrhoea and also to enrich and stimulate the flow of a mother's milk. The whey makes a tasty base for a broth or can be used as a shampoo or washing up liquid. Try using it to polish your furniture; nothing need be wasted.

Tempeh

Tempeh (pronounced 'tem-pay') is a fermented soya bean cake. Like cheese, yoghurt and ginger beer, it is made with a cultured 'starter'. It is highly digestible, smells like fresh mushrooms and tastes remarkably similar to chicken. You can pan fry it and have it with sauce, dice and deep-fry it like potato chips, add it to a stir-fry and it is very good roasted. You can buy it from the freezer cabinets of almost all health food shops.

Soy ice cream

Soy ice cream is the most commercially successful of all the soya foods introduced to the West. It has all the dietary advantages of soymilk, and comes in all the flavours of dairy ice cream.

Soy cheese

Soy cheese can be used in exactly the same way as you would use ordinary cheese. A soy equivalent to mozzarella is commercially available and there are also some soy cream cheeses available.

Soy flour

Soy flour can be mixed with wheat flour on a one part soy to eight parts wheat basis to improve the dietary value of your bread or pastry.

Soya beans are one of the easiest crops to farm. They take less labour than most crops to plant and harvest and are less finicky to handle. Not only do they grow well in ground depleted by other crops, but soya beans actually regenerate the earth by supporting colonies of micro-organisms that enrich the soil with nitrogen.

In the years that followed World War II, people in the West began increasing their consumption of meat. Soya beans were found to be an excellent animal fodder – not only for cows and chickens, but for shrimp, catfish, eels and trout. In America, hundreds of thousands of acres were planted with soya beans – gold from the land – to feed cattle.

It's time to reverse this trend. Learn to use and appreciate the soya bean as a valuable foodstuff in its own right, and you'll start to rectify the crazy way we use our world food resources.

CHAPTER 19
ZEN MACROBIOTICS – THE HEALING DIET

~

If you are overweight and also suffer from chronic disorders or disease such as hypertension, rheumatism, skin problems or constipation, then you could be just the person to benefit from the macrobiotic diet.

The macrobiotic principle helps you to discover and understand your place in the grand order of life. It deals with diet, first and foremost, and encourages you to treat your food as a healing influence in your life, rather than something that you just put in your mouth in response to a hunger pang. This simple approach to food and living can have the most profound effects on your life.

Yin and yang

The guiding principle in macrobiotics is the presence of two forces – yin and yang – present in all things, which complement and balance one another. So, for any concept or description you encounter, there is an equal, but opposite, concept or description. Men and women, cold and hot, life and death, darkness and light – these are what we often call opposites and this is the way we tend to polarize our experiences and our thoughts. The macrobiotic principle contends that these opposites are, in fact, always part of the same entity, that together they create a unity and balance that is health-giving and that provides insight into the meaning and processes of life.

Based on ancient oriental philosophies, the yin-yang concept has been popularized in the West, applied to food and given the name 'macrobiotics' by Georges Ohsawa. Macrobiotics advocates a diet of in-season, wholefoods which have been grown locally. The staple food of the macrobiotic diet is grain – rice, barley, wheat, rye, oats and millet – which makes up at least 70 per cent of the macrobiotic diet. Pulses and lentils are also important, as are seaweeds and local fruits and vegetables; these, however, are consumed in much smaller quantities than are normally recommended. Extreme foods are avoided: sugar (extreme yin), salt and meat (extreme yang) are examples of such foods.

This idea of yin and yang relates not only to food but to all aspects of our life, such as climate, temperature and movement. That's why the macrobiotic eating plan is an individual one, balancing the food you eat with the life you lead. You do not have set menus imposed upon you or fixed quantities to eat; it is for you to decide what and how much you eat. You know you have the right balance for yourself because of the powerful sense of health and well-being you experience.

Balance

A macrobiotic diet can begin to undo the errors of a life of poor or inadequate diet by re-establishing a balance in your body. This will give you a background of health which improves as the diet becomes a way of life. You gradually gain an understanding and confidence which enables you to respond, through your diet, to the needs and demands of your life and your environment.

This understanding may be particularly valuable if you are overweight because of consistently overeating or eating a poor diet. Often these errors are due to a basic misunderstanding of how your body works, how food is utilized and even how you fit into the world around you. The macrobiotic principle can help you to feel and observe the relationship between the various elements of your life clearly and calmly. You may then make active changes, sometimes called behavioural modifications, to old perceptions of yourself and the food you eat.

How to start

If you're used to following diets by measuring ingredients down to the last gram and going precisely by the book, this is going to come as something of a shock to you.
~ Georges Ohsawa recommends a strict, ten-day diet for those starting a programme to reduce their weight or stimulate health in the body's various systems. It is an extremely simple diet: for ten days eat only unrefined whole grain rice.

That's it. There's no expensive recipe book to buy, no meeting to go to, no pangs of hunger to assauge. Just whole grain rice – for ten days.

Rice is considered the most balanced food on the yin-yang scale and so it has the potential to bring balance to those who eat it regularly. Over the ten days, you may eat your rice raw, boiled, steamed or baked. You may purée or cream it. Also, you may *eat as much as you like* provided you chew thoroughly. Also, ensure that you eat *at least 1lb (455g) of raw, whole grain rice each day* to meet your calorie needs. Prepare the rice in any way you like (except frying) and use only a tiny pinch of salt in each cooked meal. Make sure you drink only clear fluids during these ten days, including water and herbal teas but not tea, coffee, alcohol and milk. After ten days you may gradually add lightly cooked vegetables, seaweeds, soups and fruits until you arrive at a diet you will be happy with in the long term.

The ten-day diet should not be repeated more than once every six months.
~ A less drastic diet, though most definitely macrobiotic, is one which Mr Ohsawa summarized, in his own words, in these five points:[52]

1) Suppress sugar completely from your diet
2) Learn that it is possible to live without being carnivorous
3) Eat primarily whole grain cereals, vegetables, beans and seaweeds – all as unrefined as possible
4) Eat as little as possible of other foods
5) Keep liquid intake down to a minimum

These guidelines should help you devise a diet for yourself that will make the greatest advantage of the ten-day diet you have just completed. Not only will your weight normalize, but you will feel a gradual, significant improvement in your general health.

Macrobiotic snacks

Rice Balls: These delicious snacks are the ultimate in convenience food, except that they are macrobiotic and very good for you. Make them the evening before you wish to use them and take them with you when you travel, work or picnic. Here's how to make them:

~ Cook up a pot of brown rice and allow it to cool to blood temperature.

~ Wet your hands and press a large spoonful of rice into one palm. Place an umeboshi plum (see below) in the centre of the rice, then place another spoonful of rice on top.

~ Mould the rice into a ball, as you would a snowball, pressing firmly to keep the plum in the centre and to make the ball hold together. Place to one side and repeat this procedure until you have the number of rice balls needed.

~ Toast one sheet of nori (see below) for each rice ball. Just hold the nori over a low flame, moving the sheet frequently, until the nori turns a brighter shade of green. Alternatively, already toasted nori may be purchased.

~ Dry your hands and place one rice ball in the centre of a sheet of toasted nori. Carefully wrap the ball in the nori, as you would wrap a package. The nori will stick to the rice. It may crack in places, but press the wrapped ball firmly between your palms, rotating it as you press to ensure that all the rice is covered.

~ Finally, wrap each finished rice ball in a sheet of non-PVC clingfilm and refrigerate until ready. Eat within three days; the umeboshi helps to preserve the rice ball.

~ Umeboshi: The ume plum is a Japanese product, originally from China, which has been in use for thousands of years as a food with medicinal properties. It has been used in Japan to kill bacteria causing life-threatening diseases such as cholera, typhus and tuberculosis and is used commonly as an antibiotic substitute. The plum is pickled and aged in a special way; the resulting salty plum stimulates metabolic processes and helps to eliminate toxins from your system. Umeboshi is available in plum or paste form from wholefood shops.

~ Eat one plum each day or serve a teaspoon of the paste with your meal.

~ Nori: This is a delicate and versatile sea vegetable, most famous for its use in sushi. You may buy nori shredded or in sheet form. Shredded, it is roasted, tossed quickly in a garlic and lemon sauce and served immediately on warm plates as a starter or accompaniment to a main course. In sheet form, nori is used to make rice balls and various sushi dishes. Here's how to make a very simple nori picnic:

~ Cook up a pot of brown rice and allow it to cool to blood temperature.

~ While it cools make a thin, spicy paste from tahini (sesame paste), mustard and finely chopped onion.

~ Place one sheet of nori on a dry surface and press a layer of cooked rice onto it. Spread the rice to the side edges, but leave the near and far edges clear.

~ Spread a thin layer of the spicy paste over the rice.

~ Lift the edge of the nori and roll it into the rice to make a 'swiss roll' with the rice and nori.

~ Wet the far edge of the nori with a little water and seal it against the roll.

~ Leave to cool completely, then wrap for later use or slice and serve immediately.

Of course, you may make your own filling and substitute other grains for rice. However you do it, this makes a very tasty and portable meal.

Chapter 20
The No-Diet Diet – The Vital Facts About Fasting

~

Lose weight, cleanse your system and purify your mind, all in one go! But if you're tempted to fast, you must know what you're doing.

Even if you eat a relatively healthy diet made up of mostly natural foods and take little alcohol or tobacco, you might still benefit from an occasional fast. We all live in an environment which is full of pollutants, chemicals and toxins. Even natural foods such as fruit and vegetables can be full of pesticides, while the tap water we drink is polluted with all sorts of chemicals. It is not surprising that our bodies are often unable to eliminate the vast quantities of waste in our systems.

This is very often the first stage of illness. How can the body be expected to rid itself of alien substances when it is already overwhelmed with the by-products of all the foods we feed it?

Fasting aids health by assisting the elimination process. As the body rids itself of environmental poisons, the digestive system, the immune system (including the blood and lymph systems), the major glands and the cells themselves all benefit. Fatigue and general lack of energy are often an immediate result of the body's inability to cope. After fasting, many report feeling more energetic and positive than ever before.

Remarkable benefits

Scientific evidence is now revealing that calorie restriction without vitamin or mineral deficiency can extend life expectancy, retard some diseases and possibly even slow the ageing process. "For over fifty years it has been known that reducing calories reduces age-associated diseases and extends life," says one researcher. But it is only very recently that science has started to discover precisely how calorie restriction can achieve these remarkable results:

~ A longer, more active life.
~ Faster healing and much reduced risk of DNA damage (the body's carrier of genetic information).
~ Enhanced ability to fight off cancer-causing substances.

All these results have been achieved simply by consuming a diet which provides 60 per cent of the calories normally taken in. But – and it's a big but – the benefits of calorie restriction can only be shown to be effective on a long-term basis. More short-term fasting is still, scientifically, controversial.

Dangers of low-cal diets

The downside of fasting is that there's a risk. And people have died.

In 1984, the US Food and Drug Administration (FDA) forced manufacturers to print this warning on all very low calorie diets being sold direct to the public:

> "WARNING: Very low calorie protein diets (below 400 calories per day) may cause serious illness or death. Do not use without medical supervision. Not for use by infants, children, or pregnant or nursing women."

The new regulation grew out of numerous reports of deaths associated with the use of very low calorie diets. An investigation by the FDA and the Centers for Disease

Control revealed a pattern of sudden death from irreversible abnormal heart rhythms in people who had been dieting for prolonged periods and had lost large amounts of weight.

It has since been found that those early diets were deficient in protein and important minerals, but some nutritionists believe they are dangerous simply because the rate of weight loss is so fast. Another possible adverse effect of fasting or very low calorie diets is that muscles could be robbed of their mass and strength. Fasting can damage the liver, cause anaemia, lead to kidney problems, and alter the body's electrolyte balance, which regulates the heart's strength and rhythm.

In fact, most very low calorie diets have poor long-term results because they are not part of a lasting change of approach towards eating.

Fasting, on the other hand, demands a measure of self control from the outset. During a fast, food loses much of its significance. Instead of being a focus (as it is in calorie restricted diets), the time spent worrying about the foods you can eat, and craving the foods you can't, is completely done away with. As decisions vanish so do your preoccupations with the eating process. In fasting the appetite is completely controlled and becomes dormant, whereas during low calorie diets the appetite is constantly tantalized and stimulated with smaller than usual portions of food.

Often, fasters report a long term reduction in appetite and increased self control. People who fast seem much more ready to continue with dietary modifications. Counselling, continued regular exercise (and not just when on the diet), relaxation and behaviour modification are all important means of ensuring the shift in attitude continues.

Preparing to fast

If you do decide to embark on a fast, first consult your doctor. Certain individuals should never fast; these include cancer patients, diabetics, people with kidney problems, pregnant women, the elderly or the very thin. If you suffer from any mental disorder or are taking any drugs, fasting could also represent a particular danger to your health. Although the evidence shows that short-term fasting (up to 36 hours) can help to boost your immune system when it's under attack (for example, when you've got a cold coming on), don't go beyond this time limit when you're ill, otherwise your immune system may not be able to cope. To be absolutely safe, visit your doctor and discuss it with him or her before beginning.

It is best not to work or carry out any strenuous activity during the first few days of a fast, although after this time you may find you are experiencing greater vitality than usual. In the initial stages, take as much rest as you feel you need and, because fasting reduces body temperature, it is important to keep warm at all times. Don't use deodorants, oils or lotions because they block the pores and halt the elimination process. Gentle exercise, such as walking, combined with relaxation and breathing techniques, are an integral part of the fasting process. It is likely that you will go through a 'healing crisis' during which you might experience headaches, nausea, muscular aches and emotional imbalance. But if you experience excessive dizziness, black-outs or vision problems, stop the fast immediately and go to see your doctor.

After the first few days many fasters report a 'high', or increased awareness. Indeed, this is the reason a lot of people fast in the first place, maintaining that their senses are heightened and they feel a great sense of well-being. Others find allergies vanish, or their desire to smoke disappears. Improved skin and a reduction in cellulite are often reported as the major beautifying effects of fasting.

The dangers of fasting are real, and shouldn't be minimized. At the same time, people who have undertaken fasts report positive benefits, both physical and mental.

The 'fast nouveau'

There are all sorts of fasts. To decide which is right for you, talk to an adviser and set a limit on the length of the fast before you begin. A fast is not something you just launch into. Your body needs to be carefully prepared beforehand and gradually reintroduced to food when it is finished. You may also need to take supplements.

Here is an example of a one-day 'fast nouveau' – not an extreme diet of deprivation, but a very gentle and mellow way of letting your body recover from the combined assaults of stress and lifeless food which are now an inescapable part of daily life.

The night before

Pour out a bowl of rolled oats, add two tablespoons of sunflower seeds, and cover with a freshly squeezed fruit juice of your choice. In another bowl, soak a cup of dried almonds in spring or filtered water.

Breakfast

Soaked rolled oats with fresh fruit – nectarines if in season, otherwise grapes (organic if possible; otherwise let them soak in salt water for 15 minutes and rinse thoroughly). Chamomile tea to drink.

Lunch

Fresh cos lettuce with a sprinkling of sunflower seeds and pumpkin seeds, with 2 teaspoons of a dressing made from cider vinegar and cold-pressed olive oil. Spring water or chamomile tea to drink.

Dinner

Mixed fruit plate consisting of your choice of banana, nectarine, grape, apple, mango (no orange or citrus fruit). Pop the soaked almonds out of their skins (discard any bitter ones) and mix with the fruit. Spring water or chamomile tea to drink.

Choose a suitable day for this fast – when you can relax a little, and unwind from the stresses of life. Be positive about it! Fasting is not a punishment – quite the opposite. It's one of the few opportunities we have of really listening to our bodies. So be receptive.

Fasting is the oldest therapeutic method of cleansing known to humans. Originally, the emphasis was on the purifying of the soul as much as of the body; abstinence was the gateway to the divine. Plato believed that it gave the spirit the chance to rise above the 'fog' of food and then, freed from the burdens of the flesh, the soul would rise towards the gods. Christians, on the other hand, saw it as an act of sacrifice or penance.

To the ancients fasting was a celebration of life itself. Do it safely, and it will be the same for you.

CHAPTER 21

WHY DIETS FAIL YOU – AND WHAT TO DO ABOUT IT!

~

Most of us have tried to lose weight, and most of us have put it right back on again! Understand what's happening to your mind and body, and you'll find the answer.

You're overweight. The prospect of another diet looms; the sure knowledge of yet another failure stands starkly behind. You'll be pleased to know that it's not just you. The figures speak for themselves: 90 per cent of people put on most or all of the weight they had lost within two years of finishing a diet.[53]

Yet there are more diets now than ever before. Surely one of them will work for you? If those statistics are to be believed, the answer is a resounding 'No!'

Let's briefly look at what happens on a weight loss diet to see if that will explain why they don't appear to work in the long term.

Only for super-humans!

All diets revolve around eating less, whether that be in general, as with the low calorie diets, or whether it relates to specific food groups, as with a low fat diet. The body does, indeed, initially react by shedding weight, but the reduction is due to water and glycogen loss. At this point, when glycogen stores drop, the body sends out a signal indicating that it needs more food! Alarmingly, this signal is sent out regardless of whether the stomach is full or not. This is the first stumbling block for most people.

Should you manage to persevere and win through this hungry stage the next weight lost is of lean tissue. Quite simply the body thinks it is in a starvation situation, and so it decides to off-load those tissues which use up most energy – the metabolically active lean tissue. Unfortunately, these tend not to be replaced after dieting. Result: a return to a normal level of eating is now excessive for the body's reduced needs; it does not have the cells available any more to burn off the extra food because you have just dieted them away. So you put on weight again! Your body thinks it's a yo-yo!

Why we over-eat

Very probably, no one has ever told you why we, as a species, over-eat.

Humans are the only species on the face of the planet to have a chronic weight problem. No other animal has so much excess body fat as we do, and no other animal so regularly commits suicide by over-eating. It's not your fault – it goes with being human. Now, once you understand why we over-eat, you'll know the truth. And for the first time in your life, you'll *really* know why you are overweight.

The key to this devastating problem lies in our deep-rooted instincts. Remember, it has only taken our species a mere 50,000 years to evolve from our pre-human forebears to the human animal we recognize today. In evolutionary terms, 50,000 years is no time at all. Today, inside our 21st century minds and bodies, there are the genetic remnants of creatures which existed many millennia ago – creatures which, by our own standards, were not even human. The appendix, the coccyx (tail bone), the webbing that still exists between our fingers – these and other physical clues indicate that our pre-human ancestry is still very much a part of our make-up. Although our human ancestors split from the ancestors of chimpanzees all of seven million years ago, there is only the smallest (about 1.6 per cent) genetic difference between modern humans and chimpanzees. That shows you just how slowly evolution takes place.

Prehistoric hunger

The fact is that humans, like all other animals, have naturally evolved to thrive on a certain type of diet. In effect, we're genetically *programmed* to survive and flourish on the sort of food we've been eating for most of our existence as a species. "If you take a particular set of genes that are involved in the metabolism of foods," says Dr. Melvin Konner from Emory University in Atlanta, who's made a detailed study of this intriguing subject, "you'll find no appreciable difference between current humans and early man." So although the genetic constitution of *homo sapiens sapiens* has scarcely changed over the past 50,000 years, the type and quantity of food available *has* changed drastically – particularly so in the last 200 years, since the Industrial Revolution.

Fifty thousand years ago, our species existed by collecting food wherever and whenever it could. Today, food is available (for some of us, at least) everywhere. The problem is too much, rather than too little. And this has created a danger of monumental proportions for millions of us.

"One should eat to live, not live to eat," said the French dramatist Molière in the 17th century. But nowadays, many of us don't follow his excellent advice. The reasons are not hard to understand, when you bear in mind that our genetic 'programming' is really designed to cope with the reduced quantity of food that was available *50,000 years ago!*

Let's take the whole question of over-eating. Animals in their natural environment never die from over-eating – the greatest threat comes, of course, from starvation. So the best survival strategy in the wild is to eat *whenever you've got the opportunity*, because you never know where your next meal's coming from. That's why many of us *still* eat whenever we get the chance – even though we know perfectly well that there is no danger of us starving to death. It is in ways like this that our instincts, which once served us so well, have now become such grave liabilities.

How they exploit you

People who sell us foodstuffs know very well how to exploit these deep-rooted, unconscious instincts of ours. Take, for instance, the routine use of the word '*NEW*' on food products of all types. Have you ever wondered why this word is repeated so incessantly? The answer, again, lies in an old and once-useful behaviour pattern which we and other successful omnivores have evolved. Omnivores are animals which have adapted to eat a highly varied diet. Their successful survival strategy is to continually search out *new* types of food, so that if one staple in the diet fails for any reason, there is always another food source ready to replace it. A great idea! But in nature, the urge to experiment with new food is precisely counterbalanced with the desire to be cautious. You can see both of these clever survival mechanisms demonstrated in the behaviour patterns of that other hugely successful omnivore feeder – the common rat.

Rats, just like humans, are always ready to experiment with anything new. When a rat finds something unusual to eat (and like us, they are on the look-out all the time) it will carefully nibble a small amount, then leave it strictly alone for a day or so. If the animal suffers no ill effects in the meantime, it will return to the new food and start to include it in its diet. However, if the rat feels sick or ill after eating that small sample, it will never return to that food again. This is a highly successful feeding strategy, which is still present deep inside all of us. Here's the proof: think back to a time when you felt sick shortly after eating a particularly distinctive type of food. It doesn't really matter whether your sick feeling was actually *caused* by the food you remember eating; what matters is that you now *associate* that food with the unpleasant feelings afterwards, and in all probability, you will never eat that particular food again.

"I remember eating a simple pasta lunch," says Neil Carr, a lawyer from Washington, DC, "with pesto sauce, which was then my very favourite Italian sauce. By the time I got back to the office, I felt pretty ill, and started to vomit. I'd actually contracted a mild case of 'flu, which was going around at the time, and it was nothing to do with the meal I'd just eaten. But ever since that occasion, I've been totally nauseated just by the very thought of eating pasta with pesto. It's a real shame, because I used to relish it!" Almost everyone has a story to tell like that. Now, you can understand it.

A new way to get fat

It's in ways like this that our old survival mechanisms try to keep us away from food which may be dangerous for us. However, it's the other side of this mechanism – the strong desire which we all have to try out anything marked 'NEW' – that gets us into so much trouble these days, simply because there's *so much* temptation all around us. It is this desire to constantly look for – and experiment with – new foodstuffs which makes us so vulnerable to all those advertising come-ons.

Now let's consider the vexed question of obesity. Clearly, we did not evolve intentionally to become such a sick species, so what exactly has gone wrong? Once more, the cause of the problem seems to lie in our omnivorous natures, and the way that our bodies have adapted to the type of diet which we used to eat thousands of years ago.

One way we coped with the uncertainty of a variable food supply was simply to become very efficient at storing food energy in the form of fat all over our bodies. Humans actually have more fat cells (known as adipocytes) in proportion to their body mass than almost *any other creature* – only hedgehogs and whales have a greater proportion of fat in their bodies! Even animals which we traditionally think of as 'fatties', such as pigs, seals, bears and camels, all have less fat than we do! It is indeed sad that we should now be paying such a dear price for an evolutionary adaptation which was, at the time, an outstanding success story. Now you understand the problems.

Twin piques

Let's come back to the present day. The answer to the problem of excess weight is first to look at the twin causes.

Sadly, your inherited characteristics are one factor, and you have to accept that these cannot be changed. The quantity of brown fat you have (brown fat is the most metabolically active), your preset metabolism and the type of fat cells you have (Alpha 2 or Beta 1) are all inherited characteristics. Changing these is just as difficult as permanently altering the colour of your eyes.

Lifestyle – the way you live – must be the other cause. Long term and sustained weight loss should be the aim of any diet, and this is where fad diets fail. A permanent change in eating habits, and therefore lifestyle, must be the answer and not a 14 day wonder diet. A slimming diet can temporarily change your weight, but it *cannot* change your lifestyle, which is what contributed to your weight gain in the first place. The only person who can change that is you. We're talking about:

~ The balance of foods you eat.
~ How your body reacts to certain foods.
~ Why you eat (boredom perhaps, or loneliness?).

~ What you do in your spare time.
~ How satisfying your life is at work, at home and in your community.
~ How much exercise you take, and your attitude to it.
~ Your attitude to shopping, cooking, and life in general.

You're not greedy

Not everyone who is fat is an over-eater. But around half of the people in this country are overweight or obese, and an inability to control their eating can be the cause. Too often people who eat too much are dismissed as greedy and they desperately try to control what they believe is nothing short of a sin. It isn't.

Food, quite often, is simply the object onto which all the eater's unhappiness is projected. Over-eaters are rarely given the support they need; in effect they can be classed as 'addicts' in the same way as a drug user or an alcoholic. Just as an alcoholic cannot just suddenly stop drinking, a person who over-eats may not be able to cut down on food without assistance. Both have other problems for which they need help as well.

Food is 'love'

Right from birth, we learn that food is gratification and reward. As babies, breastfeeding is an important part of the mother–child bonding process. Just as children sometimes cry for food when what they really want is love (or attention), so adults often eat as a substitute for satisfaction in other parts of their lives. From an early age we are rewarded with chocolate and withheld food as punishment; it is hardly surprising then, that eating is so tied up with guilt and shame and happiness.

Modify your behaviour

So what can be done? Too often fad and crash diets just don't work and leave the dieter frustrated and depressed. The very idea of 'going on a diet' can be an unhelpful one. What is needed is not a temporary abstinence, but a more permanent lifestyle change. No one is saying losing weight is easy, but *not* losing weight can cost you a lot more in terms of health risks and damaged self-esteem.

The key is to treat the cause, rather than the symptom, and look at ways to modify behaviour. This will no doubt take a little longer (and probably be more painful) than a crash diet, but the results will be a lot more real, and will even help to improve the quality of other areas of your life. This process will need to involve looking at why you over-eat. You should look at your inner self, your motivations, your feelings, even your likes and dislikes. This is not as straightforward as it might sound; many people will need the help of a therapist or counsellor to explore these deep-seated feelings.

~ There are a number of groups and individuals who specialize in eating problems so you should have no difficulty finding someone to assist you. Only then can you begin to monitor your progress, correct your misconceptions and develop ways to achieve weight loss which will work for you. This is important; most diets are not conceived with the individual in mind and people fall at the first hurdle simply because it doesn't suit them. A well-conducted group can also give you positive reinforcement – it can help you rebuild your own pride and self-esteem.

Specific techniques may involve aversive therapy. This can be somewhat extreme, as it means negatively reinforcing a person when they do over-eat. For example, a deposit is paid which is not returned if the individual fails to control their eating satisfactorily. This particular technique does work very well for certain people; it is often a matter of trial and error. Although perhaps a little bizarre, it carries none of the health risks of fasting, drug treatment or surgical intervention.

~ Eating is very much tied up with habit. If you can change your habits, your eating patterns should not be too far behind. For example, try only ever eating in one place or putting your fork on the plate between each mouthful. Include the person you live with to help you. Do other things to take the emphasis away from the actual quantity of food; make sure it is particularly delicious, or looks especially attractive. Mealtimes are important rituals in most societies, so try and make rituals out of other events. More obvious examples are going to the cinema instead of out for a meal, but you could also try making sure you are doing something else at a time when you normally eat to excess. If, for instance, you always snack mid-morning at work, try to arrange meetings or other activities which simply would not allow you to eat.

Addicted to food?

~ Just as addicts need to find something else to fill the hole that the addictive substance has left behind, so do you. For a drug addict it may be a case of rebuilding a shattered life, while an over-eater may need to establish a more positive self-image by taking part in outside activities. The answer will be different for everyone but often it is a case of filling your life with people, things and interests so that food loses some of its importance.

~ Exercise is often a help. Apart from the fact that it releases the chemical, serotonin (also produced by eating chocolate) in the brain, it can elevate the metabolic rate for prolonged periods so that fat is used up more quickly. Many people mistakenly believe that exercise increases hunger. This is not true; taking part in any exercise plays an important part in reducing food cravings and levelling out hunger patterns.

~ The sorts of food you do eat is vital. If you make sure your diet is full of natural, unprocessed, health-giving foods, you are well on the way to fighting the eating battle. If, on the other hand, you eat lots of nutritionally-empty foods you are actually increasing the likelihood of developing food cravings. You will find wholemeal bread or homemade vegetable soup will fill you up when sugary, processed foods leave you hungry for more.

Scientific evidence supports the idea that changing your behaviour is the best method for permanent weight reduction. One experiment actually managed to eliminate the desire to over-eat in all its subjects. Checks six months and a year later found that the over-eaters had not returned to their previous eating habits. Five overweight women were used in this study, for which the principle of response chaining was the basis. This holds that over-eating is a link in a chain of stimuli and maladaptive responses. The treatment was directed at the behavioural link – the urge. When each urge was felt, the women had to write a description of the desired food and examine their motivation for wanting to eat it. They also kept daily records of their eating and weight loss as well as exercising regularly.[54]

The answer to this very complex problem is to try and control hunger in a rational way. Emotion is a hard thing to fight; if you are over-eating to compensate for the love you feel you never had as a child, telling yourself how gross you are will not work. You will only end up in a cycle in which you convince yourself you are so disgusting that you eat even more. If, however, you recognize that you have a need for love that is not being fulfilled, look at ways to increase the love in your life and make you feel better about yourself. The circle will then work the other way; you will feel good (eventually), confident and in control; you will then not need food as the emotional crutch it once was.

Chapter 22
The dieter's friend – twenty answers to twenty common problems

~

Losing weight can be a lonely business. Here are some words of encouragement to keep you going through those lean times!

"Half-way through a diet, I just lose motivation. I forget what I am doing it for!"
~ Right at the start of your diet, take a little time to sit down with a pad of paper and a pen. Now list all the reasons why you would like to be a few pounds lighter. Write down every single reason that comes into your head – from fashion to fitness – without holding back. This is your private list so you can include anything in it. When you have finished, put the list where it is easy to find and read through it next time you lose motivation for reducing your weight.

"I need to be scared before I do anything like change my diet."
~ Well, there is plenty to be scared of if you are overweight or obese! Diabetes, heart disease, hypertension, joint problems – think of yourself suffering these disorders for a really terrifying view of the future.

"I'm used to being fat. I don't know how I would get along being thin . . ."
~ You will get along wonderfully. Most of us have a desire to cling to what we know. But, in fact, what we have yet to learn and experience is often the most rewarding part of our lives. Despite rumours to the contrary, change is usually exciting and happy because it allows us to mature and become more at ease with ourselves and the world around us. Clinging to your fat is like clinging to the past – you can do it, but it isn't good for you.

"Shouldn't I check with my doctor before going on a diet?"
~ Definitely yes, if you are going to try a high-protein, a very low-calorie or a food-replacement diet. And yes if you already suffer from diabetes, heart disease or are taking prescription medication. In these cases, talk your ideas through with your doctor. If you are otherwise healthy, you may discuss a change of diet with your doctor and get a basic 'check-up' at the same time to reveal any disorders you didn't know you had. Also, by discussing your plans you may feel more confident and supported in your efforts. If you are pregnant or trying to conceive, do not undertake any form of weight loss programme. Wait until after you have finished lactating.

"I understand that it will take some time to lose weight, but I want immediate rewards. How can I start to feel better now?"
~ That's not too much to ask. Reward is very much a part of successful weight loss. Here are three suggestions that work for others who also feel a need for immediate success.

First, allow a period of time each day for beauty routines or other forms of pampering. Try a proper bubble bath followed by a pedicure, a face or foot massage, a sauna or a 20 minute cat-nap. This time lets you feel good about yourself, physically and emotionally, and does wonders to rekindle your determination to get trim.

Second, begin a daily practice of deep breathing or other form of relaxation/meditation. The first few days might be difficult, but after you get used to the special quality of this time you won't want to be without it. Use these minutes to visualize yourself slim and healthy and activate these thoughts by treating each breath as the source of your success.

Third, make plans that include you as a thinner person, anything from buying a new coat to joining a rambler's club. Give yourself a further incentive by contributing some money to your own Thin Tin for each day that you successfully follow your slimming programme. Then plan celebrations for important future dates such as 'three months without butter' or 'six months below 12 stone'.

"I get very irritable when I diet. What can I do?"

~ It depends on why you get irritable. There are two common reasons, both of them important to resolve. First, you might not be getting enough calories, causing a drop in your blood sugar level which greatly affects your mood. Double-check your calorie needs against the value of the food you are eating.

Secondly, you might get irritable because, although you want to lose weight, you don't really want to change your diet in order to succeed. Try eating six to eight small snacks each day, each snack averaging 200 calories and specially made from healthy foods that you really enjoy. This way you get small edible rewards frequently and you avoid dangerous binges. The snack method also helps to solve the first problem, of low blood sugar. While you settle into this style of eating, why not begin an exercise or dance programme (class, video or cassette)? Movement has a marvellous balancing effect on your moods.

"How can I avoid nibbling at parties?"

~ Many people with this familiar problem swear by eating before they go out. Others do the opposite and promise themselves a special treat if they don't eat until they get home from the party! However, you may have noticed that parties are often held with the food and drink in one room while the dancing and games happen in another. Why not stay in the dancing room and ask your partner or host to bring you your drink rather than go through yourself and endure all that temptation?

"Sometimes I get depressed because I think I will never succeed. The feeling usually passes after a while, but I do get awfully low and begin to think I'm the worst person in the world."

~ Count your blessings – literally. Think about your good points so that you remind yourself that you really are worthwhile. You may have excellent skin, a sharp intellect, a particularly attractive colour of hair, very good posture, a soothing voice, a real flair for dressing – think about whatever you've got going for you. Then calmly promise yourself that, given time, you will succeed, but that part of that success is learning to be kind to yourself.

"I'm not just fat, I'm flabby. What can I do about that?"

~ Skin is elastic and after a time it will tighten up. But you can help it and your muscles by doing regular exercise. Join a local Keep Fit or Yoga class to use all of your muscles in a gentle, gradual stretching programme. Your muscles will alter shape as a result and you will regain some of the curves and corners you used to be so proud of.

Alternatively, begin walking as your form of fitness training. Brisk, determined walking is actually an aerobic exercise which helps you lose weight, improve respiration and increase your stamina. Start with a minimum of 30 minutes per day, four times per week. Remember, keep the pace brisk and slightly challenging – you should feel *slightly* breathless, but always able to talk as you walk.

"I'm really very overweight and I don't fancy joining an exercise class. I know that exercise helps to reduce weight, but I don't know what exercise to take – in my condition."
~ As well as walking (described above), you might purchase one of the many audio or video cassettes on the market that are aimed at stretching only. (Do not try one of the aerobic programmes at this point.) Or, if you have a staircase in your home, you may practise Stepping. Simply step up one step, then step down again. Step up with your right foot, up with your left, down with your right, down with your left – one hundred times at a speed that will enable you to continue talking. Do not become breathless, if you do – slow down. Finally, swimming is a very beneficial exercise which you may do by yourself. It is an excellent means of improving your overall muscle tone.

"Can I really lose weight just by thinking positive?"
~ No. But you can stand taller, look more alert and more interesting and show your good qualities more than you might have done. In fact, a positive attitude, when combined with a good diet, is crucial to successful weight loss. Being positive is a form of belief in yourself which keeps you determined and energetic towards the goal you have set.

"I really go to pieces at Christmas and other special occasions."
~ These occasions are full of family and social pressures and the appeal of traditional foods. The best way to keep your weight under control is to eat only plant foods during these times, avoiding flesh and dairy products as much as possible. Also, if you are preparing some of the food yourself, try making sugarless cakes and fat-reduced breads and savoury dishes. When the season or occasion is over, adopt a more strict diet programme to set you on the right track again. Don't regret your celebration, but don't neglect your weight loss diet when it is over.

"What should I do when I feel weak-willed and want to eat something fattening?"
~ Write it down. Immediately you sense this feeling, take out a notepad and write down exactly what you want to do. For instance: "I want to go into that cake shop and buy four huge cream cakes" or "I want to eat a whole family-sized pizza by myself". Now look at what you have written. Your inclination to do that thing is guaranteed to diminish.

"How can I keep dieting after that initial few weeks' success? Often I think that I've 'done it' so I stop the diet and start putting weight on again."
~ Instead of spending those first few weeks dieting, spend them training for a new way of eating. Design a Long-Life Diet for yourself following these guidelines. This diet is based on natural, unprocessed foods:

60–65 per cent of the calories you eat should be foods high in fibre and complex carbohydrates, such as whole grains, pulses, vegetables and fruit. Avoid simple carbohydrates such as sugar and honey as they really only add calories to your diet, not nutrients.

20–25 per cent of the calories you eat should be made up of fats. Only one-third of this amount should be saturated fat such as butter, lard, etc. The rest should be poly- or monounsaturated fats as found in olive or safflower oil, for instance. Most of the fat in your diet is hidden – it is already in your food so you don't have to add much fat to your diet to achieve your quota.

Approximately 15 per cent of the calories you eat should be protein. However, you should aim to avoid or greatly reduce animal products in your diet as these are very high in fat and are associated with many degenerative diseases. Rely, instead, on protein foods such as pulses, tofu, Quorn, whole grains, nuts and seeds.

This Long-Life Diet is rich in nutrients and, after a few weeks, you will begin to feel better and lighter. So treat those early weeks as an introduction, a chance to become familiar with new foods and a new way of eating. You'll certainly lose weight, but the real success happens in the rest of your life when the benefits of eating properly become permanent.

"I don't buy rubbish most of the time, but when I do my weekly shop I come home with lots of items that I bought on impulse and will only make me fat. How can I stop myself doing this?"

~ When you feel yourself reaching for that forbidden item on the supermarket shelf, stop, write down the food item and its price, but leave the packet firmly on the shelf where it belongs! When you get home, add up the list of food items you didn't buy and keep the total pinned up on your refrigerator. After several weeks of this, you should have saved enough money to buy yourself a new piece of clothing – perhaps in a smaller size!

Supermarkets are laid out so that impulse buying is easy – even encouraged. You must recognize this and resist the urge to comply. You might try standing near the checkout aisles for five or ten minutes before you start your shop, just watching what other people unload from their trolleys. Some of them seem to live on sugar and additives! Usually this observation strengthens one's resolve to stay off the junk and stick to what's fresh and wholesome.

If none of this works, then make up a strict shopping list at home and ask someone else to do the shopping for you. Give them plenty of money and firm instructions not to buy you any 'treats' unless they are of the fruit and vegetable variety. This keeps you well out of temptation's reach.

"I always start diets but then get fed up cooking two meals – one for myself and another for my family."

~ This is a difficult problem, but not an impossible one. First, sit down with your family – your spouse and your children – and explain why you want to lose weight and how you wish to do it. Then tell them that it is difficult to make two meals and that this has, in the past, caused you to 'give up' a diet programme.

Your family is certain to come up with a number of ideas that will help!

In any case, a Long-Life Diet (above) is one that will benefit everyone, even if they are already thin. It is well known for its long-term health bonuses. You will be doing your family a favour by gradually introducing them to this healthier way of eating and you'll have only one meal to prepare.

"I have always been a fast eater. When I finish my first serving, my family isn't even half-way through theirs, so I usually take another serving just to keep them company. I know this has caused a lot of my weight problems, but how can I slow down?"

~ There are a number of simple, unobtrusive little techniques you can use to help you eat more slowly.

Don't cut your food into pieces all at once (if it needs cutting). Instead, cut one bite-sized piece at a time, eat it, then cut the next piece.

Take a spoon or fork full of food, then put your fork down on the side of your plate while you chew that mouthful. Don't pick up the next spoonful until you have swallowed the first.

Buy a set of pretty cloth napkins and use one at each meal. Wipe your mouth frequently during the meal to help slow you down.

Take a slow, deep breath in and out between each mouthful of food. This will take the hurry out of eating as well as keeping you relaxed.

With all of this slow eating, you might think your food will go cold. Warm your plate before serving to prevent this. Also, take small portions of food so that the rest remains in the hot serving dish.

"I use a lot of oil and fat in cooking and I've got used to the flavour. What is a good substitute for all this fat?"

~ Cut the fat in cooking to an absolute minimum.

Ignore the fat included in the recipes you use and, when it seems essential, try cutting the amount listed in half.

Blend a little tomato or tandoori paste with 2 fl oz (60ml) water and pour into your pan. Place over a high flame and when the liquid bubbles, add your vegetables and stir frequently. This is the New Sauté method, the liquid replaces the fat normally used in a sauté. You will be surprised at how tasty this is.

Put the fat in serving dishes on the table instead of in your cooking. Each person can then add fat to their own meal. If you are faced with blocks of fat and jugs of oil, you will use very little on your food – it just isn't appetizing.

Scour your cookery books to find recipes for low fat spreads and sauces. Have several of these made up ready for use in cooking or as alternatives to butter, margarine, etc.

"I have a really sweet tooth that always lets me down when I try to diet. What can I do to stop myself eating sweet things?"

~ A sweet tooth is really a bully that always wants to have its own way. You will have to turn it gradually into a more respectable creature. First, alter the image you have in your mind of sweet things. Instead of thinking of them as 'good', 'tasty' or 'satisfying', begin to think of them as poisonous. Sugar has a very powerful effect on your body and your moods, so powerful that many people consider it addictive, like a drug.

Second, begin to deprive your sweet tooth, a little at a time, of what it wants. Instead of a chocolate bar, eat some dried figs or raisins. Instead of sugary tea or coffee, drink it unsugared with a piece of sugarless oat cake to give you slow-release energy. Every single reduction you can make in your sugar intake matters.

Third, re-train your sweet tooth to become a sour tooth. The flavours are equally strong, but the effects are wonderfully different. Every time you want a sweet 'injection', chew on a wedge of lemon, take a sip of cider vinegar in water, or eat a gherkin.

Finally, give yourself time to break yourself of the sweet habit. If you have one or two bad days, don't give up. Keep going and you will succeed. Just kicking sugar out of your diet will allow you to lose weight before other diet changes are made.

"I want to lose weight, but I know I will never look like Jane Fonda."

~ And why should you? You aren't Jane Fonda! You are yourself and you have as much human value and beauty as any other person on earth. The best any of us can do is to become as fulfilled, healthy and compassionate as is possible. The size and appearance of your body is an important part of this to the extent that it affects your health and your sense of personal quality. Do what you can to improve your physical status and you will feel better about yourself. In fact, you will feel unstoppable – never mind Jane Fonda.

Chapter 23

Fifty flavoursome superdishes for slimmers!

~

Each tasty recipe here has been personally tested for flavour, speed and convenience. They are all free of animal products, high in fibre, and low in fat. Most of the recipes serve four people, but a few serve more or less, so be sure to check the number of servings recommended. The calories are listed per portion. Enjoy!

Apple and Oat Cake

Serves 4

Calories: 210

Ingredients

2 tart apples
55g (2oz) whole wheat flour
115g (4oz) rolled oats
2.5ml (1/2 tsp) ground cinnamon
1.25ml (1/4 tsp) ground cloves
5ml (1 tsp) baking powder
285ml (10 fl oz) water
15ml (1 tbsp) oil

Method

Warm the oven to 160°C/300°F/Gas Mark 3 and lightly oil a 20cm (8in) cake tin. Peel and finely chop the apples and mix them with the dry ingredients in a mixing bowl. Stir the water and oil together and pour this liquid into the dry mix. Stir well, adding a little more water if necessary to give a smooth, moist batter. Spoon the batter into the cake tin, spread evenly to the corners and bake for 25–30 minutes. Cool for 15 minutes, then remove from the tin and cool on a rack.

Broccoli Soup

Serves 4

Calories: 223

Ingredients

15ml (1 tbsp) oil
1 small onion
3 cloves garlic (optional)
10ml (2 tsp) wholewheat flour
570ml (1 pint) soy milk
1 litre (2 pints) water
900g (2lb) broccoli
5ml (1 tsp) freshly ground black pepper

Method

Heat the oil in a deep enamel saucepan. Finely chop the onion and garlic and sauté over a medium heat for 3 minutes. Sprinkle the flour over the sauté and stir well to blend as for a roux. Mix the soy milk with the water and gradually add to the roux, stirring well after each addition. When all the liquid has been added, reduce the heat and cover the pan. Wash and coarsely chop the broccoli and add to the soup. Add the black pepper and allow the soup to simmer gently for 15–20 minutes, stirring occasionally. You may leave the broccoli in chunks, mash it slightly as you stir, or put the soup through a mouli or blender for an even texture. Serve hot.

Bubble and Sprouts Savoury

Serves 4

Calories: 60

Ingredients

5ml (1 tsp) yeast extract
60ml (2 fl oz) water
455g (1lb) Brussels sprouts
1 small onion
285g (10oz) tin bamboo shoots
freshly ground black pepper to taste

Method

Dissolve the yeast extract in the water. Wash and trim the sprouts and halve or quarter them. Chop the onion. Rinse the bamboo shoots under cold water and drain. Pour half the yeast into a frying pan and place over a high heat until it begins to bubble. Add the sprouts and onion and stir frequently for 5 minutes. Add the bamboo shoots and black pepper and stir gently together. Cook for another 5 minutes. Serve over rice, pasta or with other vegetables.

Cabbage and Red Bean Salad

Serves 4

Calories: 144

Ingredients

455g (1lb) cooked kidney beans
225g (½lb) carrots
½ small head white cabbage
2 medium oranges
25g (1oz) slivered almonds

Method

Ensure the beans are fully cooked (if they are tinned, the label should say if cooking is necessary) and empty them into a large bowl. Shred the carrots and cabbage into the bowl. Peel and thinly slice the oranges and add them, with any juice, to the salad. Sprinkle the almonds over the salad and stir gently. Serve immediately.

Carrot and Coriander Soup

Serves 4

Calories: 14

Ingredients

2 medium onions
2 medium carrots
2 litres (4 pints) vegetable stock or water
55g (2oz) fresh parsley
55g (2oz) fresh coriander
4 small bay leaves

Method

Peel and thinly slice the onions. Scrub and grate the carrots. Heat a little of the stock in a large saucepan and, when it is bubbling, drop the onion in and stir constantly as in a sauté. When the onion is tender, add the grated carrots to the sauté and stir well. Gradually add the remaining stock, stir well and reduce the heat. Wash and trim the parsley and coriander, then chop them finely. Add the herbs and bay leaves to the broth and simmer, covered, for 20 minutes. Serve hot.

Celery and Potato Soup

Serves 4

Calories: 223

Ingredients

1 kg (2lb) potatoes
2 medium sized onions
30ml (2 tbsp) cider vinegar
5–10ml (1–2 tsp) freshly ground black pepper
5ml (1 tsp) caraway seed
1–2 litres (3–4 pints) water
5 stalks celery
3 bay leaves

Method

Scrub and dice the potatoes then place them in a colander and rinse them under cold water. Leave to drain. Finely chop the onions and sauté them in the vinegar, in a large, deep saucepan. Stir constantly over a medium flame. When the onions are soft, add the potatoes, pepper and caraway. Stir well then add the water and keep stirring for 1–2 minutes. Bring the soup to a low boil, reduce the heat and simmer, covered, for 20 minutes. Chop the celery and add to the soup. Add the bay leaves. Simmer for a further 10–15 minutes and serve.

Celery Soup

Serves 4

Calories: 76

Ingredients

15ml (1 tbsp) oil
2 medium onions
5ml (1 tsp) caraway seed
1.5 litres (3 pints) water
1 head celery
1 bunch fresh parsley
juice of 1 orange

Method

Heat the oil in a deep saucepan over a medium flame. Thinly slice the onions and sauté them until they begin to soften. Then sprinkle the caraway seed over them and continue to sauté, stirring constantly. Add the water, stir very well and increase the flame to bring the broth to a gentle boil. Meanwhile, wash, trim and chop the celery and parsley. When the broth has boiled, add the celery and parsley. Stir very well, cover the pan and reduce the heat. Leave covered and simmer for 10 minutes. Add the orange juice just before serving.

Chickpea and Onion Soup

Serves 4

Calories: 256

Ingredients

170g (6oz) dried chickpeas
455g (1lb) carrots
3 cloves garlic
2 large onions
425g (15oz) tin chopped tomatoes
5ml (1 tsp) freshly ground black pepper
1–1.5 litres (2–3 pints) water
1 strip of kombu (optional)
15ml (1 tbsp) cider vinegar

Method

Soak, rinse and pressure cook the chickpeas. Scrub the carrots and slice in thin rounds. Finely chop the garlic and onions and sauté them in a large saucepan using a little juice from the tomatoes. Add the ground pepper and carrots to the sauté and stir well. Gradually add the tomatoes and water and bring the mixture to a simmer. Add the kombu and the chickpeas and stir. Simmer for 30 minutes. Just before serving, stir in the vinegar.

Country Cabbage Salad

Serves 4

Calories: 50

Ingredients

1/4 head white cabbage
2 large carrots
1 medium turnip
4 spring onions
55g (2oz) fresh watercress
2 stalks celery
5ml (1 tsp) poppy seed
5ml (1 tsp) celery seed

Method

Wash, trim and shred the cabbage, carrots and turnip and place together in a large salad bowl. Trim the spring onions, slice them thinly lengthwise and add to the salad. Wash and trim the watercress and break it into the salad. Wash and thinly slice the celery. Toss all the ingredients together in the bowl and sprinkle the salad with the poppy and celery seeds. Serve with a vinaigrette.

Fruit and Fennel Sauce

Serves 4

Calories: 28

Ingredients

1 large sweet fennel
1 green eating apple
juice of 1 lemon
2.5ml (1/2 tsp) ground coriander

Method

Wash and trim the fennel and apple and cut into small chunks. Place in a food processor. Add the lemon juice and the coriander to the processor and purée all the ingredients together to a fine consistency. Serve chilled as a dip for raw vegetables, a garnish in soups or as salad dressing.

Gardener's Salad

Serves 4

Calories: 186

Ingredients

1 large beetroot
1/4 head white cabbage
15g (1/2 oz) fresh parsley
4 stalks celery
170g (6oz) sweetcorn kernels
115g (4oz) dried currants or sultanas
55g (2oz) pumpkin or sunflower seeds

Method
Wash, trim and shred the beetroot and cabbage and place them in a large salad bowl. Wash and finely chop the parsley and add to the salad. Thinly slice the celery. Add the celery, sweetcorn, dried fruit and seeds to the salad and stir well. Serve immediately with a vinaigrette or tofu dressing.

Delicious Dhal

Serves 4

Calories: 104

Ingredients

225g (8oz) red lentils
710ml (1 1/4 pints) water
15ml (1 tbsp) oil
3 cloves garlic
5ml (1 tsp) crushed cumin seed
2 small onions
2.5ml (1/2 tsp) chili powder
1 small green pepper

Method
Wash the lentils very well. Place them in a large saucepan, add the fresh water and bring to a boil over a high heat. Stir the lentils, cover the pan, reduce the heat and simmer gently. Heat the oil in a small pan and sauté the finely chopped garlic and cumin seeds in it, stirring constantly. Finely chop the onion and add to the sauté. When the onion is tender, add the chili powder and chopped pepper. Stir well and remove the sauté from the heat. When the lentils have simmered for 20 minutes, stir the sauté mixture into them and leave to simmer, covered, for another 5–10 minutes. Serve on its own or over rice as a main meal.

Herb and Garlic Dressing

Serves 4

Calories: 67

Ingredients

3 cloves of garlic
30ml (1 fl oz) oil
90ml (3 fl oz) cider vinegar
10ml (2 tsp) wet mustard
2.5ml (1/2 tsp) dried parsley *or* mixed sweet herbs

Method
Chop or crush the garlic into a jug or jar. Add the other ingredients and shake or stir the mixture very well. Serve over any salad.

Herb and Tomato Salad

Serves 4

Calories: 110

Ingredients

115g (4oz) dried butter beans
4 medium tomatoes
2 small onions
30g (1oz) fresh parsley
1 sprig fresh mint

Method
Soak, rinse, drain and pressure cook the beans. Allow them to cool. Coarsely chop the tomatoes and place them in a large salad bowl. Finely chop the onions, parsley and mint and add to the tomatoes. Add the cooled beans and stir well. Chill the salad or serve immediately with a vinaigrette dressing.

Hot Fruit Soup

Serves 4

Calories: 152

Ingredients

2 grapefruit
2 oranges
1 lemon
1 tart apple
50g (2oz) raisins

For the Sauce
140ml (5 fl oz) red wine
1.25ml (1/4 tsp) ground cloves
1.25ml (1/4 tsp) ground cinnamon

Method
Carefully peel and section the citrus fruits and place in a shallow casserole dish. Chop the apple; add the apple and raisins to the citrus fruits and stir well. Prepare the sauce by mixing the wine and spices together in a jug. Pour this over the fruit and allow it to soak for 10 minutes. Stir again. Warm the oven to 170°C/325°F/Gas Mark 3. Cover the compote and bake for 20 minutes. Serve immediately, pouring a little of the hot sauce over each serving.

Hot Mustard and Chili Dressing

Serves 4

Calories: 80

Ingredients

1 small fresh chili
140ml (5 fl oz) cider vinegar
juice of 1 lemon
30ml (1 fl oz/2 tbsp) olive oil
5ml (1 tsp) dry mustard
30ml (1fl oz/2 tbsp) soymilk

Method
Chop the chili, including its seeds, very finely and place in a jug or jam jar. Add the remaining ingredients to the jar and stir or shake very well. Serve immediately over salad, baked potato or pasta.

Hot Scandinavian Salad

Serves 4

Calories: 245

Ingredients

900g (2lb) new potatoes
1/4 head white cabbage
3 cloves garlic
55g (2oz) fresh parsley
140ml (5 fl oz) cider vinegar
5ml (1 tsp) dry mustard
15ml (1 tbsp) olive oil

Method
Scrub the potatoes and steam them until tender. Finely chop the cabbage and garlic and place in a large serving bowl. Wash and chop the parsley. Mix the remaining ingredients together in a small saucepan and bring to a very gentle simmer. When the potatoes are tender, stir them gently into the cabbage and garlic. Now pour the hot vinaigrette over the salad and stir again. Serve immediately.

Lemon and Peanut Sauce

Serves 4

Calories: 30

Ingredients

15ml (1 tbsp) unsalted crunchy peanut butter
2 cloves garlic
juice of 1 lemon
285ml (10 fl oz) water

Method
Measure the peanut butter into a small saucepan and place over a medium heat. Finely chop the garlic and add to the peanut butter. Stir often. When the peanut butter is melted, add the lemon juice. Stir well and gradually add the water, stirring after each addition. Reduce the heat and keep covered for 5–10 minutes. Serve hot with rice or vegetables.

Lemon Bean Salad

Serves 4

Calories: 40

Ingredients

115g (4oz) dried black-eyed beans
1 bunch fresh coriander leaves
1 large sweet onion
juice of 1 lemon
2.5ml (1/2 tsp) freshly ground black pepper
50g (2oz) pimento

Method
Soak the beans and the coriander separately in very cold water overnight. Rinse, drain and pressure cook the beans. Allow them to cool. Slice the onion very thinly, break each slice into rings and place in a large salad bowl. Pour the lemon juice over the onions and sprinkle with black pepper. Wash and finely chop the coriander. Add the pimento, coriander and beans to the onions and stir together. Serve immediately or chill for later use.

Lentil Soup

Serves 4
Calories: 70

Ingredients

225g (8oz) dried red lentils
1–1.5 litres (2–3 pints) water
1 small green pepper
1 medium sized fresh chili
juice of 1 lemon

Method
Wash the lentils very well, drain them and add them to the fresh water in a large saucepan. Bring to the boil, reduce the heat then cover the pan and simmer for 10 minutes. Wash and chop the pepper and the chili and add to the lentils. Stir well and cook for a further 20–30 minutes or until the lentils have completely lost their shape and are quite mushy. Stir in the lemon juice just before serving.

Lunch-Box Marinade

Serves 4
Calories: 216

Ingredients

The Marinade
270ml (1/2 pint) cider vinegar
juice of 2 lemons
12 whole cloves
12 whole peppercorns
12 cloves of garlic, peeled but left whole (optional)
5ml (1 tsp) caraway seed
140ml (5 fl oz) apple juice
3 bay leaves
2 small pieces cinnamon
270–450ml (1/2–3/4 pint) water

The Vegetables
225g (1/2lb) carrots
340g (12oz) green beans
1 small red pepper
1 small green pepper
2 small onions
1 medium sized cauliflower
455g (1lb) broccoli

Method
Gently heat all the marinade ingredients together in a large enamel saucepan while you prepare the vegetables. Wash the vegetables. Thinly slice the carrots, beans, peppers and onions. Cut the cauliflower and broccoli into florets. Simmer all the vegetables in the marinade for 15 minutes. Keep the pan covered but stir occasionally. Remove the pan from the heat, stir the ingredients well, cover the pan and allow the mixture to cool. Serve immediately or chill and eat over the next 3–4 days.

Melon Cornucopia

Serves 4

Calories: 265

Ingredients

2 satsumas *or* mandarin oranges
55g (2oz) raisins *or* sultanas
55g (2oz) hazelnuts *or* slivered almonds
140ml (5 fl oz) orange juice
1 whole honeydew melon

Method
Divide the satsumas into segments and place them in a bowl with the raisins, hazelnuts and orange juice. Stir well and leave to soak for 5–10 minutes. Cut the melon into four and scoop out the seeds. Spoon the fruit mixture onto the melon quarters. Serve immediately.

Mint and Citrus Drink

Serves 3

Calories: 110

Ingredients

2 grapefruits
2 large oranges
2 lemons
1 lime
1 sprig of fresh mint
570ml (1 pint) sparkling mineral water

Method
Squeeze the fruits and pour their juices together into a large serving jug. Coarsely chop the mint and add to the juice, then pour the mineral water slowly over the juice. Stir gently, chill and serve.

Minty Fruit Salad

Serves 4

Calories: 187

Ingredients

1 large grapefruit
2 large oranges
2 eating apples
2 ripe bananas
225g (8oz) seedless grapes
a sprig of fresh mint

Method
Peel the grapefruit and oranges and divide them into segments. Cut the segments roughly in half and place in a large serving bowl. Wash and finely chop the apples and add to the citrus fruit. Peel the bananas, slice them into thin rounds and stir them into the fruit salad. Wash the grapes, pull them from their stalks and add to the salad. Stir the whole very well. Chop the mint coarsely and sprinkle over the fruit salad. Serve immediately or chill for one hour before serving.

New Mexico Chili

Serves 4

Calories: 194

Ingredients

570ml (1 pint) water
1 medium onion
55g (2oz) soya mince
140g (5oz) tomato purée
400g (14oz) tin chopped tomatoes
1.25–2.5ml ($^1/_4$–$^1/_2$ tsp) chili powder
450g (16oz) tin kidney beans
30ml (2 tbsp) cider vinegar

Method

Measure the water and tip a small amount into a deep saucepan. Place over a high flame and, when simmering, add the finely chopped onion. Sauté the onion for 3–5 minutes or until tender. Add the soya mince, tomato purée and the rest of the water and stir well. Reduce the heat and add the chili powder and the beans, then cover the pan and leave to simmer for 25–30 minutes. Five minutes before serving, add the vinegar and stir once again. Serve hot in bowls.

Nut Milk

Serves 2

Calories: 332

Ingredients

115g (4oz) cashew nut and sesame seed blend *or* almond, cashew nut and sesame seed blend
1.1 litres (2 pints) very cold water
molasses or dried fruit to taste (optional)

Method

Wash the nuts by rinsing them in cool water and draining well. Cover them with the clean water and leave to sit for at least 2 hours or overnight. (Alternatively, if a quick, hot milk is desired, boil the water and soak the nuts in it for 5–10 minutes.) Pour the water and the nuts into a food processor or blender and purée to a very fine consistency. Strain the milk through a piece of cheesecloth and serve immediately. Stir a little molasses into each serving if desired, or add a piece of dried fruit to each glass and pour the milk over.

Onion and Okra Stir-fry

Serves 4

Calories: 89

Ingredients

455g (1lb) fresh okra (ladies' fingers)
3 cloves garlic
2 small onions
15ml (1 tbsp) olive oil
225g ($^1/_2$lb) button mushrooms
140–200ml (5–7 fl oz) water

Method

Wash the okra and cut off the hard tip of each one. Finely chop the garlic and onion and sauté in the olive oil over a high heat. When they are tender, add the okra and stir frequently. Clean the mushrooms and add them to the stir-fry. Stir constantly and cook for another 3–4 minutes. Add the water, cover the pan, reduce the heat and cook for a further 10 minutes. Serve immediately with rice, pasta or steamed vegetables.

Onion and Olive Dip

Serves 4

Calories: 79

Ingredients

285g (10oz) soft tofu
55g (2oz) green olives
2 spring onions
1 eating apple
10ml (2 tsp) dill or caraway seed

Method

Mash the tofu in a serving bowl. Finely chop the olives and onions and stir into the tofu. Peel and grate the apple into the mixture. Add the dill and stir the mixture very well. Chill for 30 minutes before serving.

Orange and Sweet Potato Bake

Serves 4

Calories: 132

Ingredients

455g (1lb) sweet potatoes
1 large orange
2.5ml (1/2 tsp) freshly ground black pepper

Method

Scrub the sweet potatoes and quarter them, cutting only 3/4 of the way through so that you are able to open them. Lay each potato on a piece of foil *or* arrange them together in a large baking tray. Peel the orange, divide it into segments and cut each segment in half. Place orange pieces in the centre of each open potato and pour any juice in as well. Sprinkle a little black pepper over each potato. Wrap *or* cover the potatoes and bake at 180°C/350°F/Gas Mark 4 for 45 minutes. Serve immediately with other vegetables.

Parsley Potato Salad

Serves 4

Calories: 121

Ingredients

455g (1lb) new potatoes
115g (1/4lb) carrots
1 bunch spring onions
2–4 sprigs fresh parsley

Method

Scrub and steam the potatoes until tender, and allow them to cool. Scrub and shred the carrots. Trim and thinly slice the onions. Wash and chop the parsley then mix all the ingredients together in a large salad bowl. Serve with a simple vinaigrette or tofu dressing.

Pea and Tofu Purée

Serves 4

Calories: 161

Ingredients

455g (1lb) cooked peas
285g (10oz) soft tofu
1 small onion
2 cloves garlic
1 medium tomato
5ml (1 tsp) paprika

Method

Purée the peas and tofu together in a blender or food processor. Finely chop the onion, garlic and tomato and add to the blend. Add the paprika (or chili powder if you prefer it hot), stir well, chill and serve with salad and toast.

Sharp Tomato Sauce

Serves 4

Calories: 152

Ingredients

140ml (5 fl oz) water
140ml (5 fl oz) cider vinegar
4 large prunes
1 lemon
140g (5oz) tomato purée
2.5ml (1/2 tsp) ground coriander
5ml (1 tsp) paprika/
5ml (1 tsp) freshly ground black pepper

Method

Mix the water, vinegar and prunes together and leave to one side. Chop the lemon into small pieces and remove the pips. Put the tomato purée into a small saucepan. Add the lemon pieces and the spices and stir well, then add the liquid with the softened prunes. Simmer the mixture over a low heat for 20 minutes, keeping it covered except for one or two stirs. Then remove from the heat, press and remove the pips from the prunes, leaving the fruit in the sauce. You may leave the lemon pieces in if you like, as they are attractive. Serve this sauce hot over pasta, rice, vegetables or as the sauce for baked beans.

September Salad

Serves 4

Calories: 105

Ingredients

680g (1 1/2lb) green beans
1 large sweet onion
4 small new carrots
2 eating apples

Method

Wash, trim and steam the green beans (15–20 minutes) and allow them to cool. Thinly slice the onion, break each slice into rings and place in a large salad bowl. Grate the carrots and apples into the salad bowl. Stir well and serve immediately.

Slightly Sweet Tomato Sauce

Serves 4
Calories: 71

Ingredients

570ml (1 pint) water
285ml (1/2 pint) cider vinegar
285g (10oz) tomato purée
2.5ml (1/2 tsp) chili powder
2.5ml (1/2 tsp) ground cloves
3 cloves garlic
2 small onions
1 eating apple

Method

Stir the first five ingredients together in a saucepan and place over a medium heat. Bring to a simmer, then reduce the heat. Finely chop the garlic, onion and apple and add to the tomato sauce. Stir well and leave to simmer gently for 20 minutes. Cover and leave off the heat until ready to use. The flavour of this sauce improves if allowed to cool.

Smooth Lentil Pâté

Serves 4
Calories: 95

Ingredients

225g (8oz) dried red lentils
570–710ml (1–1 1/4 pints) water
55g (2oz) porridge oats
55g (2oz) rice flakes
5ml (1 tsp) ground black pepper *or* paprika
2.5ml (1/2 tsp) ground ginger
30g (1oz) fresh coriander leaves

Method

Wash and drain the lentils, add fresh water and bring to a low boil over a medium heat. Reduce the heat, cover and simmer for 30 minutes, stirring often. Add oats, rice flakes, pepper and ginger and cook for another 5–10 minutes. Wash and chop the coriander. Remove from the heat, stir in the coriander and spoon into a serving dish. Allow the pâté to cool, then chill or serve immediately.

Spanish Style Rice and Vegetables

Serves 4
Calories: 299

Ingredients

225g (8oz) wholegrain rice
850ml (1 1/2 pints) water
5ml (1 tsp) turmeric
1 bay leaf
5cm (2in) piece cinnamon
2 small onions
1 small red pepper
1 small green pepper
285g (10oz) fresh *or* frozen peas

Method

Wash and drain the rice. Bring the water to a low boil and add the turmeric, bay leaf and cinnamon. Stir well, then add the rice and bring to the boil again. Cover and simmer for 10 minutes. Finely chop the onions and peppers. Stir the onions, peppers and peas into the cooking rice and cover the pan once more. Cover the pan and cook until the liquid is absorbed. Serve hot or cold.

Special Spuds

Serves 4

Calories: 281

Ingredients

4 large potatoes
285g (10oz) soft tofu
1 small onion
1 medium tomato
5ml (1 tsp) dried parsley
10ml (2 tsp) brewer's yeast

Method

Scrub the potatoes, pierce them and bake in a hot oven for 45 minutes, or until well cooked. Mash the tofu in a mixing bowl. Finely chop the onion and tomato and add to the tofu. Add the parsley and yeast and stir the mixture very well. Cut the potatoes in half and spoon one quarter of the tofu whip over each potato. Sprinkle with a little pepper if desired. Serve hot on their own or with a salad.

Spicy Banana Milkshake

Serves 4

Calories: 250

Ingredients

2–3 ripe bananas
570ml (1 pint) soy milk
2.5ml (1/2 tsp) ground allspice

Method

Peel the bananas and break them into a large blender. Add the milk and allspice and whisk to a thick, even consistency. Serve immediately or chill for 10 minutes. Garnish with a sprig of rosemary or cinnamon.

Spicy Carrot Sauté

Serves 4

Calories: 87

Ingredients

3 cloves of garlic
60ml (2 fl oz) apple juice
30g (1oz) fresh ginger
455g (1lb) carrots
1 bunch spring onions

Method

Peel and chop the garlic and sauté in the apple juice over a high heat. Thinly slice the ginger and carrots and add to the sauté, stirring frequently. Wash and trim the onions, slice them lengthwise and add to the sauté. However, do not stir them in yet – leave them on top of the carrots. Cover the pan and reduce the heat. Leave covered for 10 minutes then remove the cover, stir the vegetables well and serve with rice.

Spicy Raisin Cake

Serves 6
Calories: 250

Ingredients

115g (4oz) wholewheat flour
115g (4oz) rolled oats
55g (2oz) oat bran
115g (4oz) raisins or sultanas
2.5ml (1/2 tsp) ground cinnamon
2.5ml (1/2 tsp) ground cloves
5ml (1 tsp) baking powder
285ml (10 fl oz) fruit juice or water
30ml (1 fl oz/2 tbsp) oil

Method

Pre-heat the oven to 180°C/350°F/Gas Mark 4 and lightly oil a 20cm (8in) baking tin. Mix the dry ingredients together in a large mixing bowl. Measure the fruit juice and oil together into a jug and pour gradually into the dry mix, stirring well after each addition. Spread the batter evenly into the cake tin and bake for 30 minutes. Cool slightly before removing it from the tin. Cool on a wire rack.

Spinach Greek Style

Serves 4
Calories: 277

Ingredients

170g (6oz) dry chickpeas
455g (1lb) fresh spinach
15ml (1 tbsp) olive oil
3 cloves garlic
2 medium onions
5ml (1 tsp) caraway *or* cumin seeds
2.5ml (1/2 tsp) freshly ground black pepper

Method

Wash, soak and cook the chickpeas. Wash, trim and drain the spinach. Heat the oil in a deep frying pan or saucepan and place over a medium flame. Finely chop the garlic and onion and sauté in the oil, stirring frequently. When the onion is tender, add the caraway and stir well. Add the cooked chickpeas and black pepper, cover the pan and cook for about 5 minutes. Roughly slice the spinach and place on top of the chickpeas. Cover the pan again and leave over a low flame for 10–15 minutes. Do not remove the cover. At the end of this time, stir the spinach into the chickpeas and serve immediately by itself, with rice or with steamed vegetables.

Split Pea Soup

Serves 4
Calories: 176

Ingredients

225g (8oz) dried split green peas
1 litre (2 pints) water
1 strip of kombu (optional)
1 bunch fresh coriander
6 cloves garlic
freshly ground black pepper to taste

Method

Wash and drain the peas and place them in a deep saucepan. Add the water, cover and bring to the boil. Add the kombu, reduce the heat and simmer for 45 minutes, stirring occasionally. Wash and clean the coriander and chop it finely. Peel the garlic and cut each clove in half. Add the coriander, garlic and pepper to the soup. Stir well and simmer for a further 15 minutes. Serve very hot.

Stuffed Pumpkin Bake

Serves 4
Calories: 81

Ingredients

a 900g (2lb) squash or pumpkin
340g (3/4lb) broccoli
30g (1oz) fresh parsley
3 cloves garlic
1 medium onion

Method

Slice the squash in half lengthwise and remove the seeds. Place each half on a large piece of baking foil. Chop the remaining ingredients very finely and blend them together in a mixing bowl. You may add a dash of black pepper if you like. Divide this filling between the two halves of squash and press well down – even so the filling will rise above the edges of the squash. Bring the edges of the baking foil up over the filling and fold them together to seal. Place the filled squash halves together on a roasting tray and bake at 180°C/350°F/Gas Mark 4 for 30–40 minutes. Serve hot with a favourite sauce.

Sweet & Sour Spaghetti Sauce

Serves 4
Calories: 254

Ingredients

1 medium sized onion
3 cloves garlic
60ml (2 fl oz) cider vinegar
225g (1/2lb) button mushrooms
55g (2oz) raisins or currants
15ml (1 tbsp) brewer's yeast
5ml (1 tsp) freshly ground black pepper
115g (4 oz) wholewheat spaghetti

Method

Chop onion and garlic and sauté in the vinegar in a large frying pan. Clean and thickly slice the mushrooms and add to the sauté. Stir in the raisins, yeast and pepper, stir well and simmer very gently while you cook the spaghetti. Serve the sauce over the spaghetti.

Tangy Tempeh

Serves 4
Calories: 127

Ingredients

225g (8oz) tempeh
150ml (5 fl oz) cider vinegar
juice of 2 lemons
5ml (1 tsp) mustard seed
12 whole cloves
12 whole peppercorns
3–6 cloves garlic (optional)
2 small onions
1 tart apple

Method

Defrost the tempeh and cut into 1-inch cubes. Place the tempeh in a casserole dish. Mix the vinegar, lemon juice and spices together in a jug. Finely chop the garlic, onions and apple and add to the marinade in the jug. Stir well and pour over the tempeh pieces in the casserole. Cover the casserole and leave the tempeh to marinate for 4–8 hours. Bake, covered, at 180°C/350°F/Gas Mark 4 for 30 minutes.

Remove the cover and bake for a further 10 minutes if you want a crispy surface to the tempeh. Serve hot with brown rice and steamed broccoli.

Tempeh Take-Away

Serves 4

Calories: 269

Ingredients

225g (8oz) tempeh
10ml (2 tsp) oil
8 slices wholewheat bread
15ml (1 tbsp) mild mustard
115g (4oz) Cos lettuce
2 medium tomatoes
½ cucumber
juice of half a lemon

Method

Defrost the tempeh and slice the block diagonally in half. Slice each half into four thin wedges and arrange these on a lightly oiled baking tray. Place the tempeh in the oven (180°C/350°F/Gas Mark 4) for 30 minutes, turning the tempeh wedges after 15 minutes. Or, for a quicker meal, place the tempeh under a hot grill for 10 minutes – turning it after 5 minutes. Meanwhile, lay out the bread, spread four pieces with mustard and arrange the salad ingredients over these four slices. When the tempeh is golden brown, place two wedges on each sandwich, close with the other piece of bread and serve. (Tempeh is *another* traditional soyabean product. What a wonderful plant! It comes as a block of fermented beans which you can buy frozen from health food shops. See chapter 18 for more information.)

Tofu Marinade

Serves 4

Calories: 78

Ingredients

285g (10oz) firm tofu
140ml (5 fl oz) cider vinegar
30g (1oz) fresh ginger
a pinch of freshly ground black pepper
115g (4oz) button mushrooms

Method

Cut the tofu into small chunks, place in a bowl and pour the vinegar over. Slice the ginger very thinly and add to the tofu; sprinkle the pepper over it and stir gently. Clean and quarter the mushrooms and add to the tofu, stir again, cover and leave to marinate for 2–4 hours. Serve cold or heat the whole mixture in a saucepan over a medium heat. Serve with rice, pasta or a salad. (You can buy tofu in all health food shops and some supermarkets, and you can even make it at home – see chapter 18.)

Tomato and Tofu Soup

Serves 4

Calories: 53

Ingredients

4 small courgettes
115g (4oz) firm tofu
1 medium onion
1 litre (2 pints) water
140g (5oz) tomato purée
2.5ml ($^1/_2$ tsp) freshly ground black pepper
5ml (1 tsp) dried basil

Method

Wash the courgettes; trim and slice them into thin rounds. Drain the tofu and cut into small cubes. Peel and thinly slice the onion. Mix the water and tomato purée together in a jug then stir in the black pepper and basil. Place a large saucepan over a medium flame and heat it for two or three minutes. Then pour approximately 60ml (2 fl oz) of the tomato sauce into the pan so that it bubbles immediately. Drop the onion into the sauce and stir constantly as you would a sauté. Add more sauce if necessary. When the onions have softened, add the courgettes and continue to stir over a medium to high heat for three minutes. Add the remaining sauce, stir well and cover the pan. Reduce the heat and leave it to simmer gently for 15 minutes. Add the tofu, stir the soup and leave it over the heat for a further 5 minutes. Serve hot.

Walnut and Onion Salad

Serves 4

Calories: 286

Ingredients

1 small turnip
2 large carrots
1 medium onion
2 eating apples
115g (4oz) broken walnuts
285g (10oz) soft tofu
5ml (1 tsp) caraway seeds
juice of half a lemon

Method

Wash, trim and shred the turnip and carrots and place them in a salad bowl. Peel the onion; finely chop the onion and apples and add to the salad bowl. Add the remaining ingredients to the salad and stir well. Serve slightly chilled with a garnish of parsley or lemon peel.

Vanilla Oat Cake

Serves 6
Calories: 146

Ingredients

225g (8oz) wholewheat flour
55g (2oz) rolled oats
55g (2oz) raisins *or* sultanas
5ml (1 tsp) baking powder
2.5ml (1/2 tsp) ground cinnamon *or* allspice
15ml (1 tbsp) oil
5ml (1 tsp) natural vanilla essence
140ml (5 fl oz) water

Method

Warm the oven to 160°C/300°F/Gas Mark 3 and lightly oil a 20cm (8in) cake tin. Mix the first five ingredients together in a mixing bowl. Mix the oil, essence and water, add to the dry mix and stir well. Spoon the batter evenly into the cake tin and bake for 25 minutes. Allow to cool, then slice and serve.

CHAPTER 24
HOW TO BE A CARING CONSUMER

~

Next time you wheel your trolley down the supermarket aisle, think of your purchase as a vote for change, not a veto!

We all know of boycotts for humanitarian or political reasons of the produce of certain countries. But why not deliberately choose an item from the United Nations of Fruit and Vegetables spread out before you to *benefit* the country of origin?

Consider the repercussions: a tin of prunes from Guatemala, say, may seem like just a tin of prunes, but what if the plums were planted in fields that used to grow maize, the staple diet of local subsistence farmers? It is true that prunes may be more lucrative and pay for imported maize many times over. But how much of the profit filters down to the peasant farmer? And if the price of prunes slumps, the peasants will be laid off and probably lose their land.

Of course, if we protest against such a pernicious system by boycotting prunes, we may precipitate the very collapse which will harm the peasants most. Then again, how much influence does the individual prune-purchaser *really* wield?

No doubt the issues are very complex, but that is no excuse for inaction, as the world is more interdependent than ever before. If you are concerned, write a checklist of what benefits you hope will accrue from what you buy. Will it help the ecology, profit the small farmer, and encourage labour-intensive farming which soaks up rural unemployment? Let's look at these issues.

Enough for all

Contrary to popular belief, the earth produces more food than is needed, enough to feed six billion people, one billion more than the world's population. Yet 950 million consume too few calories to support an active working life; and each year millions – many of them children – die from lack of food or malnutrition-related diseases, according to the World Resources Institute. The problem is that too few have proper access to food. By and large this is a symptom of a non-egalitarian system which pits rich against poor between and within nations. In relative terms, fewer people suffer malnutrition and related diseases, but in real terms more are being denied the food that could ward off illness and lethargy.

The prunes example is a variant of the old cash crops versus staples argument. If more people in the Third World grew what they needed and not what Western markets wanted, so the reasoning goes, none of them would starve even if commodity prices collapsed. Cash crops often form the basis for single-product economies and render them dependent on the world price.

Can't live on chocolates

In Ghana, for instance, one in four persons works in a cocoa industry which generates 60 per cent of the country's foreign exchange. Yet few eat chocolate there, and when the cocoa price fell from $3,789 per tonne in 1977 to $1,174 in 1989, foreign earnings dwindled and social programmes suffered. Attempts to form an international cocoa producers' cartel failed, partly because the biggest importer wanted a free market. While the long-term solution must be to diversify Ghanaian production, the short-term approach backed by the IMF was to cut back the Ghanaian cocoa marketing board's bureaucracy and pay farmers more (the Ivory Coast overtook Ghana as number one cocoa producer in 1980 simply because it paid its farmers better). Cocoa has also harmed Ghana's ecology, forcing forests to be cut back from 8.2 million square kilometres in 1900 to 1.9 million now.

Not surprisingly, many feel that cash crops are inherently bad, but farmers worldwide are business people and if given the choice (a big 'if') they will grow whatever makes a profit. In Ghana farmers are *paid* to grow cocoa, but food production is left to market forces. Yet it is wrong to say a cash crop is necessarily a luxury product and therefore useless to the locals.

Cash crops aren't all bad

In Asia small farmers now grow rice in place of previous staples. Not only does this increase their calorie intake, it also generates money with which they can buy other food to vary their diet; and as more people in the West buy their exported rice, the price stays firm and affords them the security to develop.

The Green Revolution of the 1960s and 1970s used agro-research to boost production, via new disease-resistant and fertile crop strains, greater use of pesticides and more advanced farming methods. Overall it succeeded beyond expectations (in many cases over-production has reduced prices, again at the Third World's expense), but it did not help income distribution, and upset the environmental balance. As a general rule, research funds go to farmers who through their own means or via political influence can generate some surplus money themselves – in other words, not subsistence farmers. (Incidentally, 'gene patenting', a by product of biological engineering, merely expands this trend.) The 'revolution' largely bypassed farmers in the rain-fed drylands which dominate most of Africa and much of South Asia and South America.

A strategy for success

A simple purchase cannot change these conditions overnight, but you *can* buy items to try to improve them. Research indicates that mixed cropping or intercropping can halt erosion and desertification. Farmers can grow rows of vegetables and beets between cereals like maize, which not only binds the vital topsoil but also provides an all-year-round income!

In some cases chemicals released by vegetables ward off familiar crop diseases and pests, thus obviating the need for imported pesticides, which cost money and often do more harm than good. As a consumer you could earmark producers who use intercropping, and buy their products.

One instance is found in the small-scale, but highly-productive, multi-crop gardens of Java. Another comes from Zimbabwe, where in the decade since independence small farmers have used progressive techniques, including multi-cropping, to triple their production of maize.

Do not restrict yourself to buying just vegetables from the drylands – the jojoba plant, used in shampoos, is an ideal dry soil crop.

Buy food from co-operatives

Buying a single product will not help the farmer directly – as most agriculture is dominated by huge concerns, whether multinational agribusinesses or state collectives, the individual farmer is normally the last to benefit. A better way to ensure that he or she gets something, is to earmark products made by progressive concerns, especially grassroots farming cooperatives. One such group is the Kenyan small farmers who use 'fanya-juu' – an appropriate technology system of terracing hillsides and intercropping. Another are the Mexican peasant honey farmers who got together to organize every step of the production. That includes blending, the final stage which adds value and hence profit to the good. Honey is a seasonal cash crop which brings money and security for poorer farmers when their regular crops lie fallow. Furthermore, bees pollinate other plants and so better the general ecology. As British tastes for unusual blends grows in line with Europe in 1992, we can savour these delights and benefit the peasants.

Decentralized cooperatives are still the exception to the rule. Our buying power may push up the price of a product but that does not mean tenant farmers or farm labourers necessarily benefit. Sugar is a good example. In the early 1970s GATT-Fly, a Canadian campaign group for a more equitable international trading system, earmarked the low sugar price as a cause of extreme poverty in Brazil. Yet when the price soared, actual working conditions for peasants worsened!

Instead of raising peasants' wages, plantation owners expropriated their subsistence plots to plant more lucrative cane. So GATT-Fly changed tack and encouraged local educators and politicians to organize workers to organize themselves. The message for the supermarket customer is: support countries which allow agricultural unions, and boycott those which do not. That way it is more likely that the profits will benefit the actual workers.

Here is another example of what you can do. The World Development Movement (WDM), a London-based campaign group, recently unpeeled the truth about the humble banana. Some 200 Colombian growers were killed, at the instigation of private landlords and with the connivance of government forces and multinationals, when they tried to negotiate better wages.

The governments of the Windward Islands of the Caribbean and Nicaragua, by contrast, back the interests of small farmers and allow them union rights. Currently these producers have preferential trade agreements with Britain, but all that is set to end with EC 'free trade' moves after 1992. That, says WDM, will open the door to artificially low prices for the three American multinational producers: hardly 'free' trade at all!

So pay more for Caribbean bananas in the knowledge that you are helping the peasants themselves. With that extra capital, they can diversify production to lessen their dependency on bananas.

Consumers can also support products of participatory rural initiatives, like the panchayat village parliaments in India and the Village Development Committees in Zimbabwe.

A woman's lot

Most farming in the Third World is done by women. Lacking political representation, women farmers are often compelled to surrender their income to their husbands and their families. So which countries and companies give women a voice in their work? Again, the WDM can supply you with up-to-date information on this.

Meanwhile, consider the Bangladeshi women who in 1978 organized their own clothes factories, producing low-cost but good quality goods. For many it is the first time they have worked in a money economy, independent of men. It has resulted in a virtual social revolution, and although the pay is poor, it does show the potential for female economic power and should be encouraged by Western consumers.

Another example are the sixty women's groups involved in the Kenyan Green Belt Movement, started in 1977 by Professor Wangari Maathai, which sets up tree nurseries and aims at self-sufficiency in wood. Not only is this ecologically sound, it also empowers women and provides a surer base for agriculture.

Buy less packaging

It is also worth considering in what form we buy our food or other goods. As a general rule, the more packaging and processing that goes into a product, the more likely it is that the profits will go to Western importing nations. But as consumers become more aware of their power to change things for the better, it is not too fanciful to see Third World entrepreneurs one day doing as well.

Ghana Cocoa Products, for example, are already making their own Golden Tree milk chocolate, at source. Economies of scale and weaknesses in marketing and transport mean that production of chocolate, as opposed to raw cocoa, is still dominated by multinationals, but greater consumer knowledge and the desire for positive change may one day achieve great things.

In 1973 the developing countries' percentage of world trade in manufactured goods stood at just 4.7 per cent; in 1987 that had risen to 9.5 per cent. While still trivial, much of this advance is due to the sort of 'value-adding' described above.

So before you write off the Third World as being bound to the vicissitudes of Western commodity markets forever, consider the example of the Pakistani city of Sialkot which produces most of the world's footballs; or the South Indian manufacturer who has cornered the market for 'traditional' British pub furnishings; or indeed the 'sunrise economies' of Thailand, Taiwan and South Korea, countries which till recently were regarded as aid burdens on the West and which are now overtaking our electronics industry.

A weapon of change

Until now, revolutions have traditionally been bloody affairs. The machine gun and the Molotov cocktail have, in the long run, rarely succeeded in improving the lot of the world's poorest people.

But now a new peaceful weapon is emerging. You carry it round with you in your wallet. Your buying 'vote' may be, at best, a blunt weapon, but that should not deter us from being aware of the results of our choice, and the chance, albeit limited, of using it for good rather than ill. But in order to use it, you must know how the food you're buying was produced, and what the real cost of production was. Enlightened supermarkets will start to provide this information to their customers – provide the customers ask them!

Says Ed Mayo, WDM campaigns organizer: "Our consumer power may not be geared up to tackle world market problems alone – global trade realignments are essential. Even so, we must realize we are part of the solution."

Green consumerism has already made its mark. Now it's time for the caring consumer . . .

CHAPTER 25
FOODS TO FIGHT ACNE

~

Find out how you can help your acne through watching what you eat.

For many of us, our teens are a time when our skin, and particularly the more visible parts of it, seems to lead a rebellious life of its own. Spots, pimples, blackheads, whiteheads, boils and other embarrassing eruptions – you name it, most of us will suffer from it at some point during adolescence. Some of us will go to extraordinary lengths to cure this teenage curse. When a raider in a balaclava and dark glasses held up a Scarborough chemist's shop at gunpoint, it wasn't cash he was after. Handing the startled assistant a bag, he demanded: "Fill it up with spot cream!"[55] As you might expect, the market for acne treatments is thriving – over £20 million was spent on anti-acne skin products last year in Great Britain alone.

Sex

The vast majority of people have suffered from acne at some point during their lives. Teenagers who suffer from it are not unusual – one study estimates that 90 per cent of teenagers are afflicted by it at some time. Acne often seems to develop at about the time that most people's bodies start to mature and increase their production of certain types of sexual hormones.

As the level of sex hormones increases in the body, little glands under the surface of the skin, called sebaceous glands, start to increase their production of sebum. Sebum is an oily substance that is used to lubricate the skin, and it normally moves freely to the surface of the skin. Problems develop, however, when its progress is blocked by hard plugs of skin, called keratin.

As the blockage increases in size, it may show up as a whitehead, developing into a blackhead when it becomes coloured by skin pigmentation. In the meantime, sebum production continues unabated, and may leak into the surrounding skin, causing inflammation. If bacteria are attracted to the developing mass of sebum, they may then produce free fatty acids, which will inflame the skin further. The skin becomes irritated, pus and cysts may form, and scar tissues develop.

Now although acne has traditionally been reserved for spotty teenagers, more and more adult women, even those who have never had skin problems before, seem to be suffering from so-called execu-rash. In mature women, it seems as if the stress of today's lifestyle can cause their bodies to over-produce male hormones, or androgens. Produced by the adrenal glands in response to stress, androgens stimulate oil glands in the face, shoulders, chest and back. Excess oil then plugs their pores, and bingo! Acne develops.

... and drugs

Many drugs have been used to try and control acne. Some chemicals will make the horny layer of your skin soften and peel away, these substances are termed keratolytics. The aim is to remove the plugs of keratin, so allowing the sebum to drain freely. Some of these substances can be effective, for some people.

Products sometimes contain anti-bacterial substances, but since acne is not actually caused by bacteria, although they may play a role in its continuance, it's not certain how effective these products will be. In general, drugs that are sold over the counter in chemists' shops may have some use in treating mild cases of acne, but more severe cases will require treatment by a medical dermatologist.

Spots and oil

There are more old wives' tales about the causes and cures of acne than almost any other common medical condition. Acne is not caused by masturbation or any other form of sexual activity, nor can it be cured by leading a pure and blameless life. Even if it could, would you really want to?

In recent years, it has become the received wisdom in conventional medicine that diet and acne are not related. That's because a number of experiments have failed to pinpoint any one ingredient of the diet either as a universal trigger or as a cure for acne. But we already know that acne is caused by a number of factors – not just chocolate pudding. And new evidence from all over the world is starting to indicate that, while food may not be the only cause, it may well be part of the problem.

When scientists studied clear-skinned and blemish-free Inuit (Eskimos) and Japanese who switched to eating a Western diet, they found cases of acne suddenly appearing. And the Zulus of South Africa have always had a spotless skin as well, until they were moved from their tribal villages to the cities, where they ate Western food and developed acne.

So here are some suggestions about the type of food you might consider changing to. Not everything will work for everyone, because acne is highly individual in cause and treatment. But if you find something that works for you, stick to it!

Essential fatty acids

Essential fatty acids (EFAs) are called 'essential' because your body can't manufacture them itself, and it relies on you to eat a good diet to obtain its supplies. According to research published in the *Journal of the American Academy of Dermatology*, acne sufferers have been found to have a deficiency of the EFA linoleic acid in their skin – this could well be due to too much hydrogenated fat in the diet. So you may be able to help your body fight acne by replacing the hydrogenated fats in your diet, which can actually cause a deficiency, with oils which are rich in linoleic acids, such as sunflower, soyabean, corn or safflower oil (see chapter 10).

Vitamin A

Research proves that people with very severe acne often have low levels of vitamin A in their blood. It has long been known that this vitamin is essential for skin maintenance. As the cells in the skin renew themselves rapidly, vitamin A, with its important growth properties, is particularly vital for this organ, the largest in the human body. In fact, several of the commercial drugs currently available for acne treatment are vitamin A based. Plants contain a form of vitamin A known as carotene, found in carrots, which can be converted in the human body to vitamin A. Good, natural sources are carrots themselves, green leafy vegetables such as spinach and broccoli, and fruits which have a characteristic yellow colour, such as peaches, mangoes and apricots. A diet which is rich in these foodstuffs will naturally supply all your vitamin A needs. Supplements should only be used under professional advice, because there is evidence that adverse effects, including birth defects, may be caused by doses of 25,000 IUs or higher.

Chromium

It has been estimated that as much as 90 per cent of the population may have a deficiency of this trace element. Chromium works in the body to convert blood sugar into insulin, and researchers have found that the more insulin the body uses to process sugars following meals, the more chromium the body needs. And, indeed, it has been found that people with unstable levels of glucose in their blood are more likely to develop severe acne: one researcher has even called acne 'skin diabetes'. In one experiment, researchers found that patients with unstable levels of blood glucose also experienced severe acne. When they were given two teaspoons daily of yeast containing 400 micrograms of chromium, their improvement was rapid.[56] To increase your chromium intake, eat plenty of brewer's yeast and molasses. Chromium supplements are also available in health food shops.

Hormones

The male hormone, testosterone, stimulates production of the sebaceous glands and is triggered in times of stress. This may be the reason why more and more older women are developing acne. As they are put under increasing stress from both work and family, their testosterone levels shoot up, with acne as one of the results. Since many animal foods contain hormones and hormone-like substances, it might be a good idea to avoid these foods if you fall into this category. Beauticians have also reported that women who eat a lot of meat are more likely to have body hair, because of the steroids the meat contains.[57]

Iodine

Try avoiding iodine-containing foods for a while and see if your skin condition improves. It seems that even minute amounts of iodine may lead to skin problems in sensitive people because any excess that the body cannot absorb is excreted through the pores, aggravating a condition such as acne. So try avoiding foods containing significant amounts of iodine, such as kelp, seaweed, asparagus, liver, milk, wheat and particularly cough mixtures and tonics.

Selenium

For a long time, scientists thought that selenium was simply a toxic substance which had no dietary use at all. But recent research suggests that very small amounts of selenium (200 micrograms, which is the same as 0.2 milligrams) taken twice daily for six to 12 weeks, in combination with vitamins A and E, can reduce the severity of persistent acne.[58] Selenium is naturally found in broccoli, cabbage, onions and whole-grain products, and combination selenium products are on sale in health food shops.

Zinc

Zinc is a very important weapon in the fight against acne. A good source of zinc in the diet is an essential requirement for general health. Millions of people are zinc-deficient in the West, probably due to their consumption of over-refined foods. Experiments have found that both oral and skin application of zinc has brought positive results in people with acne. In one experiment, 58 per cent of sufferers reported dramatic improvement when treated with zinc.

It is not certain how zinc actually works in the body to control acne, but it is known that low levels of zinc can lead to excessive male hormone production. Some doctors recommend an intake of 30 to 40 milligrams of elemental zinc every day for between three and four months even though the normal recommended daily allowance is only 15 milligrams. If you do decide on this course of action, consult your doctor, as a zinc overdose can be dangerous. Zinc preparations are available in health food shops, and good natural sources of zinc include whole grain products, brewer's yeast, and pumpkin seeds.

Detoxification

Another therapy to consider is bowel detoxification through colonic irrigation coupled with re-seeding the bowels with benign bacteria. See chapter 70 for more information.

Allergies

You never know, you might just be allergic to chocolate pudding! In experiments, it has been shown that about ten per cent of acne sufferers can reduce their symptoms by finding, and eliminating from their diet, a food to which they're allergic. The most common foods to produce this reaction are almonds, malt, cheese, mustard, red pepper and wheaten flour. For more information about this, see chapter 46.

CHAPTER 26

FOODS TO FIGHT ARTHRITIS AND RHEUMATISM

~

Many of us experience aches and pains and quickly dismiss them. But they could be the first, generalized signs of rheumatic disorder. Now is the time to take preventive action by amending your diet.

If you are fairly young and fit, suffering from arthritis probably never crosses your mind. Yet every year a staggering eight million people visit their doctor with symptoms of arthritis.

Arthritis and rheumatism defined

Arthritis is a specific term describing inflammation of the joints; rheumatism is used more broadly and describes all aches and pains in the muscles, bones or joints. In this sense, we have all suffered from rheumatism at some time. Rheumatoid arthritis therefore is inflammation and pain of the joints *and* the surrounding tissues. There are, in fact, some one hundred different types of arthritis, including:

~ Reiter's Syndrome, an acute form often accompanied by eye inflammation and more frequently found in young men.

~ Ankylosing Spondylitis, a chronic complaint, affecting the spine, pelvic joints, and sometimes the heart and eyes. It causes pain, fatigue and depression which can last for years.

~ Systemic Lupus Erythematosus, which is much more common in women than men and is characterized by skin rashes and joint inflammation.

~ Gout results in swelling and severe pain, normally in the big toe. It has long been known to be aggravated by diet, especially foods rich in purine, which produces uric acid.

Why do people get arthritis?

Many different causes have been suggested including stress, allergy, food and environmental pollution, malnutrition, hormonal imbalance, and digestive inadequacy. Another is that our body can mistakenly attack itself in trying to fight off foreign bacteria that closely resemble our own tissue. This is called an autoimmune response. Relevant to all of these, there is ever increasing evidence that diet has a very important role to play in the onset and control of these degenerative disorders.

How you can fight arthritis with food

~ When the bacteria colonizing their gut has been changed significantly people often experience relief from rheumatic symptoms.[59] A change of diet, such as described below, as well as a course of colonic irrigations (see chapter 70), followed by the use of *acidophilus* supplements (see chapter 52) will begin to improve your internal hygiene.

~ One interesting study of rheumatoid arthritics involved a week of fasting followed by three weeks of a vegan diet. At the end of this time, 60 per cent said they felt better, with "less pain and increased functional ability".[60] A vegan diet excludes all meat, fish, eggs and dairy products, but includes an abundance of the many and exotic fruits, vegetables, grains, pulses, seeds and nuts available. Many who eat a vegan diet avoid excess consumption of tea, coffee and alcohol as well.

~ A calorie controlled diet is of benefit to those who suffer rheumatism or arthritis and are overweight. Excess weight only adds to the strain placed on already overstressed joints. A healthy way to lose weight is to eat a vegan diet and, at the same time, cut out all refined sugar. This diet lets you drop the pounds quickly while significantly reducing joint discomfort.

~ In another study rheumatoid arthritis sufferers given a fat free diet for seven weeks reported a complete absence of symptoms.[61] When animal and vegetable fats were returned to their diets, their symptoms returned. So try keeping your intake of fat to 20-25 per cent of your total calorie intake.

~ More specifically, meat and dairy products contain the fatty acid arachidonic acid. It promotes the inflammation that is felt in rheumatism and arthritis when it is converted to inflammatory prostaglandin and leukotrienes. Replace animal fats with foods high in polyunsaturates and the omega-3 fatty acids (found in flaxseed oil supplements) to experience less pain.

~ Vitamin A is necessary for the body to fight infection, a key in many rheumatoid cases. To make sure you get enough of this vitamin, eat plenty of yellow, orange and green fruits and vegetables such as spinach, carrots, papaya, pumpkin, sweet potato, watercress and parsley.

~ If you are taking drugs for a rheumatic disease, it is probable that you are lacking in vitamin B complex. This is found in whole grains and brewer's yeast.

~ Vitamin C helps to thin the synovial fluid in your joints, leading to improved mobility. Arthritics, particularly, benefit from taking vitamin C because the aspirin they take to reduce pain and inflammation depletes the body of vitamin C. Fresh citrus fruit, blackcurrants, green peppers and cauliflower are all excellent sources.

~ Vitamins C and E and the mineral selenium are all antioxidants; oxidation is a process in which nutrients in the body are broken down before the body can use them. Selenium also reduces the production of prostaglandins and leukotrienes, both of which cause inflammation. Whole grains, vegetable oils and nuts are rich in vitamin E. Selenium is a trace mineral available from most plant foods or from supplementation.

~ Avoid purine-rich foods such as organ meats, peas and beans if you suffer from gout.

~ A New England horticulturalist has developed a theory that solanum alkaloids, found in members of the nightshade family of plants, could cause arthritis in some people. The nightshade family includes deadly nightshade, aubergine, red and green pepper, potatoes, tomatoes and tobacco. A group of 3,000 sufferers cut this family of foods from their diet and experienced reduced aches, pains and disfigurement.[62]

~ People with arthritis sometimes have an enzyme deficiency in their small intestine which means they are unable to absorb gluten, a protein found in wheat flour. In fact, maps of areas where gluten-high cereals are eaten correspond to those areas with the highest incidence of rheumatoid arthritis.[63] And countries where rice or corn is the staple grain show a much lower rate of the rheumatic diseases than those whose staple grain is wheat. Reduce your consumption of gluten by substituting rice cakes and oatmeal or corn bread for wheat bread and cake.

~ Food intolerance creates symptoms which include headaches, fatigue, depression, constipation and, in some people, rheumatic pain and stiffness. If you suspect your body cannot tolerate a particular food, eliminate it from your diet. Here's how:

- Stop eating the food in any form for eight weeks. If that food *is* causing you problems, you will probably crave it for several days and generally feel terrible.
- Were you to eat the suspect food at this craving stage and feel very much better, then you are undoubtedly intolerant of it. This may seem paradoxical – but food intolerance closely resembles addiction at this stage.
- After approximately ten days your craving will diminish.
- After 14-18 days, eat a little of the suspect food. If your symptoms return, then your suspicions are confirmed and the food has caused you problems.
- Some people may eat very little amounts of this food infrequently with no ill effect after avoiding it for 2-3 months. Others experience a complete return of symptoms if they ever eat the food again.

~ Yucca is a folk medicine which has been used for more than 1,000 years in America. In a study into its effects, 60 per cent of rheumatoid arthritis and osteoarthritis patients experienced an improvement in their symptoms of swelling, pain and stiffness.[64] Yucca is available in supplement form.

~ An alfalfa supplement may be of particular help to you. It is rich in protein, minerals and vitamins and contains chlorophyll, an excellent detoxifier of your system, reducing pain and swelling. Take it daily, in tablet or powder form, or as a tea. Also, you may like to add alfalfa sprouts to your salad or sandwich.

Chapter 27
Foods to Fight Cancer

~

You can actually minimize your risk of cancer by eating the right foods. And it is possible that improvements made to your diet *now* can have a curative effect on some developing cancers.

There are multifarious causes of cancer. Genetic, dietary, occupational and psychological factors all play an important part. In fact, it is unusual to be able to pinpoint a single cause of cancer and say: "If it weren't for this, I would not have cancer." Rather, cancer seems to form out of a lifestyle in which some detrimental factors are occupational, some psychological, some dietary, and so on.

Various observations have been made in recent decades:

~ The number of cancer cases has risen dramatically in recent years until nearly one-half of all cancers are suffered by just one-fifth of the world's population – those who live in industrialized countries.[65] And of course, industrialized populations have to cope with more stress, pollution and degenerative diseases than non-industrialized populations.

~ People who are generally viewed as 'nice' people – slow to anger, compliant, unassertive and overly cooperative and patient – seem more likely to succumb to cancer. Those who have an aggressive manner or a 'fighting spirit' seem more likely to combat or even conquer it.[66]

~ Carcinogens (cancer-producing substances) are found in many areas of life, from work to leisure to the home. Of these, many are self-administered: some knowingly as in cigarettes and radiation, others unknowingly as in various pollutants whose effects may be suspected but are not yet fully known.

~ When eminent scientists Richard Doll and Richard Peto assembled all the evidence they could find linking the occurrence of human cancers to specific identifiable causes, they estimated that diet was the greatest single risk factor – responsible for approximately 35 per cent of all deaths due to cancer. Tobacco came second (30 per cent).[67]

The influence of diet in the development of cancer is probably the most predictable and the simplest to control. Here are the components of your diet which you can manipulate to reduce your risk of developing cancer.

Fat

Generally, there is a much lower cancer rate in countries where the average diet is made up of less than 30 per cent of calories from fats. In the UK and America – where cases of cancer are much higher – the average fat intake is 42 per cent of calories from fats.[68] A wide range of cancers seems to be particularly associated with a high-fat diet, including breast, ovarian and colorectal cancers. Colorectal cancers are especially common in countries with a Western style diet, rich in meat and fatty foods.[69] In countries where a traditional low-fat, high-fibre diet is still followed, these cancers are noticeably rare.

~ Aim to reduce your fat consumption to account for *no more* than 30 per cent of your total calorie intake. Even more effective, however, is a fat intake of nearer 20 per cent of total calorie intake.

~ No more than one-third of the fat you consume should be saturated. This is easily achieved by avoiding dairy and flesh foods, and margarines.

~ Use a monounsaturated oil such as olive oil in place of other fats and read the labels of prepared foods to avoid palm, palm kernel and coconut oils, all of which contain saturated fat.

~ Omega-3 fatty acids are being studied to see whether they can reduce the risk of breast cancer in some women.[70] It seems possible, based on information available thus far, that these fatty acids may prevent or reverse an abnormal metabolism of hormones which signals an increased risk of cancer. Omega-3 fatty acids are present in flaxseed oil, available in supplement form.

Fibre

Fibre is the cornerstone of many healthy eating regimes, and a diet naturally high in fibre can almost certainly lower your risk from cancer of the colon.[71] It is thought to protect you from cancer by adding bulk to your diet – thereby preventing concentration of carcinogens as the digestive process proceeds. It may also help to eliminate potentially carcinogenic substances from the body quickly by speeding the transit of food through your digestive tract.

~ The average intake of fibre in the UK is 22g per day, but many experts recommend that this be increased to *at least* 30g per day to promote health.[72] This compares with a fibre intake of up to 120g per day eaten by Africans still following their traditional diet. Colon cancer is very rare in such communities.

~ Increase your fibre intake by eating whole grains, pulses, nuts and seeds, fruits and vegetables. Eat these foods in preference to meat and dairy foods, which contain no fibre but are high in saturated fat.

Vitamin A

A deficiency of this vitamin can contribute to the development of cancer in some people. It is available in two basic forms: retinol and beta-carotene (sometimes just called carotene). Retinol is the form which your body makes and stores in fatty tissue round your eyes, liver and heart. When necessary, your body releases small, precisely controlled amounts of retinol into your circulation. Any excess is stored away, so if too much vitamin A in the form of retinol is taken, toxicity can occur. Check the label on your vitamin supplement to see what form of vitamin A is supplied. Retinol is available in flesh foods, especially liver, eggs, milk and cheese.

Beta carotene is the form of vitamin A available in plant foods. Your body converts this form of vitamin A into retinol as and when your body requires it. Although large amounts of beta carotene may cause your skin to take on an orange colour, this is temporary and not harmful. Beta carotene does not create toxicity in the same way that retinol can. Beta carotene is strongly suspected of having cancer-preventive properties and several studies are currently underway to validate this theory.[73] In particular, it is thought to protect people from cancers of the lungs, bladder, larynx and colon.[74]

Most researchers believe that beta carotene is better than retinol for the purpose of protection from cancer. It is unlikely to cause toxicity, is a powerful antioxidant, is taken in and used according to the body's needs and it comes in a 'package' including secondary plant constituents – non-nutritive compounds that seem to inhibit the onset and growth of cancers – which may be vital to beta carotene's anti-cancer action.

~ To obtain beta carotene, eat any of the fruits and vegetables with a deep, bright green, yellow or orange colouring. Look for carrots, pumpkin, squash, spinach and broccoli, canteloupe, sweet potatoes and papaya. Eat these foods raw, fresh and organically grown if possible.

Vitamin C

This vitamin helps to minimize the effects of pollutants and carcinogens (cancer causing substances) in your food and environment. In particular:

~ Vitamin C seems to block the formation of nitrosamines. Nitrates and nitrites are added to foods to give colour, flavour and to act as preservatives (E249-E252). During digestion these substances are converted by the human body into nitrosamines, which are known to be powerful cancer-causing chemicals (they are particularly associated with cancers of the stomach and oesophagus). The good news is that if a vitamin C rich food is taken at the same time as foods containing nitrates or nitrites, then the production of nitrosamines is greatly reduced. Dr. Helmut Bartsch of the International Agency for Research of Cancer in Lyons, France, discovered that regular doses of vitamin C (100 milligrams three times a day) can dramatically reduce nitrosamine production.[75]

~ Try to avoid foods which are high in nitrates and nitrites. These include tinned, smoked and cured meats and fish, sausages, luncheon meats, bacon, pickled foods and some cheeses. In addition, tap water may contain these compounds, especially in farming areas where fertilizers containing nitrates are used on the land. Drink purified or bottled water instead, and check the label for nitrate/nitrite levels.

~ Mutagens are carcinogenic substances that can alter a cell's genetic makeup. They are readily formed when meat or fish is cooked to turn brown – for instance, when frying a burger or roasting a chicken. Although a high vitamin C intake may have a protective effect, you should reduce the amount of browned food you eat *and* increase your consumption of this vitamin.

~ Another carcinogen, benzopyrene, is produced when meat is charcoal-grilled. Benzopyrene is also present in cigarette smoke; a one-pound steak contains as much benzopyrene as in the smoke of nearly 300 cigarettes. Avoid meats cooked in this way and, if you have been in the habit of eating them, greatly increase your vitamin C intake.

~ Women with abnormal cervical smear results often have low amounts of vitamin C in their body.[76] This may shed new light on the underlying damage caused by smoking, because it has long been established that women who smoke have higher levels of cervical cancer. Smoking impairs the absorption of vitamin C but smoking also requires that you take more vitamin C to minimize the effects of it as a pollutant. If you do smoke, stop now! And greatly increase your intake of vitamin C-rich foods, such as citrus fruits, green peppers, broccoli, tomatoes, potatoes, canteloupe, strawberries and alfalfa sprouts.

Vitamin E

Vitamin E is another nutrient that provides protection against many of the damaging pollutants in the environment. It does this mainly by preserving oxygen in the blood, thus improving cellular strength and health. This vitamin is called an antioxidant because it combats the oxidation of various substances in your body. Of particular importance is vitamin E's ability to prevent the formation of free radicals (see chapter 9) as well as its protective influence on vitamins A and C and the B group of vitamins. So, while vitamin E may not be in the front line in your fight against cancer, it is essential to have a sufficiency of this vitamin in order to sustain improvements in your health.

~ Vitamin E is destroyed by chlorine in your drinking water and by rancid oils; it may be rendered useless if oestrogen is also taken.

~ Vitamin E is available in cold-pressed vegetable oils, nuts, seeds and soya beans.

Selenium

This trace mineral is essential to health, though only required in minute quantities. In America, the National Research Council has recommended a daily intake of 50-200 micrograms of selenium for adults (a microgram is one thousandth of a milligram, so 200 micrograms equal 0.2 milligrams). However, one authority – Gerhard Schrauzer, PhD, of the University of California – says that 250-300 micrograms can protect against most cancers, and that most people consume only about 100 micrograms daily.[77] At higher doses, selenium can be toxic to the human body. Although the precise level at which selenium begins to cause adverse effects is not known, it has been found that doses of 900 micrograms (0.9 milligrams) per day can make hair fall out and affect nails. This can also affect the nervous system.[78]

Selenium works best in conjunction with vitamin E, since both are antioxidants and can increase the production of antibodies by up to 30 times,[79] thereby greatly enhancing your immune response (see chapter 36). Together they help to detoxify your body and prevent the formation of free radicals (see chapter 9).

Selenium is present naturally in the soil, and the quantities available in our food relate to soil levels of selenium where the food was grown. A study of selenium included a map of its distribution in soil across the United States. This was then compared with a map detailing the national cancer rates. It was found that those areas with high levels of cancer corresponded with places of low levels of selenium in the soil. For instance, Ohio was shown to have the highest incidence of cancer and the lowest levels of selenium; South Dakota had the highest levels of selenium and the lowest rate of cancer.[80]

A study undertaken at the University of Tampere, Finland, involved taking blood samples from 21,172 Finnish men. The samples were then frozen. Eleven years after the samples had been taken, 143 men had contracted lung cancer. The researchers found that the men who eventually developed lung cancer had less selenium in their blood than those who did not. Overall, it was found that people with the lowest selenium levels were 3.3 times more likely to develop lung cancer than those with high levels. The researchers said their results were "in accord with other studies which strongly suggest that poor selenium nutrition is a highly significant risk factor for lung cancer".[81]

In West Germany, a study conducted at the University of Bonn has shown that selenium can protect against the harmful effects of ultra-violet radiation. Blood selenium levels were examined in 101 patients with malignant melanoma (a lethal form of skin cancer) and compared to a control group of healthy people. The skin cancer patients showed a significantly lower level of selenium, and the researchers concluded that their results "strongly suggest that sub-optimal selenium nutrition preceded the onset of the disease and may even have contributed to its genesis".[82]

Vitamin B Complex

Any form of stress, whether physical or mental, increases your need for the B vitamins. For instance, infection, pregnancy, the oestrogen pill, many drugs and the consumption of processed foods, coffee, sugar and alcohol all deplete your supply of this group of vitamins. The Bs are vital for metabolism, the health of your nerves, skin and liver. While not in the front line in the fight against cancer, the B group make other vitamins, such as A and E, much more effective in the work that they do.

~ A high B intake is helpful in preventing cirrhosis of the liver; cirrhotic livers are 60 per cent more likely to become cancerous than healthy livers.[83]

~ If you choose to take vitamin B in supplement form, ensure that you take all the variants together as they never work in isolation.

~ Foods richest in the B group are brewer's yeast and whole grains.

Calcium and Vitamin D

Calcium may be important in preventing both breast and colon cancer and it has been suggested that it could reduce the risk of colon cancer by two thirds when taken with vitamin D.[84] Vitamin D is necessary for the proper absorption of calcium. Your body manufactures this vitamin when sunlight reacts with dehydrocholesterol, a substance in your skin.

~ Obtain vitamin D either from fortified foods or by ensuring that you have ten minutes of daylight on your face and hands each day.

~ Calcium is available in tofu, dark green leafy vegetables such as spinach, watercress and parsley, seaweeds, nuts and seeds, dairy foods, molasses and dried fruits.

Calories

A high calorie diet may increase your risks of cancer. Cancer seems to be more common in obese people, especially those who are more than 40 per cent over their ideal weight.[85] Do your best to keep your weight within recommended limits.

Probiotics

It is possible to replace the harmful bacteria which flourish in your gut with immunity-enhancing bacteria called probiotics (see chapter 52). A diet rich in refined foods, meat and fat seems to increase your likelihood of cancer because the various by-products of digestion create bacteria which are more likely to be converted into carcinogens. The addition of a probiotic such as *Lactobacillus acidophilus* inhibits this type of conversion and colonizes the gut. This alters the ratio of 'friendly' to 'unfriendly' bacteria and improves your health in several ways. The 'unfriendly' bacteria thrive after a course of antibiotics and after years of poor diet. The friendly *lactobacilli* seem to enhance your immune function, prevent nitrites being converted to nitrosamines and convert nitrosamines back into non-carcinogenic substances.[86]

Lactobacillus acidophilus is just one of the friendly bacteria called probiotics; others are *L. bulgaricus*, *L. casei* and *Bifidobacteria*. The *lactobacilli* are found in cultured dairy products such as yoghurt.

Seaweed

Fewer women develop breast cancer in Japan than in either the US or the UK. The Japanese regularly include seaweed in their diet and some researchers now believe this has a major protective action against breast cancer.[87] Seaweed is thought to bind pollutants, inhibit the formation of carcinogens in the gut, reduce cholesterol and perform as an antioxidant. It also adds essential trace minerals to your diet.

~ Seaweed is a delicious and versatile food. Eat any of the common varieties several times each week (see chapter 16) or take kelp in supplement form every day.

Cabbage

Cruciferous vegetables include cabbage, broccoli, cauliflower, brussels sprouts and kale. These foods contain 'secondary plant constituents' – non-nutritive compounds that seem to inhibit the onset and growth of cancers.[88] These compounds, (i.e. indoles, phenols, flavones) are present in many plant foods but are particularly abundant in cruciferous vegetables. They are not available in supplement form.

~ Eat a serving of raw or cooked cruciferous vegetables three times a week.

Macrobiotics

Macrobiotics is a complete dietary system claimed by many to be a cure for all sorts of diseases, including cancer. Part of an oriental philosophy, macrobiotics takes a holistic approach to diet, maintaining that the food we eat affects our state of harmony with the universe and therefore our health. A macrobiotic diet is actually very similar to the nutritional intake recommended by the American Cancer Society, low in fat and high in complex carbohydrates and fibre, although it is not embraced by the ACS. The US House of Representatives Subcommittee on Health and Long-term Care stated in one of its publications that: "The current macrobiotic diet . . . appears to be nutritionally adequate if the mix of foods proposed in the dietary recommendations is carefully followed."[89] The Director of Clinical Nutrition at University Hospital Boston comments: "There is no denying that some people have experienced a positive change in lifestyle due to macrobiotics, and some even report remission of a disease such as cancer. Until more research is completed, macrobiotics cannot simply be ignored"[90] (see chapter 19).

The future

More and more research is being carried out all the time in this exciting area. The National Cancer Institute in America recently opened a Cancer Research Laboratory with the sole aim of investigating the connection between diet and cancer. By 1992 two important long-term experiments investigating the importance of micronutrients and cancer will be completed.

It's never too soon to start to reduce your risk of cancer. Eat a diet rich in whole grains, fruits and vegetables; avoid flesh foods and dairy products and use cold-pressed olive oil in cooking. Maintain a healthy weight, don't smoke and drink alcohol in moderation.

CHAPTER 28
FOODS TO FIGHT CHOLESTEROL

~

Cholesterol is an essential part of life. We need it to make hormones, bile and cell membranes. But if too much cholesterol builds up in your system, it can be fatal.

Every day of your life, your body produces about one gram of cholesterol. How it handles this – together with the cholesterol in your diet – can make the difference between life and death . . .

The silent killer

Because it happens so slowly, you don't notice it. No one can *feel* the cholesterol building up, and even when an artery becomes more than half blocked by this fatty, cholesterol-rich sludge known as 'atheroma', you still may not be aware of any warning signs to tell you that something is badly wrong. In fact, an artery usually has to be more than 75 per cent blocked before blood flow is seriously impeded. But by this stage, time is definitely running out. Our bodies depend on the normal flow of blood through minute capillaries, larger arteries (which transport oxygen-rich blood away from the heart) and veins (which carry blood back to the heart again) to nourish all our organs and body tissues. If this remarkable system, consisting of thousands of kilometres of blood vessels, is blocked for more than a few minutes, the heart will be damaged to such a great extent that it may be irreversibly stopped. So you see, with such a complex and awesome circulatory system, should something happen to interrupt or diminish your blood flow, the situation can become very serious, very quickly.

You will probably be shocked to learn that the very first clear, clinical account of someone having a heart attack was only written down in 1912. Until then, it seems as if heart attacks were so rare they just weren't written about or recorded. Today, of course, heart disease is the commonest cause of death in the Western world. Heart disease is an *epidemic of the twentieth century*. Over the past 80 years something has happened to make a once rare and unusual form of death so common that by the age of 65, one man out of every five has had a heart attack, and of those, one in ten has died. Although two-thirds of heart attacks happen to men in the United States, for example, about 400,000 women have a heart attack each year. But how do we go about lowering our cholesterol levels?

Soluble fibre is the secret

There can hardly be a person who hasn't heard of the benefits of eating a diet rich in fibre. But not everyone knows that there are two types of fibre – insoluble and soluble. Insoluble fibre is found in all plant foods, wheat bran being a major source. Insoluble fibre is highly effective for combating constipation, increasing stool weight, and preventing problems such as haemorrhoids and diverticular diseases. But it won't help reduce your cholesterol level.

Certain forms of soluble fibre, on the other hand, also have an effect on lowering raised serum lipids (fats in your blood). When a group of eighteen healthy volunteers agreed to add either twenty-three grams of wheat bran or one fifteen-gram oat fibre tablet to their usual diet, the researchers found that the oat fibre was much more effective than wheat bran in lowering total cholesterol. "The oat fibre tablet also proved easier to take and caused fewer side effects," reported the scientists.[91]

Now, there are only relatively few foodstuffs which contain significant amounts of this special, cholesterol-lowering soluble fibre. Here they are:

Oats – the germ of a good idea

It was observed at least as long ago as 1963 that oats could have a cholesterol-lowering effect. However, it was only in recent years that, as part of the quest for the answer to coronary heart disease, scientists have again re-examined this humble and inexpensive product. Today, many experiments have shown that oat bran can and does act to significantly lower blood cholesterol.

A group of twenty men with high blood cholesterol was admitted to hospital so their diets could be accurately measured for twenty-one days. Some were fed a 'control' diet (with no oat bran) and others were fed exactly the same diet, but with added oat bran. After just three weeks, the men receiving oat bran supplementation had lowered their serum cholesterol concentrations by nineteen per cent and had slashed their LDL concentrations by twenty-three per cent.[92]

Evidence shows that the average range of total cholesterol reduction on a low-fat diet with oat bran is in the region of ten to twenty-five per cent. Of course, it depends to some extent on how high your cholesterol is to begin with. But a diet which includes about 100 grams of oat bran and lasts for at least three weeks (the longer the better), should show a useful improvement.

Side effects

Oats are a natural substance, which have been eaten for thousands of years, so any adverse reactions should be known by now. There may be a softening of your stools, which shouldn't be objectionable (it might be a welcome change!). You may have more wind, which should calm down after a short time. It is possible that, if you are taking more than 50 grams per day, some bloating or abdominal pain could occur, in which case you should reduce your intake and consult your doctor. As with all new diets, it would be advisable to consult your doctor prior to adding this amount of oat bran to your daily diet, so that your medical history can be taken into consideration. Perhaps the only real disadvantage is that it simply seems *too* easy. If you can achieve a useful reduction in blood cholesterol simply by adding oat bran to your normal food, then you may not take further steps to improve the rest of your diet. This would be a mistake. As Dr. Basil Rifkind, chief of lipid metabolism and atherogenesis at the National Heart Lung and Blood Institute in Bethesda, says: "It would be wrong for people to start consuming oat bran and forgetting about everything else. The main thing you want to do is increase complex carbohydrates in the diet and reduce the amount of fat you consume."[93]

Corn bran

Corn bran (not available as widely as oat bran) may also be able to lower cholesterol. Researchers at Georgetown University Hospital found that when people ate raw corn bran their serum cholesterol was lowered by twenty per cent and triglycerides by thirty-one per cent. They gave about 40 grams daily to seven people suffering from hypercholesterolaemia, and to make it palatable, flavoured it with garlic powder, black pepper and celery seed, and sprinkled it over tomato juice or soup. Apparently there were no serious side effects.

Niacin

It has been known for some time that niacin – also called vitamin B_3 – can lower cholesterol levels if taken in large amounts. Niacin is found in foods such as yeast, milk, eggs, green vegetables and cereal grains, and your daily requirement of it is something in the region of sixteen milligrams. However, when used clinically to lower cholesterol, it is often taken in doses which are enormously larger – one to three *grams* – 200 times the recommended daily allowance. It is only in its nicotinic acid form that niacin has been found useful to lower cholesterol; nicotinamide does not have the same effect.

For those people who suffer from very high blood cholesterol, doctors sometimes prescribe niacin combined with one or more other types of drug (perhaps a bile acid sequestrant, such as cholestyramine) and additional diet therapy. Under these conditions, it is not uncommon to find a huge reduction in cholesterol of forty-five to sixty per cent!

You should remember, however, that your first line of attack against cholesterol should be to reduce your total and saturated fat and cholesterol intake, to control your weight, to increase your physical activity, and to control any disease (such as diabetes or hypothyroidism) which may be elevating your cholesterol. The range of side effects which have been associated with taking mega-doses of niacin make it much less suitable than other, more natural methods. Drug therapy (which is what taking large doses of niacin amounts to) should only be used when all these measures have failed, and under the supervision of your doctor.

Beans

Beans can be just as effective as oat bran in lowering cholesterol, because they contain useful amounts of the same soluble fibre. One hundred grams of oat bran contain nearly eight grams of soluble fibre. By using the following table, you can see how several different types of beans compare.[94]

Food	*Grams of soluble fibre in 100g*
Green beans, tinned	8.13
Navy beans, cooked	7.76
Pinto beans, cooked	7.52
Baked beans, tinned	6.3
Kidney beans, tinned	5.26

When researchers gave ten men suffering from high cholesterol a diet containing half a cup of tinned baked beans every day for three weeks, they found that cholesterol levels had dropped by an average of thirteen per cent and triglycerides had sunk by twelve per cent.[95] And this was on an 'average' diet which included a considerable amount of dietary fat and cholesterol! When British researchers carried out similar experiments, they also found that beans could cut cholesterol levels by about one third.[96] The researchers used plain, ordinary tinned baked beans, and asked volunteers to eat a 500 gram tin a day. Within three days of starting, the subjects showed a ten to twelve per cent drop in cholesterol! It seems, therefore, that eating some beans every day is a healthy, and easy, way to increase your cholesterol loss.

Pectin

Pectin is made from apples or citrus fruits, and is the gelling agent used to make fruit jams and jellies. It has also been used to treat diarrhoea. Like oat bran, pectin is a good source of soluble fibre, and has demonstrated its ability to lower serum cholesterol. In one trial, six men with familial hypercholesterolaemia were alternately treated with diet therapy plus cholestyramine (cholesterol-lowering drug) and diet therapy, cholestyramine and additional pectin. After eight weeks on each regime, it was found that with pectin added, total serum cholesterol was lowered by thirty-one per cent and LDL fell by thirty-five per cent. This was an improvement of twenty per cent over the diet and cholestyramine regime. The amount of pectin added was quite small – twelve grams a day, or about one scant tablespoon.[97] In another experiment, volunteers were given a daily dose of fifteen grams of pectin combined with 450 milligrams of vitamin C for 6 weeks, at the end of which it was found that their total serum cholesterol had fallen by more than eight per cent.[98] In the same trial it was noticed that for other subjects suffering from more severe hypercholesterolaemia, the drop was more pronounced – up to eighteen per cent.

Pectin is probably a useful adjunct to the dietary control of cholesterol, and since a small amount seems to produce a beneficial effect, one tablespoon a day could be easily incorporated into most diets.

Psyllium

Psyllium seeds (from the psyllium plantain, sometimes called ispaghula) have been used in bulk laxative preparations because when moistened, they swell up into a viscous mass, stimulating intestinal activity. There is also evidence that psyllium, like some other gel-producing gums, can act favourably on blood cholesterol levels. Twenty-six men were recruited by researchers, who gave them three and a half grams of psyllium at mealtimes, three times a day. No other dietary restrictions were imposed. After eight weeks of treatment, total cholesterol levels had fallen by nearly fifteen per cent, and LDL had dropped by twenty per cent. The researchers observed no adverse effects, and concluded that "psyllium is an effective and well-tolerated therapy for mild to moderate hypercholesterolemia".[99] In another trial, fibre made from psyllium husks was given to twelve elderly patients for four months, after which time it was found that blood cholesterol had dropped by twenty per cent, but triglycerides were not lowered.[100]

However, some adverse reactions have been noted following psyllium usage, including allergic reaction (anaphylaxis)[101] and hypersensitivity leading to anaphylactic shock.[102] You should therefore check with your doctor if you notice any unusual symptoms if you use psyllium, and should avoid it if you are likely to be allergic.

Rice bran

Recent research shows than rice bran (lost when converting brown rice to white rice) can be just as effective as oat bran in lowering cholesterol. But it may not work the same way. "We just don't think rice bran works by the same mechanism as oat bran," says Robin Saunders of the US Department of Agriculture. He believes the cholesterol-fighting agent in rice bran may be the oil it contains. Rice bran oil is high in b-sitosterol. It is thought that b-sitosterol and cholesterol compete for absorption in the intestines; therefore, an increased absorption of b-sitosterol means a decreased absorption of cholesterol. Rice bran oil has been widely used by Japanese cooks for fifty years, and is starting to become available in the West.

Just a few years ago, it was thought that surgery was the only way to undo temporarily the damage that cholesterol could do to our circulation. But now, we know that simply changing your lifestyle (reducing stress, lowering cholesterol levels) can effectively reverse heart disease. The evidence is there – let's act on it!

Chapter 29
Foods to fight the common cold

~

The common cold is the most widespread illness in Western countries. The average child catches about six colds a year, while adults get two or three colds annually.[103] What can we do to defeat this minor but most exasperating illness? Within five years, a drug will be available which will have the power to prevent cold viruses from infecting human cells. The drug (called soluble ICAM-1) will work by fooling cold viruses into binding to its surface, rather than infecting healthy human cells, and you'll probably buy it as a nasal spray.[104] In the meantime, however, here are some strategies worth trying.

There's always a cold around to be caught, but with a little help from you, your immune system will have the power to bring you through a whole year without so much as a sniffle.

The foods you eat can be used to both prevent and treat the dreaded sniffles, aches and chills of the common cold. A lucky six to ten per cent of the population never get colds; and by changing your diet you could become one of them. A cold is a viral infection, caused by any one of an estimated 200 different cold viruses. Each virus produces its own slightly different set of symptoms, which may include headache, chills, catarrh, sore throat, swollen glands and general malaise. Although not normally serious, colds can sometimes lead to respiratory disorders, pneumonia and meningitis. Some people still think that colds are brought about by cold weather, but a more logical explanation is that in winter we are in poorer health with a lower resistance to infection. During the colder months, we do less exercise, eat fewer fruits and vegetables and generally take less care of ourselves.

Getting rid of a cold

When your nose streams or you cough violently, it is for a reason. Your body is doing all it can to rid itself of the things making it feel so terrible in the first place. Most of the concoctions you can buy over the counter just suppress these symptoms, and do not actually help treat your cold. A much more successful approach is to assist your body in its battle:

~ Drink plenty of clear, unsweetened liquids during a cold. Do not drink honey and lemon, orange juice or other naturally sweet beverages. Although it is popularly supposed that honey will soothe your throat, and fruit juice will give you vitamin C, in fact, honey, citrus fruit and any other form of sugar or sweet food can diminish the functioning of your immune system, and so make it more difficult for your body to fight the virus (see chapter 36 for more information).

~ There is evidence that both the duration and severity of the common cold can be reduced by vitamin C intake.[105 106] Linus Pauling, pioneer of orthomolecular medicine (see chapter 85) suggests you should take two 1,000 milligram (1 gram) tablets of vitamin C at the first sign of a cold and that this dose should be repeated every hour for several hours. If the symptoms persist, Pauling suggests a total intake of 10 to 20 grams of vitamin C per day.

~ Suck a zinc lozenge as soon as you feel the first symptoms of a cold. Several scientific studies have shown that zinc can be useful in reducing the duration of a cold. In one study, a group of volunteers, all suffering from colds, were given a lozenge to suck every two hours while they were awake. Some of the lozenges contained 23 milligrams of zinc gluconate, others contained none (a placebo). After seven days, it was found that 86 per cent of the group sucking the zinc lozenges had been cured, while only 46 per cent of those sucking the placebos were without cold symptoms. The researchers concluded that the zinc lozenges shortened the average duration of colds by about seven days.[107] Side effects were usually minor and consisted mainly of objectionable taste and mouth irritation, but this high dose of zinc should not be taken for more than a few days.

~ A fever is one of your body's weapons, an attempt to heat infection out of your system; when allowed to run its course a fever is usually successful. Do not try to suppress a fever unless your temperature rises above 104°F (40°C). And try this favoured home remedy:

Boil a handful of dried yarrow herb in one litre (two pints) of water, keeping the pan covered and simmering for 30 minutes. Serve in half-cupfuls every 30 minutes to promote sweating. Keep well wrapped up and warm during this time.

~ Extra rest and sleep are *essential* to shake off a cold virus.

~ Short-term fasting can help to boost your immune system when it is under attack (for example, when you've got a cold coming on). Studies show that fasting for up to 36 hours can increase the number of active phagocytes (which form the first line of defence against infection) in your body by up to 50 per cent.[108] But don't go beyond this time limit when you're ill, otherwise your immune system may not be able to cope.

Preventing colds

Vitamins are vital for the body's immune system to work effectively. If you get a cold, supplements of these vitamins may help you fight it.

~ Taking vitamin C can protect against colds as well as drastically shorten the life of an existing cold. Linus Pauling is the scientist who 'discovered' vitamin C. He recommends taking supplements of this vitamin even when you are fit and well. Foods especially rich in vitamin C include blackcurrants, citrus fruits, strawberries, cauliflower, cabbage and brussels sprouts.

~ Increase your intake of zinc. Zinc boosts immunity, particularly benefiting the thymus gland. It is vital to the body's immune system as it assists in the growth of white blood cells. Many people in this country are thought to have a zinc deficiency, although the current RDA for zinc is only 15mg per day. Taking a regular supplement will ensure that your body isn't suffering from a shortage. Supplements are available in pill and lozenge form.

Foods rich in zinc include pumpkin and sunflower seeds, nuts, wholemeal bread, mushrooms, soyabeans and brewer's yeast.

Here is a quick recipe that will help you get a strong dose of zinc – deliciously!

Roasted Pumpkin Seeds

Heat a large frying pan over a medium flame. Measure 115g (4 oz) raw, shelled pumpkin seeds and pour into the pan. Keep the pan over the heat, shaking or stirring constantly while the seeds roast and pop. After 4–5 minutes, pour 1 tablespoon of shoyu or tamari (soy sauce) over the seeds. Stir quickly, remove from the heat and turn into a serving bowl. Allow to cool before eating.

~ Beta carotene is converted to vitamin A in your body; it is an antioxidant and enhances the action of your immune system. The mucous membranes of your respiratory tract are especially benefited by this vitamin which makes it of particular use in protecting you from colds. Both beta carotene and vitamin A may be taken in supplement form.

The following foods are rich in beta carotene: yellow and dark green fruits and vegetables such as cantaloupe, apricots, avocado, carrots, asparagus, broccoli, endive, kale, pumpkin, spinach, sweet potatoes, squash.

And two additional natural remedies:

~ Eat plenty of garlic. Garlic has a long history of use to fight infection and improve resistance to disease. You may enjoy the health giving effects of garlic without the odour (if you find it objectionable) by preparing the following recipe:

Garlic Soup

Coarsely chop 12–15 cloves of garlic including their skins and place in a saucepan with 1 medium potato, cubed, and 1 litre (2 pints) boiling water. Cover and simmer gently for 40 minutes. Add freshly grated ginger if desired. Drink one cupful every two hours if you feel the early symptoms of a cold.

~ Eat two to five umeboshi plums each day. These are a form of pickled plum originating in China and Japan which have a long and remarkable history of fighting infection. Buy them from Japanese supermarkets or your local health food shop. Available in paste or concentrate form as well.

Chapter 30
Foods to fight constipation

~

Raise the quality of your food and you'll soon have your digestive system working like clockwork.

Are you constipated at the moment? Four people out of every ten in the United Kingdom will answer 'Yes' to that question. In 20 per cent of the population, constipation is so severe that laxatives are used regularly. It is a startling fact that 77 per cent of the population only excrete between five and seven stools per week. That's over three-quarters of the total population! On top of that, a further 8 per cent of people only pass three to four stools a week. That makes 85 per cent of us with sluggish bowel movements.[109] Clearly, it's a British epidemic!

Chronic constipation

This occurs when you retain your stools in the colon and rectum so that the water they contain is re-absorbed by the body. The stools then harden even more, making defecation more difficult. Eventually, your bowel will lose its muscle tone and constipation becomes a way of life. Conventional medicine treats the symptom of constipation and brings about short-term purgative relief through the use of laxatives. However, the cause of constipation is what really needs treating in order to bring about a lasting solution to the problem. Constipation can be a symptom of a great many diseases; but for most of us, the underlying cause lies in our diets.

Good and bad foods

~ Cut back on foods which slow down the passage of food through the body. These include fatty food such as meat, cheese and other animal produce, refined foods such as sugar and white flour, and most processed foods.

~ Increase those foods that are good for your digestion and can speed up the process. You'll be pleased to know that as you do this, you'll also be cutting back on your risk of developing cancer, heart disease and other killers of our Western civilization. Fruits, vegetables, pulses and whole grains are all fibre-rich foods.

Start these simple changes to your diet now, and you will find an effective, long-term and natural cure for constipation.
~ Beetroot juice – either bottled or freshly juiced – is a very useful short-term natural stool softener and laxative.
Much heaving and straining could be prevented if only we ate a diet that was higher in natural forms of fibre! Oat bran, baked beans, pumpkin seeds, wheat fibre, bran and all the bran products, these are all excellent sources of dietary fibre. Porridge for breakfast, lots of whole-wheat products and one main meal consisting of a raw salad will significantly boost your fibre intake. The evidence shows that it will also prevent problems like haemorrhoids and diverticular diseases.

A salad with get up and go!

There is nothing more boring on the face of the earth than a traditional salad consisting of a few leaves of lettuce well past their sell-by date and accompanied by squishy but tasteless tomatoes. Yuk! This is how to make a proper salad.
~ Ingredients: tin of kidney beans, carrots, beetroot, cabbage, watercress, broccoli, potatoes, tofu, sunflower seeds, almonds, pumpkin seeds; plus any seasonal vegetables, including winter roots. Perm any six from ten! There's no need for lettuce but make it a Cos if you want it: it's got some flavour and it won't go limp.
~ Get a really large bowl.
~ Cube the potatoes and lightly steam them and the broccoli; roast the pumpkin seeds; cube the tofu; grate the raw carrot and beetroot (don't slice); thin-shred the cabbage; fine-chop the watercress; wash and roughly chop the lettuce; don't forget the sunflower seeds and almonds. All this is quick to do, but get a food processor if you want to speed it up even more.
~ Prepare your favourite dressing. Two suggestions: olive oil, cider vinegar and French mustard (real French mustard please, no appalling English substitutes). Or, for the most unusual dressing you've ever tasted – try this and you'll never try anything else! – buy some powdered black salt from your local Indian deli. Add two teaspoonsful to oil and cider vinegar, shake thoroughly until dissolved.
~ Place the lettuce in the bottom and round the side of the bowl, if you're using lettuce. Mix the other ingredients together and put them on top. Pour on the dressing.
One serving of a salad like this will give you a third of your total daily requirement of protein, almost twice your vitamin A requirement, all your vitamin C, and half your iron and fibre. It's so good you'll want to eat it every day! Tofu and, even nicer, marinated tofu are both available from health food shops.

Take your time

Get those bowels into line! Many of us become constipated simply because we don't allow ourselves time to go to the toilet! Set aside half an hour a day to do your business – yes, literally: you can take a phone in there with you if you want, or at least read the paper. Never suppress an urge to go – this is giving your body entirely the wrong message. If you can do some simple exercise just before going, stretching or yoga is good, this will help.

Non-dietary methods

Don't get hooked on laxatives. If you're already taking them, try to stop. Although a natural laxative can be useful for a few days' short-term usage; for example, if you've been abroad on a different diet, and your bowels are suffering from culture shock; all laxatives have some kind of side-effects, and they all subvert the natural processes of your body. Eventually, your bowels become dependent on them for a jump start every day.

Colonic irrigation can provide you with an internal spring-clean, and set up your bowels so that you're starting all over again with a nice, clean intestinal passage. See chapter 70 for details.

CHAPTER 31
FOODS TO FIGHT DIABETES

~

Your diet can help you overcome this disorder, which claims the lives of more and more people each year . . .

Diabetes is a disease of the Western world, brought about by both genetic and environmental factors. In the UK alone nearly one million men, women and children are diabetic; worldwide an estimated 30 million people are known to suffer it. Diabetes mellitus is "a disorder in which the body is unable to control the amount of sugar in the blood, because the mechanism which converts sugar to energy is no longer functioning properly".[110]

Energy: supply and demand

Normally, the food you eat is gradually broken down and converted to glucose (blood sugar), the source of energy for all your body's functions. The conversion of glucose into energy requires insulin, a hormone produced in the pancreas. Insulin is released into your system in order to control the level of glucose in your blood, especially to prevent your blood sugar level from climbing too high. However, in diabetics, there is either a shortage of insulin or the available insulin does not function as it should. The result is that glucose is not converted into energy, but builds up in the blood and eventually spills over into your urine. This is often one of the first signs of diabetes.

Though there is an abundance of glucose in your blood, the body is still deprived of the energy it needs (because the glucose has not been converted to energy) and so the liver begins to produce yet more glucose to meet demands. Shortly, your body's stores of fat and protein begin to break down in another attempt to supply more glucose. The resulting weight loss is often a further sign of diabetes. Thus begins a chain of events within your body that can eventually cause severe health problems, even death. In the UK alone, approximately 20,000 people die prematurely each year from diabetes related problems.[111]

A growing problem

Sufferers of diabetes are of two types. Those who are insulin dependent produce little or no insulin in their body and require injections of insulin to survive. This type of diabetes is sometimes called Type 1 or 'juvenile-onset' diabetes. Secondly, those who are non-insulin dependent produce some insulin in their body but it is not sufficient, or does not function to maintain good health. This is sometimes called Type 2 or 'maturity onset' diabetes.

Diabetes is a serious disorder and unfortunately its incidence is increasing – in Britain an estimated 60,000 new cases are diagnosed each year.[112] Further, the number of children diagnosed as diabetic has doubled in the past twenty years and this appears to be a worldwide trend. In short, this problem is getting worse. But there are simple, effective steps which you can take to prevent the onset of diabetes or minimize its erosion of your health if you already have it.

Prevent or cure?

According to a report submitted by Diabetes Epidemiology Research International to the *British Medical Journal,*[113] between 60 per cent and 95 per cent of cases of insulin dependent diabetes can be prevented. The DERI group of scientists believe that environmental factors are largely responsible for the increase in diabetes, claiming that genetic factors could not account for such great increases over such a very short period of time. Of the possible environmental causes, diet is perhaps the most significant and certainly one over which we have control.

Further, it seems that the same dietary measures used in prevention of diabetes can be used with great success in treatment. There have been several clues pointing to this possibility. For instance, Nauru, a remote island in the Pacific, had never had any cases of diabetes until it suddenly became rich and began to import American-style fast food. Now, more than 40 per cent of its population over the age of twenty have diabetes! Similarly, diabetes is noticeably rare in parts of Africa and China where the traditional diet is intact and free of Western influence. So what are the dietary influences which can prevent or treat diabetes?

~ The American Diabetes Association suggests that diabetics eat a diet in which carbohydrates make up about 60 per cent of total calorie intake, these carbohydrates to be mostly unrefined, complex and high in fibre.[114] Fat intake should total less than 30 per cent of calories consumed, with an emphasis on reducing saturated fats and cholesterol, replacing them with mono-unsaturated fats such as olive oil. Protein intake should be moderate.

~ Avoid eating meat. Diabetes is more common among meat eating people than non-meat eaters. Meat eating increases consumption of saturated fats which may affect insulin sensitivity. Also, the N-nitroso compounds in meat may actually be a trigger to the development of diabetes.

In a twenty-one-year study of 25,698 adult Seventh-Day Adventists, it was found that they were less than half (45 per cent) as likely to suffer diabetes as an underlying cause of death than the rest of the population.[115] Seventh-Day Adventists avoid consuming meat, fish, eggs, coffee, alcohol and tobacco. When other factors were taken into account, the study found that "a vegetarian diet reduces the risk of developing diabetes".[116] That means that if you are vegetarian you are less likely to develop diabetes in the first place.

~ Replace meat with protein foods such as whole grains, nuts, seeds, tofu, pulses, Quorn and soya products. In addition to meeting your protein needs, these foods contain valuable vitamins, minerals and fibre – something meat hasn't got!

~ Reduce your intake of fat, from all sources. A high fat diet is already implicated in other serious diseases such as stroke and heart disease. But too much fat in the diet also contributes to obesity; many diabetics are obese which further complicates their disorder. Start by replacing saturated fats such as butter with cold-pressed vegetable oils and cut down on dairy products generally. These are obvious sources of fat, but many packaged, frozen, or highly processed foods contain hidden fats which quickly and quietly boost your calorie count. So eat fresh produce wherever possible and in cooking, avoid frying or roasting; steam, bake or boil instead.

~ Eat at least 40 grams of fibre each day. This is twice the average intake of fibre, so you may need a week or two to adjust. A high-fibre diet can lower the amount of insulin you need to inject (if you are insulin dependent) and can eliminate the need for insulin in some Type 2 diabetics. Select foods high in fibre, especially soluble fibre, such as whole grains, beans, oats, bran and vegetables.

~ Coffee can raise the concentration of sugar in the blood. As this is the major symptom of diabetes, coffee consumption may have serious implications for diabetics and potential diabetics alike. If you drink large amounts of coffee while pregnant, your children become more susceptible to diabetes.[117]

~ Diabetics are commonly lacking in B_6 which is vital for insulin production. So give preference to foods in your diet which are rich in vitamin B_6 – oatbran and oatgerm, hummus, avocados, bananas, brewer's yeast, yeast extract, brown rice, parsley, spinach and other green leafy vegetables, molasses and whole grains.

~ Vitamin C is needed to metabolize insulin and glucose; a deficiency can lead to cell degeneration in the pancreas, where insulin is produced. Eat plenty of citrus fruit, alfalfa sprouts and vegetables such as potatoes, green pepper and broccoli. As the body cannot store vitamin C, there is no danger of toxicity from supplementation should you wish to take a high dose vitamin C tablet every day.

~ Diabetics often have a deficiency of the trace mineral chromium and can benefit from supplementation, with elderly and non-insulin dependent diabetics responding particularly well. Chromium acts with insulin to transport glucose through cell walls. Highly processed foods always have reduced levels of chromium and years of eating such foods can invite the onset of Type 2, maturity onset diabetes. A diet rich in chromium may prevent this. Eat plenty of wheat germ, brewer's yeast, whole grains and corn oil.

~ Zinc plays a crucial role in the synthesis and storage of insulin in the pancreas. It is a mineral that many of us, not just diabetics, are continually short of. Eat mushrooms, sunflower and pumpkin seeds, brewer's yeast and soyabeans to boost your zinc intake.

~ Foods rich in magnesium may help to prevent retinopathy, a deterioration of the retina which is a real threat to diabetics. Foods rich in magnesium include nuts, whole grains, dark green vegetables and molasses.

Chapter 32

Foods to Fight Eczema and Psoriasis

~

Minimize your suffering and stop your children from developing these common skin afflictions by amending your diet in simple, effective ways.

As a sufferer you will know the red, scaly, often painful skin which typifies psoriasis and eczema. Both are chronic, non-contagious skin disorders which affect people of all ages. The joints, scalp, back, chest, bottom, hands and legs, and in acute cases virtually the whole body, can all be affected. Both conditions can be brought on by allergy, stress, anxiety, viruses, 'flu, over-tiredness or injury – especially if you have a history of either disorder in the family. Rather than accept your problem as inevitable, however, you can make changes in your diet which will minimize or solve your skin problem.

~ Adopt a low-sugar or even a sugar-free diet to prevent an overgrowth of the candida albicans yeast in your gut. This yeast is normally present in a healthy person but, when present to excess, can cause disease or reduced immunity. Psoriasis is particularly responsive to a reduction in sugar intake and a few days or weeks on a sugar-free diet (sometimes called an anti-fungal diet) may improve your condition.[118] Remember, sugar includes honey, molasses, concentrated fruit juices and syrups.

~ Adopt a dairy- and gluten-free diet for two to three weeks to determine whether your skin problem is aggravated by these food groups.

~ In some people a deficiency in the B-complex of vitamins can hinder the proper metabolism of fats and proteins and problems such as psoriasis and eczema can result. To correct deficiency you may take a B-complex supplement daily. Simply ensure that your supplement includes the whole range of B vitamins as they work best when taken as a group. The B vitamins are essential to the health of the skin, mucous membranes and nerves. In fact, as stress is so often a trigger for eczema and psoriasis, a sufficiency of the B-complex may help prevent an attack by reducing the initial effects of stress on your body.

Foods especially rich in the B complex vitamins are yeasts, such as brewer's or nutritional yeast, and whole grains. Pulses and seeds are also useful sources. Ensure that you have a serving of each of these foods in your diet each day.

~ Gamma-linolenic acid is a substance which we produce in our bodies. Some people, however, do not produce enough and are more likely to suffer from eczema as a result. A bowl of porridge each day is a good source of gamma-linolenic acid,[119] as is a supplement in the form of evening primrose oil.[120] This supplement is available both over-the-counter from health food shops and under prescription through the NHS.

~ Omega-3 fatty acids reduce the itching and scaling of eczema and psoriasis in many people.[121] Sources of omega-3 fatty acids include flaxseed or soya oils which you may take as supplements.

~ Selenium and vitamin E are both antioxidants and work together to preserve and promote healthy metabolic processes. Of particular importance to sufferers of eczema and psoriasis, this combination can delay the oxidation of essential fatty acids which are so crucial to healthy skin. Selenium is a mineral found in whole grains, especially the bran and germ, and vegetables such as onions, celery, cabbage and broccoli. Vitamin E is abundant in the cold-pressed vegetable oils, in soya beans and in all raw nuts and seeds. Supplements are also available.

~ A poorly functioning digestive system results in the proliferation of various toxins within the gut. Several of these toxins can contribute to the development of psoriasis and eczema.[122] There are several dietary steps you may take to improve digestion and therefore prevent, or minimize, your skin problem.

Take a supplement of *Lactobacillus acidophilus*, a friendly bacterium which will colonize your gut and help to correct many digestive disorders (see chapter 52).

Increase your intake of dietary fibre. Start by altering your diet to include an abundance of fresh fruit and vegetables as well as two to three servings daily of whole, unprocessed grains.

~ Boost your intake of folic acid as some psoriasis sufferers have been shown to have low blood levels of folic acid.[123] Folic acid is found in green leafy vegetables and brewer's yeast. Supplements are also available.

~ Zinc is essential for the production of hydrochloric acid in your stomach, a shortage of which produces digestive problems which can lead to eczema or psoriasis. Zinc is found in whole grains, pumpkin seeds and brewer's yeast. It may be taken in supplement form.

~ Vitamin A is necessary for the health of all body tissue, especially the skin and mucous membranes. Skin problems such as eczema and psoriasis can be one sign of deficiency and may respond well to increased intakes of vitamin A or carotene, the vegetable substance which your body converts to vitamin A. To boost your intake of vitamin A, eat plenty of carotene rich foods including dark green leafy vegetables, such as spinach, and vegetables of a dark orange colour such as carrots and pumpkin.

~ Eczema or psoriasis can be an allergic response in some people. If you suspect this might be true for you, try amending your diet in these ways:

Eat only fresh, organic produce to avoid chemical residues and unnecessary additives.

Eliminate the foods which most commonly cause an allergic response. These include dairy products, eggs, fish, peanuts and soyabeans.[124] Other foods, such as chicken, citrus, tomato and corn, may also cause an allergic response (see also chapter 46).

~ Adopt a vegetarian or vegan diet for six to eight weeks. Some people have experienced an improvement in their health as a result of this type of diet.[125]

~ Moderately high alcohol consumption can aggravate psoriasis. A Finnish study concluded that men who consumed five or more units of alcohol per day were likely to suffer a worsening of their condition.[126] Try keeping your alcohol intake to the recommended twenty-one units per week for men, fourteen units per week for women.

Chapter 33
Foods to fight falling hair

~

Why me?

Losing your hair is a very common and frequently embarrassing problem. It can also be troubling psychologically. So if you are thinning on top, or know there is a family history of this problem, you will want to take steps to forestall or delay it affecting you.

There is no particular reason for the onset of hair loss. Male pattern baldness (MPB) is hereditary; there's not much you can do about it, other than a toupee or an expensive hair transplant. If a naked pate is your fate, accept it cheerfully. The human race has gradually lost its total body covering of hair since its furry primate days, and your own hairlessness is simply proof of your evolved nature – in a few millennia or so, everyone else will have caught up with you!

Women, of course, don't suffer from MPB, although it is quite common for pregnancy to produce temporary hair loss. Other possible causes may include hormone deficiency, anaemia, illness, use of steroids, antibiotics, ringworm and, increasingly in today's world, stress.

There is little that conventional medicine can do, other than investigate possible underlying causes such as skin conditions, scalp disorders and alopecia, and then refer you to a trichologist. So here is a selection of alternatives for you to investigate.

Minerals

There are certain minerals that are essential to hair growth. Zinc, in particular, has long been recognized as a means of promoting healthy hair, and more generally, zinc is essential for bodily healing. Smoking will definitely lower your zinc level – so stub it out. Keep your zinc levels high by eating fresh, leafy green vegetables like spinach; and eat lots of whole-grain products. If you are not eating a zinc-rich diet, zinc supplements may be in order. You can find them alone or in combination with other nutrients; for example, a zinc-calcium-magnesium formula, and as zinc lozenges which may also help ward off colds.

The trace mineral copper, too, is vital for healthy hair and skin. It prevents defects in hair colour and structure. Good sources of copper are, like zinc, whole-grain cereals, especially quinoa (see chapter 15). Eggs, cherries, nuts and beans are also sources of copper.

Drugs

It's a little-known fact that many prescription and over-the-counter drugs can, and do, cause temporary hair loss. While individual reactions may vary from one person to another, this side-effect can occur with all the following drugs: cholesterol-lowering drugs, arthritis medications, beta-blocker blood pressure drugs, anti-ulcer drugs, oral contraceptives, blood thinners, epileptic medications, male hormones (anabolic steroids) and vitamin A-derived drugs. If you suspect your hair loss is linked to the medication you're taking, ask your doctor if another drug without this side-effect can be substituted.

A drug called minoxidil has modest hair-restorative properties. It was originally sold as a treatment for high blood pressure, but when rubbed into the scalp can produce hair growth in some people. In a clinical study, 32 per cent of the patients using minoxidil managed to produce new hair growth after four months' treatment. The snag is that when you stop rubbing it in, the hair can recede again.

Positive thinking

Don't underestimate the power of positive thinking! In the study mentioned above, 20 per cent of the control group, who just rubbed alcohol and water into their scalps, also demonstrated positive hair growth!

Herbal remedies

Many of the foods traditionally used to combat falling hair are applied to the scalp, not eaten. An old remedy for a hair stimulant passed down amongst gypsies says that 30 grams of rosemary should be boiled in a pint of water for five minutes and then rubbed into the scalp every night. And it's true that one rarely sees a bald gypsy.

A traditional French remedy for baldness involves massaging the scalp with freshly-pressed nettle juice every night. To extract the juice, either use a modern juicing machine, or pound the nettles in a mortar, then place them in a fine cloth and press well.

Another French folk remedy directs you to rub the scalp gently with olive oil, then go to bed with your head wrapped in a towel. Next morning, shampoo with tepid water and very simple soap. Repeat for ten consecutive days every month – preferably while the moon is waxing. Two beaten eggs can be substituted for the olive oil.

Food

A good, well-balanced diet, consisting of good protein sources like beans, pulses, grains, and nuts, together with lots of fresh vegetables, will keep your hair healthy. Falling hair may be a sign of vitamin A deficiency or, paradoxically, of vitamin A overdose. The B group of vitamins, found in yeast products and whole-grain cereals, are also essential for good hair condition.

~ The Chinese eat one sheet of nori every day – a dried seaweed available in health food shops – in order to preserve the shiny black colour of their hair well into old age.

~ To make a superb hair tonic take a handful of rosemary and two cups of cider vinegar, place in a covered pan over a low heat for one hour. Cool and strain. Shampoo your hair normally, rinse, then pour half a cup of the rosemary mixture over your scalp and leave for three minutes before rinsing out.

CHAPTER 34
FOODS TO FIGHT GALLSTONES

~

Gallstones can be agony! Seventeen per cent of the population develops them. Here's how to stay out of the risk group.

If you eat a diet low in saturated fats and refined sugar, and high in fibre, your chances of developing gallstones are small. If, however, you eat a typical Western diet, high in fat and refined foods, then you could be in for real trouble. The pain of having gallstones can be intense and long-lasting. Gallstones form when the substances found in bile, such as cholesterol and calcium, begin to precipitate, forming stones which cause pain, nausea and vomiting. They can also lead to infection, resulting in inflammation of the gall bladder, colic, peritonitis, gangrene of the gall bladder, and jaundice. As the Western diet has changed, so has the incidence of gallstones, quadrupling since 1940 in many areas. Orientals and rural Africans, who traditionally consume a low-fat, high-fibre diet, suffer very little from them. In addition, only humans and domesticated animals have gallstones, wild animals do not. This also strongly suggests that the problem is connected with our modern, Western lifestyle.

Gallstones are more common amongst women than men – 25 per cent of all women and 10 per cent of all men will develop gallstones before they are sixty years old. The overweight and diabetic are also more at risk.

Protect yourself against them ...

If you are obese you are four times more likely to suffer from stones. One more good reason to shed those kilos. But be careful how you diet. Rapid weight loss can actually increase your risk of suffering from gallstones. Obese people who lose a lot of weight on very low-calorie diets are quite likely to form stones. Once the weight has been lost, however, and relatively normal eating patterns are restored, the stones may dissolve of their own accord. It's best to have your doctor supervise this.

Another possible preventive, although not yet recommended, is common aspirin. Some research suggests that aspirin can inhibit substances that may cause cholesterol to crystallize into stones. It could therefore prevent gallstones in obese people during weight loss; or halt the recurrence in people who had their stones dissolved with drugs.

Taking oestrogen or oral contraceptives can increase the amount of cholesterol in your bile fluid and thus the chances of having gallstones. At least three studies have found an increased risk of gall bladder disease among women who use oral contraceptives.

If you are a meat-eater, you are doubling your chances of developing gallstones, according to one study carried out in Oxford.[127] Two groups of women were compared to see if their diets could have any influence on the occurrence of gallstones. The first group, consisting of 632 women, were selected at random, and ate meat. The second group consisted of 130 women who did not eat meat, and had a diet naturally higher in fibre. All the women were then given a thorough inspection, using ultrasound detection techniques, looking specifically for gallstones. The experimenters found that the meat-eaters were two-and-a-half times more likely to develop gallstones than the non meat-eaters. The scientists concluded that the low-fat, high-fibre diet of the non-meat-eating women gave them protection.

... and survive in spite of them!

Once you've got gallstones, they're not easy to get rid of by dietary means alone. Conventional medicine can offer you a range of choices. Surgical removal of the stones or of the gallbladder itself is quite common. Doctors don't actually know what purpose the gallbladder serves: people who have their gallbladder removed don't seem to suffer any adverse consequences. Another possible method is the use of chemical solvents to dissolve some kinds of stones. Finally, sound waves called extracorporeal shock wave lithotripsy, or ESWL, can crush the stones into small pieces which can then be excreted.

Fatty foods are known to stimulate gallbladder contractions, causing a painful gallstone attack. So consider trying a reduced-fat diet. Also, consuming smaller, more frequent meals may help limit gallbladder contractions and attacks.

Recently, there has been scientific speculation that a diet high in soluble fibre might increase the solubility of cholesterol in the bile, and so prevent, perhaps even reverse, the formation of gallstones. Good sources of soluble fibre include oat bran, pectin and beans (see chapter 28 for more details).

The so-called olive oil cure, which involves fasting for three days and then drinking a mug of olive oil and lemon juice to make the gallbladder contract and push through extremely small stones, can be dangerous. If larger stones are ejected in this way, they could stick in the bile duct, causing jaundice, infection and a possible medical emergency.

Chapter 35
Foods to Fight High Blood Pressure

~

Why risk lack of energy, stomach ulcers, premature senility and sexual impotence – all possible side effects of hypertension drugs – when the solution to high blood pressure may lie in your diet?

Hypertension is the medical name for high blood pressure. Orthodox medicine has made impressive progress in the detection and treatment of hypertension, and this has resulted in a decline in mortality from strokes, for example, over the last three decades. But there's no room for complacency. Raised blood pressure is one of the key risk factors in the development of heart disease and cerebrovascular disease. The United Kingdom government estimates that over 240,000 people die every year as a result of a hypertension-related disease. Put another way, 33 per cent – one-third – of all deaths that occur in people under 65 are attributable to hypertensive causes.

What is hypertension?

Blood pressure can be gauged by the amount of effort put in by the heart to keep blood circulating in the body. It is measured by the height in millimetres of a column of mercury that can be raised inside a vacuum. The more pressure there is, the higher the column will rise. Since blood pressure varies with every heartbeat, two measures are taken – one that measures the pressure of the beat itself (called systolic blood pressure) and the other that measures the pressure in between beats, when the heart is resting (this is called diastolic blood pressure, and is the 'background' level). These two figures are written with the systolic figure first, followed by the diastolic figure: 120:80mmHg.

At birth our systolic blood pressure is about 40; it doubles to about 80 within the first month. Thereafter, the increase is slower, but inexorable, for the rest of our life. Many people do not realize they suffer from hypertension. There may be no symptoms, and it may only be discovered during a visit to the doctor's surgery for another complaint. In its later stages symptoms may include headache, dizziness, fatigue, and insomnia.

A pressure of 150:90 would be considered high in a young person, and 160:95 would be abnormally high. In older people, systolic pressure could be 140 at age sixty, and 160 at eighty years.

Symptoms of high blood pressure (hypertension) include dizziness, headaches, irritability and fatigue. There is also a real danger, even if you only suffer from a mild form, that it may develop into life-threatening illnesses and events such as heart attack, stroke and kidney disease. Treatment – whether through drugs or otherwise – aims ideally to reduce diastolic pressure to about 80-85mmHg.

What you can do

A diagnosis of high blood pressure is not a death sentence. There is a lot you can do to bring it down – providing you are willing to try seriously. Much research now clearly shows that many 'hypertensives' can lower their blood pressure by amending their lifestyle and dietary habits.

~ ~ GET TO UNDERSTAND YOUR OWN BLOOD PRESSURE. The instrument to measure blood pressure is called a 'sphygmomanometer'; and it is possible to buy one so that you can track your blood pressure as it rises and falls over a period of time. Blood pressure fluctuates considerably even in normal individuals – the reading taken at the doctor's surgery won't be the same as the one when you're at home later in the day. Physical activity, excitement, fear, or emotional stress can all send it shooting up. The term 'hypertension' indicates that blood pressure exceeds the upper limits most of the time, not just for short periods. When you understand how your blood pressure changes, you're on the way to controlling it.

~ One recent study has found that as many as 20 per cent of patients treated for hypertension could be receiving unnecessary medication, simply because their blood pressure rises in the presence of a doctor. They coined the term 'white coat hypertension' for this phenomenon.[128] With your own sphygmomanometer, you'll be able to rule this out in your case.

~ Drugs should not be the first step for those who suffer high blood pressure. It is now increasingly accepted that doctors should have patients with high blood pressure follow a strict diet, lose weight if necessary and exercise more to see if it improves their condition before prescribing drugs. Dr. Rose Stamler, a Chicago epidemiologist, has reported that 40 per cent of patients manage to control their high blood pressure with moderate exercise and dietary modifications alone.[129]

~ NORMALIZE YOUR WEIGHT. Most hypertensives are overweight, yet a twenty-pound reduction in weight can result in a blood pressure reduction of 20mmHg systolic and 10mmHg diastolic.[130]

~ REDUCE OR AVOID ALCOHOL CONSUMPTION. Most long-term studies have shown that blood pressure can be significantly reduced by cutting out or cutting down on the amount of alcohol consumed. For example, one study shows that among women taking more than two alcoholic drinks per day, one-third of all cases of hypertension are caused by alcohol consumption. This suggests that hypertension in these women may be treatable by restriction of alcohol intake.[131]

~ STOP SMOKING. Nicotine stimulates the heart and at the same time constricts the blood vessels – making it difficult for your blood pressure not to rise! If you are a man with high blood pressure and you smoke you are 3.5 times more likely to develop cardiovascular disease than if you were a healthy non-smoker.

~ LEARN TO RELAX AND TO EXERCISE. Both of these activities help you to feel more in control of your body and your life.

~ CONSIDER A DRASTIC CHANGE AT WORK. People in demanding jobs with little freedom to make decisions have three times the risk of developing high blood pressure compared to others who have either a less demanding job or more decision-making latitude.[132]

~ TRY A VEGAN DIET. A group of long-term hypertensives on medication ate a vegan diet for one year. In almost all cases their medication was withdrawn or greatly reduced and they all claimed to feel better. More importantly, they enjoyed a decrease in blood pressure and many additional symptoms disappeared. A vegan diet is free of all animal products: meat, fish, eggs and dairy products.[133]

~ ...OR A VEGETARIAN DIET. Vegetarians eat less saturated fat and more fibre, which gives them a lower mean blood pressure than non-vegetarians. A study of 59 healthy omnivores showed that both systolic and diastolic blood pressure fell during the period of the study when the subjects ate a vegetarian diet. They rose to previous levels when they returned to their omnivorous regime.[134]

~ EAT A HIGH-FIBRE DIET. Fibre guards against the hypertensive effects of fatty foods. In a three-day test, people with a high-fibre intake had a lower mean blood pressure than those eating less fibre. When fibre was reduced in their diet, their blood pressure rose. High fibre foods include whole grains, pulses, fruit and fresh vegetables.[135]

~ EAT A LOW-FAT DIET, but also look to the sorts of fats you are eating. You should adjust the total amount of fat in your diet to no more than 30 per cent of your total calorie intake, increasing the ratio of polyunsaturated to saturated fats. Thirty couples, in an area of East Finland with a very high level of coronary heart disease, changed their normal high fat and low polyunsaturate diet to one lower in total and saturated fats. After only six weeks, they enjoyed a significant drop in blood pressure. Consumption of olive oil, a monounsaturated fat, is linked to lower blood pressure than is the consumption of polyunsaturated oils.[136]

~ ADJUST YOUR SODIUM AND POTASSIUM INTAKE. Both of these minerals are salts (sodium is table salt) which regulate the balance of fluid in your body. An excess of sodium increases the volume of blood, which puts more strain on the circulatory system, causing high blood pressure. Thus sodium has been blamed for many cases of hypertension. However, it is now shown that potassium can protect from hypertension because it balances the effects of sodium.[137]

You can reduce your intake of sodium and increase your intake of potassium by limiting the amount of processed foods you eat – these are high in sodium and low in potassium. Instead, eat potassium-rich foods such as avocado, banana, broccoli, brussels sprouts, dates, prunes and raisins. Jacket potatoes and cantaloupes are also good sources.

~ INCREASE YOUR INTAKE OF MAGNESIUM. This mineral is lost when you take diuretics – often prescribed for hypertensives. Yet 50 per cent of magnesium-deficient patients have high blood pressure, usually normalizing when this deficiency is rectified. Foods rich in magnesium include green vegetables, nuts, whole grains and yeast extracts.[138]

~ BOOST YOUR CALCIUM INTAKE. It has been found that people with high blood pressure often have low levels of calcium.[139] In one study, researchers demonstrated a 23 per cent decrease in hypertension risk among women receiving 800 milligrams a day of calcium, compared with women consuming just 400 milligrams a day (the recommended daily allowance for adults is 800 milligrams a day, 1,200 milligrams for pregnant or lactating women).[140] Foods rich in calcium include dairy products, tofu, spinach, figs, molasses, seaweeds, nuts and seeds, watercress and parsley.

~ CONSIDER TAKING A SELENIUM SUPPLEMENT. Although its role is not yet fully known, selenium may act to prevent hypertension caused by cadmium. Cadmium is a heavy metal which raises blood pressure; intake can be derived from some water pipes, pollution, car exhaust and smoking. Dr. Raymond Shamberger and Dr. Charles E. Willis, of the Cleveland Clinic, conducted an epidemiological study which has shown that people living in an area where the soil has a low concentration of selenium are three times more likely to die from hypertension-related diseases than people who live where the selenium level in the soil (and hence in the food they eat) is higher. "We don't know selenium's precise action concerning high blood pressure," said Dr. Shamberger, "but our study strongly suggests that it has a beneficial effect on high blood pressure problems in man."[141] (See also chapter 9.)

CHAPTER 36
FOODS TO FIGHT IMMUNE DEFICIENCY

~

In today's contaminated world your immune system needs all the help it can get. The good news is that your diet may provide the key to fortifying your natural immunity.

Maintaining a healthy immune system should be a top priority for all of us because without it we are – quite literally – dead. Your immune system is the crucial means by which your body resists disease and infection; it is also a defence system you almost certainly know little about and take completely for granted. And yet there has never been a more important time than now for you to take action to bolster your body's natural defences, because every day you are exposed to an ever-increasing bombardment of pollutants, toxins, bacteria and stress which, collectively, can weaken or destroy your health. Conventional medicine has focused first on understanding and then, using drugs, on replicating the work of the immune system. But this is not the only way to fight infection. Alternative medicine has, for centuries, used natural substances specifically to boost the body's own immune system – not to replace it. And recently, mounting scientific research confirms that many of these older, natural remedies are indeed effective. We believe that it is better to have a strong natural immunity to disease, rather than to rely on drugs to cure you after you've succumbed to illness. So here we present you with a unique collection of little-known measures which have been proven to protect and fortify your body's own immune system.

What your immune system does

You and your body function, health-wise, in a hostile universe comprising a teeming ocean of viruses, bacteria, cancers, pollen, mould spores and man-made chemicals and pollutants. Collectively these are all known as *antigens*. Sometimes it seems a miracle that the body survives at all in such a potentially harmful environment! That it does is down to the strength and durability of your immune system.

When your body comes under attack from these antigens it is your immune system which comes to its rescue and fights back. Your immune system is organically programmed to respond in a flexible and adaptable manner to ward off the potentially invasive antigens which can make you fall victim to illness. It does this in a host of complex ways, some of which are still not fully understood. But to put it simply, the human immune system functions in two broad ways. First, it can produce substances known as antibodies in response to invading antigens. Antibodies circulate in the blood and other body fluids, and when they find an antigen, try to neutralize it. Second, the body's immune response can also activate cells known as macrophages, which destroy invading microorganisms by engulfing and digesting them. This second variety of immune response characteristically produces a raised red area on the skin in response to an infection. Antibodies are produced by white blood cells, which originate in the bone marrow and macrophages are stimulated by white blood cells which originate in the thymus gland. Obviously, any disease which affects the bone marrow or thymus can have very serious effects on the entire immune system.

Your basic defensive strategy

Some simple dietary measures can help to boost your immune system, fight potential immune deficiency and build resistance to illness. First, some general points:

~ A good intake of protein is essential for a strong immune system. People always think of meat as being the only source of protein, but from the health point of view, there are some serious drawbacks. Indisputable scientific evidence shows that meat-eaters consistently suffer from more serious illness than non-meat eaters (cancers, heart disease, etc).[142] So make sure you're getting several good plant food sources of protein – among the best is the soya bean and all its associated products. (See chapter 18 for more information.)

~ There is evidence that sugar (and this includes table sugar, fruit juices, and honey) can suppress the functioning of the immune system.[143] So reduce your sugar consumption.

~ Alcohol depresses your immune function, and it can also prevent your body from absorbing vital nutrients from food. There is no question that chronic alcoholics suffer from a depressed immune system.[144] What is not so clear – yet – is just how much 'ordinary' social drinking affects your long-term immunity. One study from France looked at the way the human immune system functioned before, during and after drinking a large whisky, and concluded that alcohol consumption had only a 'limited effect' on immune function.[145] But even this study did reveal some short-term immune depression. The prudent conclusion is to restrict alcohol consumption to the occasional social drink, and to eliminate it when your immune system is particularly vulnerable or run-down.

~ Short-term fasting can help to boost your immune system when it is under attack (for example, when you've got a cold coming on). Studies show that fasting for up to 36 hours can increase the number of active phagocytes (which form the first line of defence against infection) in your body by up to 50 per cent.[146] But don't go beyond this time limit when you're ill, otherwise your immune system may not be able to cope. (See chapter 20 for more information.)

~ Since you should be particularly looking to eat meals rich with vitamins and minerals, this means avoiding processed and refined foodstuffs generally. Re-train your appetite to desire a bowl full of luscious salad (see chapter 30 for instructions on how to do this) instead of over-processed food such as white sugar, white rice, white flour, and the cakes, pastries, bread, rolls and pies that are made from them. Instead, turn to complex carbohydrates such as whole grains, wholewheat pastas, and whole-grain breads.

Vitamins

Now, let's deal with specific vitamin supplementation. Vitamins always work together in the human body. This is one reason why it is generally preferable to get the majority of your vitamins from a high-quality fresh food diet – because vitamins which work together tend to be found together. Obviously, people whose diets are deficient in vitamins and minerals should consider taking appropriate supplements. But increasingly, there is evidence to suggest that many other people (not just those who are vitamin-deficient) could also benefit from vitamin supplementation. The following vitamins have been shown to be effective in producing a more responsive immune system:

Vitamin B_6

A number of studies have shown that a low level of vitamin B_6 (sometimes known as pyridoxine) in the body is connected to a generally weakened immune system, and some studies have even linked a deficiency of this vitamin to the development of cancer.[147] Additionally, several more studies have shown that high doses of B_6 can suppress cancerous tumour growth (unfortunately, some of these studies were carried out on animals).[148] Since it is well known that this vitamin plays a vital role in many physiological processes, such as amino acid metabolism, lipid metabolism and, of course, in the immune system itself, some scientists believe that a great many people could be suffering from 'subclinical' B_6 deficiency, and that this may have an important part to play in the development of diseases such as atherosclerosis, multiple sclerosis, and other degenerative diseases of the central nervous system.[149] Other studies have shown that B_6 supplementation in elderly people can be an effective way to stimulate and improve the functioning of their immunity to disease.[150] Vitamin B_6 is stored mainly in the liver, and an average adult will, at any one time, have about 16–27 milligrams stored in their body.[151] However, since B_6 is a water-soluble vitamin, it is regularly excreted from the body, meaning that we all need to provide ourselves with a continuing intake. Foods such as oatbran and oatgerm, hummus, avocados, bananas, brewer's yeast, yeast extract, brown rice, parsley, and spinach all contain useful amounts of it. A higher intake of B_6 can be achieved by taking a vitamin supplement which includes B_6 in its formulation. In one of the trials mentioned above on elderly people, 50 milligrams a day was given for two months, which is approximately 25 times the normal recommended daily allowance. A word of warning about taking extremely high doses of B_6 – bear in mind that some serious adverse effects have been reported following very high doses – 500 milligrams of B_6 or more a day has been shown to damage the central nervous system.[152, 153]

Vitamin E

The primary role of vitamin E is to protect the body tissues from oxygen damage (see chapter 9). But in addition to this, Vitamin E is a very important nutrient for the optimal functioning of the immune system. It has been shown in experiments that when diets are lacking in vitamin E, the immune response is depressed. Correspondingly, when diets are supplemented with levels of vitamin E that are rather higher than those considered to be nutritionally 'adequate', the immune response is likewise enhanced.[154] Many of us today consume considerable amounts of polyunsaturated fatty acids, because we believe correctly that this is a healthier alternative than eating saturated animal fats. However, there is in fact evidence to suggest that high levels of polyunsaturated fatty acids may reduce the effective functioning of the immune system. An intake of vitamin E can act to overcome this immunosuppression.[155] The richest dietary sources of vitamin E are seed oils and nuts, whole grains, leafy green vegetables and eggs. Wheat germ oil is a particularly rich source. As far as supplements are concerned, some experts consider it safe for healthy individuals to take 200 to 600 milligrams of vitamin E a day. This is about 20 to 60 times the recommended daily allowance.[156] Linus Pauling goes beyond this and suggests 400, 800 or even 1,600 milligrams in his orthomolecular regimen (see chapter 85). For a fat-soluble vitamin, vitamin E is usually non-toxic. However, in doses of more than 300 milligrams daily some adverse effects have occasionally been observed, including nausea, diarrhoea, intestinal cramps, fatigue, weakness, headache, blurred vision, rash, or raised serum cholesterol and triglycerides.[157]

Vitamin C

It has been proved in experiments that high levels of vitamin C can protect tissue levels of vitamin E, and may well contribute to the strengthening of the immune system that vitamin E brings about.[158] This is how specialist Dr. Stuart Berger of New York puts it: "The major factor in your immune system – the white blood cells – have a lot of housekeeping chores to do; which include isolating and destroying bad viruses and bacteria. The white blood cells cannot do this without the help of vitamin C. Vitamins help to neutralize toxins in your body – especially that overload of toxins that occurs when you are sick."[159] Despite continuing controversy over the claims made for vitamin C, there is indeed a body of evidence which indicates that it does play an important part in strengthening and maintaining a healthy immune system.[160] And there is also evidence that both the duration and severity of the common cold (one of the most persistent diseases which our immune systems have to deal with) can be reduced by vitamin C intake.[161, 162] How much vitamin C should you take to bolster your immune system? Researchers in Belgium discovered that 500 milligrams of vitamin C administered daily through intramuscular injection for one month significantly bolstered the immune system in a group of healthy volunteers over seventy. The researchers concluded that vitamin C should be considered a 'successful, non-toxic and inexpensive means of improving the immunity'.[163] Although the official recommended daily allowance for an adult is only a tiny 60 milligrams (100 milligrams for lactating mothers), Linus Pauling suggests 6 grams (6,000 milligrams) up to 18 grams (18,000 milligrams) orally every day.[164] See chapter 85 for further information and details of possible side effects.

Beta carotene

Beta carotene is a pre-vitamin A compound found in plants which is converted inside the body to vitamin A. Beta carotene has been shown to have immuno-stimulatory powers. In one study, eleven HIV infected patients were given 30 milligrams a day of beta carotene for 4 months. All of them showed greater immune system activity after treatment.[165] Beta carotene is freely available in foods such as broccoli, tomatoes, carrots, sweet potatoes, parsnips, squash, beets, spinach, and fruits like cantaloupes and papayas. Other rich sources of beta-carotene are easy to spot: bright green, orange or yellow fruits or vegetables almost always contain useful amounts.

Minerals

Zinc

This mineral has been found to aid in the healing of wounds and is crucial to proper immune cell function. A low zinc level can impair your immune response, and so make you susceptible to many infectious diseases.[166] In-depth studies have shown that lack of zinc is a major nutritional deficiency in many developed countries. The recommended daily allowances for zinc range from 5 to 10 milligrams for children to 12 to 15mg for adults (breast-feeding women need between 16 and 19mg daily). However, the zinc content of the average diet is between 10 and 15mg per day, thus putting millions of people below the recommended level.[167] The elderly consume an average of only 7 to 10mg per day. Zinc supplements have been shown to be effective against the common cold,[168] and researchers from the National Research Council on AIDS in Italy believe that zinc supplements may enhance the immune system of AIDS patients because the mineral is involved in maintaining high levels of thymulin, which is a hormone from the thymus gland that regulates immune response.[169] People suffering from AIDS often have a low level of zinc.

Selenium

The human body needs tiny amounts of this trace element. One study has shown that a concentration of 0.7 parts per million in the body can increase antibody production by seven times.[170] And with a concentration of 2.8 parts per million, antibody production shot up by 30 times! It has been known for thirty years that selenium is essential and vital to life, even though needed in only fantastically small quantities. But it is only recently – with the surge of deaths from cancers and AIDS – that serious attention has once again focused on selenium. The most minute trace amounts of selenium have a 'synergistic' effect on vitamin E – in other words, it works with vitamin E in the body to strengthen your immune response.

In America, the National Research Council has recommended a daily intake of 50–200 micrograms of selenium for adults (a microgram is one-thousandth of a milligram, so 200 micrograms equal 0.2 milligram). However, one authority – Gerhard Schrauzer, PhD, of the University of California – believes that 250–300 micrograms can protect against most cancers, and that most people consume only about 100 micrograms daily.[171] At higher doses, selenium can be toxic to the human body. Although it is not certain at precisely what level selenium begins to cause adverse effects, it has been found that doses of 900 micrograms (0.9 milligrams) per day can make hair and nails fall out and can affect the nervous system.[172] You'd be unlikely to get this much from your diet and supplements are clearly marked with the dosage they contain.

Uncommon weapons for your armoury

Conventional medicine is often very slow to consider the effectiveness of traditional medicines. Sometimes it seems the older remedies are deliberately overlooked in favour of the more exciting – but also more expensive – new drugs. The irony is, of course, that many drug developments are themselves based upon traditional folk and plant pharmaceutical preparations. So here are some of the traditional remedies that you may wish to consider. It is always advisable to have the assistance of a qualified herbalist or other practitioner when deciding on treatment and dosages.

~ Purple cornflower (*Echinacae angustifolia*, also *Echinacae purpurea*). This plant produces rich purple flowers, and was originally used by native American Indians as a blood purifier and snake bite remedy. It is now cultivated in Britain and elsewhere. The dried root is used to prepare a liquid extract. It has been shown to be able to stimulate macrophage cells, which seek out and destroy invading bacteria and viruses.[173] The suggested dose is 0.5–1 drachm of the liquid extract.[174] (A drachm is an apothecary's measure, approximately 3.8879 grams.)

~ Goldenseal (*Hydrastis canadensis*) was also discovered by American Indians, who valued the root for its medicinal properties, and used the yellow stain from the rest of the plant as a dye for clothes and faces. Goldenseal root contains approximately 4 per cent of an alkaloid called berberine, which is the main active ingredient of the plant (and is very poisonous if the prescribed dose is exceeded). Berberine has been proven to be a powerful stimulator of macrophage activity.[175] Standardized preparations and suggested doses are: Elix. Viburn. et Hydrast.

B.P.C. 1949 0.5–1 drachm; Ext. Hydrast. Sicc. B.P.C. 1949 (Hydrastin) 0.5–2 grains; Ext. Hydrast. Liq. B.P.C. 1949 5–15 minims; Tinct. Hydrast. B.P.C. 1949 0.5–1 drachm.[176] (A grain is approximately 0.0648 grams, a minim is approximately 0.0592 millilitres.)

~ Liquorice (*Glycyrrhiza glabra*) is so well-known to most people that it needs no introduction. However, the liquorice most of us are familiar with is the rather sickly flavouring found in children's sweets. By this stage in the manufacturing process, it has no useful medicinal activity left. Liquorice root was first recorded as being used by the Greeks in the third century BC for asthma, dry cough and all diseases of the chest, and since then it has a long history both as a food flavouring and a medicinal ingredient. Recent research has shown that some of the active ingredients in liquorice root can actually increase the production of interferon (a protein produced by cells when they are invaded by viruses. When released into the bloodstream, it acts as a messenger to instruct healthy cells to manufacture an enzyme that counters the infection.).[177] In the laboratory liquorice has also been shown to inhibit the growth of viruses such as herpes simplex,[178] and it has also been shown to act against a number of common bacteria (including streptococcus) and candida albicans.[179] Standardized preparations and suggested doses are: Ext. Glycyrrh. B.P.C. 10–30 grains, or Ext. Glycyrrh. Liq. B.P. 0.5–1 drachm, or Pulv. Glycyrrh. Co. B.P. 1–2 drachms.[180]

~ Consider taking spirulina, which provides a wide range of nutrients (see chapter 14). Chlorella is a similar edible algae, which also provides a broad-spectrum mega-dose of natural nutrients to bolster the immune system in multiple ways.

~ Many people find a macrobiotic diet (see chapter 19) to be very effective in helping to enhance the immune response. One specialist, Dr. J. D. Kaiser, who practises medicine in San Francisco, recommends a 'modified macrobiotic' diet for the treatment of AIDS patients, including fruits, vegetables, whole wheat pasta, whole grains and shiitake mushrooms. Garlic, ginger, olive and sesame oil are recommended; sugar, alcohol and caffeine are not.[181] Says Dr. Kaiser: "I believe that we stand today on the cutting edge of using natural therapies as a means of treating many medical conditions that to this point have been poorly managed by standard medical therapies alone."

~ Germanium has been shown to induce production of interferon, enhance normal killer-cell activity and activate macrophages in laboratory studies. Dr. Stephen A. Levine, PhD, writing in the *Journal of Orthomolecular Medicine*, states that organic germanium has demonstrated marked anti-tumour effects, as well as interferon-inducing activity. It also has restored immune function in immune-depressed animals. "These immunostimulant effects were achieved with oral doses, and no harmful side effects were noted," he said.[182]

~ Garlic has been shown to improve the natural killer cell activity in AIDS patients. Garlic is thought to be a particularly valuable tool for reviving the immune system because it is one of the richest sources of organic selenium and germanium. It also contains magnesium, 17 amino acids, vitamins B_1, A and C.

In one study, ten AIDS patients were given garlic extracts as a food supplement for twelve weeks. A 5 gram dose of the extract was taken daily during the first six weeks, and a 10 gram dose was taken each day for the second six weeks. During the experimental period, three patients experienced gastrointestinal and neurological problems and were unable to take the supplement (they later died). All the seven patients who were fit enough to take the supplement showed signs of a strengthening immune system. They reported fewer bouts of diarrhoea, genital herpes, candidiasis and pansinusitis with recurrent fever.[183]

~ The following natural medicines have been used by Japanese nutritionists to stimulate a jaded immune system. Many of these substances, although very familiar to oriental cooks, are largely unknown in the West, and untested by Western science. However, some good scientific news does surface from time to time. For example, it is now established beyond doubt that Japanese green tea has anti-tumour properties. Researchers from the National Cancer Centre Research Institute in Tokyo discovered that fewer people die from cancer in the Shizouka area of Japan than in other regions. Shizouka produces much of Japan's green tea, and the locals drink it in large quantities. After isolating one of its active ingredients (epigallocatechin gallate, or EGCG), they discovered that EGCG can indeed block tumour activity.[184] Unfortunately, it is only green tea which contains sizeable quantities of EGCG – ordinary British tea contains virtually none. Here are some other substances which, one day, we hope may prove to be equally useful:

- LEM (*Lentinus Edodes Mycelia*, an extract from the shiitake mushroom)
- Hijiki (a sea vegetable)
- Iwanori (a sea vegetable)
- Beer yeast
- Yoghurt
- Natto beans (fermented soya beans)
- Wild taro (a type of starchy potato)
- Umeboshi (salt pickled plum)
- Kumquat (a fruit)
- Jujube
- Pine seeds
- Green tea

The scourge of AIDS

AIDS (acquired immune deficiency syndrome) is without doubt the most complex and baffling collection of diseases ever to have affected humankind. It is caused by infection with the human immunodeficiency virus (HIV), which slowly suppresses the immune system's ability to resist invading organisms. As the immune system weakens, so the body becomes prey to a whole collection of opportunistic diseases, and to the development of unusual cancers.

HIV is a retrovirus. One of the distinctive qualities of retroviruses is that they mutate rapidly, changing part of their genetic makeup for adaptive purposes. The greatest fear of AIDS researchers is that the virus might undergo some major mutation that would make it far more infectious, perhaps by different routes. This is a 'nightmare' scenario, but one which becomes more conceivable as the virus spreads and more and more people become infected. If this were ever to happen, those with weakened immune systems would be the first to suffer.

Conventional medicine is hostile to the notion that nutrition and holistic medicines may have a part to play in the treatment of this disease. Nevertheless, a few dedicated researchers and patients are pioneering new treatments, some of which seem at least as promising as any therapy conventional medicine has yet to offer.

Natural therapists believe that AIDS is an immune system deficiency which is intensified by poor nutrition, stress, drugs, and pollution. Since AIDS manifests itself as a combination of diseases (with many different causes) common sense suggests that we should adopt a combination of strategies in dealing with it. Any 'cure' for AIDS will need to combine:

~ Something to act against the HIV virus.

~ Something to work against those secondary opportunistic infections which are so characteristic of the AIDS onslaught.
~ Something to strengthen our immune systems so that our bodies can fight the infection themselves.
~ Something to fight tumours such as Kaposi's sarcoma and other AIDS-related cancers.

No one drug is likely to provide all these characteristics, so it seems only sensible to investigate natural therapies which could complement the efforts of conventional medicine.

Dr. Laurence E. Badgley, a Californian physician specializing in the treatment of AIDS patients with natural therapies, believes that opportunistic germs, including certain retroviruses like HIV, can only invade an already-weakened immune system.

"When confronted by a strong immune system, opportunistic germs are either defeated or forced to remain quiescent within the body," he wrote in a newsletter for doctors. "Investigators have discovered persons who have been HIV-positive for 10 years and who remain asymptomatic. Most wives of haemophiliacs with AIDS have not become HIV-positive even though they have had 'unsafe sex' for months and years, while their husbands were infectious. Some HIV-positive individuals have even become HIV antibody negative."[185]

Dr. Badgley undertook a six-month study involving 36 HIV-positive patients, twelve of whom were diagnosed as having AIDS proper. The patients were advised to 'take charge' of their situation, initiate dietary changes, take nutritional supplements, meditate, exercise and have a positive outlook on life. Homoeopathic remedies, herbal therapies and acupuncture also were recommended. Every day, they supplemented their diet with:
~ 7,800mg of vitamin C
~ 48,600 IU of beta carotene
~ 14,400 IU of vitamin A
~ 615 IU of vitamin E
~ 176mg of vitamin B_6
~ 203mcg of vitamin B_{12}
~ 970mcg of folic acid
~ 312mg of pantothenic acid
~ 23mg of iron
~ 62mg of zinc
~ 184mcg of selenium
~ 172mg of germanium
~ 55mg of coenzyme Q10

Twenty-five per cent of the patients also used garlic, and 36 per cent used *echinacea*. After six months, 83 per cent said that their health had improved. The average absolute T4 helper lymphocyte count (a measure of immune strength) had increased 13 per cent. Many of them stopped taking AZT (the only drug then approved to combat the HIV virus).

"The study results suggest that natural therapies are cost-effective treatments for AIDS," concludes Dr. Badgley. "Most of the participants paid less than $400 for their office visits to the natural therapists. Many AIDS patients who pursue orthodox medical-pharmaceutical care spend $30,000-$50,000 yearly on their outpatient care."

Neither complementary therapies nor conventional medicine can claim a 'cure' for AIDS. But it is very likely that each may have its own part to play in the treatment of the disease. The long-term survivors of AIDS teach us that there's much more to conquering this syndrome than simply taking your medicine when you're told to. Attitude is vitally important. People who are diagnosed as being HIV-positive, and who are willing to take control of the new circumstances in their lives, are far more likely to stay the course than those who passively accept the diagnosis as terminal.

"What I began to understand was, maybe you can't change the virus but you can change yourself," says one six-year survivor. "It became a teacher instead of a death sentence."

"I set about to enjoy my life on a daily basis, moment to moment, and I'm still here," says a seven-year survivor, who has thrown himself into dance therapy, meditation, praying, massage, acupuncture, support groups and visualization. He eats a first-class diet and exercises regularly, too. We can all learn something from people like that.

Chapter 37
Foods to fight insomnia

~

Sleep is certainly a healer – of body, mind and spirit. Yet approximately one-third of people have trouble finding it. Here is help for your sleeplessness.

Insomnia is a pattern of either waking repeatedly during the night or having persistent difficulty in falling asleep in the first place. For some people insomnia is a temporary affliction, passing within days or weeks; but for others it is a seemingly permanent part of their lives. Most of those who suffer from insomnia would agree that it is a frustrating condition that often drives people to despair and the bottle of sedatives.

The cause of insomnia is usually psychological. It has always been associated with depression, anxiety and general stress, so if you suffer from insomnia you will probably benefit from learning a relaxation technique (see chapters 57 and 59). Some people find that an hour or two with a counsellor helps them resolve a problem that has encroached on their sleep. Allow 20 minutes each day for brisk exercise such as swimming, walking or cycling. A regular exercise regime is often all that is needed to break a pattern of insomnia. For very persistent, severe cases attendance at a sleep clinic might provide insight into the cause of your insomnia, and help you resolve it. Your doctor will know if there's one near you.

All insomniacs should take a good look at their diet to see whether they are eating, or not eating, something which could be the cause of their sleeplessness.

~ Sleeplessness in children usually means sleeplessness in parents, too! Recent research from Belgium has revealed that a previously undiagnosed intolerance to cow's milk may be a cause of insomnia in children.[186] In the Belgian studies, once milk had been eliminated from the children's diet their sleeping problems dramatically improved. An intolerance to cow's milk is also common in adults, so try eliminating all dairy products from your diet – and that of your children.

~ Tryptophan is an amino acid which is synthesized into serotonin, a compound in your brain which can initiate sleep. Nuts such as peanuts, pecans, walnuts and brazil nuts all contain tryptophan and a snack of these before retiring may help you fall asleep. A serving of baked beans is also effective. Tryptophan used to be recommended in supplement form but in this form it is now believed to be capable of causing a blood disorder (eosinophilia-myalgia syndrome – EMS);[187] you should therefore avoid taking a tryptophan supplement.

~ Increase your intake of the B group of vitamins. These vitamins help your body to cope with stress, a common cause of insomnia. The B vitamins are essential to the proper functioning of your nervous system and influence your moods and your emotional well-being. Foods rich in the B vitamins are brewer's yeast, nuts and seeds and all whole grains.

~ You might think a nightcap will help you conquer your insomnia, and it might work once. However, alcohol is one of many dietary factors which can actually inhibit sleep. Reduce your intake of alcohol and avoid a nightcap altogether. Coffee, chocolate, tea and many other drugs (such as marijuana and certain prescription drugs) also inhibit sleep and should be avoided.

~ Reduce your intake of refined sugar as it can cause large fluctuations in your blood sugar level. Wakefulness at night is often caused by a sudden drop in your blood sugar level. Eat an evening meal low in sugar but high in complex carbohydrates to correct a tendency to wake, perhaps feeling hungry, in the middle of the night. Complex carbohydrates are unprocessed grains, legumes and vegetables.

~ A hot cup of chamomile, hop or lemon verbena herbal tea has relaxing properties and makes a good bedtime drink. Serve with a slice of lemon and a piece of cinnamon to make it really special.

~ There are several natural herb tablets on the market (such as Lane's Quiet Life Tablets) which are non habit-forming but sleep- and rest-inducing. The chief active ingredient in most of these tablets is the herb valerian. Try using them just for a week to break the established pattern of insomnia.

Chapter 38
Foods to Fight Migraine

~

A migraine differs from an ordinary headache in that it is often difficult to pinpoint its cause. And the severity and duration can be quite awesome.

We all have headaches from time to time, and when we do, we often have a good idea as to their cause – too much to drink the night before, eyestrain from working in a badly-lit environment, or the prospect of an unpleasant event in our lives, to name but three. Headaches are generally divided into two categories – tension headaches and vascular headaches. The first is caused by muscle spasms in the neck and head (about 90 per cent of headaches are thought to fall into this category). Tension headaches which continue on and off for years are often associated with chronic depression or other emotional problems, and are sometimes effectively treated by psychotherapy or relaxation training. A migraine is typical of the second category, the vascular headache. The symptoms may include a severe throbbing pain, often just on one side of the head, vertigo, visual disturbances, nausea and vomiting, and the attack may last a day or more. Basically, what seems to be happening is that blood vessels inside the head are dilating, so stimulating and causing pain to the membranous linings of the brain. Conventional therapy often includes treatment by vasoconstricting drugs, which attempt to reduce the swelling of these blood vessels.

Whilst prescription medicines can sometimes solve the immediate problem of a migraine attack, none of them treat the underlying cause. So the sensible way to fight migraines is on two fronts: first, try to prevent it from happening; and second, conquer it when it does!

Prevent ...

The evidence shows that many migraines are frequently triggered by certain foods. So this is a good starting point – if you are a sufferer, you may already suspect which foods are liable to bring on an attack. If not, then follow this plan to identify the culprit.

First, make arrangements to eat a simple 'elimination' diet for several days – up to a week if you can. This should consist only of those foods which are least likely to cause an allergic reaction, such as:

Brown rice
Rice flour
Puffed rice
Cooked fruits (not citrus)
Simple cooked vegetables (potatoes, cabbage, broccoli, etc.)

It should definitely *exclude* these foods, which experience shows are most likely to provoke an attack:

Cheese
Chocolate
Red wine
Wheat
Corn
Eggs
Milk
Shellfish
Citrus fruits
Coffee
Tomatoes
Strawberries

If you feel better after your elimination diet, and haven't had an attack, then that is a promising indication that food allergy may indeed be responsible for your attacks. To confirm this, re-introduce each one of the suspect foods into your diet every two days. At the first sign of an attack, you've found one of the culprits! This process sounds easy, but actually requires a considerable amount of dedication to make it work. It is a painstaking procedure, but the rewards, if your detective work succeeds, will be worth it. A study published in *The Lancet* has established that 93 per cent of long-term sufferers can obtain relief by eliminating offending foods from their diet.[188] So give it a try!

... And conquer!

Even if your migraine is not directly triggered by a specific food, diet can still be an important factor.

~ At the University of Missouri, research has shown that people who suffer from migraine frequently suffer from hypoglycaemia as well.[189] Hypoglycaemia, or low blood sugar, has a wide-ranging list of other symptoms, including fatigue, irritability, indigestion, breathlessness, and blurred vision. The condition can be diagnosed with a glucose tolerance test which identifies any abnormal over-reaction to glucose. An over-reaction brings about a severe drop in the blood sugar level and symptomatic headaches or migraine can result. People who have been identified as suffering from this condition have also been shown to have a magnesium deficiency. If you are a migraine sufferer, try including more magnesium-rich foods in your diet, preferably from organic sources. Magnesium is found in fresh green vegetables, whole grains, nuts and yeast extracts.

~ Probably the most interesting dietary remedy for migraine is the common herb feverfew, which has been used to treat headaches since early Roman times. Several very exciting recent studies have proved that feverfew can prevent migraine attacks.[190] One study found that 70 per cent of the people who consumed two or three fresh leaves of the bitter-tasting plant each day had fewer and less severe attacks than a comparable group of migraine sufferers who didn't use the plant.[191] Just how feverfew works is not clear – it contains sesquiterpene lactones, substances which are known to inhibit the release of a brain chemical called serotonin, thought to be one of the precipitating factors of the migraine attack. Be aware, however, that taking any drug, including feverfew, for a long time might lead to side effects – so talk to your practitioner before embarking on treatment.

~ Another foodstuff with possible anti-migraine effects is cayenne pepper. It contains an ingredient, capsaicin, which might be able to prevent and control migraine attacks by inhibiting platelet aggregation, one of the biological changes which may underlie attacks.[192]

~ It is also possible that certain bacteria active in the colon may produce substances which produce an allergic migraine reaction in sensitive people. A course of colonic irrigation could therefore be of help, see chapter 70.

~ Not all migraine headaches are caused by the food you eat. Stress, bad posture and a poor working environment have all been identified as possible causes. As long ago as 5000 BC, the Chinese used acupuncture to relieve head pain. So consider other options available to you, outlined in this book, such as:

- Ionizers and air purifiers
- Probiotics
- Chiropractic
- Herbalism
- Hypnotherapy
- Massage
- Naturopathy
- Reflexology

Finally, if you are a chronic sufferer, it is worth supporting the British Migraine Association, who can keep you up to date with new developments and research, see the Help section for details.

Chapter 39
Foods to Fight Multiple Sclerosis

~

You may not think of multiple sclerosis as a diet-related disease but, in fact, the type of food you eat may be linked with its onset and progression.

Multiple sclerosis (MS) is a degenerative disease of the central nervous system. In the course of the disease, myelin (a white, fatty substance that acts as an electrical insulator for the nerves) is progressively destroyed, and the formation of hard scar tissue on the protective myelin sheath which surrounds nerves stops the nerve cells from working. This scarring results in permanent loss of nervous control to areas of the body. It is a crippling disease which attacks every body function; and with time MS can be fatal. It affects both men and women, usually first being diagnosed between the ages of 20 and 40.

Suspected causes

The cause of multiple sclerosis is still unconfirmed. Dozens of causes have been suggested over the years but no conclusive proof of any one cause has yet been found. A great deal of research has gone into investigating the possibility that MS is caused by a virus, although to date, it has not proved possible to pinpoint precisely which one. Similarly, it has long been suspected that MS is an autoimmune disease, a sort of allergic reaction in which the body responds to an antigen by acting against itself. Again, pinpointing the antigen in question has proved very difficult. Another theory proposes that giving cow's milk to infants predisposes them to nervous system injury later in life, because cow's milk has only a fifth as much linoleic acid (an essential fatty acid) as human breast milk, and linoleic acid makes up the building blocks for nervous tissues.[193] The list could go on and on. But while waiting for conclusive proof of cause, it is possible to deal with multiple sclerosis so as to minimize its crippling effect and, perhaps, prolong life.

Diet and MS

Most health professionals have traditonally dismissed the idea that multiple sclerosis might be linked to diet. However, Dr. Roy Swank, former Professor of Neurology at the University of Oregon, was intrigued by some wartime research. During World War II, the consumption of animal fat decreased in Western Europe. Meat and dairy products were rationed, and instead, consumption of grains and vegetables increased. It was noticed at this time that patients with MS had 2 to $2\frac{1}{2}$ times fewer hospitalizations during the war years, when saturated fat consumption was low.[194] Greatly excited by the possible implication of these findings, Dr. Swank began treating his own patients with a low fat diet. Over the next 35 years, he treated thousands of MS patients in this way. By any medical standard his results have been remarkable: patients' conditions improved by as much as 95 per cent.[195] Patients fared better if they had detected the disease early and had had few attacks, but even long-time MS sufferers experienced a slowdown of the disease's progression. The basics of his diet are:

~ No more than 10 grams saturated fat per day
~ 40 to 50 grams of polyunsaturated fat (but *no* margarine or other hydrogenated fats), per day
~ At least 1 tsp cod liver oil daily
~ Fish three times a week, other animal foods cut out.[196]

Protein intake should be kept up with a good supply of mixed vegetable proteins (see chapters 11 and 18). The long-term results of the Swank diet show that of those who ate less than 20 grams of fat per day, only 31 per cent have died (close to normal) and the condition of the rest has deteriorated only slightly. Of those who ate more than 20 grams, 81 per cent have died.[197, 198, 199]

Many orthodox medical practitioners, however, are still very wary of accepting such evidence. As an editorial in *The Lancet* recently stated, "there are still no firm answers as to whether a relationship (between MS and dietary fats) does indeed exist and if so, what its mechanism might be . . . more work is needed at the biochemical level . . . Until such studies are undertaken, the role of lipids in MS cannot be said to be proven."[200] But in the words of another doctor who uses the Swank diet to treat patients: "I've been very gratified by the results of this dietary treatment, not only because the progress of most of my MS patients' disease has been halted, but also because their overall health has unquestionably improved."[201]

Chapter 40
Foods to fight osteoporosis

~

If you are a woman, by the time you are sixty, there is a one in four chance that osteoporosis will have caused you to break a bone.[202] And more than 10 per cent of people who suffer a hip fracture caused by osteoporosis will die.[203] So be wise, and take steps now to protect yourself from this insidious threat to your health.

What is it?

Osteoporosis literally means porous bones. You may not even realize that you suffer from it until you suddenly break a bone – by which time the harm has been done. Other telltale signs can include severe back pain, loss of height or deformities such as a curvature of the spine. It is estimated that more than 50,000 women fracture their hip each year due to osteoporosis.[204] And the number of deaths from fractured hips is greater than the number of deaths from cancers of the cervix, uterus and breast combined,[205] making osteoporosis one of the major killers of our time.

Osteoporosis is caused by a slow loss of bone mass. By the age of 35 or so, your bones will be as strong as they're ever likely to be. The rest, as they say, is all downhill! Hormones in our bodies are responsible for continuously balancing the growth of new bone with the reabsorption of old bone. When levels of these hormones fall significantly, as happens in menopause, this balance is lost and a gradual loss of bone mass occurs. Eventually, the bones can become very brittle and break easily. In some women this process is sufficiently slow to avoid fractures, pain and loss of height. In others, however, the loss is rapid – some women can lose up to half of their bone mass within ten or so years of menopause, leaving them very vulnerable to easy fracture. Since it is clear that oestrogen, the female sex hormone, plays a protective role in the maintenance of bone mass, one current treatment for women suffering from osteoporosis is Hormone Replacement Therapy (HRT).

Unlike some modern epidemics, osteoporosis is not an equal opportunities disease. It discriminates on the grounds of gender, race and age. Both men and women *can* suffer from osteoporosis, but it is rarer in men (one estimate holds that only one in 40 men are ever diagnosed as having it).[206] Oriental and Caucasian women are most at risk due to their tendency to have thinner, lighter bones. Women of African, Mediterranean or Aboriginal extraction are less likely to suffer.

Hormone replacement therapy

HRT provides your body with a supplement of the female hormone oestrogen. While every last detail of the mechanism by which oestrogen slows down bone loss is not yet known, doctors have known about its usefulness in treating this complaint for over fifty years,[207] and there is no doubt that it works. HRT has a number of very worthwhile advantages:

- It slows down the loss of bone mineral content, so decreasing the likelihood of fractures of the spine, hips and wrists
- It prevents loss of height
- It lowers LDL cholesterol in your blood and increases HDL cholesterol, thus prolonging life expectancy by decreasing the risk of heart disease
- It decreases hot flushes
- It decreases the risk of ovarian cancer[208]

On the other hand, concerns have been expressed about its long-term safety (as they have for the oestrogen-based contraceptive pill). Although many women – and some doctors – are concerned about an increased risk of cancer from HRT, most of the scientific evidence does not confirm these worries. While some scientific studies do indeed show that oestrogen therapy may increase the risk of developing cancer,[209] today's HRT includes other hormones (progestogens) which studies show can actually reduce the cancer risk appreciably.[210, 211] This is an area of ongoing research, and it is worth keeping up to date with the latest findings. There are, however, some problems associated with HRT, as with all drugs. These can sometimes include breast soreness, gallstones, weight gain, return of periods, and breakthrough bleeding. You should obviously discuss these and other aspects of HRT with your doctor.

How to battle brittle bones

Treating osteoporosis successfully is one thing, but preventing it is even better. Here are some simple changes you can make to your lifestyle which can slow the rate of bone loss and, if started at a young enough age, prevent osteoporosis from developing in the first place. The potential for suffering osteoporosis is now thought to be laid down in childhood. So if you have a daughter, begin now to instil in her the importance of following this four-point prevention programme:

1 Make exercise part of your way of life

Especially important are forms of exercise that are weight-bearing such as walking, dancing, running and many sports. Swimming, for example, is not a weight-bearing exercise. Proper exercise exerts the muscles around your bones, stimulating them to maintain bone density. Leading a sedentary life will increase the likelihood of osteoporosis developing later in your life.

2 Avoid smoking, caffeine and excess alcohol

~ Smoking can increase your risk of suffering from osteoporosis.[212]

~ Caffeine can affect calcium levels in the body. It is found in tea, coffee and chocolate. A study of women aged thirty-six to forty-five found that those who drank two cups of coffee a day suffered a net calcium loss of 22 milligrams daily. One cup meant a loss of 6 milligrams a day. The authors concluded that a negative calcium balance of 40 milligrams a day (about four cups) was enough to explain the 1 to 1.5 per cent loss in skeletal mass in postmenopausal women each year.[213] So cut down your caffeine consumption.

~ Alcohol, except in moderation, speeds bone loss because it interferes with the way your body absorbs calcium. If you are a woman, keep within the fourteen units per week recommendation.

3 Get regular doses of sunlight

Sunlight reacts with a substance in your skin – dehydrocholesterol – to produce vitamin D. This vitamin is essential to the proper absorption of calcium and a deficiency will cause you to lose bone mass. Most people get enough vitamin D just by being outside for part of the day with their face, hands and arms exposed.[214] If you don't get out regularly, you may need to eat food which is fortified with vitamin D.

4 Choose the right food

When selecting foods, take these factors into consideration:

Calcium

The UK recommended daily allowance of calcium for adults is currently 500 milligrams a day, and the American one is 800 milligrams. Yet a consensus at a recent conference on osteoporosis in Virginia, USA, put the recommended level as high as 1,500 milligrams per day for women,[215] and another experimental study shows that about 1,200 milligrams a day is the right level to keep the body in calcium balance.[216] So how much calcium do you actually need? Obviously, different people will need different amounts. At a symposium organized by the National Osteoporosis Society, Dr. Chris Robinson, a lecturer at Newcastle-upon-Tyne Medical School, suggested intakes:

Age	*Calcium in mg*
Normal adult	800
Adolescent growth	1100
Pregnancy	1000
Lactation	1200
Elderly with HRT	1000
Elderly without HRT	1500

But 1,500 milligrams is nearly half a pound of hard cheese, four cups of yoghurt or five cups of milk a day! Most people would find it difficult to include these amounts of dairy food in their diet, and in any case, there are undesirable health implications in eating such quantities of these foods:

~ Dairy foods tend to be very high in fat, especially saturated fat, and cholesterol. A regular consumption of such large amounts would increase the risk of obesity, cardiovascular disease, and stroke. If you wish to eat dairy foods, choose those with reduced fat content.

~ Consuming large amounts of animal protein is undesirable for a number of reasons. When scientists from Andrews University, Michigan, studied the bone mass (by direct photon absorptiometry) of 1,600 women living in southwestern Michigan they found some surprising results. Women who had eaten a vegetarian diet for at least twenty years had only lost an average of 18 per cent of their bone mineral by the time they were eighty. On the other hand, women who did not eat a vegetarian diet had lost an average of 35 per cent of their bone mineral. Interestingly, there was no statistical difference in the nutrient intakes between the two groups.[217] The difference in bone loss could be explained by the different type of protein consumed. A diet high in animal-based proteins increases the amount of acid in the body. This triggers a buffering mechanism, which releases stored calcium from the bones. The body would normally reabsorb the calcium released, but the animal protein inhibits the parathyroid function that orders this reabsorption. The body then excretes the calcium, causing bone loss. One researcher who put this theory to the test concluded: "This study suggests that a diet higher in vegetable protein might actually be somewhat protective against osteoporosis."[218]

So how can you take in enough calcium to protect yourself from osteoporosis without consuming excessive quantities of animal-based foodstuffs? Non-meat foods rich in calcium include:

~ Dairy products (low fat, please!)
~ Tofu
~ Sesame seeds and paste (tahini)
~ Pumpkin and sunflower seeds
~ Molasses
~ Carob
~ Dried figs, currants and apricots

~ Almond and brazil nuts
~ Porridge
~ Spinach, seaweed and other green leafy vegetables

If you are unfamiliar with any of these foods, there are many good wholefood and vegetarian cookbooks which include them in their recipes. Of course, the easiest way to ensure that you get the right amount of calcium in your diet is to take a mineral supplement with your food.

Magnesium

This mineral works with other vitamins and minerals, including calcium, to promote bone growth and the healthy functioning of nerves and muscle tissue. A deficiency of magnesium can affect the manufacture of vitamin D, so it is important in preventing osteoporosis. Magnesium is a constituent of chlorophyll and so is abundant in green vegetables. Other excellent sources are whole grains, wheat germ, molasses, seeds and nuts, apples and figs.

Boron

This trace mineral helps to prevent calcium loss and subsequent loss of bone mass. It is also thought to help in the manufacture of vitamin D in the body. The first study ever to look at the nutritional effects of boron in humans took place in 1987. Twelve postmenopausal women were fed a diet very low in boron for seventeen weeks, after which they were given a daily supplement of 3 milligrams for a further seven weeks. The addition of boron had a dramatic effect – the women lost 40 per cent less calcium and 30 per cent less magnesium through their urine. The study therefore concluded that boron can reduce bodily losses of elements necessary to maintain bone integrity and to prevent osteoporosis. What was even more exciting was the discovery that the boron supplement could double the most active form of oestrogen (estradiol 17B) in the blood of the women – their estradiol levels equalled those of women on oestrogen replacement therapy. Curtiss Hunt, of the US Human Nutrition Research Center, said he "suspects the body needs boron to synthesize estrogen, vitamin D and other steroid hormones. And it may protect these hormones against rapid breakdown."[219]

Foods rich in boron are easily obtained and include apples, grapes, pears, prunes, dates, raisins, almonds, peanuts and hazelnuts. Yet another good reason to include fresh food in your diet every day.

And finally ...

~ The vitamin B complex and vitamin K are both thought to play a role in the prevention of osteoporosis. The B group is available in brewer's yeast, whole grains, molasses, nuts and seeds and dark green leafy vegetables. Vitamin K is present in cauliflower, soyabeans, molasses, safflower oil and, again, dark green leafy vegetables.

~ Several commonly used drugs can induce significant calcium loss, particularly aluminium-containing antacids. If these antacids are used for prolonged periods of time, they may produce bone abnormalities by interfering with calcium and phosphorus metabolism, and so contribute to the development of osteoporosis.[220] So if you want to use an antacid, choose one which does not include aluminium in its ingredients.

CHAPTER 41

FOODS TO PROMOTE LONGEVITY AND FIGHT SENILITY

~

Does the government want you to die young? The idea isn't as preposterous as it might first appear. The truth is that the world is getting older. In 1950, the 'median age' of the world's population was 23.4 years (this simply means that half the population was older than 23.4, and half was younger). By the year 2025, the median age of the world's population will have risen to 31.1 years – and in Europe, the median age will be as high as 43. Now it is an indisputable fact that old people cost governments money – lots of money. To tell the brutal truth, most governments seem to regard older people as a drain on their country's resources. At the very least, it is conceivable that your government may not want you to live too long.

Of course, no government is going to admit this. But examine the facts. In the United Kingdom, for example, people generally assume that their state pension contributions are invested on their behalf, and will be repaid to them when they reach pensionable age. However, this is not the case. Pension contributions paid by today's workers are used to pay the pensions of *today's* pensioners. This system only works as long as pensioners and workers keep in rough balance with each other. However, in the future, the labour force will shrink in size, while the number of older people is forecast to mushroom dramatically. Eventually, a point will come when the number of pensioners will exceed the number of workers paying to support them. At that time, bankruptcy and financial chaos will be staring us in the face. Before this point is reached, however, a crafty government is likely to take steps to ensure that the number of old people it has to care for does not reach crisis levels. To put it bluntly, they may have a financial interest in seeing you die young.

If you still think this is inconceivable, try explaining why governments still tacitly encourage smoking; why none of them spends any significant amount on preventive health care; why so little priority is attached to rectifying the environmental causes of illness; why so much ballyhoo is made about finding 'cures' for cancer and heart disease yet no significant effort is made to eradicate the causes; why many governments are trying to renege on their state pension obligations; why most of the public and many doctors are kept in the dark about optimum levels of nutrition; and why the public health services in many countries are being deliberately eroded. If they really want you to live forever, they're not making a very good job of it, are they?

Of course, ageing is an inevitable process – there is as yet no elixir of youth – but we can certainly take action now to delay its effects and protect ourselves from such ravages as senility. Because if *you* don't no one else is likely to – least of all the bureaucrats who are worried about supporting a greying population.

How many years?

If you were born in the baby boom of the fifties and sixties, you can expect to live longer than any other previous generation: to seventy-six if you are a man, or eighty if a woman. You might live even longer – the Office of Population Censuses and Surveys estimates that the number of British people aged eighty-five and over will grow to nearly two million in the next fifty years.

Although we are living longer than our grandparents, and medical research is at its height, we are not in the golden age. In fact, children are now more at risk from cancer, heart disease and strokes than were their parents, according to a study of 15,000 children from sixteen different countries.[221] So what *is* our maximum possible human lifespan?

Unfortunately, the evidence isn't clear-cut. Even the experts disagree among themselves. The pessimists believe that the human body has a natural upper limit to its useful life, beyond which normal ageing processes do their deadly work. "Once you go beyond the age of 85," says S. Jay Olshansky of the University of Chicago, "people die from multiple-organ failure. They stop breathing. Basically, they die of old age. And there's no cure for that. Barring a reversal of human ageing on a molecular level, the rapid increases in life expectancy are over."[222] However, the optimists take a different view. "We have all the basic science to postpone human ageing right now," says Michael Rose, an evolutionary biologist from the University of California at Irvine, who has written a book about it.[223] He believes that ageing is "a problem that is well on its way toward a scientific solution".

In the face of so much scientific uncertainty, what is our best course of action? We propose a three-part strategy:

~ Don't Kill Yourself Prematurely
~ Make Quality Count
~ Squeeze Those Extra Years

First – Don't kill yourself prematurely! This simply means really looking after yourself. In particular, there are 'Seven Deadly Sins' of modern life which, if allowed to get out of control, can put an early end to your hopes of a long and happy life. Here they are:

1. *High Blood Pressure*

Many people with high blood pressure don't know they have it until it is measured by their doctor. Others suffer from frequent headaches, chronic fatigue or kidney problems which eventually leads them to have a check-up. In fact, the general symptoms of high blood pressure can be quite vague. But there is nothing vague about the *effects* of high blood pressure on your heart and arteries. It is one of the leading causes of heart and circulatory disease and can result in handicap or death from heart attack or stroke. High blood pressure erodes your health, whether you are aware of it or not. It can gradually rise to an unhealthy level without you knowing a thing about it. This is why having your blood pressure measured once each year is a good idea. And if it is too high – then do something about it! See chapter 35 for more information.

2. *Salt*

Table salt or sea salt consists largely of sodium chloride. Sodium works with potassium in your body to balance the level of fluid inside and outside each cell. Too much of one or the other of these salts will create an imbalance. An imbalance – and it need only be a very small one – will create health problems particularly focused on the arteries, heart and kidneys. High blood pressure is one of these problems.

Most of us probably take in more salt than is good for us so a general recommendation here to **reduce your salt intake** is in order. Here are three simple steps which can reduce your salt consumption by as much as half – without it being difficult or tiresome.

~ Don't add salt to your food as you cook. Let each person add a little salt to their own meal when it arrives at the table, if they really want it. Taste tests have shown that food *tastes* saltier when the salt is added after cooking – even though less salt is generally used. And make sure that the salt shaker on the table is transparent and only one-quarter full. This seems to encourage people to use rather less than usual.

~ Substitute ordinary table salt for a balanced salt, such as Biosalt™, which contains potassium as well as sodium. Then add other condiments to your table, such as celery seed, dried herbs and spices, which will introduce other flavour-enhancing tastes – not necessarily salty ones.

~ Shop with an eye for salty foods. Check the labels. Tinned foods, yeast extract and many 'instant' products are all potential salt traps – read the fine print carefully. Thankfully, many manufacturers have responded to consumer interest and produced excellent low-salt versions of many of these food products.

3. *Alcohol*

When it is part of a lifestyle 'package' that includes over-eating, smoking and lack of exercise, alcohol can contribute to liver and psychological disorders, obesity and, of course, heart and circulatory disease. Some scientific studies point to alcohol consumption as a probable factor in the development of breast cancer.[224] Certainly, most doctors agree that excessive drinking is not good for any aspect of your health.

Obviously the choice is yours. But if you decide to drink you should know the risks and practise moderation – which is crucial if you wish to preserve your health.

The Risks Are:

~ Alcohol can cause obesity and high blood pressure.

~ Even moderate drinking during pregnancy can cause low birth weight and premature birth. Heavy drinking can cause deformity, blindness, retardation and heart problems.

~ Alcohol taken with aspirin can cause abnormalities in the way your blood clots.

~ Women may experience menstrual or gynecological disorders from moderate to heavy drinking. Use of the contraceptive pill may, for some women, compound this effect.

~ Men and women who smoke, overeat or are overweight and who also drink will increase their risk of illness – of any sort – from this combination. Heart and circulatory disease is especially likely.

Moderate Drinking Is:

~ **Women** – consume *no more* than two to three units of alcohol, two to three times in a week.

~ **Men** – consume *no more* than four to six units of alcohol, two to three times in a week.

~ **All drinkers** – have three or four drink-free days in each week.

~ All drinks should be consumed slowly: one unit per hour, one unit at a time, preferably accompanied by food.

One unit of alcohol equals:
= one-half pint of beer
= one measure of spirit
= one glass of wine
= 1 small glass of sherry
= 1 glass of vermouth or aperitif

A final caution: Heavy drinking is *definitely* damaging to the heart, liver, stomach and brain. Avoid it!

4. *Obesity*

Today, over thirty-four million Americans are so fat as to be considered 'obese' – that's one in every five adults. In Britain, the government's COMA Report revealed that there has been a progressive increase in the average weight of adults since the war until – currently – more than 40 per cent of middle-aged men and women are overweight.[225] Currently, between 50 and 80 per cent of British children are thought to be overweight and underactive – these children are the obese adults of the future. Obesity is linked to the development of many serious illnesses – for example, high blood cholesterol levels occur *more than twice as often* in the overweight than in the non-overweight.

In fact, it seems likely that being overweight by only 10 per cent can greatly increase your risk of death from coronary heart disease, and this is especially likely in young men. Diabetes, hypertension and an increased level of blood cholesterol are all more likely to happen to you if you are overweight, and particularly if you have been overweight since childhood.

Many people learn to be obese as children and their bodies simply remain obese for the rest of their lives. One health care group has conducted studies which reveal that nearly one-third of all school children eat a lunch-time diet that is so high in fat it virtually *guarantees* they will suffer from obesity later in life.[226] Many voices have been raised in protest against the unhealthy diet that our children are eating, but not enough positive action seems to emerge. The 95,000-strong Assistant Masters and Mistresses Association produced a report some years ago which heavily criticized nutritional standards.[227] "There is now ample evidence that our national eating habits are unhealthy," it said, "and it could be that education authorities, however accidentally, are reinforcing bad eating habits which children should be educated out of, not encouraged to carry over into the home."

The fact is, most of us have a well established diet and lifestyle by the time we're ten years old, and these patterns are often difficult or impossible to change in later life. If we've been taught bad eating habits, then we'll probably go on eating badly all our lives. If you want to try and break this vicious circle, you'll find help in chapters 21, 22 and 23.

5. *Smoking*

There is no doubt that smoking causes ill health and literally robs you of the best years of your life. Heavy smokers (who smoke twenty-five or more cigarettes per day) are *fifteen times* more likely than non-smokers to have a fatal heart attack. Smoking also creates the ideal conditions in your body for the development of hypertension, atherosclerosis, lung, throat and respiratory diseases – and of course, cancer. But if you stop smoking, within five to ten years your chances of developing these crippling or killing diseases will drop to about the same risk level as a life-long non-smoker. So do it now.

6. *Stress*

Stress is a reaction to a situation, a person, or an event. Anything can cause stress or trigger a stressful response. Even the smallest frustrations – apparently quite trivial in themselves – can contribute to a stress build-up. "Microaggressions happen to us on a daily basis," says Dr. Michelle O. Clark, Assistant Clinical Professor of Psychiatry at the University of California in San Francisco. "It may seem like a small thing when it occurs, but these small things add up, day after day, month after month, year after year. They wear you down and you may begin to manifest physical symptoms."[228] Stress creates a sense of urgency which, though possibly arising from an emotional or mental reaction, nevertheless has physical symptoms too. Here is what happens:

When you feel stressful, your adrenals make a hormone called adrenaline which prepares your body for immediate hard work and urgent action. This is a physical response – often called the 'fight or flight' response – which is an inheritance from our ancestors who used it to deal with dangerous situations. The situations in which we live are significantly different from theirs, but the same mechanisms are at work in our stressful responses.

During stress your body needs additional oxygen in order to help you either beat the problem or beat a fast retreat (fight or flight). To supply this oxygen, your heart beats faster and harder, your blood pressure rises and your rate of breathing increases. You also begin to perspire, anticipating the need to keep cool during your efforts!

To give you the instant energy you will need to fight or flee, your liver gets the stress message and triggers the release of fats and sugars directly into your bloodstream. This set of responses is an excellent means of ensuring self-preservation and will occur even when the stressful situation is left unresolved. In fact, much of our modern experience of stress is because we cannot resolve problems in the simple 'fight or flight' way. We have conditioned ourselves *not* to fight or flee, but to resolve our problems in a more 'civilized' manner. Unfortunately, our bodies haven't got the message yet.

Your body will react to stress in this age-old manner no matter how your social training tells you to respond. So, while you might *appear* cool, calm and collected, your body is still sweating and speeding – a case of 'all revved up and nowhere to go.' Those extra fats released by your liver, for instance, if not used for energy are left circulating in your bloodstream until they eventually clog your arteries. Other manifestations of stress are more apparent, and *very* common. They include: asthma, eczema, headache, hostility, indigestion and ulcers. Unresolved stress can cause serious health problems and even death from stroke, heart attack, and maybe cancer too. Even depression and manic depression appear to be triggered by stress. Stress is one of the most insidious killers of our Western way of life, and it is imperative that each and every one of us learns how to defuse this timebomb before it destroys us. Otherwise, the symptoms of stress will ensure that your life is not only pretty short, but pretty miserable too.

Here are a few ideas to start with:

~ Raise your stress threshold. Decide, and then train yourself, to become stressful *only* after all other possibilities have been considered. If you are prone to stress, you almost certainly believe that the problems you face are 1) insurmountable and 2) can only be dealt with by you and you alone. Rubbish! Here are several other alternatives to consider:

Try laughing
Try crying
Try walking away from the problem
Try making an appointment to solve the problem later today or this week
Try asking someone else to solve it
Try asking someone to share it with you
Try telling the perpetrator of it to go elsewhere

~ Change the way you react to the stress in your life. If you currently internalize it, why not try hitting cushions instead! Or if you are a person who goes red with rage but still doesn't feel de-stressed, try some rhythmic breathing routines to expel the demon from your system. Here is the most basic breathing pattern for this purpose:

~ take one long, deep breath in
~ hold it for three seconds
~ then let the breath out slowly and, if you like, noisily
~ repeat this five to ten times – usually long enough to stop the stress reaction from developing fully.

~ Take a nap! Researchers from the University of Athens, in Greece, studied people at risk from coronary heart disease and found that a half-hour nap in the afternoon could reduce their risk of heart attack by as much as *30 per cent.* Elsewhere, scientists are 'discovering' what many people have known for ages – that holding and stroking a warm, furry animal soothes your *human* cares away too.

In fact, it is possible that this gentle, sharing activity actually slows the heart beat and lowers blood pressure. What more encouragement do you need?
~ Exercise combines movement, breathing, relaxation and the personal space and time for private contemplation. Just twenty to thirty minutes per day seems to dissolve worries, muscular tensions and those dreadful headaches that appear out of nowhere and are surely stress induced.

Because stress is such an increasing problem in our Western society, *Superliving!* has a number of special chapters which will provide you with many other ideas and techniques for dealing with 'the enemy within'. In particular, see chapters 57, 58, and 66.

7. Lack Of Exercise

When the computer company IBM surveyed the health of its UK employees, it found that four fifths of them were classified as 'unfit', and 32 per cent of them had a significant risk of heart disease due to high cholesterol levels in their blood.[229] "They are not just a bunch of obese slobs," said a medical officer. In fact, IBM's employees tend to live longer than the national average. "It raises the question" said the medical officer, "of what the others are like if these are the results from a relatively healthy company."

The survey found that 79 per cent of men, and 75 per cent of women, were obese according to standard medical definitions. On an overall measure, 83 per cent of men and 76 per cent of women aged twenty-five to forty-four were found to be unfit. Only 6 per cent of men and 10.8 per cent of women were judged 'very fit'.

IBM paid for the cost of the health screening programme (about £70 per employee) and is also investing a large sum in healthcare facilities, including running tracks, gymnasiums and healthcare experts. Now if a company such as IBM is prepared to invest considerable sums of money in its employees' health – presumably in order to keep them as productive as possible – shouldn't you also consider investing a little time and perhaps money in your own body? After all, an employee can always be replaced, but your body is the only one you're ever likely to be given!

If you can move and breathe and control your posture, then you can exercise, because exercise is only a particular way of combining movement and breath and posture. Virtually every moving activity you engage in can become an exercise if you add a special attention to detail and a special change in attitude. These special additions can be summarized as:
~ an awareness of what is correct and appropriate exercise for you
~ an eye for opportunities to improve your movement, posture and breathing pattern
~ a willingness to learn and to achieve exercise skills
~ an attitude of care towards your body

For example, walking your dog twice a day can be a chore which brings you slouching and grumbling out into the open air. Or it can be transformed into an opportunity to get a regular, brisk walk that will increase the strength of your heart and lungs, improve your stamina, muscle tone and possibly the health of your skin. It may also enable you to meet people or observe things you would otherwise have missed. Put like that, it sounds appealing, doesn't it? Yet the majority of us simply do not make the most of such opportunities.

An American study found that 87 per cent of women and 68 per cent of men in their mid-forties do not exercise regularly.[230] In the United Kingdom, a report on the health of women showed that fewer than 20 per cent of women over the age of nineteen take regular exercise, even though most women know that regular exercise will benefit their health.[231] This report was funded by the Association of the British Pharmaceutical Industry who no doubt want to know just how many of us will be in need of medication for cardiovascular ills in the near future. Quite a few, it seems.

That same American study also found that men and women who are not physically fit have nearly three times the risk of dying from heart disease compared to those who are fit. The report states that "a lower level of physical fitness is associated with a higher risk of death from coronary heart disease and cardiovascular disease".[232] And the good news is that even moderate exercise can reduce this risk. A thirty-minute exercise session, repeated three times per week, will get you fit! For help choosing an exercise program, see chapter 54.

Quality time

So much for the Seven Deadly Sins. The second rule for a long and happy life is to Make Quality Count. When you realize that there's more to life than just staying alive, then you're beginning to appreciate the quality of living. Sadly, many of our friends and colleagues never seem to reach this stage in their lives. It's one long rush from the cradle to the grave, often selfishly persuing the illusory happiness which money can't buy, with little time for their real needs and even less time for other people's. Often, the only thing that wakes these people up to the miraculous experience of living is a close brush with death – a heart attack, a cancer, or a near-fatal accident. Then, as they lie in their hospital beds somewhere between life and death, they suddenly realize what they've been missing. Does something in this paragraph strike a chord with you? If it does, the remedy lies in your own hands.

Squeeze those extra years

Our third rule is to use every trick in the book to steal a little extra time. Here, we can learn a great deal from other cultures and other diets. The Japanese, for instance, live longer than any other nation in the world. The traditional Japanese diet consists of small amounts of protein from fresh fish and tofu, as well as a high level of fibre in the form of rice and buckwheat noodles. This ancient diet contains little or no meat and is very low in fat and sugar. It has been largely responsible for keeping the Japanese healthy throughout their very long lives. Sadly, all that is changing. As Japan rapidly becomes a wealthy, Westernized country, its young people are having to deal with all the diseases of affluence — cancer, diabetes, cardiovascular disease, obesity. And it is no wonder. Since the 1960s, the country's consumption of junk food calories has rocketed. Meat consumption has quadrupled. There are more obese Japanese than ever before and an increased fat intake has resulted in a corresponding increase in cardiovascular disease. The rate of lung cancer has risen a soaring 85 per cent in the period from 1975 to 1985, with breast cancer shooting up 105 per cent in the same period.[233] "The westernisation of Japanese disease is picking up speed," says *The Economist* magazine, which predicts that by the year 2000 Japan will be "groaning under the weight of a long shuffling line of patients with geriatric complaints".[234]

Paradoxically, while the Japanese are busy importing the worst of Western civilization (and paying the price for it), we in the West are more interested than ever in the lessons we can learn from traditional societies such as theirs – and also the Georgians in Russia, the Hunza in Pakistan, the Vilcabamba in Ecuador and others who are renowned for being long-lived. Their traditional diets usually consist of 1,800-2,400 calories per day, compared with an average of 3,600 per day in the

West. Their diet is also low in fat, sparing in protein and high in complex, unprocessed carbohydrates. It is not unusual for these people to live to one hundred years.

So what kinds of food should we be eating – and what should we avoid – in order to live a long life and escape senility? First, the forbidden foods:

Foods to avoid

Metal fatigue

Alzheimer's disease is the most common form of senile dementia. In Britain alone, close to one million people suffer from this incurable disease, with the number expected to double by 1995. In fact, it looks set to be one of the most serious problems of the next century as forecasts warn that 50 million people worldwide will be suffering from the disease by the year 2025.[235] The symptoms of Alzheimer's disease include depression, irritability, general mental and physical degeneration and often complete loss of memory.

What causes Alzheimer's disease is not yet precisely established, but there is one prominent clue. People with this illness have been found to have high levels of aluminium in their brains. Once considered harmless, aluminium is now recognized as a toxic metal. People with kidney disease, and the elderly, are particularly at risk as they are likely to have difficulties ridding aluminium from their bodies.

~ You can minimize your intake of aluminium by avoiding the following foods: processed cheese, baking powder, cake and pancake mixes, self-raising flour, pickled vegetables and baby milk powders.[236] These foods often contain the metal in the form E541. Aluminium is sometimes used to bleach flour and may be found in table salt, where it helps to keep a dry flow of salt. Check the label carefully.

~ Medicines, aspirins and some indigestion formulas contain E541. Again, check the label.

~ A few plants, notably those of the tea family, also accumulate aluminium from the soil.[237] So cut out or decrease your tea consumption.

~ Don't buy those 'healthy' fruit juices which are sold in cartons lined with aluminium foil (pull the carton apart to check). Fruit juices stored for some time in these cartons can dissolve some of the metal, and the citric acid contained in the juice can act to increase the amount of aluminium that the body absorbs.[238]

~ In water, aluminium sulphate is often added by your water company to give the water sparkle and brightness. In July 1989, the worst incident of water pollution in Britain for years occurred when a lorry driver dumped twenty tonnes of aluminium sulphate in the wrong water tank at a small town in Cornwall called Camelford. Many people in the area soon started complaining of nausea, blisters, mouth ulcers, sore throat, irritation of the skin and scalp, rashes and even hair which turned green. Predictably enough, an inquiry found that long-term adverse health effects were 'unlikely'. But the people who were poisoned – and who are now suffering a deterioration of their mental functions – know differently. What can you do about aluminium in your water supply? First, write to your local water company and ask them if they routinely add aluminium (mercifully, not all do). If they do, then read chapter 1 for advice on testing your water for aluminium and ways to reduce it.

~ In the kitchen, saucepans, household utensils, 'tin' cans, baking foil and many forms of packaging all contain aluminium. Stop using any aluminium cookware you may have and replace it with cast iron, enamel or glass. Some people suffering from symptoms such as headaches, indigestion, diarrhoea and nausea report an improvement after throwing out their aluminium saucepans and altering their shopping patterns.

~ Increasing your intake of vitamin C, calcium and magnesium may help to inhibit aluminium absorption.

Shun sugar

Scientists have described sugar as a potential ageing agent.[239]

Many people eat foods, such as convenience foods, which are infused with hidden sugars. Yet a high sugar consumption carries the risk of cardiovascular problems, cataracts and stiffening of collagen in the skin and tendons. Further, people with high glucose (sugar) levels in their blood may be at risk of the complications diabetics face, such as kidney, circulatory and neurological disorders. There are also suspicions that glucose can have an adverse effect on DNA, affecting genetic chemistry and speeding up cellular ageing.[240]

~ Greatly reduce your intake of processed sugar and honey and eat fresh or dried fruit to satisfy a sweet craving.

~ Cut out all obvious dietary sugars for fourteen days to retrain your appetite and curb a sweet tooth. After this period of abstention, your craving for sweet foods will have disappeared or greatly diminished.

Give meat the chop

Avoid meat and meat products. There are many good reasons to do this. One is mad cow disease, properly called bovine spongiform encephalopathy (BSE). It is called 'spongiform' because the disease – quite literally – makes an infected brain resemble a sponge. Head-hunting tribes of Papua New Guinea also suffer from a similar disease, known as kuru, which is contracted by eating diseased human brains. BSE has a long incubation period, which means that the meat on sale in butchers' shops today could have come from infected but undiagnosed cows. While government scientists and politicians placidly tell us that there's no risk to humans, the truth of the matter is that *they simply don't know for sure*. Says Dr. Gerald Forbes, director of the government-funded Environmental Health Unit in Glasgow: "We have heard all the assurances that beef is safe. But how can we really give an assurance on something that we do not know the answers to?"[241] Dr. Forbes, who was previously senior medical officer at the Scottish Office's Home and Health Department, told *The Independent* newspaper that he would not have been able to make his comments had he still been employed by the Scottish Office. And he believed a number of government scientists shared his views.[242] More information about BSE can be found in chapter 44.

Foods to favour

Vital vitamins

~ Eat plenty of foods rich in vitamin E, such as cold-pressed vegetable oils, raw seeds and nuts, and wheat germ. Vitamin E is an anti-oxidant; it protects the integrity of vitamins and minerals in the body and prevents the formation of harmful free-radicals and other by-products of oxidation. Vitamin E is thought to increase immunity and, as our immune system usually deteriorates with age, this vitamin should become an important feature in your diet.

~ Expose your face, arms and hands to the sunlight — in Britain it's called skylight! — three times each week for ten to fifteen minutes each session. This simple precaution will ensure that you produce enough vitamin D to protect you from deficiency. Vitamin D is essential to prevent rickets and osteoporosis, maintain healthy nerves and heart function and in the formation of healthy bone.

~ Vitamins A and C are antioxidants which fight off free radicals, which attack and destroy vulnerable cells in your body — greatly contributing to the ageing process. These vitamins strengthen the immune system and seem to protect against cancer in particular. Eat an abundance of green leafy vegetables, dark yellow vegetables such as carrots, squash, pumpkin and sweet potato, and apricots for your vitamin A. Eat peppers, citrus fruit, parsnips, potatoes and cabbage for your vitamin C.

Long life from the oldest tree in the world

The Ginkgo tree (*Ginkgo biloba*) is the most ancient of all trees – so ancient that Darwin called it a 'living fossil'. The species first appeared 300 million years ago and flourished throughout the time of the dinosaurs. It is sacred to Buddhists and is often found near temples in China and Japan. It has been a popular remedy in Chinese and Hindu medicine for over 5,000 years. The leaf of the Ginkgo tree has recently come under intense scientific scrutiny for its possible use in a whole host of age-related ailments, including Alzheimer's disease, various circulatory disorders, depression, memory loss and tinnitus (ringing in the ears). Ginkgo has also been found to inhibit blood platelet aggregation, suggesting that it may offer protection against strokes and heart attacks.

In a recent scientific trial in Germany, sixty patients suffering from cerebral insufficiency and depression were treated with a daily dose of 160mg of Ginkgo extract. After six weeks, two-thirds of the patients showed an improvement compared to a control group who were given a placebo.[243]

In another German study, thirty-six patients suffering from dizziness, memory and concentration loss and orientation disorders were given 40mg of Ginkgo extract three times a day for eight weeks. A control group of patients was given placebo capsules of identical external appearance. At the end of the trial, a whole battery of tests was conducted, including EEG monitoring of the brain's performance. "A highly significant difference" could be observed in the patients who had taken the Ginkgo extract, concluded the scientists.[244]

Numerous further studies have shown that Ginkgo can protect the brain against damage caused by hypoxia (reduced oxygen supply),[245] that it can help recovery from penetrating brain injury,[246] that it can improve alertness,[247] that it is effective against many kinds of cerebral disorders due to ageing,[248] and that it can be used to successfully treat dizzy spells.[249] Indeed, one scientist concluded:

"*Ginkgo biloba* extract seems to be effective in patients with vascular disorders, in all types of dementia and even in patients suffering from cognitive disorders secondary to depression, because of its beneficial effects on mood. Of special concern are people who are just beginning to experience deterioration in their cognitive function. *Ginkgo biloba* extract might delay deterioration and enable these subjects to maintain a normal life and escape institutionalization. In addition, *Ginkgo biloba* extract appears to be a safe drug, being well tolerated, even in doses many times higher than those usually recommended."[250]

Although Ginkgo is the oldest tree on earth, it is rather new to medical science. At the moment, it has not been established whether there are any long-term side effects of its use, so it would be wise to consult your doctor first if you are thinking of using this truly miraculous plant to counteract the effects of ageing.

CHAPTER 42
FOODS TO FIGHT ULCERS

~

"I wish my ulcers and I could get together on a mutually satisfactory diet" – Irvin S. Cobb

You can! Ulcers are a common and debilitating problem which can often be relieved by making simple adjustments to your diet, thus allowing you to eat your pain away!

Ulcers are sore-like flaws in the mucous-membrane lining of the upper digestive tract which leave the lining vulnerable to damage from gastric juices and the digestive enzyme pepsin. The gastric or stomach ulcer and the duodenal ulcer are both forms of peptic ulcer – the duodenal ulcer is the more common, and affects men more than women. The main symptom of an ulcer is upper-abdominal pain suffered about an hour after a meal or during the night. The development of an ulcer is usually associated with smoking, over-reliance on aspirin, food allergy or, in some people, stress.

To treat your ulcer and prevent recurrence, use this three-step plan:

1 Search and destroy

Identify those aspects of your lifestyle which are implicated in the development of your ulcer – then change them!

~ One person's stress is another's holiday. You must decide whether the level of stress you live with is suited to you or not. If not, make a firm commitment to yourself to drastically lower your stress level, using some of the techniques described in *Superliving!*

~ Monitor the drugs you take. Aspirin damages the lining of the stomach, and if you take it regularly you are simply inviting an ulcer to happen! Only take it when absolutely necessary, and investigate other forms of pain relief outlined in this book.

~ Antacids are commonly taken to soothe the pain of an ulcer. However, there may be some unwanted side effects which you should know about. For instance, antacids containing calcium carbonate can cause kidney stones; and others containing aluminium are suspected of contributing to a build-up of this metal in the brain (see chapter 41).

~ If you take other drugs on a regular basis, consult your doctor to ensure they are not complicating your ulcer problem. Or look up the particular drug in the British National Formulary, available for purchase or at your local library.

~ Stop smoking. Smoking seems to seriously complicate, perhaps even cause, ulcer problems.

~ Try an elimination diet (see chapter 46) to determine which food or foods aggravate your ulcer. It is possible that some ulcers are a particularly painful form of allergic response. If you allow yourself two or three weeks to do the diet properly, you may well discover one or two culprits which you can then exclude from your diet. Those most often excluded are milk, strong spices, garlic, onions, red meats, beer, cheese and chocolate.

2 Promote healing

~ Continue to avoid smoking and the drugs, foods and levels of stress which you have addressed in Step One.

~ Eat your evening meal at least four hours before you go to bed. The level of acid in your stomach usually drops as your stomach empties; this precaution helps ensure you get a good, pain-free night's sleep.

~ Drink hot beverages rather cooler than you normally would, certainly cooler than scalding temperature. Very hot drinks are suspected of damaging the lining of the stomach, and it has been shown that peptic ulcer sufferers have a tendency to prefer much hotter beverages than other people.[251]
~ Drink one litre (two pints) of raw cabbage juice each day for seven to ten days. Researchers at Stanford University School of Medicine have discovered that it can have a profound healing effect on ulcers.[252] Try to prepare it yourself from organic cabbages, or buy one of the bottled organic cabbage juices available in health food shops.

3 Protect and prevent

Now begin to include substances in your diet which will actively improve the health of your intestines and perhaps prevent your ulcer from recurring.
~ Avoid coffee, alcohol, tea and fried foods in addition to the food or foods you have eliminated from your diet.
~ Eat foods rich in the vitamin B complex. These include whole grains, legumes, molasses, brewer's yeast, nuts and seeds and green leafy vegetables. These foods help to counteract the effects of stress on the body, and studies have shown that patients with low levels of the B group of vitamins also have high levels of stomach acid.[253]
~ Increase your intake of vitamins A and E. Both are fat soluble vitamins which benefit the health of the mucous membranes that line your stomach and duodenum. They are available in supplement form, but you can find them in your food, too. For vitamin A, eat dark yellow and dark green fruits and vegetables such as carrot, squash, pomegranate, spinach, broccoli, avocado. For vitamin E, eat cold-pressed vegetable oils, wheat germ, molasses and leafy vegetables.
~ Zinc is a mineral which helps digestion and promotes healing. It is available in supplement form, or you can eat foods rich in zinc such as pumpkin and sunflower seeds, mushrooms, soyabeans and brewer's yeast.
~ Amend your diet to include foods high in fibre. A high-fibre diet is known to improve intestinal health *provided* the food is well chewed. Select foods from the whole grain, beans and pulses, fresh fruit, and vegetable groups to ensure an intake of approximately 40 grams of fibre per day.

Chapter 43
What you can do about world hunger

~

Do you know how many people in the world are hungry? Do you know why they are? The answers to these questions may surprise you; they will certainly make you realize that world hunger is an issue we all can and must do something about.

Last year between 14 and 18 million people died of hunger – that's 35,000 a day. Most of them didn't die as a direct result of pestilence, drought or even war – they simply starved to death. Right now, 50 million people, most of them children, almost all of them in the Third World, are hungry.

Contrary to popular belief world hunger is not 'a fact of life'. It is a human-made problem – and a soluble one. In many countries hunger has already been dealt with, and a concerted effort could eradicate it in the others within our lifetime. But the effort cannot be left to 'them' – it has to be made by us.

World hunger is not caused by:

~ Lack of food. There is enough food produced in the world for everyone. Even in famine-stricken countries there *is* food – but it's either in the wrong place or people can't afford to buy it.

~ Overpopulation. Europe contains five times as many people per square kilometre as Africa. The problem is not the amount of land, but who owns it and what it's used for.

~ The weather. Harsh extremes of weather are nothing new in the Third World; it is human action or inaction that turns drought into famine.

People are hungry for one simple reason – they are poor. The 50 million hungry people are the poorest inhabitants of (usually) the poorest countries – small farmers, landless tenants and labourers; people who can neither grow the food they need nor buy it. And, in a way, it's our fault.

The story of a cup of coffee

Say you buy a jar of coffee from the supermarket.

The coffee bean was grown in a Third World country, but the finished product was sold to you by one of the Western multinational companies that effectively control the coffee trade. It bought the coffee from a plantation owner for a third of the price you paid. Some of the proceeds go to the owner, some to the government. Eventually, about 3 per cent of the price of your jar is divided among the people who actually did the work.

Since coffee is that country's only export, the government encourages plantation owners to grow as much as they can. It allows them to seize land from small farmers, who must then either work on the plantations or starve. If the demand for coffee falls, the owners lay people off or reduce their wages in an attempt to be more price-competitive. The workers are powerless, because someone else is always willing to work, for however little.

Over the past thirty years the price of coffee and other commodities has gradually fallen, as demand in the West has levelled off. So much coffee has to be grown to provide a national income that there is no longer enough food produced to feed the country. So basic foodstuffs have to be imported – and these imports rarely find their way to isolated rural areas.

Western banks are happy to loan the government money until things improve, only they don't. Now the government has interest payments to fund as well as food imports. If payments are not met, the International Monetary Fund forces the government to adopt stringency measures, which means cuts in health, education and the supply of food to isolated areas. The rural poor starve.

Hunger and land deprivation provoke unrest, especially in urban areas. The government fears for its survival and buys arms from the West. Arms cost money, and cause consternation in neighbouring countries, which also begin to arm themselves. The results fill our newspapers and TV screens daily.

Aid isn't the answer

It's a grim picture, and one that government-funded aid programmes have done little to change. In fact, Western governments have in many ways worsened the plight of the rural poor through their aid programmes:

~ Aid programmes are politically motivated. Any government that tries to upset the economic or political status quo is not supported.

~ Money given to a government is used in that government's best interests – so it is far more likely to end up helping plantation owners or buying arms than feeding the rural poor.

~ Development programmes are often misguided, because the people they are supposed to help are not consulted. A new road may be a great idea from our point of view, but for a poor farmer it's a disaster because it brings increased competition from outside the area.

It's up to us!

What does all this add up to? Just this – if any meaningful change is to happen, it will be people like us who initiate it.

Governments are concerned first and foremost with self-protection, and there are too many very powerful interests – landowners and military people – to make reform a viable proposition for them.

So what can we do?

The first option is to support one of the non-governmental development organizations, such as Oxfam.

Oxfam is independent of any government. Its campaigns on behalf of the Third World poor are driven by the poor themselves, who draw its attention to local issues and needs. These might be:

~ A lorry for a group of small farmers to cut transport costs.

~ Support for an embryo trade union campaigning for fair pay in the coffee industry.

Every project is planned by the poor, for the poor. Oxfam provides cash and expertise, and helps to spread public awareness in the West.

How you can help

~ By donating money or buying goods from Oxfam shops. Eighty per cent of your donation will end up exactly where it is needed.

~ By helping out with fundraising activities, or organizing your own. Oxfam will lend their name to almost anything you could think of – a sponsored walk, a pub quiz, a disco. The list is endless.

~ By offering your services as a volunteer to work in a shop or for one of the local campaign groups. Any expertise you have – as a graphic designer, for example – will be invaluable.

~ By offering the use of a facility, like a theatre or mobile disco.

~ If you have an idea, Oxfam will give you the facilities to make it happen. You can also pinpoint a particular project you want to help, so you know exactly where your time, energy and money are going.

But if none of this appeals to you, there are still plenty of other ways you can help:

~ Be informed and inform others. Compare what the papers say with what you learn from more informed sources. If a newspaper gets it wrong, write to the journalist and the paper explaining your point of view. Next time, the journalist may get it right.

~ Use your political power. Ask your MP awkward questions about aid, debt, arms control, etc. Oxfam and the other groups organize mass petitions and letter-writing campaigns so you should ideally aim to coordinate your efforts. MPs take notice when enough of their constituents take up an issue.

~ Use your power as a consumer (see chapter 24).

~ Form a consumer group. A small vociferous group can alter a nation's shopping habits. Your best targets are women's magazines and your best tactic not a 'boycott this' but a positive 'buy this and help Colombian children' kind of approach.

~ Use your power as an investor. Everyone invests money somewhere – even if it's just in the bank – so choose where it goes (see chapter 24).

~ Action is the key. It's no use giving up coffee in protest because no one gains from this action – unless you take the money you save on coffee and put it to good use. When everyone knows the truth about world hunger its days will be numbered. Already, this century has witnessed the eradication of mass hunger in seventy countries – forty-one of them since 1960 – so it is *not* an impossible task! The technology is there, the knowledge is there; what's needed is the political will. Just remember:

~ There are a lot of hungry people in the world.

~ There need be none.

~ It is up to us to bring this about.

Book Two

SUPERHEALTH!

CHAPTER 44

PLAGUES OF THE FUTURE – WHERE THE DISEASES OF TOMORROW WILL COME FROM

~

Will they be the products of sinister research conducted behind the closed doors of biological warfare laboratories; or will they be the accidental results of genetic engineering experiments gone wrong?

In all probability, neither. We predict that the plagues of tomorrow will originate in exactly the same way that the diseases of the past have done. They will originate from the human race's exploitation of animals, and – as in the past – the new diseases will prove highly unpredictable, extremely virulent and increasingly difficult to prevent or cure. The chilling fact is, the diseases of tomorrow are already with us, now.

You'd have to have been living in a time capsule not to have heard of salmonella. Every year, hundreds of thousands of people succumb to this very common form of food poisoning, whose symptoms include diarrhoea, abdominal cramps, vomiting and fever, and which can sometimes prove fatal. Salmonella is just one example of a disease called a zoonosis – the scientific term for any disease which originates in animals and can be passed on to humans (sometimes in a much more virulent form). Other examples of zoonoses include anthrax, rabies, leptospirosis, listeriosis, toxoplasmosis, brucellosis, tuberculosis and trichinosis – all serious, often fatal, diseases which are transmitted from animals to humans across the species barrier. But outside of the research laboratory, few people realize how grave a health threat zoonoses pose to all of us.

Zoonoses behave in strange, often unpredictable ways. The process of human-animal disease transmission is going on all the time – new diseases are continually being created, transformed, mutated and activated. Some diseases may lie dormant for hundreds of years, just waiting for suitable conditions to appear before they re-emerge and decimate a population that has little or no immunity to them. The stark reality is that today, *three-quarters* of the world's rural population suffer from one or more diseases which have been passed on to them from a reservoir of infection in the animal population. But don't make the mistake of believing that it's only people who live in Third World countries who are at risk. Apart from a few widely-publicized diseases (such as rabies and salmonella) most people – and a surprising number of doctors and scientists – are hugely ignorant of the legacy of disease which humans and animals jointly share. For example, very few people indeed know that:

The common cold came from our ancestors' contact with horses

As a species, humans first succumbed to rhinoviruses (the group of viruses which produce the common cold) from their association with horses. The cold is a recent disease in humans – we have only suffered from it since we became urbanized, about 10,000 years ago. At that time, the rhinoviruses present in horses mutated and crossed over into the human population, where they are now quite numerous.

Measles originated in the wolf population

Measles emerged as a new disease in humans about 6,000 years ago. The evidence shows that wolves first passed on the distemper virus to dogs. It then mutated and became the rinderpest virus, which infected cattle, which once again mutated and established itself in the human population as the disease we now know as measles.

Syphilis first arose from contact with monkeys

Syphilis originated in Stone Age populations between 25,000 and 18,000 BC from a reservoir of infection existing in monkey populations. Originally a disease disseminated by bodily contact, it evolved to become a sexually-transmitted disease as the wearing of clothes increasingly restricted skin-to-skin intimacy solely to the act of copulation.

Cholera originated from sheep and cows

Few people appreciate that this process of animal-human disease transmission *is going on all the time.* For example, cholera is one of the newest of all human pandemics, first making its appearance in Calcutta in 1817, from where it quickly spread all around the world. The cholera organism almost certainly mutated from similar infections present in sheep and cows, and its rapid (and opportunistic) transmission is frightening evidence that, whether we realize it or not, zoonoses are our constant companions.

Today, there is considerable reluctance among governments and many health professionals to admit that new and alarming forms of zoonoses may be in the process of developing. Nevertheless, the evidence is steadily building up, and it demands to be heard.

Mad cow disease

Bovine spongiform encephalopathy (BSE) is an alarming new disease first found in British cattle, which riddles their brains with holes and drives them mad. A hastily-convened government working party concluded that the chances of humans catching BSE (from eating meat, drinking milk or occupational contact) was 'extremely remote'. But this was largely for public relations purposes. The truth is, no one can really be sure.

BSE belongs to a strange and little-known class of diseases sometimes called 'transmissible virus dementias', affecting both humans and other animals. They work by destroying the nervous tissues of the brain, they are invariably fatal, and there is no known cure. BSE first originated in sheep as a disease called 'scrapie', and was passed to cows because rendered-down sheep carcasses were included in cattle feed. The major concern about BSE was expressed by Dr. James Hope, head of a government-funded but independent research unit, when he was quoted as saying: "Because it jumped from sheep to cow, it might better be fitted to jump from cow to human."[254]

Two very similar diseases to BSE already exist in humans – kuru and Creutzfeldt-Jakob disease. 'Kuru' means 'shivering' or 'trembling' in the language of the Fore tribe of Papua New Guinea, where uncontrollable trembling is the first outward sign of the disease's onset. Loss of speech and complete motor incapacity soon follow, and death results within twelve months. Like some other transmissible dementias, kuru has an exceptionally long incubation period – the time from initial infection until the first sign of symptoms can be anything up to thirty years. Kuru is contracted by eating brains taken from dead tribespeople in traditional funeral rituals. Over 90 per cent of all those taking part in such rituals have been found to develop kuru eventually. Kuru is readily transmissible *from* humans to other animals, and in goats it is identical to scrapie.

Unlike kuru, Creutzfeldt-Jakob disease is geographically widespread in humans, and its symptoms are impossible to differentiate from Alzheimer's disease without a neuropathic examination. Consequently, some presumed cases of Alzheimer's disease could, in fact, be Creutzfeldt-Jakob disease, meaning that this illness may be much more common in the population than has been assumed. Like kuru, it can be transmitted from humans to a variety of other animal species, where, again, it produces a disease indistinguishable from scrapie. But the really bad news is this – cats whose diet has included offal from BSE-infected cows are now starting to develop the disease.[255] Pet food manufacturers are extremely worried, of course. This proves beyond doubt that BSE can jump the species barrier. And if cats can catch it – then why not humans, too?

Whatever agent causes this type of disease, it is very resistant to radiation, high-temperature sterilization, and many powerful antiseptics. At present, it is not detectable in its host for many years, is capable of becoming highly contagious, and is invariably fatal. The precise nature of the infectious agent is even open to scientific question. Under the circumstances, the bland reassurance that 'there's nothing to worry about' is rather less than convincing.

Cancer viruses

Recently, when a cancer charity conducted an opinion poll enquiring into the public myths and misconceptions which surround this disease, it found that 10 per cent of teenagers believe that cancer is infectious. The charity later cited this finding as evidence of the confused attitude of the public towards cancer. However, the truth is that it illustrated perfectly the confused attitude which many doctors themselves have towards cancer – and the reality that many cancers are, indeed, transmissible – both within species and *across* them.

It has taken a long time for the scientific community to accept that cancer could be caused and/or transmitted by a virus. In experiments conducted as far back as 1908, it was demonstrated that tumours taken from one chicken and implanted into another would infect the second chicken with a cancerous growth. Despite this early evidence, it took many more years for most scientists to accept the facts. Here is a selection of the accumulating evidence:

~ Cows, chickens and turkeys suffer from leucosis, a form of cancer that is known to be produced by a virus. Leucosis produces multiple tumours and sometimes goes on to produce leukaemia. In one unpleasant experiment, scientists fed young chimpanzees on milk taken from cows known to be infected with bovine leukaemia virus, with the result that all the chimps died from leukaemia.[256] But like many such animal experiments, results which are disturbing or contradict received wisdom are rarely widely broadcast.

~ If bovine leukaemia virus can kill chimps, why can't it also kill humans? Maybe it can. It has already been experimentally shown that bovine leukaemia virus can survive and replicate itself when placed in a human cell culture.[257] Surely this is most alarming evidence.

~ Extensive experimental work with the viruses that cause leucosis in poultry has proved that they can be transmitted from chickens to other animals, including rats, mice, hamsters, guinea pigs, rabbits, dogs, and monkeys. It has also been shown that these viruses can affect human cells kept in culture.[258] Again, if 'chicken cancer' can infect so many other species – and can be shown to infect human cells – why do we so blithely assume that it can't also kill humans?

~ One authority has estimated that a group of viruses called 'bovine papillomaviruses' are the biggest killers of beef cattle in Britain.[259] Nationally, 3 to 4 per cent of all cows are affected, but on some farms epidemics of cancer affecting up to 25 per cent of the herd have sometimes occurred. The human papillomavirus (HPV) family is a large one, and includes the viruses which cause plantar warts, genital lesions, and choking growths in the throat. It is also thought that cervical cancer in women may be linked to papilloma viruses. The evidence connecting bovine papillomaviruses to human infection is most disquieting. One recent study compared the health status of two groups of slaughterhouse workers – one group working in an older slaughterhouse where the slaughtermen have direct contact with the animals and meat, and the other group working in a more modern slaughterhouse where the work was almost completely automated. Only 9 per cent of the second group suffered from human papillomavirus infection (in this case, HPV-7, the so-called butchers' wart virus). But in the first group, 50 per cent of the workers were infected.[260] The clear implication is that people having direct contact with meat and meat products are at much greater risk of contracting a papillomavirus infection from the animals.

~ Statistical analyses of human deaths from leukaemia and other cancers show that those people who have close contact with food animals (vets, farmers, butchers) run a significantly higher risk of dying from certain types of cancer than would be expected. In a Nebraskan study, it was shown that men having regular contact with cattle were twice as likely to die from leukaemia.[261] In a Polish study it has been shown that farmers, butchers, and tanners are also more likely to develop leukaemia.[262] In another, a Minnesotan investigation of leukaemia patients, it was found that a larger than expected number of them were farmers who had regular contact with animals.[263] And a further large-scale study which tracked the health of American butchers over a thirty-year period found that deaths from Hodgkin's disease, bone cancer and cancer of the buccal cavity and pharynx were up to nine times more likely to occur in this group than in the general population – again, strongly suggesting a viral, occupation-related cause.[264]

Can meat which has been taken from cancerous animals enter the human food chain? The problem here is deciding precisely what a 'cancerous' animal is. While visible tumours can be removed at the slaughterhouse, and the meat condemned, it is by no means so easy to detect an animal which may be in a pre-cancerous condition. "Virtually all commercial chickens are heavily infected with leucosis virus," says one expert pathologist from the University of California. "Since the tumours induced are not grossly apparent until about 20 weeks of age, this virus is not economically as important as is the Marek's disease herpes virus (another infectious virus-induced cancer of chickens) which induces tumours by 6–8 weeks of age." So the answer is Yes – animals with cancer can indeed get into the human food chain.

How could an animal cancer virus induce the disease in humans? There are several possible routes. One theory suggests that a 'helper virus' can form an association with another relatively harmless one, and in the process produce a virus that can induce cancer. An animal virus may not, therefore, *directly* precipitate the disease in humans, but it may be able to convert otherwise harmless human viruses into killers. The full story is by no means known. But there *is* enough evidence for the prudent to take sensible precautions.

AIDS

Although there is widespread speculation that AIDS originated in central Africa, possibly as a zoonosis arising from contact with the African Green Monkey population (which also suffers from an AIDS-like disease), there are also a number of other possibilities. One, in particular, has received little publicity but is, nevertheless, plausible. This theory, advanced by a team of Boston scientists, holds that AIDS could be initiated by infection with African Swine Fever Virus (ASFV). This virus causes similar symptoms to AIDS, including initial fever, loss of appetite, swollen lymph glands, and the appearance of skin lesions and immune suppression of T-cells. The Boston scientists theorize that a new, less virulent strain of ASFV emerged among pigs in the 1960s (partly as a result of a counter-productive vaccination project), which subsequently became adaptable to human transmission. They argue that several Third World nations with the highest AIDS rates have also had ASFV epidemics, and AIDS consistently develops about two years after an ASF infection. Their theory, which is deeply unpopular with the pork industry, has very profound implications for all pig meat eaters.

Time and time again, we have seen that human diseases and animal diseases are intimately linked and inter-connected. And yet it seems that we never learn the lesson. Humans persist in keeping intensively-farmed animals in grossly unnatural conditions, despite accumulating evidence that by doing so we are simply creating a breeding-ground for the next generation of new and ever more appalling diseases. Until humans eventually learn this simple lesson, it would be a wise defensive measure to restrict or eliminate your contact with such perversely-reared animals.

Chapter 45

Feeling SAD? What to do about Seasonal Affective Disorder

~

Do you become gloomy during the darker days of winter? If you do, then you might be suffering from SAD, seasonal affective disorder . . .

There may be more than half a million SAD sufferers in Britain alone, and most are thought to be women. There is nothing new about getting winter blues – over 2,000 years ago Hippocrates noted "Some are well or ill adapted to winter" and advised doctors to study meteorology before getting to grips with medicine!

SAD usually starts in autumn and continues winter to spring. You might feel low, have less energy, put on a few pounds, and experience difficulty in getting up in the morning.

Clinical SAD is so overpowering that it can affect jobs and relationships for the larger part of each year. Shift workers are particularly prone to it: they have to change normal patterns of behaviour so that their natural body rhythms are disrupted on a regular basis. They tend to be unhappy, unproductive in their jobs, and suffer a higher incidence of illness. Research suggests that shift workers must eliminate noise and interruption from their lives as much as possible in order to cope with the syndrome.

Scientists do not know yet why women are four times more likely to suffer from SAD than men. The link between depression and premenstrual tension and the existence of postpartum depression suggest that hormonal changes may influence women's moods. Originally, it was thought that SAD sufferers had an imbalance of the light-sensitive hormone melatonin, which is secreted into the blood stream at night by a gland at the base of the brain, but the hormone's role in SAD, if any, is as yet unclear.

Very often, a sufferer from SAD will also have a craving for carbohydrate-rich foodstuffs. It is thought that carbohydrate consumption sets off a complex biochemical chain of events, eventually leading to higher levels of serotonin in the brain. Serotonin is a neurotransmitter, one of the chemicals in the brain that is involved in sleep, pain perception and motor activity and helps to control moods. And it is possible that a seasonal serotonin deficiency may be brought on by low levels of sunlight during the winter months.

What you can do

Diagnosing SAD is not easy. There is no simple laboratory test you can do – instead doctors rely on case histories. If you feel that you are a SAD sufferer, seek advice from a psychiatrist, psychologist or a social worker, and ask to complete a Seasonal Pattern Assessment Questionnaire or SPAQ. This assesses whether your sleep, social life, mood, weight, appetite and energy vary according to the seasons. If you have a low score, your depression is probably caused by something else.

There are many ways of approaching and treating SAD. Here are some options:

~ You could move house to sunnier climes nearer the equator or take long winter holidays in an area with more available natural light! If you scoff at this ("How on earth could I afford to do that?") just remember that housing prices and the cost of living generally in many sunnier countries is a fraction of what it is in the northern countries.

~ Psychotherapy may help you cope with the symptoms, even though it may not prevent the oversleeping, the overeating and the blues.

~ Some people benefit from antidepressants, but these can have harmful side effects.

~ Light therapy can clear this depression completely and has few known side effects. The treatment is simple. Sufferers regularly expose themselves to intense levels of light, often in the comfort of their own homes. You should not look directly at the light but you are free to read, write or eat meals. You can bathe in it from thirty minutes to three hours, once or twice a day, depending on your needs and the equipment you are using. But the lamp's light must match the light outdoors shortly after sunrise or before sunset. Light intensity is vital too. You must remember that everybody varies in their reactions to light and different equipment gives out varying amounts of light. The light must be at least 2,500 lux; normal indoor lights are about 400 lux and have no effect on SAD.[265]

Users should stick to a regular schedule because skipping a few days of treatment will bring back the blues. Light therapy usually starts in the autumn or winter and continues through to the end of April. By then, natural light is usually sufficient to create a happy mood and plenty of energy!

Light therapy can cause eye irritation but if this is the case, just sit further away from the lights or use them for shorter periods. If you have cataracts, retinal detachment or other retinal problems or if you are diabetic, you should inform your doctor before seeking light therapy.

What our society seems to have forgotten is that it is entirely natural for the seasons to affect us. Humans, just like other animals, have the urge to slow down and even hibernate in winter. It is, after all, a sensible way to save precious calories and to conserve heat. Living indoors probably makes us more susceptible to this seasonal depression, because we spend less time in the sunlight. Our ancestors certainly led more of an outdoor life, and perhaps we should too. Those of us with indoor jobs should use our spare time to treat ourselves to generous amounts of outdoor, natural light.

Chapter 46
Foods that bite back – are you allergic?

~

A man goes berserk in a McDonalds restaurant and kills 21 people before being shot dead by police. Another man goes crazy and strangles his father with a tie – at his trial, the judge accepts his plea that his behaviour was caused by an allergy to potato crisps. In both these cases, food allergy was blamed. What's the truth about this baffling – and some say non-existent – illness?

The word allergy comes from the Greek words 'allos' and 'ergon', literally meaning 'altered reaction'. For reasons which are not always clear, some people may suddenly become abnormally sensitive to normally harmless substances – such as pollen, dust, household chemicals, fur, feathers, cosmetics, textile dyes, smoke . . . the list is endless. When this happens, the body's immune system, which normally defends us against dangerous foreign substances such as invading bacteria and viruses, is tricked into mounting a full-scale attack. Antibodies are released, histamine is produced, and the vastly complex immune system swings into action against a non-existent enemy – producing unfortunate side-effects, and some extreme cases as in the two incidents reported above.[266, 267]

The most common symptoms of allergy often involve the upper respiratory system – the nose, inner ears, mouth and throat. Hay fever reactions such as sneezing, itchy, watery eyes and a sore throat are also very common reactions. Other sufferers may experience breathing problems, with asthma, wheezing and shortness of breath, or flu-like symptoms, migraine, depression or fatigue. In more serious instances, these reactions are accompanied by vomiting, loss of appetite, diarrhoea and weight loss – sometimes, a life-threatening anaphylactic shock can rapidly occur which, unless promptly treated, can lead to asphyxiation and death.

This much is established medical science. What is far more controversial is the idea that 'food allergies', 'masked food allergy' or 'food intolerance' may be a previously unrecognized cause of widespread ill health. Typically, the symptoms of food intolerance take far longer to appear than conventional allergies, and are much more varied. Charles Darwin, the father of the theory of evolution, suffered all his life from intermittent nausea, vomiting, headaches, fatigue, palpitations and eczema. These symptoms were never adequately explained (conventional medicine concluded that they were 'psychosomatic' – the label that's always pinned on disease of unknown origin). Today, there is growing support for the view that Darwin may himself have suffered from a type of food intolerance.[268] Certainly, those few medical specialists who treat patients for food intolerance often report favourable results. John Mansfield, a British doctor with more than ten years' experience in the field, remarks: "Of the patients I see, at least a third have been told by a doctor that their symptoms are psychosomatic. Yet they respond very well to dietary treatment, and they remain well afterwards, which is what matters."[269]

So does food intolerance exist, or doesn't it? Most conventionally-trained allergists insist that only 2 to 5 per cent of children and fewer than one in one hundred adults are truly allergic.[270] On the other hand, in a recent survey, 43 per cent of 3,300 adults reported that they experience adverse reactions to foods.[271] So while many medical, government and food industry spokespeople dismiss food intolerance as exaggerated and even imaginary, the common-sense experience of many thousands of sufferers flatly contradicts them. Certainly, when conventional medicine is incapable of finding a cure for your lethargy, aches, nausea or other persistent ill health, there's little to lose by trying an elimination diet (see below) – and maybe everything to gain!

How to test

Means of testing for food intolerance vary greatly from one doctor to another. RAST tests (radioallergosorbent test) and ELISA tests (enzyme-linked immunosorbent assays) are designed to detect the effect of possible allergic substances on blood samples. Their results are often difficult to interpret and the tests are quite costly to undertake. Some alternative practitioners use dowsing – where a pendulum is swayed over a patient's hair sample or photograph in the presence of certain foods. Another 'alternative' technique is applied kinesiology (sometimes called muscle testing). Here, food is placed under the tongue and the arm is then tested for strength. Any apparent weakness supposedly indicates a particular sensitivity. Many of these tests have poor accuracy. When the Consumers' Association carried out an experiment on five allergy testing clinics in Britain, they found that all five failed to spot genuine allergies of real sufferers, while issuing lists of problem foods to those who had no known complaints. All eighteen patients were told they were allergic to an average of fifteen foods.[272]

Ultimately, the best and most accurate diagnostic test for possible food intolerance is to follow an elimination diet. Dr. Harold H. Hedges of the University of Arkansas College of Medicine is an expert in the diagnosis and treatment of patients with chronic reactions to foods. "I consider the elimination diet to be the most useful tool for food reactivity," says Dr. Hedges. "In my opinion, this is the single most cost-effective diagnostic strategy for patients with many types of chronic symptoms, including arthralgias, depression, anxiety, and bed-wetting and hyperactivity in children."[273]

The elimination diet

It may seem like a detective's nightmare: an endless list of suspects and no real evidence. But as any budding Sherlock Holmes will tell you, it is simply a process of elimination. To identify the culprit, you need to begin what is called an elimination diet: only by excluding certain substances will you discover if they are at fault. All foods are potentially guilty, but proteins, dairy products, chocolate, fish, wheat, corn, tomatoes are some to particularly look out for. So how does it actually work?

"The rationale for our elimination diet is based on the concept that many adverse reactions to food are, in my opinion, addictions," says Dr. Hedges. "Like the alcoholic who masks his or her symptoms with a large enough dose of alcohol, or the smoker who staves off nicotine withdrawal with another cigarette, the person who is addicted to a food craves that food and needs regular doses of it to prevent withdrawal symptoms. Many people will have a headache if suddenly deprived of their morning coffee: this is a manifestation of caffeine addiction. The extreme example is the person who drinks 25 cans of Dr. Pepper in a day.

"I believe that [when] certain foods are eaten with sufficient regularity in a given society that potentially susceptible individuals may become addicted to them. So the diet I use avoids anything that is likely to be eaten regularly: milk and milk products; all grain products – wheat, corn, rice, rye, and barley; beef, chicken, and pork; refined sugar products; egg products; apples and citrus fruits; and peanuts and soya beans. Any food that contains yeast is removed. Alcohol, chocolate, coffee, tea, and cola beverages are not allowed. If the patient improves by the end of seven days, we begin adding individual foods back into the diet, and it usually takes about two weeks until the most important foods are back in the person's diet."[274]

The first week

For the first week of the elimination diet, you will be eating very plain food, which is unlikely to cause a reaction – some examples are given below. You should also keep a 'food diary' in which you should record details of your daily menus, and any symptoms which occur. This can then be used to discuss your reactions with your doctor or therapist.

Vegetables

Artichokes
Asparagus
Avocados
Broccoli
Brussels Sprouts
Cabbage
Carrots
Cauliflower
Celery
Cucumbers
Kale
Leeks
Lettuce
Okra
Parsley
Parsnips
Pumpkins and other squashes
Radishes
Rice
Spinach
Swede
Turnips
Water Chestnuts
Watercress

Fruit

Apples
Apricots
Bananas
Cherries
Coconuts
Dates
Figs
Grapes
Kiwi Fruit
Mangos
Melons
Nectarines
Peaches
Pears
Pineapples
Plums
Prunes

Nuts

Almonds
Brazil nuts
Cashews
Chestnuts
Hazelnuts
Pumpkin seeds
Sesame seeds
Sunflower seeds

Seasonings

Bay leaves
Celery seed
Cumin
Tahini
Vinegar

Beverages

Mineral or spring water
Juices from allowed fruits

A typical day's menu

For Breakfast:
Half a canteloupe melon
Mineral water or fruit juice

For Lunch:
Avocado salad, consisting of

One medium avocado
Quarter of a crispy iceberg lettuce head
Half a cup of sliced radishes
Half a cup chopped watercress
One ounce each sesame seeds and sunflower seeds
Tablespoon of vinegar to dress
Mineral water or fruit juice

For Dinner:
Rice and vegetables, consisting of
One cup of brown rice
Half a cup of boiled spinach
Half a cup of boiled, mashed pumpkin
Half a cup of steamed, chopped broccoli
Tablespoon of tahini to dress
Mineral water or fruit juice

As a Snack Anytime:
A mixture of 2oz dried almonds and 2oz roasted pumpkin seeds
Fruit

This menu supplies 1,794 calories, and is high in protein and other essential nutrients. Another elimination diet is shown in chapter 47.

The second week

In the second week you can start to add other food back into your diet again (for example, wheat and dairy products). Remember to keep a record of your reactions in your food diary. Foods should be added to your diet in their simplest form. For example, when adding wheat start with plain puffed wheat rather than bread, which contains other substances, such as yeast, that might contribute to your symptoms.

When you find a food which brings your symptoms on again, try eliminating it from your diet again completely for a few days. If your symptoms clear, the chances are you have found your enemy!

When you have identified the offending food or foods, you are then faced with the prospect of avoiding them. If you sneeze violently every time you eat a papaya, this won't be too much of a problem. If, however, you discover you have an egg allergy, you will need to become an expert in reading food labels and questioning restaurants. This is not always as simple as it sounds; for example, 'albumin' listed as an ingredient on a product means it contains egg. Also, of course, different recipes and replacement foods will need to be on your new menu. In baking, half a teaspoon of baking powder can be used in place of each egg, and you can buy products such as eggless mayonnaise and corn noodles.

If you encounter difficulty in getting support from your own doctor, remember that there are a number of groups which offer support and all-important information. Action Against Allergy is a charity which encourages research and provides an information service giving details of relevant medical assistance in your area. They also have a reference library. For details, see the Help section.

Chapter 47
What makes your child hyperactive – and what you can do about it

~

Are you the parent of a child diagnosed as hyperactive? Is your child a restless, impulsive, disruptive ball of uncontrollable energy? Then read on – help is at hand.

Hyperactivity – sometimes called Attention-Deficit Hyperactivity Disorder (ADHD) – is an increasingly widespread problem among children. It arouses great medical controversy, because it is so difficult to give the condition a specific definition – one person's 'emotional disturbance' is another's 'spoilt child'. One thing's for sure – if your child exhibits more than half of the following behaviour patterns, there *is* cause for concern:

~ Easy distraction
~ Low attention-span
~ Difficulty following instructions
~ Constant fidgeting or squirming
~ Never completing an activity
~ Excessive chattering and shouting out in class
~ Constantly interrupting, not listening
~ Wild and dangerous play
~ Inability to play alone or quietly
~ Disrupting others
~ Excessive impatience

The causes

Hyperactivity is a uniquely individual condition, and no single cause is likely to apply to all children affected. Possible causes fall into four major groupings:

~ Genetic. An inherited tendency to hyperactivity. It is also speculated that excess alcohol consumption during pregnancy may predispose the child to later hyperactive behaviour.

~ Medical. Head injury; mental illness; sight and hearing problems; meningitis and hypoglycaemia can all result in hyperactive behaviour.

~ Environmental. Social upheaval, family breakdown and disturbed homelife, and lead poisoning may all be factors.

~ School-related. Hyperactivity which is brought on by academic failure, stress, lack of rapport with the teachers or antagonism within the class.

What to do

Hyperactivity is a doctor's diagnostic nightmare and, indeed, your first problem may well be to get your physician to acknowledge its existence – for often during a visit to the doctor, your child will appear normal, showing none of the moodiness, the clumsy indiscipline, the aggression/depression and perpetual motion you've observed when he/she is at home or at play. It is therefore important to gain the help and collaboration of a teacher to convince your doctor that there really is a problem.

In all probability, your doctor's next course of action will be to refer you to a child psychologist or specialist. If so, you must find one who is sympathetic and who can offer constructive advice – one that suits *you* and your child.

Conventional medicine has developed a 'pill for every ill' attitude which is only recently being challenged by a younger and more open-minded generation of doctors. It is not surprising to learn, therefore, that several drugs exist which are claimed to be effective in the treatment of hyperactive children. In the United States, the most popular drug is methylphenidate, and it is estimated that over 750,000 children are currently receiving treatment.[275] Paradoxically, methylphenidate is actually a stimulant, which seems to have the incidental effect of slowing down hyperactive children. According to an article in the *Journal of the American Medical Association*, well over a million children are now estimated to receive stimulant drugs to 'treat' hyperactivity and classroom inattentiveness.[276] It is sadly ironic that, while the war against illegal stimulant drugs becomes ever more intense, doctors are busier than ever before prescribing legal stimulant drugs to young children and teenagers.

Increasingly, however, there is evidence to show that individual cases of hyperactivity are related to factors which can be controlled without resorting to drugs. Here are some key areas to investigate:

Allergic reactions

~ IN THE HOME. Try this – watch your child and keep a note of the severity of the symptoms from day to day. Does he appear more symptom-free when away from home? Does he seem more hyperactive, say, in cold weather when increasingly housebound? If so, then he could be allergic to something in your home. Possibilities include dust, feathers, pets, mould spores, odours, chemicals, kapok – the list is endless. If you have grounds for suspicion, your doctor will be able to recommend a consultation with an allergy specialist, and skin tests can determine the answer.

~ OUTSIDE. Check the pollen calendar. If a higher count relates to hyper-behaviour, a connection is worth considering. At school, is your child's behaviour worse by lunchtime or when he returns home after class? There are a myriad of possibilities ranging from allergy to an element in school lunches, through certain classrooms (like the gym, metal/woodwork room, art/cookery class) to heating/cleaning materials. They all have to be investigated, with the help of a friendly teacher.

~ FOOD. A number of studies have been conducted which point the finger at a causal relationship between diet and hyperactivity. For example, a 1985 study at Great Ormond Street Hospital suggested that food additives such as tartrazine could seriously affect children's behaviour.[277] Seventy-six children who had been clinically diagnosed as being hyperactive were treated with a simple, bland diet which contained none of the usual substances associated with hyperactivity. After treatment, sixty-two of the children had noticeably improved, and in twenty-one of them the symptoms of hyperactivity entirely disappeared. The researchers found that artificial food colourings and food preservatives were the ingredients most likely to provoke bouts of hyperactivity. Some parents have also noticed that consumption of brightly coloured sweets and fizzy drinks transform the behaviour of their kids. One mother compared her son to the 'Incredible Hulk' after he ate foods containing additives. Tartrazine is already banned in some countries. Other studies have caused suspicion to be cast on sugar, caffeine and cow's milk.

Criminologists, too, are showing interest in the relationship between anti-social behaviour and poor diets. Stanislaus County Juvenile Hall is a detention centre for 3,000 juveniles in Northern California, where researchers modified the diets of all inmates over a two-year period. Junk food was banned, and instead, the facility's staff prepared nutritious snacks and treats, which did not contain as much sugar or food additives. Snacks such as popcorn and unsweetened orange juice were also substituted for candy bars and soft drinks. The results showed that the incidence of serious anti-social behaviour declined by 21 per cent, assaults and fights declined by 25 per cent, and there were also reductions in suicide attempts, verbal threats, and disobedience.[278]

Another remarkable study carried out among young offenders in a similar institution found that, on average, displays of anti-social behaviour could be cut by about 50 per cent *simply by reducing their sugar consumption.* The researchers replaced soft drinks and junk food snacks with fruit juices and nutritional snacks, and eliminated high-sugar desserts and cereals. After twelve months, the number of assaults had been lowered by 82 per cent, thefts had been cut by 77 per cent, general rule violations were reduced by 23 per cent, and fighting was diminished by 13 per cent. Most significantly, after the experiment ended and the inmates were allowed to eat 'junk' food again, it was found that incidents of anti-social behaviour once again climbed to their previous levels.[279]

The one-week diet

If you suspect a food allergy is related to your child's hyperactivity, try the one-week diet. This is based on the idea that hyperactive behaviour will – if it is caused by an allergy to a foodstuff – disappear while your child is eating a plain diet, and return when the offending food is reintroduced.

This diet requires attention to detail, diligence and accurate recording but it is definitely worth trying. So for the first week make sure your child doesn't eat any of the following seven foods, which are thought to be the most likely to produce an allergic reaction:

~ Milk
~ Wheat
~ Egg
~ Cocoa
~ Sugar
~ Corn
~ Food colourings

It's not going to be very easy for you, because many of these substances are present in much of our diet. But stick at it – just for a week, at least.

After one week without any of these suspect seven foods, see if there's an improvement. If there is, you're on the way to discovering what causes your child to be hyperactive, and to curing the problem, too. So during the second week, re-introduce them, one by one:

~ Sunday – Milk (dairy products, cheese, yoghurt)
~ Monday – Wheat (bread, cake, bakery stuffs)
~ Tuesday – Sugar
~ Wednesday – Egg
~ Thursday – Chocolate
~ Friday – Food Colouring (observe labelling)
~ Saturday – Corn

Should you discover a food affecting your child's hyperactivity, then permanently alter his or her diet, to eliminate the offending foodstuff.

More techniques to fight hyperactivity

On a wider level, you can use other techniques to reduce your child's hyperactivity:

~ Create a routine. A smooth-running day has a calming effect. From getting up, through breakfast, to tea, TV, homework and bed should be a routine as regular as clockwork. Consistency is the keynote, with any changes carefully explained.

~ Reduce distractions. Reduce all stimuli at home. Less noise, movement, sounds, and changes of light all quieten hyperactivity and aid concentration. Aim for a peaceful home. Fluorescent light might also be a triggering element.

~ Obtain school cooperation. Ask teachers, if possible, to reduce distractions at school, such as being near windows or doors. Smaller classes, special teaching and private tuition could also help.

~ Explore nutrition. A diet of natural foods, high in vitamins and minerals, and the exclusion of foods with artificial flavours and colours can be crucial.

~ Hypoglycaemia. This can occur when the body's blood-sugar level rapidly drops in response to the consumption of high-energy carbohydrate foodstuffs. It can produce symptoms similar to drunkenness, and must receive medical treatment.

~ Give personal attention. Your behaviour is intrinsically linked to that of your child. Try not to make him feel 'naughty' or a failure. Give simple, achievable tasks – success breeds success – and set reasonable limits of behaviour. Discipline is counterproductive. Explain the situation to your child's brothers, sisters and friends.

Many parents of hyperactive children feel guilty and powerless over their inability to control their children's bizarre and upsetting behaviour. It is not your fault! Instead of being negative, look to the positive and determine to explore what you and your child *can* achieve together. By learning about hyperactivity, about your child's individual problems and responses, you will become better equipped to deal with the more extreme manifestations of behaviour. Your child will already have low self-esteem, few friends and find it difficult to cope. Don't add to his or her problems through misunderstanding and intolerance.

Chapter 48

Worn out? How to combat the hidden epidemic of chronic fatigue

~

Are you persistently tired? Has your doctor failed to identify the cause? You may be suffering from Chronic Fatigue Syndrome.

Chronic Fatigue Syndrome, CFS, Myalgic Encephalomyelitis, ME, Postviral Syndrome, PVS, Chronic Mononucleosis-Like Syndrome or Chronic Epstein-Barr Virus Syndrome – whatever you call it, it's a debilitating disease which is still creating enormous controversy amongst orthodox medical practitioners. At the heart of CFS lies a severe disabling fatigue, lasting for at least six months, with a variety of other symptoms, including recurrent sore throats, headaches, muscle and joint pain, low fever, lymph node swelling, intestinal discomfort and depression. The symptoms of CFS can last an average of $3^1/_2$ to 4 years. Many people tend to get somewhat better after a year or so, but only 15 to 20 per cent of CFS patients seem to recover fully and 5 per cent remain homebound or bedridden.[280]

People with CFS are sometimes dismissed by doctors as hypochondriacs. While it is true that most sufferers do have an accompanying psychological disorder – usually depression – it is quite wrong to label the illness as 'psychosomatic' simply because of this. In America, the Centers for Disease Control now recognize CFS as a disease and are spending $1.5 million to study its frequency and impact.

Currently, there is no real laboratory test for CFS, although one may be on the horizon. Researchers in America have identified an abnormal level of certain white blood cells in persons with CFS. These cells are known as CD8+ cytotoxic T-cells

(T-cells help the immune system fight infection). Along with a high level of CD8+ cytotoxic T-cells, researchers have found a low level of CD8+ 'suppressor' cells.[281] A future laboratory test could conceivably be based on these findings. Normally, CFS is only diagnosed when other illnesses – such as anaemia, cancer, depression, diabetes and allergies – have been ruled out. A physical examination and routine laboratory tests often reveal nothing, and blood tests fail to show up any viral infection. Part of the difficulty with diagnosis is tied up with the vagueness of the very definition of fatigue and the wide range of symptoms involved.

CFS particularly seems to target over-achievers in the twenty to forty age group. That's why it has been called 'yuppie flu', because it so often affects successful people. This glib term fails to take into account the very real severity and length of the illness.

The cause

The cause of CFS is still basically unknown, but a number of theories have been suggested. One theory proposes that it may be caused by chronic infection with Epstein-Barr virus (EBV). Part of the herpes group of viruses, EBV can produce a lifelong latent infection. Almost all of us have become infected by EBV by the time we are adults, but with a healthy immune system, it will not become troublesome.[282] However, CFS has not been consistently linked with Epstein-Barr (or any other) virus and the American Centers for Disease Control have now dropped the EBV label.

Another theory involves overgrowth of the common yeast *candida albicans.* Candida is normally present in every person's body and can sometimes cause minor infections of the mucous membranes of the mouth or vagina (thrush). With a healthy immune system, candida causes few problems, because it is kept under control. However, with a weakened immune system, candida may flourish, creating symptoms similar to CFS. The idea that CFS might be connected to candida infection was first proposed in 1977 by C. Orian Truss, MD, a certified internist from Birmingham, Alabama.[283] Truss found that many of his chronically ill patients improved on a treatment regime which featured a sugar-free, yeast-free diet and nystatin, a safe antifungal medication taken by mouth.

Apart from a malfunctioning immune system, other factors in the proliferation of candida may include the use of antibiotics which, while killing both 'good' and 'bad' bacteria in the body indiscriminately, allow candida to grow unchecked. Dr. Belinda Dawes, a British doctor who has specialized in the treatment of CFS says: "I would now say that without doubt, candida infection plays a role in the ill health of all of the patients I see. Although their illness may not be directly related to the candida problem, eliminating the candida from their body and its related consequences has certainly been one of the factors in their recovery."[284]

However, the candida/CFS connection is by no means accepted by all doctors. At least one study has failed to show any benefit at all to CFS sufferers of taking anti-fungal drugs such as nystatin.[285]

Dr. Peter Nixon, a cardiologist at London's Charing Cross Hospital, has attracted much controversy by stating his belief that CFS is simply a result of chronic exhaustion. "We're always getting fashionable diseases – ten years ago it was total allergy syndrome," he says. "Then it was spasmophilia. After that it was food allergy – have you noticed how that's fading away? Now it's ME. To my mind they're all basically the same – people have got into terrible fatigue and they can't get out. Nowadays, people simply aren't allowed to be tired. Yet nobody can do a high-performance job, working 14 hours a day, for ever. We have to behave like winning people all the time – and our systems can't stand it."[286]

Some researchers even believe that the epidemic of Chronic Fatigue Syndrome may be related to the AIDS epidemic. Brain scans of some CFS patients show the same abnormalities seen in scans of AIDS patients. More than a hundred physicians and 3,000 nurses have come down with CFS, and almost all of them have treated AIDS patients (they are not positive for HIV).[287]

Ultimately, the root cause of CFS may well involve a wide combination of factors – environmental toxins, food allergens, activated viruses, a higher than normal presence of *candida albicans*, lack of good quality sleep and far too much prolonged stress.

What can you do?

Because the cause hasn't yet been pinpointed, conventional medical treatment is directed towards alleviating the most distressing symptoms. But most studies have generally had little success using drugs such as anti-inflammatories, antibiotics, tranquillizers or anti-herpes medicines.

On a personal level, your aim must be to take responsibility for your own state of health. Gently, both the body and the immune system should be strengthened, to the point where they can naturally re-establish an optimum degree of health. For many busy, go-getting people, who have previously taken their own robust good health for granted, this will be the first time in their lives that they have actually considered their own body's needs. Progress will not happen overnight. It must be gradually and solidly achieved, step by step. Here are some stepping stones:

~ First, get a thorough medical check-up, in order to exclude treatable, physical or psychological problems that may be producing the symptoms. An underactive thyroid, problems with the temporomandibular joint (TMJ, the jaw joint), parasite and yeast infections, mitral valve prolapse (incomplete closing of a heart valve), sugar intolerance and low blood sugar, and various allergies and hypersensitivities to food and environmental substances can all produce symptoms similar to CFS.[288]

~ A combined daily programme of gentle exercise with breathing instruction will help to restore a state of inner balance prior to recovery (see chapters 53 and 54 for help).

~ Time set aside for daily meditation or relaxation is a key part in recovery, especially as CFS sufferers often have a lot of stress in their lives. Stress affects the immune system, and can be part of a vicious circle – fatigue causes stress, which in turn leads to more stress. This book contains many possible avenues to explore which can help you conquer stress: for example, try chapters 57 and 58. Other techniques to combat stressful living may include biofeedback, visualization, counselling, psychotherapy, massage, aromatherapy – the list is potentially endless. See the relevant sections for more information on each of them, and then decide if they seem appropriate for your personal needs and circumstances.

~ Many CFS patients respond well to a diet of natural, unprocessed foods with lots of fibre and plant food, and very little fat. Protein is kept to a minimum and around ten glasses of water are drunk every day. See chapter 36 for ways to boost your immune defences.

~ Dr. Jesse Stoff, a consultant in viro-immunology and a qualified homoeopath, believes that patients with CFS should try to sleep from 9pm to 3am, because it is during this time that the liver regenerates its exhausted Kupffer cells, which are vital to the body's immunological function.[289]

~ Stoff also recommends a wholefood diet, together with extensive dietary supplementation including zinc, selenium, magnesium, beta carotene, vitamin C, calcium lactate, and vitamin B complex.
~ A detoxification diet to remove both internal and external toxins is a vital step towards achieving optimum immunity. A good naturopath or homoeopath will be able to prescribe individually the right detoxification programme for your personal requirements.
~ Certain herbal medicines may be useful in stimulating the immune system and thus overcoming fatigue. These should only be prescribed by a qualified herbalist who will choose the appropriate non-toxic dose.

- Pokeweed (*Phytolacca decandra Americana*) can improve immunological response and act as an antiviral agent.
- Liquorice root (*Glycyrrhiza glabra*) is useful for its antiviral activity.
- *Radix astragalus* has long been known for its role in strengthening the body's resistance, particularly in wasting and exhausting diseases.
- *Lomatium dissectum* and *Ligusticum porteri* are both used in native American and naturopathic medicine to treat viral infections. Although there is no specific research to indicate their value in viral-related infections, there is a great deal of empirical evidence to suggest their role in treating CFS.
- Shiitake mushroom (*Lentinus edodes*) has always been used in traditional Chinese medicine to help improve resistance to disease. It has been found to contain a complex which stimulates the immune system while remaining non-toxic.

~ According to ayurvedic medicine, CFS is a 'pitta' excess or disorder. Pitta is one of the three basic humours or 'doshas', and controls digestion and metabolism. The Ayurvedic Institute and Wellness Centre, Albuquerque, New Mexico reports good results within two or three months of beginning a programme which includes laxatives and enemas to relieve colonic constipation, natural remedies such as aloe vera juice and psyllium husk to cleanse the colon, and herbs such as arogyavarenini for liver cleansing.[290]

~ In Incline Village, Nevada, a two day workshop is available to CFS sufferers. Here patients experience the 'bio-psychosocial' approach which encourages the healer within. The workshop includes behaviourial work which looks at the often vital need for change in the sufferer's way of life. The idea is that the patient has to learn to recognize the body's messages and act on them; indeed, the symptoms of CFS can be seen as a blessing – a warning sign to slow down and think again. Information, meditation, relaxation and breathing are all an important parts of the programme. It is stressed that the patients are not victims, and change and growth are the key to recovery. This message of hope is vital for people to get well. Healing must encompass the rebuilding of the self, especially as many sufferers are successful people experiencing tremendous setbacks.[291]

CFS is real. If your doctor takes the attitude that 'it's all in the mind', then find another doctor. The cure for CFS is very much in your own hands, and in order to succeed, you'll need a friendly and sympathetic medical advisor, who is open to exploring new possibilities with you. A holistic approach, which combines nutritional, botanical and psychological treatments, is currently your best strategy for cure. As CFS is an illness which affects the whole being, a treatment which takes account of all the needs of an individual would seem to be the only really sensible response to this multi-dimensional disease. Keep up to date with new research and maintain contact with other sufferers by joining a support group (addresses in the

Help section). And remember – since CFS seems to strike clever, resourceful people, you've got a head start!

Chapter 49
What your mother never told you ...

~

No matter how old or young you are, things have changed since you were a child – in no area more so than in women's health. What you were told a decade or more ago probably isn't true now. So here's an update on what you may have missed. Men – read and take note! Women – read and take action!

. . .About the pill

In spite of some scares about it, the Pill continues to be the most popular and the most reliable reversible method of contraception. Instead of placing a mechanical obstruction between sperm and egg, the Pill's hormonal messages deceive your ovaries into not releasing an egg – they can also make your cervix inhospitable to sperm, and your womb lining inhospitable to any egg which might get released.

The Pill is the least messy, the least intrusive and the least inconvenient of all contraceptive methods – particularly popular with men, from whom it seems to remove all sense of responsibility for any consequences. But of course there are side effects, both short-term and long-term, and we're still finding out about them. If you are or want to be part of this enormous experiment with women's bodies, you'll be pleased to know that at least some of the side effects are good ones. Also that most of the research on the long-term effects is based on samples with a far higher hormone intake than any Pill prescribed in the Western world during the last decade or so. That means that both benefit and damage may well be much lower in future.

~ The new low dose Pill. Most versions of the Pill these days combine synthetic oestrogen and progesterone in extremely small amounts – even a contemporary 'high dose' Pill contains less than a quarter of the standard Pill of the sixties. Those with the lowest dosage are adjusted to three phases, with varying quantities and proportions of the different hormones for different times of the month. They are known as 'triphasics', contain less than 4 per cent of the old-style Pill, but are just as effective with fewer apparent side effects.

~ The minipill. Another sort of low dose Pill has no oestrogen in it at all. This progesterone only contraceptive is known as the minipill. It doesn't suppress ovulation so efficiently, and has a failure rate of 3 to 10 per cent – missing even one pill could mean an unwanted pregnancy. It may cause irregular periods, with bleeding between, and it increases the likelihood of dangerous ectopic pregnancy.

So, why does anyone use the minipill? One reason is that most of the breast cancer anxieties (see below) centre on oestrogen, which this doesn't contain. Also, some women get extreme side effects from oestrogen, such as nausea, headaches, and bloating. It may also be prescribed during breast-feeding because, unlike oestrogen, it will not reduce the quantity or general quality of milk produced. But both hormones are secreted into the mother's milk, so nursing mothers should really use some other sort of contraception.

Side effects

Obvious and immediate side effects of the standard modern Pill vary from person to person. Many women report a steeply reduced sex drive, which rather spoils the point of taking the Pill in the first place! And there is scientific evidence to confirm this effect. Researchers at McGill University in Montreal studied a group of eighty-two women who were attending a clinic for severe premenstrual syndrome. Half of them took a triphasic Pill and the other half received a dummy pill with no active ingredients. Neither group knew which they were taking. Women in both groups had fewer premenstrual symptoms after three months. "What was really surprising," says Cynthia Graham, one of the researchers, "was that women in the Pill group showed a marked decrease in sexual interest over the trial."[292]

Many women also report general depression. Nausea, raised blood pressure, breast tenderness and weight gain are also common, periods may dry up, fungal infections like thrush could take hold, and allergies you didn't have may start to plague you. But lots of women have none of these problems, and appreciate having lighter, perfectly predictable periods with less pain.

Cancer links

In May 1989 a major British study was published which showed that young women who used the Pill for eight or more years increased their risk of breast cancer by almost 75 per cent. The study, which was jointly funded by the Cancer Research Campaign, the Imperial Cancer Research Fund and the Medical Research Council, interviewed 755 women with breast cancer under the age of 36, and compared them to another similar group of women who had not developed cancer. The researchers found a "highly significant trend in risk of breast cancer with total duration of oral contraceptive use". In other words, the longer they took the Pill, the greater the risk. They also found some evidence to show that oral contraceptives containing less than 50 micrograms of oestrogen had a lower risk of breast cancer than Pills with a higher oestrogen content.[293]

Alarming though this was, it fell short of absolute proof. For a start, the conclusions of the study would seem to indicate that there should be rising rates of breast cancer among young women. But so far, such a trend has not appeared. And some of the women in the study would have taken the older, higher-hormone Pill, which might have raised their risks more than today's Pill. Also, the methodology of the study could be questioned – there is always the possibility that the data could be skewed in some way.

When the figures of this and other studies are carefully analysed, it seems that women in their mid-thirties or over will not be at greater risk through taking the Pill, especially if they've had children (this is true even though most of those in the samples analysed were exposed for some time to the old much higher doses). However, in many studies, younger women – especially if they've never given birth – *do* show some increased likelihood of coming down with this very common cancer.

In America the Public Citizen Health Research Group (founded by consumer activist Ralph Nader) has demanded that the Pill should carry a printed warning that long-term use of oral contraceptives may raise a woman's risk of breast cancer. The US Food and Drug Administration has indeed acknowledged that some studies do show an increased risk in certain women, including those under 45, those who are longtime users or those who began taking the Pill at an early age or before having children. But, they say, no uniform risk pattern was found across the studies, and when viewed as a group the findings appeared contradictory.[294]

And it's true that the Pill does seem to reduce the likelihood of contracting some less-common cancers – primarily, cancers of the ovaries and of the womb. One report in the *British Journal of Obstetrics and Gynaecology* suggests that the Pill may have saved 1,500 women's lives in this way between 1973 and 1986.[295]

While no one can yet come to a definite conclusion one way or the other, it is sensible to consider the words of the authors of the British study: "The simplest and most plausible explanation must be that there is a substantial causal relation between prolonged oral contraceptive use and breast cancer risk in young women

. . . prolonged oral contraceptive use beginning at an early age produces a persistent and substantial increase in risk."

Heart disease

Oral contraceptives affect the clotting of the blood, raise cholesterol levels, and carry a greater risk of thrombosis – which can be fatal or disabling. The much lower doses now seem to have reduced that substantially, though if you're unlucky enough to be a tobacco addict then you should either quit the habit or give up the Pill since it's a high risk combination. Obesity should be enough to stop doctors even thinking of prescribing you the Pill, partly because it can make you fatter, and partly because of the raised risk of thrombosis.

In the past, the Pill was associated with an increased risk of heart disease, but newer formulations are thought to be much less harmful, and there is some limited evidence to show that some low dose Pills could actually reduce your chances of heart disease.

Drugs

The Pill can interact with other drugs, increasing or decreasing the efficiency of either. Some antibiotics, barbiturates, anticonvulsants, analgesics, tranquillizers and anti-migraine preparations can increase the metabolism of contraceptives. This means that the liver breaks down the hormones in the contraceptive faster and they are eliminated from the body more quickly. Thus, the levels of hormones in the body are reduced, sometimes so much that they no longer suppress ovulation. Breakthrough bleeding is often a symptom of this reduced effectiveness, and you may be more likely to get pregnant while you're taking such drugs – particularly if you're taking a low-dose Pill.[296]

Taking oral contraceptives can make the breakdown of other drugs you're taking much slower, thus increasing their potency (for example, some tranquillizers, hydrocortisone and Theophylline). Alternatively, oral contraceptives can reduce the effectiveness of certain other drugs (for example, medication taken for high blood pressure, some anticoagulants and diabetic drugs).[297] It is always a good idea to ask about possible drug interactions such as these when you are taking an oral contraceptive and are concurrently prescribed another drug. Also, taking the Pill can affect the results of some medical laboratory tests, so be sure to mention the make of contraceptive you're using to your doctor before any tests are carried out, in order that this can be taken into consideration when evaluating the results.

Vitamins

The evidence shows that taking oral contraceptives can reduce some vitamins in your body. One such is vitamin B_6 (pyridoxine). In rare cases, anaemia is thought to have occurred as a result of Pill use.[298] The other possible vitamin deficiency is that of folic acid, which is involved in the body's absorption of iron.[299] So it would be a sensible precaution to supplement your diet while on the Pill with a multivitamin pill which is a good source of both vitamins.

Also, some studies have shown that vitamin C may increase the quantity of natural oestrogens in your body. This means that women using birth control Pills who take large doses of vitamin C may be risking increased side effects from the Pill's own oestrogen. For this reason, some experts suggest that oral contraceptive users take no more than 1 gram (1,000 milligrams) of vitamin C daily.[300]

Taking the Pill can have a wide range of effects, but the statistical picture isn't all bad. If you're a healthy, reasonably slim non smoker, with one pregnancy behind you and only thinking of taking it for a short time, then you're unlikely to suffer any long-term ill effects, and the risk may be worth it!

. . . About pregnancy

A great deal of what you experience during pregnancy is just 'Fate' – some people find pregnancy a doddle, others have a really miserable time. Some women expect the worst and surprise themselves by having a great time. Others confidently expect to sail through it unscathed, but have problems at every turn.

Some women feel and look radiant almost from the moment they conceive; while others get varicose veins, constipation, piles, and swollen ankles. If you're one of the unlucky ones, then you should make doubly sure to look after yourself.

Being pregnant is just as much a matter of major status change as major physical change. Once people know, they'll treat you quite differently, you'll acquire new respect, and new rights. Being treated as a fully-fledged adult means goodbye to irresponsible youth, and you may not be wholly glad of that . . .

Your rights

~ Your rights to benefits vary according to how well off you are, and whether you have worked and paid national insurance. You can find out details from the Post Office, the Social Security or at your ante-natal clinic. If you're employed you should talk to your personnel officer about maternity leave – you are entitled to eighteen weeks' paid leave, and the right to your job back. But everyone, regardless of whether they've had paid work or not, has the right to free maternity care, free classes or groups for parenthood preparation, free prescriptions, and free dental care.

~ Your rights to consideration may be harder to secure. Nevertheless, they're very important. If you have bad nausea, try not to let people dismiss it as trivial just because it's commonplace – it's still vile! As time goes by, one problem replaces another – the larger the load you're carrying, the more strain your musculature is under, and the more often you'll need to sit or lie down. If seats reserved for people who are old, disabled, or pregnant are occupied by people who clearly don't qualify, do insist on your rights – you'll be fighting for all pregnant women.

~ Your rights to choose the kind of care you get and the kind of birth you want are also hard to secure, sometimes. If you're keen to have minimum intervention, or a home delivery, you may have to fight hard for them. You must check out the options available in good time, because you may have to seek out a willing midwife. The earlier you do this, the better your relationship will be with those who'll be there at the birth.

~ Your rights to enjoy life fully (before you acquire the major responsibility of another person) are important. Sometimes advice to expectant mothers seems to be a long list of Don'ts! But the fact is that pregnancy can be – and should be – one of the most special times in your life. It's a particularly good idea to make sure you get some time off for you and your partner to enjoy each other's undistracted company for what may be the last time in years.

Eating

Whatever you eat, nature makes sure the baby gets whatever it needs for healthy growth – only if your diet is *really* bad will the baby suffer. But that means you should take special care to eat well for your own sake as well as the baby's – you really are eating for two! There tends to be a lot of emphasis on not putting on too much weight, but if you breastfeed later you may lose weight drastically (to the baby's gain) unless you have a good layer of fat to draw on. So, unless there's a family tendency to obesity, don't worry about getting fat when you're pregnant if you plan to breastfeed.

Part of eating well when you're pregnant should be to eat organic food as far as possible. Remember that poisons from crop sprays don't just affect fruit and vegetables, they also get stored in the fat of animals that eat them. Since animal feed is much less strictly controlled for chemical residues than human food, animal fat can be very high in toxins – and since you're an animal too, you'll wind up storing them in your body fat and so passing them on in your breastmilk.

Drinking

Accepted wisdom tells you not to drink alcohol during pregnancy, but there is scant evidence that light drinking (around the one unit a day level) does either of you any harm. If you've had a history of miscarriages, if you want to be super cautious, or if you've just gone off the booze, by all means cut it out entirely – but don't feel guilty if you don't.

Smoking

Of course it's better for both of you to give up entirely.

VDUs

"There are enough indications of health risks from the type of electronic fields emanating from computer screens (VDUs) to justify significant new studies," according to the US Environmental Protection Agency.[301] The worries began in 1980, when four out of seven pregnant VDU operators at the *Toronto Star* newspaper gave birth to infants with serious birth defects. This raised the suggestion that electromagnetic radiation emanating from VDUs may somehow be responsible for damaging cells – which, in a developing baby, could be catastrophic.

Since then the debate has raged, and it's far from over. Some scientific studies found no connection between VDUs and birth defects or spontaneous abortion, but others weren't so reassuring. While there's so much uncertainty over the subject, the safest course for you and your baby is to request not to work near VDUs as soon as you know you are pregnant. And if your boss won't cooperate, then change jobs.

Nine months is a long time to be getting larger and larger while the little person you're carrying around acquires more and more of a life of its own. By the end of it, you'll probably be longing for it to be over – but only a tiny proportion of births happen on the predicted day, so you may have to be patient.

When your baby's ready to be born, it'll send a hormone message to your body, and birth will get under way. Sexual arousal and medical interference can also get that hormone circulating. Medically-induced births tend to involve other sorts of intervention too, and can cause more violent contractions, so avoid that if you can.

Remember that your pregnancy is your own. It is unique – no one has ever had it before, and no one will ever have it again. Don't let 'them' take you over. If all you end up doing is obeying the instructions of well-meaning doctors and midwives, you'll miss the best parts. Never be afraid to ask awkward questions. Never be afraid of being a nuisance. Pregnancy is about growing up, and growing up is about self-knowledge. Don't miss out!

. . . About childbirth

Your choices about how you give birth can make a lot of difference to the experience, even though (as with pregnancy) there's a good deal of luck involved.

Attitude makes a huge difference to the perception of pain, but at the same time, the body you happen to have can make a huge difference to what you go through physically – so, be prepared to suffer however well-prepared and relaxed you are. It can still be a wonderful experience if you are caringly supported, and making sure of that in advance is the most important thing.

Natural or less natural?

They've got pretty good these days at spotting high risk births, and if yours is likely to be one, you'll probably be grateful for all appropriate intervention. Anyone else should feel completely free to insist on the minimum possible.

Home or away?

The medical establishment is deeply reluctant to admit it, but study after study has produced evidence in favour of home births. If yours isn't a high risk birth, then the evidence favours home birth – the statistics clearly show that home births are no more risky than delivering in hospital.[302] Even when high risk births aren't included in the comparison, intervention is far likelier to occur in hospital. One study summed it up like this: "Home births entail a definite small risk, of unknown magnitude. Hospital births entail a wider range of risks, whose magnitude may be large but is also unknown."[303]

A study of home births in 26 medical practices in Essex, England, compared the risks of two similar groups of women – the first group giving birth at home, the second opting for hospital delivery under the supervision of a consultant. It came to these conclusions: "The principal difference in outcome was the induction rate of 19 per cent in the hospital group compared with 8 per cent in the group booked for delivery at home. A higher rate of episiotomy and second degree tears were found in those who were booked for hospital. There were no perinatal deaths in either group. The results of this study showed no evidence of an increased risk associated with home confinements but indicated that there were fewer problems than were encountered in the deliveries in mothers confined in hospital."[304]

Interestingly, if you have a home birth, it seems as if you may suffer less pain than in hospital. With all the hi-tech pain relief available in hospital, you might suppose that the opposite would be the case, but a study carried out in Canada concluded that women birthing in hospitals experience 'significantly higher' pain.[305] Another interesting finding of this study was that the women giving birth at home actually suffered less pain than their male partners *thought* they did! But in hospital, the men thought they were suffering much less than they actually were.

If you do opt for a home delivery, it is likely you'll have to fight for it (see the Help section for information about organizations in this field). It is possible that your own doctor may not want you to have a home delivery, and you may be struck off his list. Don't worry if this happens, you'll find another who is more sympathetic. If you can afford it, go privately – paying for a doctor's services actually gives you a great feeling of power and control over him or her – for a change!

If you don't feel like fighting for a home birth (and it *can* be a struggle) it is worth knowing that some hospital maternity units are far better than others, both in terms of atmosphere as well as results. So ask around locally, and speak to other mothers.

Hospital doctors who attend births are likely to be either obstetric consultants, who specialize in non-normal births, or inexperienced beginners. There will certainly be a midwife around, but she's almost sure to defer to the doctors' opinions. In Britain, as in most Western countries, pregnancy and birth is still viewed by the medical profession as an illness, not as a normal part of life. For this reason, there is a tendency among doctors to assume control, which can be difficult to resist. So it is well worth making your feelings and preferences known well in advance, and if you can, have a friend or partner there to make sure your wishes are acted upon.

Hospital births do have one major advantage – you immediately get to meet other mothers, so you can moan and groan in sympathy together!

Drugs

Some midwives believe that post-natal blues are caused by the suppression of endorphins, the body's natural painkillers, by intervention with drugs. So you should take that into account when deciding if you need them.

~ Pethidine is the most common drug used in labour; it's given as an injection to reduce contraction pains. Quite a bit of it goes straight through to the baby, and it can make a baby so drowsy for the first couple of days that it won't begin to suck (though you'll get more chance to rest yourself).

~ Gas and air is actually a mixture of laughing gas and oxygen, which you can help yourself to if contractions are getting really bad. You control the quantity and frequency completely and it doesn't affect the baby, though it'll make you feel a bit daffy.

~ An epidural involves a needle through which painkillers flow, being inserted near the base of your spine. It keeps your lower half so anaesthetized that you can't feel what's going on in your womb at all – great if you're having a Caesarean, but many people find the detachment unnatural. Only some of the drug gets through to the baby, but it can be enough to stop the foetus moving into the birth position at the right moment, in which case a dose of oxytocins may correct this. If not, then a forceps delivery may be necessary.

Forceps

These are metal tongs, which are sometimes used to help speed the baby's birth. Their use is not without risk, and babies born in this manner can show more facial scars, and sometimes facial paralysis (palsy) than babies born without this intervention.[306] A survey conducted by the National Childbirth Trust has shown that a forceps delivery also doubles the risks of infection to the mother.[307] These possible risks must, however, be weighed against the dangers of a prolonged delivery. A good midwife or obstetrician will discuss this possibility with you, and give you confidence that forceps will only be used when absolutely necessary.

Vacuum suction

Vacuum suction (or ventouse) can be used instead of forceps. A suction cap is applied to the baby's head, and the baby is removed by gentle pulling. One study has found that less analgesia is required for mothers whose babies are delivered by vacuum extraction compared to mothers who have forceps deliveries.[308] Again, this is something you may want to discuss with your midwife or obstetrician. Unless there are good medical reasons to use either forceps or vacuum suction, it may be worth taking a little more time and letting the baby be born naturally.

Episiotomy

This small cut, usually from the vulva toward the anus, is meant to help let the baby out without your flesh tearing, and it can speed up delivery. Put like that, it sounds well worth it, but it can be sore for days and days, and increases your risk of infection. Urge the birth team not to do it unless they are absolutely convinced you would be worse damaged without it – a bit more endurance now can save much later misery.

Caesarean

A Caesarean birth involves making an incision in the mother's abdomen through which the baby can be safely extracted. This is useful in cases where the baby is in distress – for example, if the umbilical cord has become compressed. However, emergencies such as this only occur rarely. The growing concern is that too many Caesareans are routinely performed, for inadequate medical reasons. This is particularly true in the United States, where Caesareans can account for 40 per cent or more births at some hospitals.[309] Most Caesareans are performed simply because the woman had a previous Caesarean birth. As many as 95 per cent of the women who have had a Caesarean and are having another child have a second Caesarean, despite studies that have shown at least half could safely deliver vaginally.[310]

Another reason commonly given for performing a Caesarean is 'failure of labour to progress', which can sometimes simply mean that the doctor and medical team have become tired of waiting around, and want to go home. Also, epidural injections to ease pain can have the unfortunate side effect of slowing labour.

As far as private medicine is concerned, Caesareans are more profitable to perform than natural births. A study of 245,854 births in Los Angeles has shown that women from high-income brackets have twice as many Caesareans compared to women from low socio-economic backgrounds.[311] And sadly, many Caesareans are done simply because doctors are frightened of being sued for malpractice – making a Caesarean a 'defensive' medical procedure carried out for the benefit of the insurance company rather than the patient. Unfortunately, 'defensive' medicine such as this may be on the increase in Britain, too.

Once again, you should discuss the possibility of a Caesarean with your midwife or obstetrician, and agree beforehand what approach you will jointly adopt in this eventuality.

Birthing positions

You won't know what suits you until you're doing it, but it does seem that you run less risk of injury to your perineum (the bit between your front and back passages) if you give birth in a semi-sitting position, especially after the first baby. Also, you may want to investigate the possibility of a water birth.

Midwives

Whether at home or in hospital, more than three-quarters of births in this country are delivered by a midwife. They are *the* specialists in normal births:

~ Community midwives work with GPs and will attend your birth in hospital or at home. In each area there are just a handful. If you're lucky, you'll meet the one who'll be there on the day. Whoever it is, it's certain to be a woman with a great deal of experience – and she'll visit and help you learn to breastfeed your baby after the birth.

~ Hospital midwives are also specialists, but there's almost no chance that you'll meet the one who'll bring your baby into the world, and after the birth you may never see her again.

~ Independent midwives are most likely to give you most control over your birth. They are highly experienced women who believe that the interests of mother and child are paramount; and unless safety dictates otherwise, they will deliver you at home. They will not press on you any intervention you don't want, they will discuss everything with you, and having someone you know and trust at the birth will be guaranteed. Unfortunately they can be expensive, although many have a sliding scale adjusted to their clients' incomes.

After the long months of pregnancy and the long hours of labour, a satisfactory birth tends to feel like an end – but it's really a beginning, of course. For a while, at least, your life is going to be completely ruled by this new small person's needs. Out of the cosy womb into the harsh world, it needs comfort and it needs nourishment – and it's down to you to provide them. You know how to give the comfort, but what about the nourishment?

. . . About breastfeeding

Everyone agrees that 'breast is best' – even the manufacturers of formula milk. And it is. Even a few weeks on the breast will give your baby advantages in the health stakes. In spite of this, many women give up much sooner. Why?

Privacy

We spend our lives learning that breasts are for male titillation, and must therefore be kept concealed from all but the targeted males. If you want to breastfeed, you'll find it much easier if you can get over this inhibition – the most private room in most places is not a pleasant or hygienic spot to feed a baby! No adult would willingly eat his or her dinner in a toilet – so why should your baby?

Pain

Few women manage to breastfeed without some initial discomfort, and some go through a lot of pain. Engorgement of the breast means it's swollen, hard, and tense, full of milk that's not moving on. In the first days, especially with the first baby, this is a very common problem – whether you're breastfeeding or not, nature lays on the milk. It doesn't just hurt, it makes getting the baby to take the nipple much harder. With help from someone who knows what you're going through (a friend who's actually done it may be more helpful than an 'expert'), you'll get the baby sucking properly and the problem will quickly sort itself out. Later on, you may suffer engorgement because you're not feeding evenly from both sides, and the neglected breast may swell up. It's important (and easy) to correct this because if you don't you risk mastitis (inflammation of the breast), which used often to be fatal before antibiotics.

Cracked nipples can be agony for those who suffer them, but they don't usually last long once the baby's holding the nipple right, which may well prevent them happening in the first place. It's a matter of getting the whole pinky brown area into the baby's mouth, and not just the teat tip. As well as being painful, these can also cause mastitis, so tell your midwife or health visitor about them at once (don't be 'brave'!).

Leaking

Your breasts will tend to leak at first, especially when your baby cries. But breastpads are easy to find to blot it up, and the problem is usually over in a few weeks.

Time

Your time will not be your own if you breastfeed. They tell you you can squirt it out into a bottle (with or without a pump), and get your partner to share the load. But it's hard to get out enough even for one feed, and lots of babies won't touch a bottle if they're used to breast (though some go quite the opposite way). The baby will naturally develop a schedule (with a little help from you) after a few weeks or so, and you'll be able to plan your life a bit.

But do understand this fact: *none of these problems lasts*, while most of the benefits do!

Pleasure

Though much love and tenderness can be given with a bottle, along with great joy, it cannot replace the feelings in your own body which come from giving the breast. That little mouth sucking on you for sustenance causes sensations which are also accompanied by hormonal changes: it naturally helps to clean your womb out after the birth, and it helps tighten the vaginal walls, too.

Weight loss

If you're worried about getting back to your normal weight after giving birth, exercise will help, but nothing beats breastfeeding because it draws on your subcutaneous fat! In fact, if you're underweight that can be a problem – if you don't eat especially well now, you'll find you're exhausted and losing weight rapidly, because Nature sees to it that the baby gets the goods even if you don't! Those gaunt women in the Third World feeding their babies nutritious breastmilk are starving themselves to do it.

Convenience

Breasts can be ready anywhere at all times, night and day – no mixing and measuring, no sterilizing, no scrubbing.

Nutrition

Your breastmilk will have the best possible selection of nutrients to ensure healthy growth in the baby. There is, quite simply, nothing better.

After a mother gives birth, her breasts produce a yellowish fluid, called colostrum, for a few days before her milk flows. Foolishly, doctors used to advise throwing colostrum away, but we now know that babies who suckle on colostrum have increased resistance to bacterial and viral infections, and don't contract diarrhoea, colds, gastrointestinal disorders and respiratory infections so easily, because colostrum contains protective proteins and antibodies. In fact, mother's milk is better all round than cow's milk. It comes at precisely the right temperature, it is more digestible and it is not nearly so likely to provoke allergic reactions in the baby. It also contains essential human growth-promoting substances, and most important of all, it contains precisely the right nutritional balance for young humans. Despite this, the manufacturers of artificial baby milk (also known as infant formula) sometimes try to give the impression that their product is in some way superior. This misleading practice has a serious consequence – it kills babies in the Third World.

This has become a major issue in many developed and less developed countries, and it is something that all mothers – wherever they live – should know about. The problem starts when representatives from the manufacturers of infant formula visit hospitals (sometimes dressed up as nurses) soon after a mother has given birth, and leave free milk samples for her baby. These free samples are often described as 'charity' or 'donations'. But their purpose is actually much more commercial:

"When you've got your first baby," says Patti Rundall of the Baby Milk Action Coalition, "you are often terribly worried. You just don't know whether you *can* breastfeed or not. You actually need to put the baby to the breast frequently and often in order to stimulate the milk. But for the first three to six days there won't be any milk – there will just be colostrum. Now if you start giving your baby substitute milk, you are going to inhibit your own milk supply. Even if you just give water to your baby, it won't suck as hungrily on the breast next time. The more substitute milk you give, the more you inhibit and slow down your own milk. And what's even worse is, you won't *believe* that you can do it. And that happens very often. It undermines your confidence, and that's what we're talking about here. It's about believing that you can breastfeed this baby. The more it sucks, the more milk there is – it's physiological. The milk itself has an inhibitor in it, and if it's not actually being pumped out, it will think there's no baby there, so it doesn't produce any more."

This is why some infant formula manufacturers find it so profitable to go into hospitals and give away free milk samples. "When one considers that for every one hundred infants discharged on a particular formula brand, approximately ninety-three infants remain on that brand," a sales training manual stated some years ago, "the importance of hospital selling becomes obvious."[312]

"The only purpose that the donation of free milk supplies to hospitals and maternity wards serves is sales promotion," says Nancy Gaschott, staff attorney at Action for Corporate Accountability. "Promotion in the hospital is particularly effective," adds Douglas Johnson, chairman of ACA, "because once bottle-feeding starts, breastmilk starts to dry up. When mother and baby leave the hospital, there is a physical need to buy more formula – both mother and baby are 'hooked'."

To try and curb the dubious promotional practices of some formula manufacturers, the World Health Assembly adopted resolution 39.28 in 1986 which states: "the small amount of breast-milk substitutes needed for the minority of infants who require them in maternity wards and hospitals should be made available through the normal procurement channels and not through free or subsidized supplies."

Just how does infant formula kill babies? "As a paediatrician," says Professor R. K. Anand of Bombay, "I have discovered three facts. One – bottle feeding continues to kill a large number of babies in India and other developing countries. Two – even poor mothers can produce enough breast milk for their babies for at least the first four months of life. And three – restraint on the aggressive marketing of infant formula is essential. Otherwise, more and more babies will be displaced from their mother's breast by big business."[313]

Professor Anand's work shows that, out of 200 babies studied in one survey, 111 were artificially fed. He estimates that safe use of infant formula requires a per capita income of 200 Rupees (about $7) a month, yet in half the cases of bottle feeding, their income was less than 100 Rupees a month. Not surprisingly, he found that for ninety-one children, infant formula was being incorrectly diluted. And in virtually every case, the bottle was not being properly sterilized. Only fourteen homes had a continuous water supply. Half the mothers using bottles were illiterate (so much for written instructions on the milk containers). The result? Thirteen bottle-fed children died.

So by feeding your own baby on breastmilk you're not only giving him or her the best possible start in life, you're also refusing to support a baby milk industry which puts profits before lives. On both counts, well worth doing.

Toxins

Not only will you pass many of the good things in your diet on to the baby, you'll also pass some of the bad ones. So it's a good idea for both of you to eat organic food, and reduce or cut out any substances which pose a health risk.

Immunization

Your breast milk passes on antibodies which, many scientific studies have conclusively shown, will protect your baby from many childhood illnesses.[314, 315] Breastfed babies are less likely to suffer from allergies than their bottle-fed peers, and some studies also suggest that brain development is speeded by breast rather than bottle.[316] One study also shows that there are natural tranquillizers present in the milk of mothers who've just given birth.

Protection against breast cancer

Several studies have found that breastfeeding reduces your own chances of getting breast cancer in later life.[317] If you breastfeed for a total of two years you'll cut the risk of getting this cancer by one-third!

Costs

Breastfeeding is not free – you pay for it in the extra food you eat. But it still costs you less, and you can have the satisfaction of depriving unethical companies of some profit.

Whatever you wind up doing, you'll still be an animal feeding her young, and you'll still be giving your baby the love and care it needs to grow and flourish. There's no more important relationship, and no more responsible job – but it can be fun too! Remember that when the going gets rough and make sure you appreciate the good times!

. . . About premenstrual syndrome

In some primitive tribes, menstruating women are beaten if they do not warn approaching males of their condition. Most of us today escape such severe treatment, but the myths surrounding periods and PMS live on.

If you dread those days before your period, you are not alone. As many as 90 per cent of women experience varying symptoms of premenstrual syndrome.

For many years the condition was known as premenstrual tension. 'Syndrome' is the usual term now, and much more appropriate as it covers the whole range of symptoms women can experience. PMS was first described in medical literature as long ago as 1931, so it seems incredible that the problem is only now being fully addressed. Part of the answer must surely be that the medical system seems to depend on a very male profile of health. PMS is unique in that it cannot really be described as an illness. A PMS sufferer's body is not in a state of sickness or ill health which needs to be cured. The menstrual cycle is an ongoing natural phenomenon. It is not an epidemic, but a cyclically recurring syndrome.

There is no doubting, however, that PMS symptoms can be very unpleasant. Some women can experience weight gain and painful breasts, or depression, mood swings, acne, fatigue, dizziness, headaches, cramps, stiffness and digestive problems. These may occur at any time between two and ten days before menstruation. Often the only real way of finding out if you have the syndrome (which simply means a collection of symptoms) is to keep a record of how you feel, both mentally and physically, for about two months.

PMS is a subject which has implications far beyond the medical sphere. For instance, women complaining of PMS too loudly in the work place are faced with the fact that the question of poor performance will loom large in many employers' minds.

Recently PMS has been used as 'mitigating circumstances' in criminal proceedings. In 1981, publicity reached its peak when two women charged with serious criminal offences were given reduced sentences because they were suffering from PMS at the time of the crime. One of the women, who killed her lover by running him over in a car, was given a conditional discharge of twelve months and banned from driving for a year.[318] It has also been claimed that many women prisoners had committed their offences within four days of menstruation.[319]

The causes

The causes of PMS have, until now, been largely unknown. This has meant that most treatments deal only with the obvious symptoms rather than the underlying problem. Many women, for example, are given diuretics to help with fluid retention. One doctor compared this with mopping up the floor after a pipe has burst, while failing to call the plumber to mend the hole. Apart from this, diuretics do not always work and may cause depletion of vital salts and minerals.

Hormone therapy is another common treatment, given in various forms. All provide progesterone supplementation, based on the theory that PMS is caused by a lack of this hormone. More extreme is bromocriptine therapy. This is sometimes given to women whose pituitary gland produces a very high level of the hormone prolactin, which causes a hormone imbalance and a progesterone deficiency. This drug works by reducing prolactin levels, but is known to have side effects, which include nausea, dizziness and headaches. Tranquillizers are sometimes given to PMS sufferers to relieve irritability and mood swings. Here, the problem is that, because they dull the brain, they often result in depression and lethargy. Tranquillizers can also become addictive.

What to do

~ You may have strong food cravings during the days just before your period. If so, follow them! These are caused by changes in the body altering your blood sugar levels. Often cravings are for sweet, starchy foods and carbohydrates. Traditional advice has always recommended that premenstrual women avoid such foods, because it was thought that, as PMS sufferers have been found to eat a lot more refined sugar and carbohydrates than average, these foods somehow contributed to the condition. But, more recently, it has been found by researchers at the Massachusetts Institute of Technology that women who eat more of these foods can significantly reduce their PMS problems. One experiment gave a high carbohydrate meal of a big bowl of cornflakes and low protein milk to PMS sufferers who all ate large amounts of carbohydrates prior to their periods. One hour later 47 per cent reported less fatigue, 43 per cent less depression, 42 per cent less tension and 69 per cent less anger.[320] "The women with severe PMS ate significantly more food," reported Judith Wurtman, one of the researchers. "Primarily carbohydrates – not just sweets, but rolls, pasta, and potato salad – but only when they were premenstrual. Eating a high carbohydrate diet before menstruation could be enough to reduce a severe case of PMS to a mild one."[321] So try eating larger amounts than usual of complex carbohydrates – a large bowl of pasta, for example, when you feel low.

~ If you suffer from fluid retention, try to keep your liquid intake to a minimum, although don't go thirsty. Also, cut down on your salt intake, which contributes to the problem.

~ It is important to try and eat breakfast to minimize the risk of hypoglycaemia (low blood sugar) later in the day. Although you may really not feel like eating, try at least to drink some weak herbal tea or juice and have a piece of toast.

~ Magnesium has been found to help in some cases. The stress PMS causes can precipitate a deficiency in this mineral, which often aggravates the syndrome. Magnesium supplementation works by acting as a diuretic which can ease the problem of fluid retention too. Taken with calcium, it can help to soothe the nervous system. You can find natural sources of magnesium in green leafy vegetables, nuts, peas and brown rice.

~ Pyridoxine (Vitamin B_6) has sometimes been called the anti-depressant vitamin. The theory is that increased oestrogen production may cause depression because it affects levels of vitamin B_6 in the body. In one study conducted by researchers in Oxford, women whose ages ranged from 18 to 49 were asked to take 50 milligrams of pyridoxine daily for three months. They kept a diary in which they were asked to record their symptoms, classified into three groups: Emotional (depression, irritability, tiredness); Somatic (headache, breast discomfort, swollen abdomen, swollen hands or feet); and Menstrual (stomach cramp, backache). The study revealed that pyridoxine could significantly affect emotional-type symptoms (depression, irritability, and tiredness). However, no significant effect was observed on premenstrual symptoms of any other type.[322] If you suffer from these symptoms, it could be worth experimenting with vitamin B_6, taking it three days before your period is due and continuing for two or three days after it has stopped. A word of warning about taking extremely high doses of vitamin B_6 – bear in mind that some serious adverse effects have been reported following very high doses – 500 milligrams of B_6 or more a day have been shown to damage the central nervous system.[323]

~ That calming cup of tea you drink when feeling stressed may – believe it or not – also be a factor. One study in China has found that out of 124 female student nurses with low tea consumption, only 39 per cent suffered from PMS. This compared with 77 per cent of 64 female tea factory workers who had a high tea consumption. The researchers also found a direct correlation between the quantity of tea drunk and the severity of the symptoms, with those drinking more than four cups a day experiencing the worst reactions.[324] So try cutting it out!

~ The seeds of the evening primrose plant contain appreciable amounts of a substance known as GLA (gamma-linolenic acid), which may lower the level of prostaglandins in the body which cause PMS-related inflammation and pain. Oil from the evening primrose has long been used by American Indians for medical purposes, and is now being studied in laboratories all over the world. It is available in capsule form containing between 250 and 500 milligrams of the oil. Many doctors are now prescribing the oil for PMS sufferers. One of the world's largest PMS clinics at St Thomas's Hospital in London carried out an experiment with evening primrose oil. Women who had not responded to other treatments were given two 500 milligram capsules twice a day after food, three days before the start of their periods. Their symptoms, which included depression, anxiety, headaches, breast discomfort and fluid retention, were all severe, but 61 per cent reported complete relief and 23 per cent partial relief.[325] Recommended doses are two 500 milligram capsules three times a day throughout the cycle for the first two months, and then one two or three times a day. While some estimates claim that as many as nine out of ten PMS sufferers are helped by evening primrose oil, in America, the Food and Drug Administration recently won a lawsuit to prohibit the sale of evening primrose oil, on the grounds that the oil is not generally recognized as safe and is not approved for use as a food additive.[326] Evening primrose oil is still on sale in Britain, and is worth trying.

~ Jogging is probably the last thing you feel like doing when you are premenstrual, but if you exercise at other times of the month, you may find it improves your PMS symptoms. In a study at the University of British Columbia, eight sedentary women who began to run an average of thirty-two miles each menstrual cycle found that after three months they had less breast pain and 'puffiness' than the six women who didn't.[327]

~ Yoga is also well worth trying. Not only does it aid relaxation, and so help with tension problems, but the posture exercises can be of particular assistance with lower back pain common in premenstrual women. Certain positions, such as the plough, the fish, the cobra, Uddiyana and the shoulder stand may all help to relieve congestive dysmenorrhea.

Not all methods work for all women. But somewhere in the advice given above, you'll almost certainly find a technique of alleviating your own PMS problem. It is very much a case of experimenting; no blanket recommendations can be given because the symptoms vary so much. But keep trying – you'll succeed at last!

Chapter 50

Ten over-the-counter medicines you don't need

~

There's a pill for every ill, so they tell us. But how much of your medication is really necessary?

1 Expectorants exposed

When you've got a cough, you probably buy an expectorant. An expectorant is a substance that is supposed to help you cough up sputum and so clear your bronchial airways. If you read the labels on over-the-counter cough medicines, you'll often find they contain substances such as acetic acid, anise oil, cocillana, or ipecacuanha – which are dilute emetics (substances which, in stronger doses, would make you vomit). Ipecacuanha, for example, is used both as an expectorant and, at higher doses, as an emetic for the emergency treatment of certain types of poisoning. Expectorants like these are *supposed* to stimulate coughing – but there is no scientific evidence to show that they can really do this.[328]

Verdict: unnecessary medication – best avoided.

2 Demulcents demystified

Can cough medicines which include demulcent substances (glycerine, honey, chondrus, linseed, marshmallow and many others) really soothe away that irritating cough? Frankly, no. Pleasant-tasting as they are, most demulcents are quite inert pharmacologically. And the fact is that the areas of the throat and chest which become most inflamed by a cough are not even reached by cough mixtures when swallowed. Home-made remedies such as lemon and honey are likely to be just as appetizing as the more expensive commercial preparations.

Verdict: save your money.

3 Cough suppressants condemned

No doubt about it – cough suppressants work all right – but the question is: should we use them? Many cough suppressants sold over the counter contain drugs such as codeine, paperavine, noscapine and pholcodine, all chemically related to opium

and its derivative, morphine. Be aware that narcotic analgesics such as codeine may depress breathing, particularly in the elderly and in children, and may prove toxic to infants. And remember that coughing is a natural process, it is the body's way of clearing an obstruction in your respiratory tract, the airway. When you suppress or immobilize the 'cough centre' of your brain, side effects could occur: breathing may become depressed (which may be dangerous for asthmatics) and the sputum retention they cause could be harmful to those suffering from chronic bronchitis.[329] Furthermore, such preparations will *only* suppress your cough, they will *not* shorten the course of any respiratory infection you may be suffering from. In most cases, an acute attack of coughing will sort itself out after a day or two, without the need to resort to medication. On the other hand, a cough that does *not* quickly resolve itself needs medical investigation.
Verdict: marginal usefulness for most people.

4 Decongestants demolished

We are all familiar with the stuffy nose which can be a miserable symptom of a cold or an allergy such as hay fever. This congestion can be temporarily relieved by using a decongestant (most cases of stuffy nose will, however, clear up without any medication). Decongestants come in two styles: topical (which are applied onto the inflamed area) or systemic (taken orally it works on your whole system). Both types work by constricting the blood vessels in your nose, causing the tissue inflammation to subside.

As far as topical decongestants are concerned, doctors have discovered a phenomenon known as 'rebound congestion'. Just as the effects of the first dose of the drug begin to wear off, the mucosal blood vessels can swell up even more than before, making your nose feel even more stuffy than it was originally. The more you use the drug, the more likely you are to experience this effect. Eventually, it may damage the nose and lead to dependence on these substances, a condition doctors have termed 'rhinitis medicamentosa' (inflammation caused by drugs).

Systemic decongestants can have their own problems. Most of them are 'sympathomimetic' drugs, so-called because they affect the body's sympathetic nervous system (which amongst other things controls the 'fight or flight' reaction in emergencies). Generally, these drugs tend to stimulate the heart's force and contraction, arouse the central nervous system (increased alertness, faster breathing, reduced appetite, etc.), and raise your blood pressure and blood sugar level. Adverse effects could include nervousness, anxiety, headache, nausea, palpitations, difficulty in passing water and difficulty in sleeping. Paranoid psychosis, delusions and hallucinations can result from overdosage. People who have high blood pressure, prostate or thyroid problems, or who suffer from glaucoma, heart or circulatory impairments certainly shouldn't use these drugs without medical advice.[330]
Verdict: very doubtful therapeutic value.

5 Sore throat sorcery

We know from scientific evidence that the majority of sore throats are caused by viral infection. Most medicines sold over the counter which claim to treat sore throats actually contain one or more antiseptic drugs. There's just one problem with this: most of these antiseptics won't kill viruses. So sucking an antiseptic lozenge almost certainly won't shorten your suffering. Local anaesthetics are sometimes incorporated into oral preparations, and are effective in providing short-term symptomatic relief. However, they are inappropriate for anything more than

occasional pain relief, because 1) they may mask the symptoms of a problem that requires medical attention, 2) with continued use the risk of sensitization (allergy) increases, and 3) absorption into the system may cause toxic effects. In addition, anaesthetizing the throat before eating could be dangerous since it might result in choking.
Verdict: don't waste your money.

6 Antiseptic anxiety

Antiseptics are often sold to consumers as essential requirements to life and health. No home is *safe*, the advertisements suggest, unless the 'right' brand of antiseptic or disinfectant is readily available. Of course, you can't tell whether an antiseptic is working or not, but, like life insurance, you're supposed to feel more secure because you've got the protection. Whether you *need* such protection is another question. The fact is that there is *no* ideal antimicrobial substance that selectively kills all disease-causing microorganisms without also causing other, unwanted, toxic effects. Many experts believe that such products do *not* significantly improve the standard of hygiene in the home. Soap and water is just as good a way of keeping people and places clean and hygienic.[331]
Verdict: don't be frightened into buying them.

7 The bottom line on piles

Piles (haemorrhoids) are veins that have become distended, or varicosed, in the rectum. This is often the result of chronic constipation and the straining to produce a motion which this causes, so a good way of preventing piles is to avoid constipation by increasing the fibre in your diet. Pile remedies sold over the counter will not cure the underlying condition which gave you piles in the first place. Some pile medications contain local anaesthetics (such as lignocaine or benzocaine) which will temporarily relieve pain when applied to the surface of the skin. These substances can also produce allergic reactions in some people (the skin around the anus is particularly sensitive). In addition, local anaesthetics are sometimes formulated into suppositories which are intended to be inserted *into* the anus. However, there are few known pain-receiving nerve endings in the rectum – so there's nothing really to anaesthetize there! Some products contain 'vasoconstrictors' such as ephedrine. They are included in these preparations because of their ability to constrict blood vessels, but they are less effective on veins (and therefore on haemorrhoids) than on other vessels, and their use is questionable. Vasoconstrictors should not be used if you have heart disease, high blood pressure, hyperthyroidism, diabetes, difficulty in urination or are taking tranquillizers or nerve pills. Antiseptics are present in many anal preparations, but, again, there is nothing to justify their use. Regular washing with soap and water is an effective method of reducing the number of microorganisms on the skin, and (because of regular contamination from faeces) the additional use of antiseptics is scientifically unsound because of the high percentage of anaerobic organisms present in the faeces.[332]
Verdict: unnecessary medication.

8 The perils of phenylpropanolamine

Phenylpropanolamine (pronounced 'fee-nile-prop-an-olly-meen') is found in some products which are sold to reduce nasal congestion, but it has also been used in weight-reduction pills and 'pep' pills. In some countries (Britain, for example) the maximum amount of phenylpropanolamine that a non-prescription product may

legally contain has been significantly reduced – by as much as 50 per cent – in recent years. The problem with phenylpropanolamine lies in its ability to constrict blood vessels and to produce raised blood pressure. Fairly small doses have been found to be sufficient to produce an acute rise.[333] When taken with other commonly used drugs (such as caffeine or ephedrine) the rise in blood pressure has sometimes resulted in haemorrhage and death. It has also been reported to have caused psychotic disorders – in Sweden, during the course of one year there were sixty-one reports of psychic disturbances occurring with phenylpropanolamine usage, a number of them children who had taken the drug in a cough linctus.[334] Another report suggested that some people may experience severe headache, visions of coloured lights, tightness of the chest and heart pounding after taking phenylpropanolamine and eating cheese.[335] A number of medical experts have now called for this drug to be withdrawn from sale.[336, 337, 338]
Verdict: avoid it.

9 Poisonous phenol

Phenol is an old-fashioned antiseptic and disinfectant (sometimes called carbolic acid). In the 1860s Lord Lister showed that he could prevent septic infection in the operating theatre by using phenol as a disinfectant. Unfortunately, phenol can be very poisonous, a fact which it has taken a long time to recognize. Phenol can be rapidly absorbed through the skin, with toxic consequences. For this reason, phenol should not be used over large areas of skin or on large wounds, or even on small wounds on a regular basis. Studies suggest that the surface area of skin treated with phenol is more critical in determining absorption than the concentration of the solution. Some people may be hypersensitive to even very small amounts. Today, it is obvious that the level of phenol required in an antiseptic formulation to be effective (2 per cent or greater) is higher than the level that can be safely used on the skin or mucous membranes. Phenol is toxic in concentrations geater than 1.5 per cent.[339]
Verdict: avoid it.

10 Analgesic anarchy

There are scores of analgesics (painkillers) available for sale without a prescription. Despite widely different advertising and packaging, most of them contain very similar major ingredients, usually aspirin, paracetamol or ibuprofen. Here are some points to consider when trying to choose between the confusion of products on the market:

~ Ignore the pretty packaging, just look at the ingredients. Check the cost of the 'generic' or 'own brand' form of the major painkiller – you'll be surprised how much cheaper it is.

~ Both aspirin and paracetamol are pain relievers and will reduce fever. Aspirin also has anti-inflammatory properties and may be more useful than paracetamol where pain is due to tissue inflammation. Ibuprofen works in all three ways.

~ Since aspirin can cause stomach irritation, its inclusion in 'hangover cures' presumably taken by people whose stomachs are likely to be irritated by alcohol, is dubious, and many doctors would advise you not to use aspirin if you have indigestion.

~ Sometimes manufacturers will include substances other than straightforward analgesics in their analgesic products. Caffeine is one such example. It is claimed that caffeine enhances the pain-relieving ability of the product, but this is open to question. Caffeine can certainly stimulate the nervous system, sometimes leading to nervousness, irritability, and – paradoxically – headache. Headache can also result from caffeine withdrawal symptoms, and, like aspirin, it may also irritate the stomach. Sleep may be the best form of treatment for some headaches or migraines, but since caffeine is a stimulant it will, of course, tend to oppose this natural process. It has also been suggested that the inclusion of caffeine in these products could stimulate analgesic abuse amongst some people, who find its stimulant properties addictive. And it is conceivable that caffeine might be included in some products to give you the sort of 'lift' you get from a cup of tea or coffee, and thus inspire some brand loyalty in a highly competitive market.

~ Substances such as salicylamide, sodium salicylate and codeine are sometimes found in combination analgesics. They are not such effective painkillers as aspirin or paracetamol in the doses found in over-the-counter products.[340]

~ Children under twelve years of age should not take aspirin for fevers associated with 'flu or chicken pox because the use of aspirin during these illnesses in children has been associated with a serious illness known as Reye's Syndrome.

~ You should remember that some preparations for children come in attractive flavours and colours (one paracetamol product, for example, is made in a banana-flavoured elixir). The wisdom of making such potentially dangerous drugs as paracetamol attractive to children in this manner is questionable, and you must keep such tempting items well out of a child's reach.

Verdict: forget the ads and the packaging, just read the ingredients when buying.

Chapter 51
How to avoid being cured to death

~

Who's in charge of your body when you visit the doctor's surgery? Do you always accept that he or she knows best? Your life could depend on handling your doctor the right way.

Too often, visiting the doctor is a subtle game of power, consisting of little rituals whose purpose is to instil a sense of awe into the patient. Fighting your way past the dragon of a receptionist . . . that feeling of terror as you're met with a silent scowl on entering the inner sanctum . . . the barked diagnosis when you're only half-way through explaining your symptoms . . . Seeing the doctor is not really like any other form of human communication. In fact, all too often, it's not much like communication at all.

How to understand 'medspeak'

If you can't decipher the words your doctor uses when he or she talks to you, then your health could be in real jeopardy.

Frequently, doctors use language that seems calculated to be obscure, deceptive or fraudulently erudite. For example, why should a headache be labelled 'cephalagia', or itching as 'pruritis'?

The truth is, physicians have their own ancient and mysterious jargon which is only intended to be understood by insiders. More than 2,000 years ago, the Greek physician Hippocrates warned doctors: "Those things which are sacred are to be imparted only to sacred persons; and it is not lawful to impart them to the profane until they have been initiated in the mysteries of the science."

Today, many doctors still seem to be following his advice. Before a medical student can become a doctor, he or she must be initiated into the secrets of a language which, it has been estimated, contains 10,000 unfamiliar words, which, to the rest of us, seem just as extinct as the Greek or Latin from which they originated.[341] Nevertheless, and contrary to the impression that it is designed to create, 'Medspeak' is *not* difficult in itself to learn or understand. Here are three steps that will help you to crack the code when jargon rears its head:

~ First, ask your doctor to explain precisely what they are trying to tell you in clearer language. This should give you a broad idea of the meaning of the terms being used, although don't expect a comprehensive or even strictly accurate explanation of your condition and its treatment. Write down any words you're unsure about.

~ Later, check a medical dictionary (see the Help section for details) to expand and define the terms used.

~ Finally, and working with the dictionary if necessary, use a current, general-purpose medical textbook (see the Help section) to give you a deeper understanding of your disorder, its causes and options for treatment.

Once you understand the jargon your doctor is using, you will be in a much stronger position to evaluate, control and, if necessary, query your diagnosis and treatment. At the very least, it should give you some idea of what they're talking about – if, indeed, they know themselves! Sometimes they really *don't* know – if your disease has 'idiopathic', 'agnogenic', 'essential' or 'cryptogenic' in its name, watch out – these are all obscure ways of saying "we don't actually know what's causing your problem, but don't wish to say so in plain language".

A Beginner's Guide to Medspeak

Jargon	*Meaning*
Ambulatory	You can walk
Pruritis	You itch
Ecchymosis	You've got a bruise
Pyrosis	You've got heartburn
Acute rhinitis	You've got a bad cold
Rhinorrhea	Your nose is running
Sternutation	You sneeze
Cephalagia	Your head aches
Xanthochromic	You look yellow
Adverse patient outcome	You've just died

And finally: *Sesquipedalian loghorrhoea*: A disease which prevents doctors from communicating with ordinary people.

How to talk to your doctor

Doctors often say that about half of the information they relay to patients is either misunderstood or not acted upon. There are no reliable estimates, however, that reveal how often doctors fail to listen well enough to their patients.

Although they are supposed to learn the subtle art of being a good listener in medical school, many physicians either never acquire this, or lose it under the pressures of work. It is dangerous to assume that all – or even the majority – of what you say in the surgery gets through. A busy doctor may jump to a wrong diagnosis too soon, perhaps ignoring vital information that only becomes apparent after a few minutes' conversation. Computer programmers have a phrase which describes this situation: 'garbage in, garbage out'. If you don't 'program' your doctor with the right information, you're obviously not going to be satisfied with the diagnosis and treatment. The answer is to plan your interview before your visit. Follow this model:

~ First – briefly describe the *Chief Complaint*. "I have a sore throat/pain in my lower back/chest pain," etc. Be simple and direct – confine yourself to an accurate description of your symptoms, don't try to present your doctor with a ready-made diagnosis.

~ Next, describe the *Present Illness*. When did the problem start? Are you taking any medication? Could you be pregnant? Have you been exposed to sources of infection (e.g. foreign travel)? Also report changes in your temperature, pulse, weight or other bodily functions which you may have noticed, even if they don't seem to be directly relevant.

~ Finally, describe those areas of your *Medical History* which could be important, such as allergies, similar illness in the family, childhood diseases, exposure to chemicals at work, or social and emotional problems. It really pays to give a lot of thought to all these areas before your interview – your doctor will be impressed with your thoroughness, and the time available to you both will be used to maximum effect.

Be your own second opinion

Years ago, it used to be common practice to ask for a 'second opinion' whenever a doctor's judgement was in doubt. This was, and still is, prudent. Doctors frequently make mistakes in diagnosis, and, what's more, they often don't agree among themselves upon the best course of treatment. The shocking reality is that unnecessary and incompetent medical treatment kills millions of people every year in Western countries (more than 200,000 in America alone[342]) and malpractice lawsuits are one of the biggest growth areas of all for lawyers.

Apart from killing their patients through negligence, surveys have shown that doctors may demonstrate poor judgement in matters such as coronary artery bypass operations, diagnosis and treatment of cancer, pacemaker implants, Caesarean sections, and removal of tonsils, prostate glands, the uterus, breasts and other parts that are *not* diseased.

By the age of forty, it is likely that your doctor will no longer know about many of the advances in medical science that have taken place since he or she qualified.[343] Therefore, the diagnosis and treatment you are offered today could well be ten or more years out of date.

For all these reasons, you can't regard your doctor as an infallible dispenser of correct advice and appropriate treatment. This means that you must become your own second opinion by acquainting yourself with the basics of medicine as it applies to your own complaint. In order to do this, you need access to information. Libraries and bookshops offer a wide range of consumer health books, many of which have little value, often being aimed at people who 'like to read about' their diseases as a hobby.

Far better to find an authoritative handbook that medical professionals themselves use. Although many medical textbooks are extremely specialized, difficult and expensive to obtain and may be nearly incomprehensible to outsiders, there is one area of medical publishing which will be invaluable to you: nursing textbooks. These are almost always clear in their language, concise and up to date. They are widely available in towns where nurses train, are not expensive, and make a good starting point if you want to carry out further research (see the Help section for some suggested titles). With this information, you will be more able to answer these key questions: "Have I been properly diagnosed?" and "Am I being offered the most appropriate treatment?"

Calculate the risks and know your options

Former US Secretary of State Henry Kissinger once said that his most vital job was showing the President that he always had more options than his advisers led him to believe. This is true not just for presidential decisions, but for every sphere of human activity, especially medicine.

The more serious your complaint, the greater your need to be sure that the proposed treatment will be effective. As a patient, you will almost invariably be offered one diagnosis for your complaint and one proposed course of treatment. A wise patient will check both. Some key points:

~ DIAGNOSIS. Ask your doctor just how certain they can be that the diagnosis you are offered is accurate. It is a medical maxim that 70 per cent of every diagnosis comes from what the patient tells the doctor; 20 per cent from the physical examination; and only 10 per cent from medical tests.[344] The more tests your doctor orders, the less certain they are likely to be about your problem. Check with professional medical textbooks to confirm for yourself whether your symptoms really match the complaint. Effective treatment depends on an exact assessment of your condition, and in many cases, doctors are simply wrong.

The fact that mis-diagnosis is not uncommon was dramatically confirmed in a study conducted by two British pathologists. They carried out 400 careful examinations on patients who had died in hospital, and found that over half the patients had been wrongly diagnosed! Additionally, they found that potentially treatable disease had been missed in 13 per cent of cases; 65 of 135 cases of pneumonia went undiagnosed and untreated; and of 51 patients who had suffered heart attacks, 18 had been completely missed by their doctors. The pathologists concluded their study by writing: "The findings closely parallel those from other units both in Britain and overseas, and suggest that there is currently a high diagnostic error rate, which varies remarkably little from one institution to another.[345]

~ TESTS. If you have a laboratory test, ask your doctor about the per cent error rate, and what they propose to do to confirm the test results. Medical testing can be both dangerous and inaccurate. Although many doctors seem to regard lab tests as invariably trustworthy, the American Centers for Disease Control point out that an average of one out of every seven test results reported back to doctors from laboratories may either be in error or unreliable.[346] Some examples:

- The stress electrocardiogram, in which your ECG is taken while you are exercising, has been rated at best as only 21 per cent accurate, and may 'reveal' heart disease in 50 per cent of patients who are ultimately shown to have no heart disease at all.[347]
- The accuracy of most blood tests can be affected by your physical activity, diet, stress, medication and even your body's position while giving blood. Or the lab can let your blood sample sit around for hours before testing, use chemicals that are out of date, operate the testing machine incorrectly or mislabel your specimen. Dr. Edward Pinckney, a fellow of the American College of Physicians and a former editor of *The Journal of the American Medical Association*, has pointed out that one of the most common blood tests used to diagnose a heart attack, called creatine phosphokinase, can show a false positive result in a healthy person simply because he did nothing more than exercise moderately a few days earlier.[348]
- Some tests are notoriously unreliable: for example, the accuracy rate of gallbladder X-rays, where the patient swallows chemical dyes to help make

the gallbladder more visible, is reported to be only from 13 to no more than 30 per cent accurate.[349] A 'false positive' result can lead to being treated for a disease you don't have.

~ Side effects. Insist on being told (and check for yourself) of any possible side effects associated with any test that your doctor proposes. Another hazard of medical testing is the damage the test may directly inflict: it has been estimated that 800 people die every year in America alone as a consequence of reactions to the dyes used in gallbladder X-rays.[350] Other side effects of this test may include kidney failure, mental aberration and chromosome damage. Invasive tests, such as biopsies, catheterizations and bronchoscopies, all carry a degree of risk. Even some non-invasive procedures, such as X-rays, carry some risk, and often reveal no useful information.

~ Treatment. Find out for yourself about the possible side effects of any drugs you are prescribed. Your doctor uses a small paperback called the *British National Formulary* for impartial information about drugs, and you can use it too as an authoritative guide to prescription medicines and their drawbacks.[351]

Doctors have also been notoriously backward in reporting adverse reactions to drugs. This means that a drug may be prescribed for years (recent examples include Eraldin, Opren, and many others) before a significant body of adverse reactions is accumulated. Older drugs are therefore likely to be safer than newer ones, whatever the pharmaceutical industry's salesmen say to the contrary.

At the first sign of an adverse reaction, discuss it with your doctor, and request him to file a report to the Committee on Safety of Medicines. Another recommendation: don't fall into the repeat prescription trap. Although some people with long-term disorders (such as diabetics) need regular supplies of medication, about half of all prescriptions issued by British doctors are written *without the doctor seeing the patient.* This leads to continuing dependence on medication, which may well have its own adverse consequences on your health. All prescription drugs are potent, and therefore potentially dangerous. You should aim to reduce, and eliminate if feasible, your need for medication as soon as you and your doctor agree that it would be possible. Obviously, this will never happen if your doctor automatically issues repeat prescriptions without meeting you and reviewing your case.

~ Alternatives. If surgery is suggested to you, ask about alternative therapies and ask for the surgeon's success (and survival) rates. Being operated on is a traumatic experience for the body. About one out of every one hundred patients will die as a result of it.[352] It is well worth considering an alternative to the knife – for example, peptic ulcers can be treated with drug therapy with greater success than surgery. Remember that specialists in surgery will automatically tend to recommend their own procedures above other therapies, and in fact may not be knowledgeable in other treatments.

When the Rand Corporation (an independent American think-tank) examined coronary bypass operations, they found that of 400 operations studied, only 56 per cent of them met approved medical standards to balance benefits against risks, and 44 per cent were done for inappropriate reasons.[353] And despite a huge programme of coronary bypass operations in many Western countries, the hard evidence to show its overwhelming usefulness (compared to other forms of treatment) is often absent.

There are, quite simply, too many operations performed. Britain's *Drug and Therapeutic Bulletin* has reported that 20,000 appendix operations are performed unnecessarily every year. Even the Chief Medical Officer at the Department of

Health has stated that many of the 90,000 tonsillectomies (removal of tonsils) are of 'questionable' benefit.[354] The truth is that medical procedures follow fashions. Very recently, it became fashionable to prescribe cyclotron treatment for certain cancers (it kills cancer cells by bombarding them with neutrons). Millions of pounds were raised by charities to buy cyclotrons, and even the then British Prime Minister supported the appeal. Then the side effects started to be reported – holes appeared in flesh and bone, and patients suffered persistent ulcers and lockjaw, rendering them unable to eat or drink. Eventually, the Medical Research Council and a number of cancer specialists called for the treatment to be abandoned.[355] So before agreeing to an invasive procedure, it would be wise to consider these questions:

~ What is the overall success rate for the procedure? (And how is 'success' defined?)
~ What is the likely outcome in my own situation?
~ What other therapies are available, and how do they compare?
~ What is the individual success rate of the specialist/surgeon involved?
~ How does this compare to other specialists in the same field?
~ What is the quality of my life going to be after the procedure?

A good doctor will take the time to answer these questions with you.

Chapter 52

Probiotics – the Friendly Antibiotics of the Future

~

Think of 'bacteria' and most people think of 'germs' – the evil, mean-looking bugs which the television advertisements for antiseptics and disinfectants encourage us to kill. A good mother, the ads seem to imply, uses a disinfectant that 'kills 99 per cent of all known germs'. But the fact is, humans did not evolve to live in a sterile, 'germ-free' environment. Over the thousands of years we have evolved and developed as a species, we have established important, health-promoting relationships with a number of bacteria that naturally colonize our insides. And in the past few years, scientific research work has confirmed that these 'good' bacteria (probiotics) are, indeed, essential for good health.

Did you know that the word 'antibiotic' literally means 'anti-life'? And that's what antibiotics do – kill both the good and bad bacteria inside us. Probiotics, on the other hand, are 'for life'.

The idea that certain types of bacteria could be beneficial arose about eighty years ago with the publication of a book, *The Bacillus of Long Life*, by Loudon Douglas (a Fellow of the Royal Society of Edinburgh), which popularized the work of Russian bacteriologist Elie Metchnikoff. Metchnikoff was interested in the remarkable longevity of certain groups of Russian peasants, who regularly seemed to live up to and beyond the century mark. Metchnikoff came to the conclusion that the common factor shared by all these people was that they regularly consumed sour milk. Being a bacteriologist, Metchnikoff set about trying to discover precisely what it was in sour milk that was so good for them. The answer, it turned out, was a particular bacteria – *lactobacillus acidophilus*.

Douglas's book became a bestseller, and, incidentally, helped to give yoghurt and sour milk products the healthy image they still have. But the scientific community took little notice. Then, just a few years ago, things started to change, ironically, not in the field of human health (where many doctors still regard the claims made for *lactobacillus* and other probiotics as 'alternative quackery') but in the area of animal health.

The trend in meat production over the past few decades has been towards massive intensification. Poultry, for example, are no longer allowed to scratch around in the farmyard, but are kept in vast battery units, often consisting of thousands of birds. Here, there is very little that is natural or pleasant about their short lives. They are often kept in such cramped conditions that it is impossible for a bird to turn round in a cage. Cannibalism is rife (which is why many of them have their beaks painfully removed), and excrement lies everywhere. In such grossly unnatural conditions, the farmer must guard against any outbreak of disease, because one sick bird can infect and kill thousands of others, wiping out thousands of pounds of profit.

The usual way of ensuring that no lightning epidemics strike is for the animals to be fed a constant diet of antibiotics and other drugs. However, in recent years, consumers have reacted against eating meat which comes from animals who have been drugged all their lives. And additionally, drugs can do very little about the presence of salmonella food poisoning bacteria (meat is the most common cause of salmonella poisoning in humans).[356] The problem, therefore, was to try and find a way of maintaining animal health without using antibiotics. Which is where probiotics came in.

Work at the Finnish National Veterinary Institute pioneered the field in the 1970s, and showed that young chicks, naturally reared, soon acquired a number of 'friendly' bacteria from their mothers, which colonized their own intestines and prevented 'unfriendly' salmonella bacteria from invading.[357] The phenomenon was labelled 'competitive exclusion', meaning that the 'good' bacteria keep out the 'bad'. These friendly bacteria were not acquired if the chicks were kept under intensive conditions. But they could, however, be acquired if the feed which the chicks ate contained probiotics such as *lactobacillus*.[358]

Today, the use of *lactobacillus* and other probiotics is one of the most promising growth areas in commercial animal health products. "What we are doing with the probiotic treatments," says one group of researchers, "is re-establishing the natural condition which exists in the wild animal but which has been disrupted by modern trends in conditions used for rearing young animals, including human babies, and in modern approaches to nutrition and disease therapy. These are all areas where the gut flora can be altered for the worse and where, by the administration of probiotics, the natural balance of the gut microflora can be restored and the animal returned to its normal nutrition, growth and health status."[359]

Although probiotics are one of the hottest new products to hit the animal health market, conventional human medicine still lags way behind in its acceptance of the value of probiotic therapy. Nevertheless, some interesting experiments have been conducted, and their results have been published in scientific journals.

~ Researchers at the University of Lille, in France, recently undertook the first controlled experiments on human beings. Ten volunteers took two three-day treatments with the antibiotic erythromycin, chosen because of its ability to cause diarrhoea. During each treatment, the subjects also ate yoghurt three times a day. One group of volunteers ate yoghurt which contained live cultures of beneficial probiotic bacteria. The other group ate yoghurt which had been heated to kill off the probiotic bacteria.

The researchers discovered that only one of the subjects who ate the yoghurt with active probiotic cultures developed diarrhoea while taking antibiotics. But eight of the ten volunteers eating the heated yoghurt (containing no active probiotic bacteria) developed diarrhoea![360]

~ Colitis is an inflammatory condition of the large intestine that causes diarrhoea. Research at Tufts University School of Medicine shows that *lactobacillus* can help that condition, too. This study looked at the effect of *lactobacillus* on five people who suffered from colitis which had been induced by repeated treatment with antibiotics. Every day, the subjects took a concentrated dose of *lactobacillus acidophilus* bacteria. After ten days, four of the five colitis sufferers had complete relief from their diarrhoea. One subject needed a second treatment, which then completely cured her symptoms.[361]

These studies are just the tip of the iceberg. Medical research in this area is very slow, and it may be years until we know the full extent of the power of probiotics. There are, however, early signs that three of the best-known probiotics – *lactobacillus acidophilus, lactobacillus bulgaricus* and *bifido bacteria* – could be useful in a very wide range of disease. Here are some of them:

~ People who eat a typically high-fat Western diet are known to suffer from colon cancer. But there's one exception. People in Finland do not have the same high rate of colon cancer that other inhabitants of the West suffer. And yet they eat the same unhealthy, high-fat diet.

"That led some of us to wonder whether the low colon cancer rate in Finns had anything to do with the huge amount of yoghurt they eat – more per person than any other country in the world," commented Dr. D. R. Rao of Alabama University.[362]

The theory is that *lactobacillus acidophilus* may stop bad bacteria in human colons from making enzymes that produce carcinogens (substances which will produce cancer). Pork products, for example, often contain nitrites, added to prolong the shelf-life and give a pink colour to the meat. Nitrites combine with other substances in the human body to form nitrosamines which are powerful carcinogens. Research shows that people who eat significant amounts of nitrites have a greater risk of cancer.[363] It is possible that *lactobacillus acidophilus* could prevent or reduce nitrosamine production in the human body, thus lowering the risk of cancer.

~ A high cholesterol level is known to be a factor in the development of heart disease, and there is evidence to suggest that probiotics can play a useful part in controlling it. Every day, your body manufactures about one gram of cholesterol, and takes in a further half gram from your diet. However, this is much more than you actually need – about four times as much, in fact. Now if your body doesn't process it properly, a little cholesterol will probably stick around in your system, slowly building up year by year, until eventually the level of cholesterol in your blood can become dangerously high – just like sediment builds up in a river. Interest focused on *lactobacillus acidophilus* when it was observed that members of the Masai tribe of Africa have low cholesterol levels, despite eating a high-fat diet, which normally raises cholesterol in Western societies. But like the Finns, the Masai also consume large amounts of cultured milk products which contain probiotics.

So far, the results of human experiments have been intriguing. "I've had some very puzzling results," says Dr. Sherwood L. Gorbach, a researcher at Tufts University School of Medicine. "I have tried to lower cholesterol levels with yoghurt in about 150 people. Sometimes cholesterol went down, and sometimes nothing happened. I have no idea why yoghurt worked sometimes and not others, but I just know there's something there."[364]

It is quite possible that certain strains of *lactobacillus acidophilus* work more effectively against cholesterol than others. So if you have no success with one type, try another. And you should also consider how many viable organisms there are present in pills and supplements (see below).

~ Many other claims have been made in favour of probiotic use. At the moment, many of these have not been tested according to conventional scientific procedures. But that doesn't mean they don't have any value! It could be well worth trying probiotic treatment in some of the areas below – the risks are non-existent, and the benefits may be considerable.

- Probiotics may help to control acne
- They may protect against the effects of toxic pollutants
- They may enhance protein digestion and absorption
- They may help to relieve cases of anxiety and depression
- They may affect blood levels of sex hormones which in turn affect menstruation, fertility and osteoporosis
- They may control *candida albicans* infections, and all the problems associated with it.

Where to find them

Probiotic bacteria are present in 'live' yoghurt and other cultured milk products, such as cottage cheese. Most yoghurt sold today, however is 'dead', because it has been pasteurized (much of it is contaminated with appalling fruit flavours, too), and is therefore worthless from the probiotic point of view. Only yoghurt which has been 'started' with the *lactobacillus bulgaricus* or *streptococcus thermophilus* will yield useful amounts of probiotics, so look for this on any food label (if it doesn't say, write to the manufacturer and ask). Also check that the product has not been pasteurized. At the moment, you are only likely to find such products in a few pioneering health food shops.

Probiotics can also be bought in capsule or powder form in health food shops. Here, the problem lies in knowing precisely what you're buying! A survey in the *Journal of Alternative and Complementary Medicine* in March 1985 analysed three popular *acidophilus* products. One claimed to contain not less than a billion viable organisms per gram; the independent scientists actually counted 8 billion. Another claimed 10 billion viable organisms per gram, whereas the scientists only found 2 billion. The third, which made no claims on the label, contained one billion per gram. Leon Chaitow, an expert in the field, suggests that anything with a potency of one billion viable organisms per gram may provide benefits, but he believes that the method of production also has considerable significance.

"It is particularly important to look for the information 'not centrifuged' on labels of *acidophilus* products," he says. "If no such assurance is forthcoming, ask the manufacturer directly whether this process is used in their production methodology. Ask also whether the count (so many million or billion organisms per gram) given on the container represents intact viable chains of bacteria or fragments of spun cultures, and whether this count represents the numbers present at the time of manufacture or that anticipated at the time of purchase, and through to the expiry date of the label. If you fail to take these precautions you may end up with a product with seemingly large numbers of organisms which are actually only fragments of useful material, not possessing the major ability to re-colonize your gastro-intestinal tract or to produce natural antibiotic substances for your protection."[365]

Chapter 53
How to find out how fit you are

~

Everyone knows that life gets better when you're fitter. But who decides what 'fit' is? This selection of simple, do-it-yourself tests can tell you how fit you are for the life you want to lead.

Fitness increases your self confidence and improves your health. Fit people can be more physically active with greater ease for longer periods of time than their unfit colleagues. Fit people are able to recover from exertion more quickly. When you are fit, you take a more active role in life and enjoy yourself more. So, what are you waiting for? Find out how fit you are!

Fitness consists of these elements:

~ Endurance

Also called stamina, endurance indicates a cardiorespiratory (heart/lung) system which allows you to use the large muscles with efficiency over a sustained period of time. It also indicates an ability to recover quickly from exertion without suffering fatigue.

~ Strength

Strength is the force which a muscle can produce when it contracts. Strength can be acquired either by contracting the muscles in a static position with little or no movement of the joint (isometric), or by contracting them in resistance to a weight or force while moving the joint (isotonic).

~ Flexibility

Flexibility is indicated by the range of movement available in the joints. Flexibility involves connective tissues, such as ligaments and tendons, and the joints themselves. Flexibility determines posture and ease of movement as well as suppleness.

To find out how fit you are, test yourself in each of these areas using these common 'rule of thumb' tests:

Endurance

Run on the spot, lifting your knees high, breathing regularly.

~ 1 minute or less = poor endurance
~ 1–1.5 minutes = average endurance
~ 2 minutes or longer = good endurance

STOP if you start to feel dizzy, sick, winded or experience any discomfort in the chest.

Strength

First test your abdominal muscles. Lie on the floor with your arms folded and *roll* up into a sitting position. Abdominal strength is

~ Poor – if you can't do it
~ Average – if you can get halfway up
~ Good – if you can sit up easily and do so repeatedly

Now test your arm, shoulder and chest muscles. Find a sturdy table and stand approximately three feet from it. Now do press ups against it by bringing your chest down to the table edge, and lifting it away again. Keep your legs straight all the while.

~ 1–3 press-ups are poor
~ 4–6 press-ups are average
~ 7–10 are good

Flexibility

Sit on the floor, legs together and stretched straight in front of you. Reach for your toes without straining. Reaching

~ between the ankle and knee is poor
~ just the ankle is average
~ over the toes is good

General tests

You may wish to try other means of testing fitness before you choose an exercise programme for yourself. Here are a selection of general tests:

~ Your resting pulse is a good general indicator of how fit you are, although it obviously cannot measure strength or flexibility. Men should have a resting pulse rate of between 70–85 beats a minute and women between 75–90 beats a minute. If your pulse rate is past the hundred mark then you definitely need to improve your fitness, but you must avoid vigorous exercise to begin with.

When you are very unfit your pulse rate increases quickly when you exert yourself and takes longer to return to normal after exercise than that of a fit person. A fit person not only has a low pulse rate to start off with, it also stays lower for longer and quickly returns to normal after activity.

~ Another simple test of your fitness is whether you can complete a three-mile walk without effort or discomfort.

~ Assuming you do need to regain your fitness, start by walking one mile in 20 minutes each day. Combine this with some gentle stretching and strengthening exercises before you consider doing more vigorous exercise.

~ Self awareness is perhaps the most vital element in deciding how fit you are. Most people know where their shortcomings lie. If your lack of fitness is stopping you from engaging in your favourite sport or activity, then you will know it before anyone, or any test. Using the simple tests above, you can establish which aspects of fitness you most need to work on.

Measure your fitness every year on your birthday. Write the results in a diary for easy comparison. This method provides a powerful incentive to gain fitness!

Chapter 54
A consumer's guide to evaluating exercise programmes

~

You're always being told 'Exercise is good for you!', but what kind of exercise should you be doing? There are so many alternatives! What you need to do is evaluate the different types on offer and decide which one is really for you.

In fact, to say 'Exercise is good for you' is not really true; only exercise suited to your age, physical state, interests and budget can really be good for you. And exercise is an exact science; there are certain kinds of physical activity that your body needs, and others that it certainly doesn't.

Suitability

How do you decide which exercises will suit you? For real benefit exercise should cause:

~ Your muscles to both stretch and contract. As well as improving your shape and establishing strength and endurance, developed muscle tissue is necessary to support your joints and internal organs. Many serious health problems arise out of poor muscle tone, such as hernia, back problems, prolapse and digestive problems.

~ All your major joints to move. Movement stimulates the circulation of blood and lymph and keeps the joints mobile.

~ You to breathe deeply and regularly, perhaps becoming *slightly* breathless though still able to talk. Many kinds of exertion have this effect, but you need to keep yourself exercising to this level for several minutes to benefit your cardiovascular system. Exercising to this level helps to keep blood pressure down, arteries clear, and heart and lungs strong and healthy. If you under-exert you do not gain fitness; and over-exertion to the point of breathlessness does not improve fitness either and can lead to serious problems, such as heart attack.

~ Your heart to pump strongly and regularly. You should monitor this by watching your breathing, as above. Do not allow yourself to go red in the face, dizzy, or to feel the thumping of your heart in your ears!

~ Your brain to deal with co-ordination or movement patterns. This aspect of exercise creates opportunity for relaxation, stress reduction, creativity and fun. No exercise should be without these.

In addition, an exercise only really suits you if:

~ It is enjoyable and affordable

~ You can practise it at least three times each week, for approximately 30 minutes each session

~ It includes warm-up and cool down movements in each session

~ It is interesting to you, so that you welcome its practice as a regular feature in your daily life.

Which exercise?

Pick an exercise after first deciding what sort of practice schedule and environment best suits you. For instance:

~ a group exercise such as a game or class *or* a solitary exercise

~ a morning-only, daytime-only, evening-only, etc. exercise session

~ an exercise that is silent *or* accompanied by rhythmic music

~ exercise that involves a little expense, to keep you motivated

~ exercise that is free except for the clothes you will wear

~ a strict routine *or* a lot of variety

~ three or four seasonal exercises *or* one year-round exercise

Here are basic evaluations of some of the more common forms of exercise. The summary for each exercise follows the format:

~ where or how is it done?
~ for how long is it done?
~ why or for whom is it especially beneficial?
~ what are its special attractions?
~ what are the clothing requirements?
~ what are the drawbacks or disadvantages?

Aerobics

~ indoors with an instructor; many sports centres, church halls
~ 15 minutes excluding warm-up and cool down, average total of 45–60 minutes
~ challenges the cardiovascular system, best for the youngish and fairly fit
~ very social, usually to music and therefore quite dance-like
~ minimum of loose or stretchy clothing with good training shoes
~ quality of exercise dependent on quality of teacher, (see Help section) also some floors are too hard for this exercise and injury can result

Cycling

~ indoors on a stationary bicycle *or* outdoors on a geared bicycle
~ minimum of 20 minutes without stopping
~ especially good for the elderly or those with hip or back problems
~ little likelihood of injury to muscle, tendon, ligament, etc.
~ wear non-chafe clothing and a helmet for outdoor cycling
~ outdoor cyclists should plan a safe, non-stop route with few hills

Dancing

~ ballroom, rock 'n' roll, disco, folk, Scottish country or any other
~ minimum of 12 minutes without a complete break
~ very social and pleasant for those who like music and rhythm
~ an attractive activity which makes one feel competent and controlled
~ wear flat, comfortable shoes to avoid foot injury
~ dance with a partner who can also dance for 12 minutes!

Games

~ volleyball, squash, tennis, golf or similar
~ minimum of 30 minutes as these are usually stop-start activities
~ especially good for those who like to compete or follow a set of rules
~ social yet with a chance for individual accomplishment and skill
~ wear shoes and clothing suited to the game, allowing free movement
~ play with a partner who will challenge you, but not too much

Jarming

~ sitting in a chair and 'jogging' with your arms
~ minimum of 15 minutes without stopping
~ particularly for those who are elderly or in any way infirm
~ achieves cardio-respiratory goals safely and effectively
~ may be performed to rhythmic music
~ maintain a size and pace of 'jarm' that will allow adequate breath

Jogging

~ in an indoor court *or* outdoors on track or field
~ minimum of 15 minutes without stopping
~ for those who are able to exercise strenuously without pain
~ may be social or solitary with scope for competition if desired
~ select very supportive shoes and non-chafe clothing
~ weather, dogs and mud are always hazards

Keep Fit

~ in a class *or* at home using an audio cassette or video tape
~ minimum of 30 minutes
~ for a complete fitness programme of stretch, strength and mobility
~ for all ages; classes are usually very social and full of variety
~ wear loose or stretchy clothing
~ make sure your teacher is qualified and gives you personal attention

Rowing

~ on an indoor machine *or* join an outdoor rowing club!
~ minimum of 15 minutes without stopping
~ an excellent way to exercise the whole body
~ for all ages; having particular effect on arms, legs, back and abdomen
~ wear minimum, non-chafe clothing
~ indoors, select a machine with a comfortable, sliding seat

Skiing or Skating

~ cross-country skiing *or* ice or roller skating
~ minimum of 20 minutes without stopping
~ all the benefits of running or jogging, without trauma in the joints
~ mostly lower-body exercise, though arm movement improves breathing
~ wear stretchy, non-chafe clothing and appropriate skis or skates
~ skiing is seasonal, and you need to find rink space for skating

Swimming

~ usually an indoor exercise in this country
~ minimum of 20 minutes without stopping
~ excellent to loosen joints and muscles and improve heart and lungs
~ a variety of strokes ensure the majority of joints and muscles are used
~ wear minimum clothing
~ finding a clean, uncrowded pool is sometimes difficult

Walking

~ can be done anywhere, anytime
~ minimum of 20 minutes without stopping
~ an excellent exercise for heart, lungs, back and lower body
~ for all ages; a no-trauma way to travel, entertain yourself or exercise
~ wear high-quality supportive shoes
~ it is necessary to maintain a brisk pace for maximum benefit

Weight Training

~ using a multi-gym or poly-gym arrangement in a sports centre
~ aim for 20–30 minutes of sustained training

~ improves strength, muscle tone and posture in specific body parts
~ for all ages; provides an opportunity to become more physically aware
~ wear supportive shoes and loose or stretchy clothing
~ a qualified coach is essential in your first month of training

Yoga

~ at home from memory *or* at a class run by a certified teacher
~ most classes last at least one hour, some up to two and a half hours
~ increases your mobility, suppleness, posture and improves breathing
~ for all ages; also gives you time and mental space to contemplate
~ wear loose or stretchy clothing and have an extra layer at hand
~ it can take time to find the teacher and type of yoga class that suit you

Precautions

Do NOT exercise if:
~ you are ill
~ you are injured
~ you are undernourished
~ you are *very* tired, physically, mentally or emotionally
~ you have already exercised today
~ you have a medical condition which requires a doctor's advice – get their opinion on the exercise programme you wish to follow
If you have an idea you would like a particular form of exercise, attend one session before you enrol for a course or spend out on expensive equipment. Look for a new teacher if you find that:
~ You're not given the opportunity to warm up and cool down properly.
~ You're pushed straight into complex exercises you don't understand.
~ You're not taught the correct style, so that you feel confused and your muscles are hurting before the session ends.
If you like the teacher, the place and, so far, the type of exercise, decide finally if it is an appropriate exercise for you by asking yourself the following questions:
~ Will it make my heart and lungs work hard but not too hard? Remember – you want to be slightly breathless.
~ Will it tone my muscles and make me move all major joints?
~ Will I be able to do it regularly? Remember – half an hour three times a week is a good guide.
~ Does it require a bit of brain work in the form of co-ordination or remembering movement patterns?
~ Will I like it?
~ Does it suit my age and current level of health and fitness?
If you don't have time for exercise, you'll certainly have time for illness. Exercise keeps you well. Get to know and like two or three different types of exercise and simply rotate your practice of them to keep yourself interested and active.

Chapter 55
What you need to know about exercise during pregnancy

~

The joy and excitement of pregnancy brings with it many new demands, both physical and emotional. Exercise helps you to deal with these demands and benefits you in several ways.

Selected forms of exercise can increase your enjoyment of pregnancy and speed both your labour and your recovery.

A more comfortable pregnancy

You will enjoy a more comfortable pregnancy if you exercise regularly throughout, because your body is dealing with the changes of pregnancy more successfully. Here are some specific benefits:

~ Improved circulation will combat the tendency to suffer varicose veins, haemorrhoids, cramps and swelling – especially in the third trimester.

~ Your posture will improve. The tendency to suffer lower back pain, 'sway back' and aching knees and hips during pregnancy can be prevented or minimized by corrective exercises. These are very simple and are beneficial long after you have given birth.

~ Your muscles will be kept in good tone and specific muscle groups will be prepared for labour. Most important of these are your back and abdominal muscles, your pelvic floor muscles and your pectorals, the muscles that support your breasts. Good muscle tone during pregnancy helps to maintain good posture, circulation and respiration.

~ You will feel an increased sense of well-being. Exercise seems to create more energy than it uses so you will feel less lethargic and tired. You will breathe more fully and with this will come a reduction in levels of stress. Finally, exercising throughout pregnancy heightens your bodily awareness – no mean feat when your body is daily changing size and shape! This awareness is crucial to maintaining your self-esteem and confidence.

~ Other, more specific benefits may be felt, such as relief from high blood pressure, nausea, and insomnia.

A healthy labour

No one can say what your labour would have been like if you hadn't exercised, but it is generally accepted that the more healthy and fit you are before labour, the more straightforward your labour will be. Barring complications, women who have exercised throughout their pregnancy will experience:

~ shorter labour
~ less painful labour
~ a sense of control while in labour
~ less fear of labour

A quicker recovery

The ten to fourteen earth-shaking days following the birth are too short a time to recover – you need a full nine to twelve months to regain your physical and emotional equilibrium. However, most women would like to speed this process along. They want to look and feel 'normal' as soon as they possibly can. Exercising during pregnancy can help you to a speedy recovery. All the changes of pregnancy are reversed now and the bodily strengths and improvements you gained during pregnancy can be used:

~ to reclaim tone in the pelvic floor
~ to maintain correct posture even through the demands of lifting, carrying and feeding the baby
~ to improve your stamina for the challenges of parenthood
~ to keep you on an even keel, mentally and emotionally

Which exercise?

Most women feel best during pregnancy if they can carry on as normal, doing the things they have always enjoyed doing. This is a comfortable, relaxed and usually sensible attitude which can also apply to exercise. But there are a few exceptions. Broadly speaking it is inadvisable to continue with aerobic dance training, horse-back riding, jogging, trampolining or gymnastics beyond the fourth month of pregnancy. If you feel inclined to continue with these or other strenuous forms of exercise, discuss your plans with your midwife or doctor first. There are certainly four types of exercise which you should feel completely at ease to practise during your pregnancy:
~ WALKING: wear low-heeled shoes throughout your pregnancy and good trainers when walking any distance. As an exercise, walking improves your circulation, challenges the heart and lungs, and keeps your lower-body joints mobile. In later pregnancy it can ease lower back pain, later still it can help the baby engage in the pelvis. Walk briskly for 30 minutes at least three (preferably five) times per week.
~ SWIMMING: most public pools have a 'pregnant and post-natal only' session somewhere in their schedule, in case you're shy about your shape. If not, just get a maternity swimsuit and take the plunge anyway! Swimming helps to strengthen and tone muscles throughout your body and enables you to move your joints easily and without awkwardness. Women with varicose veins find it enables them to exercise without having their problem aggravated. In fact, swimming is altogether marvellous in pregnancy – the water supporting your weight and the chance to work hard without getting hot are both welcome changes.

You don't really need to know how to swim in order to benefit from this exercise. Simply stand in chest-deep water and perform a collection of kicks, floats and stretches while holding on to the side. Thirty to 40 minutes twice a week is a good level to aim for, more if you can.
~ STATIONARY CYCLING: all you need is the cycle and the time. No special shoes are needed and you can do this exercise anytime of day or night in the privacy of your home. Cycling exercises the large muscles of your legs, increasing your strength there. But it also affects the abdominal and back muscles to some extent and, of course, challenges your heart and lungs. Like swimming, cycling is excellent for those who feel the need to take the weight off their feet as they exercise. Circulation is improved so that varicose problems and swelling are still benefited.

Make sure you sit tall while cycling and aim to cycle hard for 15 minutes each day. Cycle an additional 2--3 minutes at a low tension to warm up, the same again to cool down.
~ YOGA-BASED MOVEMENT: if you already attend a yoga class, ask your teacher if she is happy for you to continue attending throughout your pregnancy. Some teachers have no experience of teaching for pregnancy and are nervous to do so. In this case, or if you have not attended a yoga class before, consult your midwife, the local fitness centre or look at your library bulletin board about ante-natal exercise classes.

Such classes are generally excellent because you are able to meet and discuss with other pregnant women. Often a midwife attends to answer questions. Yoga-based exercise focuses on movements that:
~ stretch and strengthen your muscles
~ mobilize your joints
~ correct your posture
~ prepare you for various labour positions and the demands of motherhood
A typical session will last one hour and include a series of stretching and joint mobility movements for:
~ the face and neck
~ the upper arms, shoulders and pectorals
~ the spine and torso
~ the hips and thighs
~ the calves, ankles and feet
Various postures will be practised as they would be used in labour, such as:
~ squatting
~ knee-chest position
~ hands and knees
~ pelvic rotations
~ kneeling squat
In addition, some emphasis will be placed on breathing as a form of stress and pain relief. All movements taught in these sessions are designed with the pregnant body in mind. Occasionally, however, you may find that a movement you enjoyed one week is no longer comfortable for you. In this case, simply substitute another of your favourites. Your teacher should help you to personalize the exercises in this way. If she can't or doesn't, look for another class to attend. As yet, there is no qualifying body for this sort of teaching and you may have to rely on word of mouth and sampling a class for yourself. The main features which should indicate a good class are:
~ personal attention and modification of the exercises
~ a relaxed but steady pace
~ attention given to the needs and disorders of pregnancy, through both discussion and relevant exercises. Some medical background or support would help.
~ women of all stages of pregnancy attending
~ an avoidance of aerobic dance-style jogging and other very strenuous forms of movement
~ plenty of time allowed for explanation of the purpose of each exercise
~ time given to questions and discussion of anything related to pregnancy, labour and the post-natal months.

Remember – pregnancy is not an illness! It is a normal and usually healthy phase in a woman's life. It is natural and beneficial to want to keep supple, strong and active during this time.

CHAPTER 56
EXERCISING INTO YOUR EIGHTIES

~

So what if you're old? Exercise is as important now to your health and well-being as it is to a toddler's development. The rules are slightly different, but the rewards are quite similar.

Exercise is really just a way of challenging your body to function at its best while moving and breathing. Of course, it is often associated with games, sports, hard work and dieting, but it needn't include any of these. All it need be is a time and activity set aside specially for you to enjoy using your body. You can exercise all your life and, if you do, it is likely to be a long one!

The benefits

The benefits of exercise for those over sixty years of age are well chronicled. Regular exercise helps to:

~ keep your weight normalized
~ keep your joints flexible
~ keep your muscles strong and elastic
~ keep your cardiorespiratory system (heart/lungs) healthy
~ keep your posture well-aligned
~ maintain good circulation
~ improve skin tone
~ reduce stress
~ lift your spirits and improve self-esteem
~ minimize the discomfort and progress of some disorders such as rheumatoid arthritis and osteoporosis
~ boost your level of energy
~ improve the quality and/or length of your sleep

How to start

You may be one of those people who have never exercised in their lives, but you can start now, no matter what your age. Exercise begins to benefit you *the moment* you start, with benefits mounting the longer you stick with it. However, you should take a safe and sensible route into your exercise programme:

~ discuss with your doctor your intention to begin an exercise programme or take up a new activity
~ select a form of exercise that really suits you (see below and chapter 54)
~ begin slowly and extend your practice gradually
~ set yourself a daily target that you know is comfortably within your scope, walking a certain distance, for example. Practise that amount every day for a week or two, then try adding ten per cent to the distance. Continue in this way for several weeks until you arrive at a level of exercise you feel happy doing.

How much is too much?

If you exercise regularly, the fitness you acquire will enable you to do more exercise more safely than when you first started. If you're doing more than you're currently fit for, however, your body has a number of ways of letting you know. Slow or temporarily stop your exercise if:

~ you get so breathless you cannot speak
~ you feel pain of any sort anywhere in your body. There is a difference between a mild muscular discomfort sometimes felt while exercising and real pain. Trust your body's pain reflex, it's there to protect you from damage.

~ you still feel 'puffed', a pounding heart or racing pulse more than ten minutes after stopping. This is a definite sign that you should be doing less. Remember, improvement is gradual.
~ discomfort in the joints lasts more than a couple of hours after you've stopped, or if your joints feel worse, not better, the next day. If you have joint problems, exercise can improve their condition, but you may have an initial few days of discomfort.
~ Stop at once and let your doctor know if you experience chest pain or pressure, dizziness, fainting or visible facial pallor.

Avoiding injury

~ If you take regular medication, or if your general health is poor, then ask your doctor about suitable sorts of exercise.
~ Make sure a drink of water is nearby when you exercise. The older you get the more prone you are to dehydration. Avoid perspiration-inducing rubberized clothing for this same reason.
~ If your exercise is an outdoor activity, avoid exercising in temperature extremes. With age, you are more prone to excessive heat-loss in cold weather and to overheating in the sun.
~ Do not begin active or strenuous exercise until at least one hour after a meal.
~ Don't exercise on concrete or asphalt. Surfaces with a bit of natural 'give' like wood or grass will jar your limbs much less, as well as being less painful and injurious if you fall.
~ Wear shoes which cushion your foot. Add a good insole if necessary, or you will transmit undue shock to weight-bearing joints.

Enjoy your exercise

Misery is bad for your health. Select a type of exercise that you enjoy the look and feel of, one that fits in with other aspects of your lifestyle (see chapter 54). A little trial and error here will make all the difference, so allow yourself a month or so to experiment with different classes and activities. When you find one or more that you like, schedule them into your life so that you can enjoy them with gusto.

Which exercise?

~ Walking is an excellent form of exercise. Because it uses the large muscles in your legs, it offers maximum benefit for least cardiorespiratory effort. Your whole body benefits, not just your legs, especially if you walk briskly and with a slight swing to your arms. The benefits will be undercut if you have to pound along hard city streets, so try to find a park or unpaved lane to enjoy and become acquainted with. Walking is especially beneficial for people with rheumatism, arthritis or osteoporosis as it mobilizes the joints and strengthens bone. This exercise is best done briskly, for 30 minutes at least five times per week.
~ Swimming is another excellent all-body exercise, good for people with advanced osteoporosis and other disorders that make weight-bearing exercise difficult. In fact, because the water supports your weight, swimming can make you feel that all your physical impediments have temporarily vanished, at the same time as exercising all your muscles. Most swimming pools have cheaper rates for pensioners, and many have special sessions for the over fifties or sixties. These are great fun, child-free and full of new people to meet.
~ Dancing is something you can do in your own home to your favourite music whenever you like. It's nice to have a partner, but it's not essential. Dancing

includes any movement that feels graceful or rhythmical to you – it doesn't have to comply with anyone else's idea of a dance! *Any* movement you make helps to exercise your joints and muscles, so all of it does you some good. Check your local paper for traditional dance classes, if you prefer that style and the company, or go ahead and organize regular tea dances in a local hall.

~ Tai Chi is an ancient oriental form of martial art used as an exercise by millions of people of all ages. Tai Chi is a series of slow movements designed to keep your *chi* (energy) flowing properly; it is believed to prolong health into great old age and is certainly an excellent way to stay limber without making excessive demands on your body. Check your local paper or library for the nearest class.

~ If you are chair bound, try 'jarming' – nothing other than jogging with your arms! Make the regular, pumping movements with your arms that you would make if you were jogging to improve upper-body muscle tone and challenge the cardiorespiratory system. Most jarmers find it more fun if they jarm to rhythmic music, or 'conduct' their favourite symphonic music.

~ Stretch like a cat when you wake and any other time you feel like it. Stretching feels good and stimulates improvement to your posture, joints and muscles. This movement is usually accompanied by a deep intake of breath which is an excellent way to reduce stress.

~ Find exercise in the ordinary activity: walk instead of drive, hide the remote controls so you have to get up, take the stairs instead of the lift.

~ Many games provide an element of exercise along with their social aspect. Try boule, darts, croquet, golf or bowling.

~ There are dozens more forms of exercise which you can do safely for many years, including stationary cycling, rowing or yoga.

Keeping it up

~ If you stop enjoying your exercise, find a new one to replace it.

~ Practise your exercise at a regular time, whenever possible, so that it becomes an important part of your day. Ideally, you should really regret missing a session.

~ Most forms of exercise are stimulating, so try not to do yours just before bedtime.

~ A supportive partner or friend, joining in or just applauding, is usually an encouragement to continue your exercise.

~ Have one or two exercise options up your sleeve if, for any reason, you can't practice your favourite form. This way you won't lose the place in your schedule reserved for exercise.

~ Keep an exercise diary. Chances are that if you record several days' neglect these will coincide with several days of lethargy, depression, aches and pains, and so on.

~ Practise two or three different forms of exercise in rotation to keep variety in your life.

~ Ask that your birthday and Christmas gifts, etc., be things such as clothing, music cassettes or equipment, that you can use in your exercise sessions.

CHAPTER 57

RELAX AND HEAL YOURSELF!

~

Forget pills, you can heal yourself simply by relaxing! Here are two techniques which are rapidly gaining ground as an antidote to our sick, over-stressed, lives.

Autogenics

Autogenics consists of a series of exercises which enables you to slow down your heart and body processes. Once you have learnt the techniques of autogenics you can do them in any stressful situation.

Dr. H. Schultz developed this therapy in the 1930s in Berlin. A psychiatrist and neurologist, he experimented with hypnosis and noted the way it could induce feelings of heaviness, warmth and deep relaxation. He realized that people could learn to induce these feelings through self-hypnosis.

You can use autogenics as an alternative to tranquillizers, sleeping pills, and beta-blockers. It is also effective for treating high blood pressure, heart trouble, ulcers, gastritis, gall bladder attacks, irritative colon, haemorrhoids, constipation, weight or smoking problems, arthritis and many other complaints. It is used in antenatal clinics and to treat people who are recovering from major surgery.

But autogenics is not limited to medical purposes. Athletes use it to improve their performance by increasing the oxygen flow to their muscles. Managers are now using it to become more decisive and solve problems effectively. Even writers and artists who are suffering from an artistic block can benefit because it frees their creativity.

The Canadians have gone even further by introducing it into schools. Studies have shown that it reduced behavioural problems and exam results improved.

But autogenics therapy must initially be done under the supervision of a doctor because medical conditions, such as diabetes or asthma could otherwise worsen. At the beginning it can also bring repressed anxieties and tensions to the surface so that you have headaches or pain in your chest.

What happens

The techniques are reasonably straightforward. You must imagine you are in mental contact with a part of your body and repeat a given formula to yourself, either mentally or verbally. And you should have a relaxed, casual attitude towards its effects. There are six standard 60-second exercises which allow you to influence your arms and legs, your heart, breathing, and your nervous system. Once you have mastered these techniques you can progress to a series of meditative exercises. Through these you can visualize colours, objects, concepts such as happiness, feelings and people, and begin to know your unconscious, deeper self. The healing, calming effects of the six standard exercises are reinforced by the meditation.

Biofeedback

Biofeedback is 'the feedback of biological processes to the person whose biology it is'. In biofeedback, the electricity generated in your own muscles is picked up by electrodes on your skin, and fed back to you in the form of sounds or, more recently, through visual displays on a TV monitor.

So if you learn relaxation techniques and then perceive your body processes in the form of sounds or pictures, you can lower your blood pressure, for instance, and affect other healing changes in your body.

Patricia Cowings has carried out research into biofeedback at NASA in America in an attempt to help astronauts avoid motion sickness, which is a serious problem (half of them become sick during a space flight mission). Drugs do not work in space because of the effects of weightlessness on metabolism and fluid distribution. "It seems kind of mystical to some folks," says Dr. Cowings, who is director of the feedback experiment at NASA's Ames Research Center in California. "However, we are a NASA laboratory and we have been producing results for 12 years."[366]

Like autogenics, biofeedback is helpful for people who suffer from anxiety or have disorders which are aggravated by severe stress. Biofeedback enables you to relax your body and avoid the fight-or-flight response that causes headaches, hypertension and other stress-related problems.

Stephen P. Hersh, one of the founding psychiatrists of the American Medical Illness Counseling Center, believes that biofeedback is a way for people to master some of the techniques "that otherwise were only accessible from years of study of Yoga or Zen or other forms of meditation. So it is tapping into a real ability that has been known for at least 4,000 years that humans, and probably many mammals have."[367]

Hersh believes that biofeedback can be useful in treating excessive anxiety, and illnesses associated with it – skin diseases like psoriasis, bowel diseases, some asthmatic conditions and headaches. One recent study involved a group of children with headaches, sent to him by neurologists at a children's hospital. All of them were regarded as 'treatment failures' by traditional methods. The biofeedback program was 100 per cent successful.[368]

Most biofeedback patients are taught to quieten or relax their systems, to overcome the fight-or-flight response that can induce headaches, hypertension and other stress-related problems.

For information on where to get both these promising new therapies, see the Help section.

Chapter 58
How to get a good night's sleep

~

Do you have a problem sleeping? Sleep disturbance troubles many people, and the tendency to insomnia increases as one gets older. The problem can become chronic and debilitating, so it is important for you to know how to succeed in sleeping.

You will spend up to one-third of your life asleep. Sleep is essential for your mind and body to function effectively, yet there is great dispute over why we sleep and how much we need. What is clear is that sleep allows rest, recovery and recuperation, while sleep deprivation leads to health problems ranging from headaches and irritability, through inability to concentrate and hypersensitivity, to psychosis.

Sleep problems can broadly be split into two:

~ Primary problems. This term is used to describe a situation where sleep itself is the main difficulty. Apart from rare conditions like narcolepsy and apnea, primary sleep problems can be either:

- Insomnia – a condition where you are slow to go to sleep or suffer from repeated awakenings. Three types are discernible. *Transient insomnia,* initiated by disturbance in your routine – for example, jetlag or shift work. *Short-term insomnia,* brought on by worries, emotional upset such as bereavement, or illness; and *long-term insomnia,* triggered by more severe problems.
- Psuedo insomnia – you feel you haven't slept when in reality you have. This is surprisingly common. One study showed that during observation of sleep

patterns of a group of insomniacs, in reality half were awake for no more than half an hour per night. Lack of sleep was a subjective illusion!

~ Secondary problems. These are sleep problems caused by use of stimulants or sedatives, excess alcohol use, depression or mental disturbance, or acute worry and anxiety. By focusing on the primary problem, sleep will be found to come much more easily.

Some good techniques

You can try a number of proven techniques to conquer your insomnia:

Dream therapy

This is a radical approach to insomnia, in which you control your dreams to help you sleep. Here's how to do it – first choose a morning on which you can oversleep (because most dreams occur in the early morning). Allow yourself to wake up naturally and gradually, and make an effort to remember your last dream image. Now put it into words – write it down in a dream diary, or record it on an audio cassette. Replay the image the next night while going to sleep. This will help you make the transition between ordinary everyday consciousness and your sleep state. To sleep, you must surrender your grip on the world, and replaying a dream is the ideal method of doing this gently and pleasurably. So choose a good dream!

Dream therapy can also help with secondary problems like depression. One doctor, for example, claims that a dream equals six months' therapy. Indeed, you can use your dream after reshaping it, to give an improved format – a better ending. If people stop having unpleasant guilt-ridden, anxious dreams, they wake in the morning better refreshed. If you are a creative, imaginative person, dream therapy could be just what you need. And as a bonus, you may end up with an extraordinary diary of highly original themes, ideas and stories.

Reduce stimulants

Cut out tea, coffee, drinks with additives and caffeine, alcohol, and tobacco. Instead, try a herbal tea before bedtime. Valerian, chamomile and yarrow all have soothing properties, and generally are available at your local health food shop.

Exercise

It's a fact that exercise taken during the day promotes greater relaxation and better sleep the following night. The problem with many of our lives is that while our minds become fatigued with the mental strain of modern life, our bodies are basically under-used. Exercise is your chance to re-establish the equilibrium which should exist between mind and body.

Amino acids

Tryptophan, an amino acid, has a variety of important roles in mental activity. Serotonin is a neurotransmitter, one of the chemicals in the brain that helps control moods. To have enough serotonin you need enough tryptophan, which is essential in its formation. Tryptophan can act as a natural sleeping pill – it has also been proved to be as effective as prescription drugs in relieving severe depression. However, a recent outbreak of a rare blood disease has been linked to the use of tryptophan, and currently it is no longer on sale in tablet form.

At the time it was taken off the market, health officials suspected a chemical contaminant was responsible for illnesses that have so far affected 1,500 Americans and resulted in twenty-two deaths.[369] Virtually all cases of illness could be traced to a few batches of tryptophan from one Japanese manufacturer. But you don't have to resort to pills to get tryptophan. It can be found naturally in foods such as peanuts, baked beans, wheat germ and brewer's yeast. So try to include some of these in your diet, eating them from the early evening onwards.

Relaxation tapes

Pre-recorded gentle, repetitive, rhythmic music (some created by hypnotherapists), is best for soothing your mind and promoting a restful state prior to a relaxing sleep. The tapes are best played on your personal hi-fi, because this will allow you to sink back into the bedclothes and just drift away. It will automatically switch itself off when the tape has ended and the earphones will block out extraneous, disturbing sound. Many New Age shops sell these tapes.

Visualization

Visualization is, as yet, a little known technique but its success has been shown by people suffering from cancer and other serious diseases who use it to build up their resistance to pain and to add mental support to their treatment. You can use it for many purposes, and it can certainly help you to relax and find deep, natural sleep.

The visualizer creates in his mind an imaginary world to which he can escape at will, where he can relax away from the pressures of real life and reaffirm positive statements about himself, his body and his life. The two main ingredients of successful visualization are:

~ Patience.
~ Practice.

Anyone can do it—it just takes time to learn. To start with, you should:

~ Find a quiet room where you won't be disturbed.
~ Lie comfortably on a bed or carpet, making sure there is nothing to distract you, such as uncomfortable clothes
~ Close your eyes and relax.

Relaxation is essential. If you have trouble relaxing try using a meditation technique to clear your mind of persistent thoughts. There are many relaxation aids available—tapes of environmental sounds, for example. Use these if they help.

Next, try to conjure up mental impressions, one for each of your senses. These could be:

~ The image of a black square.
~ The sound of running water.
~ The feel of sawdust, followed by that of ice.
~ The smell of apples or fresh coffee.
~ The taste of vinegar.

At first you will find it very difficult to concentrate on a particular image. Don't try to wrestle with your imagination. Let the images come, then choose the ones you want to keep.

Practise until you can recall chosen images easily. Gradually work towards more complex impressions, adding details in stages. Once you've mastered this, begin creating impressions that use a combination of senses.

~ See, pick up and unpeel an orange. Then eat it. Concentrate on each sense and practise until it really seems as if you are eating an orange.
~ If you have difficulties with accuracy, eat a real orange and practise visualizing each stage after you've done it.
~ Make your imaginary activities more complicated, until, for example, you can pick up and play with an imaginary kitten—as if it were real.

Secret places

Now you can set about creating your own secret places, one indoors, one outside—the places you can always return to when visualizing.

~ The first will be a room or building. It doesn't have to be realistic, but it must be detailed. And consistent.

~ The same applies to the outdoor scene, usually a natural setting. You need to invent distant objects as well as immediate ones like a beach or river bank.

You can return to either of your individually tailored places at any time, when you need to relax, for example, or escape a stressful situation, to mull over problems, or to find a safe, restful place to sleep.

This will take time; fifteen minutes three times a day for several weeks. But once you have created your secret places you will have the skills necessary for any kind of visualization. You will be able to recreate past scenes, alter them and imagine alternative or future scenes, like a film director.

Before you begin, however, there are some guidelines to bear in mind:

~ Always picture yourself positively when visualizing, otherwise it will reinforce your negative conceptions of yourself.

~ It's helpful to have someone to discuss your problems with, so visualize yourself some kind of friend, be it man, beast, cartoon character or whatever. The existence of this creature will make 'shall I, shan't I' dialogues easier and more satisfying.

Once mastered, visualization is an easy and valuable means of combating stress and improving yourself in countless ways. Enjoy it, and it will work for you.

Yoga and massage

Try a slow, relaxing massage, or some peaceful yoga techniques last thing at night. Late night sex helps too.

Deprivation

Deprivation is a controversial treatment which involves going without any sleep at all. If you want to experiment with it, do it over a weekend. It requires mental resolve and a 'helper' to goad you into keeping awake, even when you finally wish to fall asleep. Some research shows that after missing a night's sleep, you will feel better and more energetic the following afternoon. This allows you to do and achieve more, hence tiring yourself out more for the next night!

The last resort

Doctors now use hypnotic drugs as a last resort, and prefer to look for the underlying reasons for sleep troubles. Sometimes, however, they are necessary, for the right patient at the right time. Health food shops, however, sell a range of safe, natural pills (such as 'Quiet Time' made by G. R. Lane Health Products Ltd) which are in many ways preferable to orthodox sleeping pills, and non-addictive.

Perhaps the most important rule with sleep troubles is *not to worry*.

Over-concern about 'required' sleep levels merely adds to the problem by making you more tense and less able to relax. Everyone has phases when they either can't sleep or need less sleep – it's natural and normal! Merely being aware of this can help. Don't have unrealistic expectations about the length and depth of your sleep. Don't build sleep up into a big deal – go to bed when you feel sleepy and not before. If you do sleep, and wake up later and can't get back to sleep, *get up* and catch up on some task or other you missed that day. Read a book or play music – fill that time constructively. You may find that you just don't need as much sleep as you thought!

CHAPTER 59
WHAT TO DO ABOUT A SICK HOUSE

~

When you think you're shutting out the world's dangers, give a thought to the dangers you're shutting in. Read how you can evict them and really make your home a haven.

Your home is your castle, right? A place of safety and comfort in an ailing world. Yet, environmentally speaking, your reassuring cocoon may be a potential house of horrors. The plain truth is that your home contains the means to seriously damage your own health and that of your family. Sick building syndrome (SBS for short) isn't just something that only happens in offices and factories. It can also affect many homes, including yours; and many people, including you.

Don't take the air quality in your house for granted. Because of poor building design, new construction techniques, and the increased need to conserve energy, today's home now resembles a sealed box. That expensive double glazing you installed certainly keeps in the heat, but it also stops fresh air from circulating. According to studies by the US Environmental Protection Agency, the air inside energy-efficient houses often is two to five times more polluted than the air outside![370] Indoor pollution will be one of the major environmental issues of the 21st century. You should know more about your home's invisible dangers so that you can start taking preventive action right now.

Spotting a sick house

A 'yes' answer to two or more of the following questions strongly suggests that something may need fixing at home . . .

~ Do you suffer from the symptoms of ill health (a persistent runny nose, for example) which go away when you leave the house and return when you return?

~ Does more than one member of the family suffer like this, especially those who spend the most time at home?

~ Do the symptoms get worse when the heating is turned on?

~ Did you start feeling bad when you moved into a new house, remodelled your house, got new furnishings or curtains, sprayed with pesticides, or changed your activity level?

~ Did symptoms develop after energy conservation work (lagging, cavity foam, etc.) was done on your house?

~ Do the symptoms become most severe when the house is tightly sealed in cold weather?

A table of troubles

Where do you start looking for the cause of SBS? Unfortunately, there are, quite literally, hundreds of potential indoor air pollutants, ranging from dust, smoke and airborne bacteria to the paints, cleaners, solvents, dyes, glues and household sprays you use every day to supposedly clean and improve your home. They all pollute your inner space. Here are just a few possible sources to consider:

~ In your home office, your computer generates heat, radiation and stress.

~ The copier produces ozone.

~ Electromagnetic radiation from household appliances, like the TV, fridge and even your electric blanket, can also adversely affect your health (see chapter 61).

~ Your new curtains and carpets may give off formaldehyde which is a carcinogen.

~ Your home insulation may discharge man-made fibres, or even asbestos, into the air you breathe, threatening cancer and respiratory problems.

~ Your pressed wood and fibreboard furniture and fittings can emit trace chemicals.

~ Even taking a refreshing hot shower to wash all the pollution away can be risky – studies have shown that you can actually absorb more pollutants by taking a shower (from breathing the fine water spray) than you would from simply drinking the water.[371]

All this makes rather gloomy reading. But all the more reason to take action now, and *cure* your home!

Health through indoor plants

First of all, you should seriously consider filling your home with living plants. Some remarkable research by NASA scientists shows that plants can actually remove health-threatening pollutants (such as formaldehyde, benzene, and trichloroethylene) from the air we breathe. And why not? They already remove carbon dioxide and emit oxygen. While researching life-support systems for future space stations, NASA found that three common house plants – golden pothos (*Scindapsus aureus*), nephthytis (*Syngonium podophyllum*) and the spider plant (*Chlorophytum elatum vittatum*) – can all remove substantial amounts of chemical contamination from the air. For example, the spider plant can remove an astounding 95 per cent of formaldehyde in just twenty-four hours. Later research suggests that other plants, especially philodendrons, may be even more effective.[372] So get some pollution-fighting vegetation now!

Health through chemical vigilance

On a basic level, you can cure a sick house by becoming chemically vigilant. Remove as many chemical products from your environment as you can, especially air fresheners, moth crystals, carpet shampoos, aerosols and stored chemicals (including paints and solvents). Store those chemicals you just can't do without in a locked outdoor shed or container. Read product labels carefully and use non-toxic alternatives where possible. Your motto should be: eliminate or minimize.

Health through air cleaners

Air filtering systems trap particles like pollen by drawing air through filters. High-efficiency particulate systems use extra filter layers to trap gases, odours and smoke. Air purifiers and ionizers use negatively-charged ions to bond with pollutant particles which are collected in a filter trap. As a spin-off, these ions seem to counteract depression, too! Consider a humidifier for air which seems too dry or dusty (a side-effect of central heating). Although cheap air 'cleaners' costing ten or twenty pounds may seem like good value, they often do little more than perfume or deodorize the air. A good air filter will probably cost £200–£300, and its filters need changing every month or two. If you value your family's health, you'll find the expenditure worthwhile. Addresses of manufacturers can be found in the Help section.

Timber treatment

Chemicals used in timber treatment can cause potentially deadly illnesses. Fatal blood disorders (aplastic anaemia) and toxic poisoning cases are known to have resulted from living in contaminated houses and from DIY usage. Bought over the counter, or used by the big infestation treatment firms, these products may contain lindane, pentachlorophenol (PCP) and tributyltin oxide (TBTO). These chemicals may linger in the home for a long time after spraying.

What to do about it:

~ Don't use products containing these chemicals, or allow them to be used, in your house.

~ Check the history of any house you move into for evidence of usage.
~ Ask any timber-treatment company you think about employing for full, written safety data about the chemicals they use, and a written guarantee saying they'll be responsible for any adverse health effects.
If, after all this, you decide to go ahead with chemical treatment in your home, be aware that concentrations of lindane reach a peak four weeks after application, even though government guidelines advise evacuation for only 48 hours.

Radon

Radon is an odourless, invisible, radioactive gas which emits high-energy alpha particles as it decays. When you breathe it in, it damages lung tissue and can cause lung cancer and leukaemia. One in eight US houses suffers from radon seepage. In the UK about 140,000 homes are affected, but the number keeps rising as more and more homes are tested. In Britain alone, the National Radiological Protection Board says that radon causes 2,500 deaths each year from lung cancer. It's the second most important cause of lung cancer after smoking.[373]

Radon is produced from uranium-rich rock and slowly seeps up into houses through gaps in floors and walls. The World Health Organization believes a safe radon level is below 200 becquerels (Bq) of radiation per cubic metre. Above 400 Bq per cubic metre and you must apply to your local council for a grant to have your home protected. Radon hot-spots exist in Devon, Cornwall, Northamptonshire, Avon, Cumbria, Staffordshire, the West Midlands and Wales.

What should you do about it?
~ First, ask your local council's environmental health department for help in determining if you have a radon problem, and if so, for financial assistance in curing it.
~ Radon can be prevented from seeping into your home by building a suspended concrete floor. This can either be done during construction (if the area is known to be a high radon one, for example) or later.
~ In the case of an existing home, underfloor fans beneath the building can suck the gas away. Check with your council about grants for this.
~ Radon's harmful effects are magnified if you smoke – another good reason to give it up!
~ A machine called the No-Rad has shown some promising results in scientific trials in radon reduction.[374] It grew out of experiments conducted at the Harvard School of Public Health, and works in an unusual way by removing the radioactive substances that radon creates when it decays. An address for the No-Rad can be found in the Help section.

Further tips for a non-toxic home

~ Make sure you ventilate your home regularly, with the use of air conditioners or a kitchen exhaust fan; even merely opening a window helps to disperse pollutants.
~ Clean your house regularly and thoroughly using vacuum cleaner, mop and duster. Use a damp cloth – not a cleaning solution – on surfaces and change your vacuum cleaner bag frequently. Use borax in hot water with a dash of vinegar for walls and floors. Wash all fabrics and bedclothes regularly. Hot water and elbow grease beat chemicals hands down!
~ Water filters can deal with any concerns you may have over water contamination (see chapter 1).
~ In the garden, ask your local council's environmental health department for help in determining the amount of lead in the soil. Anything over 500 parts per million

(ppm) is risky. Lead concentrates in plant leaves, so avoid planting leafy vegetables such as lettuce and those with edible tops such as broccoli and cauliflower. Lead is absorbed in lesser amounts in root vegetables – and only in their skins – so peel carrots, potatoes and other root crops before eating or cooking them. Fruits or plants like beans, tomatoes and strawberries also absorb smaller amounts of lead, so growing them is less of a problem.

~ Wash all plants thoroughly in running tap water before eating them. Rotavate the soil (the top few inches are usually the worst contaminated); add organic material and lime; and grass-over kids' play areas. Consider topsoil replacement if pollution is very bad.

~ Leave creosote, weed killers and those pesticides well alone. They all have organic alternatives.

You will spend up to 75 per cent of your life in your home. Given a toxic blend of pollutants and poor ventilation, any house can become sick. Develop a protective attitude towards your house and those who live in it, and you'll beat the threat of a poisoned home.

Chapter 60

How to fly successfully

~

Colds

Most people who are frightened of flying believe that the greatest danger which faces them is the risk of crashing. Not so. The chances of dying in an air crash are minuscule. On the other hand, flying does involve some real, but little-appreciated, health dangers which, with a little good sense, you can take steps to eliminate or minimize.

People who fly while suffering from colds can face severe pain and headaches. If you have ever used an inflatable travel pillow, you'll know that when the plane is at 35,000 feet your pillow is rock-hard, but after you've landed the pillow is soft and needs inflating. This isn't because it's sprung a leak, but because when you ascend the gases inside the pillow expand, and when you descend, they contract. Your external organs – ears and nose mainly – behave like that too.

As you ascend and the outside pressure decreases, so the gases in the chambers inside your ear expand. When the gas escapes round your ear drums it causes that typical popping sensation. Similarly, when you descend, the gas needs to get back in, and it bends your ear drum inwards to create a gap through which the gas can flow.

However, when you have a cold (or even if you are suffering from hay fever or blocked sinuses) then mucus gums up your channels and the gas has to build up a lot more pressure to get back in. Something similar happens in your nasal passages. This pressure can cause severe headaches and can occasionally burst the ear drums. Decongestants may help, but if you have a bad cold, it's best to delay your flight if at all possible.

Hyperventilation

The most common medical complication on commercial flights is hyperventilation or over-breathing. During hyperventilation, oxygen levels in the body increase and carbon dioxide levels decrease. This disorder can result in dizziness, numbness in the hands and feet, feelings of suffocation, panic, and fainting. It is often accompanied by palpitations. Hyperventilation happens while flying for the same reasons as it occurs on the ground, over-excitement, fear and acute anxiety, all frequent emotions while flying. You feel breathless, numb and your face and limbs tingle. The cure is simple – breathe into a paper bag until you've calmed down. This will increase the amount of carbon dioxide you inhale, and so bring the amount of oxygen in your blood down to its normal level again.

Medication

Medicines may become more potent when taken before or during a flight. You should ask your doctor about the suitability of prescribed medicines for air travel. Of the over-the-counter medications, antihistamines – used primarily to treat colds, 'flu and hay fever – should be avoided because the side effects (drowsiness and dehydration) are increased by air travel.

Plaster casts

Plaster contains gases which may expand causing the space inside the cast to shrink. This will squash your broken limb and can even cause gangrene. You should avoid travelling for the 40 hours after the cast has been put on, and consider splitting it for long hauls.

Pregnancy

Women who are pregnant should be very circumspect about flying. They should never fly after the 34th week (flying tends to accelerate the birth process) and should also avoid it altogether in the first trimester, because of exposure to cosmic radiation. If you must fly while you are pregnant, check with your airline well in advance about any special requirements they may have.

Children have special needs when flying. For a start, their bodies have a higher water content than adults, and more prone to dehydration. Therefore they should be given small amounts of water to drink at frequent intervals. Newborns should not fly until they are, at the very least, twelve days old.

Scuba-diving

Going scuba diving is foolish less than twelve hours before take off (or twenty-four hours if you've gone deeper than thirty feet) because it may bring on decompression sickness – sometimes called 'the bends' – which can be fatal.

Surgery

Having an operation inevitably leaves air trapped inside the wound which needs to be re-absorbed into your body. If you fly less than ten days after surgery, the air could expand and possibly cause a haemorrhage. Similarly, defective dental fillings often have air trapped inside them. If you are having problems with your teeth then see your dentist before you fly.

If you have a cardiovascular or respiratory disease, or a blood disorder; if you have had liver or kidney failure; if you suffer from severe diabetes, a large hernia, or are an alcoholic then you *should consult your doctor before flying.*

Ozone

The protective ozone layer that surrounds the Earth, and which is being alarmingly depleted at the moment, starts at around 40,000 feet. So the higher you fly, the more concentrated ozone you will encounter. Concorde – and the coming generation of airplanes – cruise at 60,000 feet, where ozone levels are more concentrated still. Ozone can irritate the throat, chest, nose and eyes, and people with health problems in these areas – asthmatics, for example – should be particularly aware of this problem. There is also research to suggest that it may cause cancer.

Ozone normally reaches its maximum concentration in the northern hemisphere from February to May, so flying outside this period will tend to reduce your exposure. Airlines install catalytic converters to reduce the amount of ozone in cabins, by heating it to 400°C, at which point it decomposes to oxygen. However, when the engines are throttled back as the plane starts its descent, the catalytic converter temporarily loses efficiency for about three minutes, as its temperature falls to about 300°C. At this time, ozone concentrations in the cabin can rise. The obvious solution to this problem is for the airlines to install more effective ozone reduction equipment. Until this is done, however, F. S. Kahn, an expert in the study of aviation medicine, suggests that one way to reduce your intake of this irritant substance is to hold a handkerchief to your nose and mouth for three minutes as soon as you feel the engines throttle back prior to descent.[375]

Radiation

When you fly, you are likely to encounter radiation from two sources – galactic radiation (which comes from the galaxy in which our Earth resides) and solar radiation (which is generated by the Sun, and is particularly intense during sunspot activity). The International Commission on Radiation Protection has suggested that the maximum permissible dose for air travellers should be set at 5 milli-Sieverts a year. However, research among air crew indicates that they receive anything up to 9.1 milli-Sieverts a year – almost twice the suggested limit.[376] There is still a huge amount of dispute and uncertainty over the whole question of radiation exposure. There are strong arguments to be made, for example, that the limits set by the International Commission on Radiation Protection are far too high. A sensible policy is to strive to reduce your exposure wherever you can. This means:

~ Flying less. If you can travel another way, consider it – particularly if you may be pregnant (remember that the growing baby is at its most vulnerable to radiation damage in the first three months). Since your radiation exposure increases with each flight, take fewer flights, and arrange to get more accomplished per trip.

~ Avoid polar routes, which tend to be exposed to more galactic and solar radiation (the cause of the aurora borealis).

~ Don't fly during periods of maximum sunspot activity. The sunspot cycle peaks about every eleven years. Even so, there may be sudden solar flares which can, on occasion, produce as much radiation at 40,000 feet as 20 milli-Sieverts an hour.[377] Familiarize yourself with the sunspot cycle and don't fly when it is at its peak. National meteorological offices will be able to warn you about solar flare activity. Also, long-range radio communication is disrupted during times of maximum solar radiation, so if your short-wave radio can't pull in the stations it normally can, consider waiting for the flare to pass before flying.

Chapter 61
What you can do about electromagnetic pollution

~

Every time you switch on your VDU (visual display unit) screen it emits possibly dangerous electromagnetic radiation. But what can we do to protect ourselves from this, the latest – and perhaps most insidious – form of pollution?

"There are enough indications of health risks," say the US Environmental Protection Agency, "from the type of electronic fields emanating from computer screens to justify significant new studies."[378]

In Texas in 1985, a jury ordered a local electricity utility to pay a school district $25 million in punitive damages after the utility built an electricity line through school property without permission. The jury's award was based almost entirely on the potential cancer threat, according to H. Dixon Montague, the school's attorney.[379] In Florida, juries have awarded more than $1 million to owners of land next to high-voltage power lines, again on the basis that such power lines can be linked to an increase in cancers among those people living nearby.[380]

Today, we all live in the electric, electronic age. Society as we know it simply couldn't function without electricity – industry and offices, hospitals and entertainment, all depend on electricity to keep them going, and all would instantly grind to a standstill without it. Yet the evidence is growing all the time that the side effects of our electric society may be killing us.

Electromagnetic pollution explained

The story begins with epidemiologists Nancy Wertheimer and Ed Leeper, who in 1979 published a bombshell report *Electrical wiring configurations and childhood cancer.*[381] They told how they had painstakingly conducted research into the deaths of children with cancer in the Denver, Colorado, region of America from 1976 to 1977. After plotting the precise location of the children's homes on maps, they found that there was a clear connection between deaths from cancer and their proximity to high-current power lines. The evidence pointed to the fact that children who grew up within a few metres of power lines were more likely to contract cancer than those living further away. At the time, the report seemed hard to take seriously – critics pointed out that the Earth's natural magnetic field is at least one hundred times stronger than anything the power lines seemed capable of generating, and no one had ever suggested that the Earth's magnetic field might be bad for humans. However, the critics overlooked one crucial detail – while the Earth's magnetic field is steady and changes very little, the magnetic field produced by alternating-current power lines is in a state of constant flux. Today, it is this fluctuating magnetic field which is thought to be capable of bringing about adverse changes in the human body. At the heart of the electricity/cancer connection lie two fundamental scientific principles.

The first is the innate dependence of the human body upon its own extremely subtle electric forces. Ever since 1780, when Galvani showed that the muscles in a frog's leg could be made to contract by the application of a weak electric current, it has been known that all animal life (including, of course, humans) is dependent upon internally-generated electricity for many of its most vital processes. For example, our very thoughts are – in essence – electric. Nerve cells (called neurons) in our brains are intrinsic to the processes of thinking, creating, analysing and, of course, receiving information from the outside world, in the form of vision, hearing, smells, taste and touch. In its 'at-rest' condition, the membrane surrounding a neuron allows potassium ions (a charged atom or grouping of atoms) to pass through, while keeping sodium ions out. This creates a situation where the inside of the neuron is electrically negative compared to the outside – like a cocked trigger waiting to be released. When stimulated, the neuron fires and releases this stored electrical charge. The actual amount of electricity involved is, of course, infinitesimally small.

The second basic scientific principle is the ability of a moving magnetic field to generate electricity. This was first demonstrated in 1831, when the British scientist Michael Faraday showed that a continuous electric current could be produced by rotating a copper disc between the poles of a permanent magnet, a process called electromagnetic induction. This is the underlying principle behind the dynamo and the transformer. It is important to note that it is the *movement* of an object within a magnetic field which creates electricity – a stationary field or object will not do so.

Put together, these two simple scientific observations prompt the conclusion that moving magnetic fields (such as those generated by the alternating current of power lines) could be capable of inducing subtle changes in the electrical system of the human body.

Simple though this theory seems, it is still very difficult to provide conclusive proof that these subtle electrical changes in the body could lead to cancer. There are many powerful interests (the electricity companies, computer manufacturers, electric goods manufacturers, employers of VDU operators, etc.) who resolutely oppose such a conclusion. Nevertheless, a steadily-growing body of epidemiological research tells a worrying story.

After their first piece of research, Wertheimer and Leeper also analysed adult deaths from cancers in the same geographical area, and – once again – found a clear connection.[382]

Another piece of research looked at the electromagnetic fields generated by electric blankets and heated waterbeds, and found that pregnancies among women who use these appliances were more likely to end in miscarriages than those among women who do not use them.[383]

In 1982, occupational health physician Samuel Milham, from the Washington State Department of Social and Health Services first connected jobs which involved exposure to electromagnetic fields with an increased risk of cancer. "In the course of updating a study of occupational mortality," he wrote in the *New England Journal of Medicine*, "I noticed that among men whose occupation required them to work in electrical and magnetic fields there were more deaths due to leukaemia than would be expected."[384] This sparked a number of pieces of research, all of which were designed to test the possible link between occupational exposure to electromagnetic fields and cancer. By 1986, seventeen surveys had been conducted amongst electrical and electronic workers, and fifteen of them had revealed a link between electromagnetic fields and cancer.[385] Jobs with a particularly elevated risk included telegraph, radio, and radar operators, electricity and telephone linemen, and electrical and electronic engineers.[386]

Then in 1987, yet another damning report was published. Back in 1973, the New York Power Authority had declared its intention to erect a 765-kilovolt power line to import cheap hydroelectricity from Canada. After pressure from environmental groups, New York's Public Service Commission directed that a five-year research study should be conducted on the possible health implications of the power line. This led to the publication of a meticulously-executed landmark study, which – once again – provided good evidence that exposure to low-level magnetic fields increased the risk of developing cancer in children. The study found the cancer risk for children who lived near the power lines to be 1.7 times higher than for those who did not. The risk of getting leukaemia was 2.1 times higher.[387]

Many of these studies were challenged by scientists who disagreed with the research or with the findings. But by 1990, the US Environmental Protection Agency wrote in a Working Review Draft, *Evaluation Of The Potential Carcinogenicity Of Electromagnetic Fields*: "There have been six case-control studies of cancer in children examining residential exposure from power transmission and distribution systems. Two additional studies have examined childhood cancer in relationship to father's occupation. Five of the six residential exposure studies showed positive associations with ELF (extremely low frequency) field exposure; three were statistically significant and the other two had odds ratios greater than one but not statistically significant. Where different cancer sites were evaluated, leukaemia, nervous system cancer and, to a lesser extent, lymphomas were found to be in excess in the five residential studies showing positive associations."[388]

The paper concluded: "In conclusion, the several studies showing leukaemia, lymphoma, and cancer of the nervous system in children exposed to magnetic fields from residential 60Hz electrical power distribution systems, supported by similar findings in adults in several occupational studies also involving electrical power frequency exposures, show a consistent pattern of response that suggests, but does not prove, a causal link. Frequency components higher than 60Hz cannot be ruled out as contributing factors. Evidence from a large number of biological test systems show that these fields induce biological effects that are consistent with several possible mechanisms of carcinogenesis . . . . With our current understanding we can identify 60Hz magnetic fields from power lines and perhaps other sources in the home as a possible, but not proven, cause of cancer in people."

To summarize, the evidence connecting electromagnetic fields and cancer is strong, but not yet conclusive (and it may never be conclusive, until adequate funding is provided to conduct more research). But there *is* enough evidence to alert prudent people to take preventive action now.

What you can do now to reduce your risk

~ Tame your computer. Every time you switch your VDU screen on it emits electromagnetic radiation. Depending on the machine, this ranges from low to high frequency. Write to the manufacturer of your particular model of computer monitor, asking for details of the sort of radiation it gives out (all manufacturers hold this information, but not all will be happy to release it) and what they intend to do to reduce it.

- If you are pregnant, don't work on a VDU. This is even more important in the early months, when the possibility of damage to the baby is at its greatest. One scientific study followed the health of 1,583 pregnant women who attended three obstetrics and gynaecology clinics in northern California in 1981-1982. It found that women who used VDUs for more than twenty hours per week during the first trimester of pregnancy were 1.8 times more likely to suffer a miscarriage compared to other women who did not use a VDU.[389] While the evidence is, as yet, not conclusive, it is enough to justify taking sensible precautions. Your employer is likely to take a sympathetic attitude – in 1987, managers in British government departments were instructed to consider 'sensitively and sympathetically' all such requests.[390]

- Try to sit some distance from your computer screen (about an arm's length is a good guide). If this isn't possible, change the place you are sitting in from time to time, so that the same part of your body isn't always in the 'firing line'.
- Stay away from those sides! It has been found that most radiation is given out at the sides and the back of a machine, with less than one fifth being emitted from the front. So, if you work in an office close to other computer workers, try to position yourself so that you are not in line with these areas of their machines.
- "The construction of some forms of workstation and office desk may considerably enhance the magnitudes of the Very Low Frequency (VLF) and Extremely Low Frequency (ELF) fields produced by VDUs," says Dr. Stuart A. Kingsley, a respected optoelectronics consultant. "If a non-metallic workstation or desk top is supported by a closed horizontal metal frame running around the (inside) perimeter of the surface, it is possible for relatively high levels of magnetic field to be generated, that are in close proximity to the lower part of the torso."[391] This phenomenon could be caused by magnetic induction, which generates eddy currents to circulate in the frame, which in turn create their own localized magnetic fields. So use an entirely non-metallic workstation.
- Various shielding devices are on the market, but many of them do no more than reduce eyestrain from glare. Even those shields which say they reduce radiation may not reduce ELF radiation. Unless you see specific safety data, don't be fooled into thinking they automatically give you protection.
- Colour screens are more likely to have higher emissions than monochrome ones. Do you really need a colour monitor? Many tasks – word processing, for example – don't demand it.
- A few enterprising manufacturers are already producing low-emission screens. At a time when some manufacturers are still trying to discredit the evidence, the more progressive manufacturers should be rewarded for their initiative. So buy one! One such manufacturer is Sigma Designs Inc, which has a range of screens meeting the Swedish government's new regulations, the most stringent in the world so far. For their address, see the Help section.

~ The watchwords for controlling other forms of electromagnetic fields at work or at home are 'duration' and 'distance'. For example, the motor in an electric shaver may create an electromagnetic field while it is working, but any risk is likely to be very small because of the brief duration of use. And although a television set may be switched on for some time, viewing at the recommended distance of 12 feet or so will considerably reduce the effects of any electromagnetic field.

~ An electric blanket, on the other hand, could produce unacceptable electromagnetic fields, if it is used as an all-night over-blanket. Never use an electric blanket while you are in bed. Instead, use it to heat the bed before you get in, and make sure you switch it off before settling in.

~ Although microwave ovens were once a cause of concern because many had a high level of microwave leakage, standards have tightened and there is probably no cause for concern on this score. However, both microwave and conventional electric cookers may both generate significant electromagnetic fields, due to the large currents they consume.[392] Since no scientific work has been conducted in this area at the present time, any risk must be classified as speculative, but if you are concerned, you can reduce your exposure either by using electric cookers less, or by cooking with gas.

~ Finally, if you live in a house located close to power lines, should you move? Dr. Samuel Milham's advice reflects the ambivalent nature of scientific research to date. "I wouldn't say you should sell your house because it's under a power line," he says. "But if you were considering buying a house under a line, I'd tell you to buy a different one."[393]

Chapter 62

When Nightmares Come True – How to Survive a Nuclear Disaster

~

"Nikolai Fomin, the plant's chief engineer, believes that both man and nature are completely safe. The huge reactor is housed in a concrete silo, and it has environmental protection systems. Even if the incredible should happen, the automatic control and safety systems would shut down the reactor in a matter of seconds. The plant has emergency core cooling systems and many other technological safety designs and systems."

from Soviet Life, February 1986, concerning the nuclear power plant at Chernobyl.

Two months later, on 26th April, a fire started in one of the four 1,000-megawatt reactors of the Chernobyl nuclear power complex, eighty miles north of Kiev, capital of the Ukraine. A core meltdown and explosion followed, sending huge quantities of radiation into the atmosphere.

We are regularly told that the risks of an accident at a nuclear power plant are so remote as to be insignificant. Yet it happened at Chernobyl. Before then, it happened at Sellafield in 1957. And it happened again at Three Mile Island in 1979. Where will it be next time?

According to Britain's former Central Electricity Generating Board, the probability of a catastrophic accident in a nuclear power station was one every 10,000 years.[394] On the face of it, this sounds very reassuring. After all, 10,000 years ago, much of the northern hemisphere was still covered with ice, and humans were just starting to discover agriculture. But even simple statistics such as this can be most deceptive, as Ian Stewart, Professor of Mathematics at the University of Warwick points out. "A probability of one every 10,000 years sounds very reassuring, but it is worth taking a closer look. What it means is that for each nuclear reactor, the probability of a catastrophic accident in any given year is one in 10,000; that is, 0.0001 per year. There are roughly 40 nuclear power stations in Britain, so the probability that at least one will have a catastrophic accident in any given year is the sum of the 40 probabilities, which is 0.004. The probability of at least one catastrophic accident in Britain during the next 25 years is 25 times this, or 0.1. That is, the chances are one in 10 . This does not sound as reassuring as 'one every 10,000 years'. But it is just a different way of saying the same thing."[395]

React and survive

Here are some steps for you to consider taking to protect yourself against some of the effects of a nuclear accident:

~ Develop awareness. All governments regularly and routinely lie to their populations about nuclear power. Soviets and Americans, British and French – all of them try to minimize the impact on our health of nuclear radiation. The French, for example, told their citizens in the days after Chernobyl that "by dint of our distance from the Ukraine, we have been completely spared from the fallout of Chernobyl".[396] And the British (who have been lying about emissions from Windscale (Sellafield) since the fire in 1957) also deceived the public. So do not expect to be told the truth about any incident. They may even try to conceal incidents, as the Soviets initially did at Chernobyl.

Ideally, you should buy a radiation monitor (addresses in the Help section) and periodically check for any sudden increase in radioactivity – particularly if you live near a nuclear installation. If you can't do this, at least develop an awareness of the local news so that any mention of a 'radiation problem' at the local nuclear plant will trigger you into action. It is quite possible that a major incident will, initially, be downplayed by the media.

~ After a release of radioactive material has occurred, your first step must be to avoid contamination by any fallout. This is easier said than done. Should you evacuate, or sit tight? In the case of a major disaster, such as a Chernobyl-type meltdown, you should evacuate, no matter what the authorities say. In any case, they may be so disorganized as to be incapable of arranging a mass evacuation, and there is also the possibility that deliberately false information will be broadcast, to prevent mass panic. If you live close to an airport, take your family and leave immediately for a distant destination – if you have relatives abroad, for instance. At all costs, you must avoid moving into an area which is more heavily contaminated than your own. You can always return after a day or two if the danger doesn't materialize.

In the case of a lesser release of radioactive material, it is essential to know just how the radioactive plume is spreading. Wind speed and direction will determine this. Although it's difficult to fight an enemy that moves with the wind, you can try to estimate the approximate direction of the plume on a weather map in your newspaper. If your house lies in the path of the plume, and you're sure it hasn't yet reached you, then consider evacuating to an area which is not downwind of the disaster. Rain will make radioactive material fall to earth much sooner than otherwise, so you should avoid being caught outside when it's raining.

If you are not evacuated, but know the plume is approaching, take any washing in off the line and go indoors, shut all windows and switch off any ventilation. Seal off fireplaces and put away carpets, curtains and clothing which could harbour radioactive dust. For the same reason you should take plenty of baths and showers. Any objects likely to accumulate dust which can't be removed should later be decontaminated by experts. Contaminated sand from children's play pits should also be removed. Avoid pregnancy during high levels of contamination. You should stay indoors for as long as possible, until monitoring bodies say the shorter-lived radionuclides have decayed to safer levels.

~ Food. Avoid eating local produce which may be contaminated. Certain foods – especially milk products, eggs, mushrooms and honey – retain more radioactivity and should be particularly avoided. During this time, a radiation monitor (geiger counter) is essential to check the contamination of food you buy (suppliers' addresses in the Help section).

- Infants are much more sensitive to radioactive contamination through food than adults, so stock up on baby food in sealed containers and use it for them exclusively.
- The basic rule is: everything you used to think of as 'healthy' is now *un*healthy. Fresh food, for example – salads, vegetables, fruit, dairy produce – are all now off-limits if they have been exposed to radioactive material. Tinned or dried food, or food in a refrigerator or freezer, however, should be safe to eat.
- Remember that cooking cannot get rid of contamination.
- Make up for any nutritional deficiencies (e.g. vitamin C) with multi-vitamin pills. If possible, keep a stock of water and bottled drinks handy in case the water supply is contaminated.
- Some foods may actually counteract some of the harmful effects of radiation, and if you can find an uncontaminated source of them, use them

as much as possible. They include apple and sunflower seeds (rich in pectin), miso paste, Kola nuts and Spirulina. Research currently being conducted with children who suffered the tragic effects of Chernobyl may also reveal that other natural foodstuffs can have powerful radio-protective effects (we will return to this subject in the free *Superliving!* update mentioned at the beginning of the book).

~ Potassium iodide tablets can block your body's uptake of lethal radio-iodine, and so counter the effects of radiation on your vital thyroid gland. They should be made available from police stations, hospitals, and pharmacists. Another lethal radioactive by-product is radio-strontium, but Selenium Alginate formula (see the Help section) should prevent its absorption. Because doses vary according to the radioactive material released, and the age of the person concerned, you should ask your doctor about applicable doses of these substances.

We hope you never have occasion to put these suggestions into practice.

Chapter 63
Plain talk about complementary therapies

~

"Should I consider using alternative medicine?" and "Which therapy should I choose?" are the two most common questions people ask themselves about this often confusing area. Here's some straightforward advice.

In today's high-pressure world, the idea of returning to a kinder, gentler type of medicine is increasingly attractive to millions of people. With unnecessary and incompetent conventional medical care killing more than 200,000 people a year in America[397] (there are no reliable estimates for Britain), you can see why so many people are turning to less lethal forms of treatment.

But before you rush off to have yourself perforated by the nearest acupuncturist, pause to consider. Sadly, the first thing to realize is that sick people are fair game the world over for sharks, shysters and scoundrels. Conventional medicine certainly has its share of fraudsters; but so does complementary medicine. It's all too easy to assume that orthodox = bad, complementary = good. But it isn't necessarily true.

The war between orthodox and complementary medicine

Basically, the two sides of the medical conundrum have never really liked each other. The orthodox point of view tends to be that complementary practitioners are playing at being doctors, and in the process could do real damage to their patients. The complementary viewpoint is that orthodox doctors treat their patients as a ragbag collection of symptoms encased within a walking cadaver, whose next stop is the dissection room.

This mutual antipathy means that complementary and orthodox medical practitioners generally leave each other pretty much alone. Occasionally there are encouraging examples of both sides working under one roof within a group practice, but these are, as yet, rare. The underlying reasons for this mutual disregard are complex. Perhaps the adherents of orthodox medicine consider that the scientific examination of complementary therapies might endow them with a spurious respectability; perhaps, too, some complementary practitioners have been unwilling to submit themselves to evaluation by an authority they do not acknowledge.

This odd relationship was temporarily disrupted, when the British Medical Association published its report *Alternative Therapy*.[398] The BMA had been requested to examine 'the other side' by some provocative remarks made by their then President, the Prince of Wales, during his term of office.

"Today's unorthodoxy is probably going to be tomorrow's convention," he told them. Some 'unorthodox' practitioners seemed to take this as royal endorsement of their therapies, and Prince Charles's visage could be seen adorning the covers of complementary health magazines, and other publications, for months afterwards. The complementary health movement clearly thought it had gained a new form of respectability.

Of course, the BMA had to respond to their President's implied request to re-examine the whole area. Therefore, an eminent panel was assembled, and a 164-page report was produced. Not to be outdone in the report-publishing business, the British Holistic Medical Association promptly assembled its own expert panel which proceeded to criticize the BMA's paper.[399] Here are some of the conclusions on various aspects of medicine from both reports – useful and interesting for the medical consumer, because it allows us to compare the strengths and weaknesses of both sides.

Acupuncture

The BMA's report accepted that there *is* a scientific basis for claims that acupuncture is effective as an analgesic (pain-reliever) although it pointed out that since it is an invasive procedure, the practice of acupuncture should conform to the same ethical and technical standards as orthodox medicine.

Some people undergoing acupuncture treatment have certainly experienced adverse effects: infections such as hepatitis have been transmitted by non-sterile needles, for example, and the BMA's report warned that the AIDS virus could be transmitted in such a manner. The BMA's report is, however, rather dismissive of traditional Chinese medicine, and it is obvious that they felt much happier with the concept of acupuncture when set in the context of conventional Western medicine, as practised by conventionally-trained doctors.

The counter-punch from the BHMA pointed out, quite rightly, that the BMA's report did not take regard of some important clinical trial work concerning the effectiveness of acupuncture, and also accused them of being alarmist in their assertion that AIDS could be transmitted by acupuncture.

The most serious criticism of the BMA's report, however, lies in the fact that they did not suggest or propose, as they were required to do under their terms of reference, any detailed study methods by which acupuncture could be assessed.

Herbalism

The BMA's report concluded that despite herbalism's 'pure and harmless' image, some herbal medicines can give rise to adverse reactions. This conclusion is hardly earth-shattering, for many modern pharmacological substances are directly or indirectly derived from herbs, and if modern medicine is capable of producing adverse reactions, there is no reason why their precursors should not also produce adverse effects.

But the BMA was right to point out that 'herbal' does not necessarily mean 'harmless'. Furthermore, not all herbal medicines have been evaluated by clinical trials, and evaluation of their safety, efficacy and quality is difficult.[400] And like other over-the-counter medications, the majority of those using these substances will probably buy them without taking expert advice. For example, here is a selection of reported adverse effects for some common herbal substances:

~ Senecio, Crotalaria and Heliotropium Species

Many of these species are reported to contain pyrrolizidine alkaloids, which have been associated with liver disorder.[401] Some common names for these species are: Senecio (Groundsel, Ragwort, Fireweed), Crotalaria (Sunn Hemp, Jubbulpore Hemp), Heliotropium (Heliotrope).

~ Comfrey

This herb has been incorrectly reported as containing useful amounts of vitamin B_{12}. It does not,[402] but it does contain pyrrolizidine alkaloids, and is thought to be capable of causing liver cancer.[403]

~ Coltsfoot

This herb also contains pyrrolizidine alkaloids.[404]

~ Sassafras, Nutmeg, Anise, Mace, Cinnamon

Sassafras contains safrole (as do the other spices mentioned above, but in smaller amounts), which is also believed to be toxic to the liver and capable of causing liver cancer. It may also act to prolong the action of other drugs.[405]

~ Mistletoe

There are many species of mistletoe which vary in their constituents. The berries contain alkaloids, viscotoxins and lectins which are toxic and have caused gastroenteritis.

~ Ginseng

Ginseng has been associated with high blood pressure, swollen and tender breasts, vaginal bleeding, excitation and arousal, nervousness, insomnia and tension.[406] It also contains oestrogen-like substances which may precipitate the development of male breasts.

~ Liquorice

Liquorice contains substances which can be useful in healing peptic ulcers.[407] It may also produce sodium retention, high blood pressure, and loss of potassium in the body.

~ Aristolochia Species

These species (Birthwort, Snakeroot) contain aristolochic acid which may be carcinogenic.[408]

~ Pennyroyal, Devil's Claw and Broom

The oil of Pennyroyal contains pulegone which can cause severe liver toxicity and is an abortifacient (a substance which causes abortion).[409] Devil's Claw and Broom also contain abortifacients.

~ Apricot, Bitter Almond, Cherry, Pear, Peach, and Plum Seeds

All these seeds contain cyanogenic glycosides which may produce cyanide poisoning. Amygdalin (Vitamin B_{17}, Laetrile) is a cyanogenic glycoside extracted from apricot, peach and plum kernels and has been sold as a 'miracle cure' for cancer in the United States. It is ineffective and has caused cases of cyanide poisoning.[410]

After perusing the above list, you'd have to be a hero to risk even a herbal tea again! A compromise conclusion was offered in the *Drugs and Therapeutics Bulletin* when the editor wrote: "Most (herbal) remedies appear to do no harm and they may help some people but some occasionally cause adverse effects. They may interact with conventional medicines taken concurrently and can carry hazards for pregnant women who should anyway avoid medicines as far as possible. The efficacy of herbal medicines is difficult to verify. Patients ought not to abandon conventional treatment without their doctor's knowledge and should say if they are taking a herbal medicine. Doctors need to ask about such remedies."[411]

Homoeopathy

The practice of homoeopathy is one of the more 'respectable' complementary therapies – its adherents include conventionally-trained medical practitioners, it has its own hospitals, and its patrons include royalty. Despite this 'established' image, it is still very difficult for orthodox medicine to endorse the principles upon which homoeopathy is believed to be based. "What then," asks the BMA's report, "is the explanation for the survival of the practice of homoeopathy essentially in the form developed by its founder, by which alkali or metallic salts, the metals themselves or their oxides, or the more toxic of the then used simples are prescribed, usually in dilutions so great, and in doses so minute as to have no pharmacological action, and sometimes in dilutions that are unlikely to contain a single surviving molecule of the original substance?"

So how does orthodox medicine account for the effectiveness of homoeopathy? The BMA's report concluded that "there is no rational basis for the potency theory which is claimed to explain the mode of action of homoeopathic remedies". It went on to postulate that the placebo effect (always a worthy stand-by in tight corners) may be the underlying mechanism, and gave homoeopathic practitioners a pat on the head for, at the very least, withholding unnecessary medication "in accurately diagnosed conditions that ordinarily resolve without treatment".

These dismissive and patronizing comments are most unsatisfactory. The BMA's report seemed to be arguing:

1. There is no rational medical basis for the way homoeopathic medicines are supposed to work.
2. If they *do* work, it's probably due to the placebo effect.
3. If it's *not* due to the placebo effect, the illness would probably have cleared up in any case by itself.

But one investigation into the effect of homoeopathic medicine examined this placebo effect using randomized, double-blind trial methods. A total of 144 patients with hay fever were selected, and some given a homoeopathic remedy, while others were given a placebo (i.e. an inert, therapeutically valueless substance). Those taking homoeopathic treatment showed a significant reduction in symptoms – although, interestingly, their symptoms initially seemed to get worse, which was quickly followed by an improvement (this is just what homoeopaths say happens – they call it a 'healing crisis'). This study concluded that: "No evidence emerged to support the idea that placebo action fully explains the clinical responses to homoeopathic drugs."[412]

And what about the veterinary surgeons who are successfully using homoeopathic medicines on animals? Does the BMA really suppose that animals, too, are victims of the infamous placebo effect? One vet, John Nicol, who has a practice in Surrey, finds acupuncture particularly useful for alleviating chronic pain in animals. The treatment has, he says, sometimes saved animals who would otherwise have had to be destroyed.[413]

Conclusion

Orthodox medicine's attitude, as expounded in the BMA's report, towards complementary therapies is at times very patronizing in its tone, and fails to adopt an open-minded approach to unorthodox procedures. Some of its disparaging comments do seem to be quite gratuitous – for example, there's a curious little section about the growth of 'religious cults' in the report, which is strangely out of place in such a document.

The BHMA's report provides a generally good critique of the BMA's paper; it would, however, have been more valuable if it had included references to more hard, scientific fact.

So there, in a nutshell, the two sides rest uneasily. Both factions have their own strengths and weaknesses. The problem for us, the patients, is – how to choose?

Deciding between them

Here is some simple advice to help you choose:

~ HAS YOUR ILLNESS BEEN DIAGNOSED PROPERLY?

Orthodox medicine is, on the whole, better than complementary therapies at diagnosing straightforward medical conditions. This applies particularly to infectious illnesses. However a diagnosis does not always mean the same as a 'cause'. For example, pain during urination may be diagnosed by your GP as a prostate condition. But this does not really tell you what the cause is, nor does it dictate one universal treatment for all. However, an accurate diagnosis by an orthodox medical practitioner is always a good starting point for any complaint.

~ IS YOUR ILLNESS MINOR?

Many illnesses are self-limiting (they'll clear up by themselves if left alone). In these cases, it is probably best not to accept conventional drug therapy, but to either wait for the problem to go away by itself, or to find a complementary therapist who may help the healing process, and prevent the problem happening again. For example, a back ache caused by bad posture will usually attract a prescription for a painkiller from your GP. This is not useful to you in the long run, because it does nothing about the cause of the problem – it'll keep on recurring until your posture is corrected. In this case, an acupuncturist may help you deal with the immediate pain, and Alexander technique can help you to prevent the problem from happening again (see chapter 65).

~ IS YOUR PROBLEM AN EMERGENCY?

If it is, you won't have much choice. The skill of a surgeon in setting a bone, for example, is unparalleled. The victim of a heart attack must be treated immediately. In cases such as these, complementary medicine has, as yet, little role. 'Natural first aid' is indeed available, but at the moment only a very few therapists have the knowledge to put it into action. So let conventional medicine help you through the emergency, and use complementary medicine from then onwards, to facilitate healing.

~ IS YOUR ILLNESS MAJOR?

If so, then this is the time for you to ask some hard questions. Above all, you must inform yourself of *all* the options available to you, so both you and your doctor have the widest possible choice available. Your first move should be to find an orthodox doctor who has, at the very least, an open mind towards complementary therapies. You don't want advice based on dogma, you need accurate and fair-minded help! You need a doctor who is capable of admitting that orthodox medicine has its limits, and beyond that you're in unexplored territory. In short, you need a doctor who will be a guide and helper.

Change your doctor if necessary to find such a person. Make it clear to them right from the beginning that you want to assume responsibility for your treatment, that you may at times disagree with their suggestions, but that you need them to be your advisor and pilot. Good doctors will find this challenging and will be prepared to involve themselves wholeheartedly in your task. At every stage of your treatment, you'll need their advice on your options, and the risks involved.

Then you need to summarize your options. Your doctor should let you know about the therapies orthodox medicine can offer. You'll have to find out about complementary therapies for yourself (see below). At each stage, you must carefully consider:

- What are the possible risks of each course of treatment?
- What are the possible advantages of each course of treatment?
- Where's the proof? (See it with your own eyes!)
- How can you hedge your bets? (Aim for the best of both worlds.)

The last point is particularly important. 'Complementary' means 'something that makes up a deficiency in another thing'. In this case, that 'other thing' is conventional health care. Use both judiciously, and you can win.

How to choose your complementary therapy

There are so many – as you'll see from the following pages – that the choice may seem baffling at first. However, it's not really so difficult:

~ DO IT BEFORE YOU NEED IT

A major difference between complementary and orthodox medicine is that with the orthodox version, you only see a doctor when you're ill. Not so with complementary medicine – the aim should be for regular consultations right from the start, with the specific aim of preventing you from falling prey to disease or illness. If you preserve the health of your mind and body, you won't get ill. So don't just wait until you have an acute problem – familiarize yourself with the therapies now, and reap the reward of continued good health.

~ GO BY WORD OF MOUTH

When you need a therapist, the right person will often materialize. This may sound hard to accept, but it happens. Ask your friends, colleagues, family for personal recommendations. Use your instinct, too. If you are stumped, consult one of the directories produced by the complementary medical organizations (see the Help section).

~ YOU ARE *NOT* GUILTY!

Many forms of complementary medicine have a streak of right-wing libertarianism in them. Whether or not it accords with your own personal political beliefs is not the issue. The point is, it must not be allowed to interfere with the healing process.

Orthodox medicine initially seems to take responsibility for your illness away from you, and in return you agree to follow the prescribed advice. Traditionally, we take our sick bodies to the doctor, he or she tells us what to do, and we unquestioningly do it. And people have mainly been happy to 'give away' control of their bodies to the medical profession, in return for the promise of a cure. But this 'social contract' only works when a cure is possible. If a mistake is made, or if the cure simply doesn't work, orthodox medicine all too speedily turns its back on its 'failures'. As one cancer specialist said to his patient: "Sixty per cent of my patients get better, 40 per cent don't. You're in the 40 per cent. Goodbye."[414]

Complementary therapy is quite different in its attitude. It generally holds that disease (literally dis-ease) is your own responsibility – some would say fault – anyway. If the cure doesn't work, the blame is essentially yours.

This attitude must be resisted. You are not guilty of anything beyond being ill. It is your doctor's job (complementary or orthodox) to help you get better. If you make the relationship clear to them from the outset, you won't get into this futile and distracting game.

~ SELECT A THERAPY TO COMPLEMENT THE PROBLEM

To some extent, all complementary therapies are interconnected. Bad posture, for example, may have other consequences than simply a back ache – it can affect your view of the world, your self-image, and possibly make you prone to other health problems. So start with the therapy which seems most likely to match the symptom, and work onwards from there. An openness of mind and a willingness to continue your journey into unexpected places is the best attitude you can have – together with an unshakeable desire to be well again.

CHAPTER 64
WHAT TO EXPECT FROM ACUPUNCTURE

~

If you think that prevention is better than cure and the reinforcement of the body's natural defences preferable to modern medical intervention, acupuncture could well become the technique you favour most.

You may shudder at the idea of needles being inserted into you, but acupuncture is actually much less painful than a standard injection. As the oldest form of medicine known to man, some mystery obviously surrounds its practice, but this shouldn't cause suspicion. Aldous Huxley very simply exposed the prejudice tied up with so many present-day criticisms of acupuncture when he said: "That a needle stuck into one's foot should improve the functioning of one's liver is obviously incredible. It can't be believed because, in terms of currently accepted physiological theory 'it makes no sense'. Within our system of explanation there is no reason why the needle-prick should be followed by an improvement of liver function. Therefore, we say it can't happen. The only trouble with this argument is that, as a matter of empirical fact, it does happen."

The force of chi

Acupuncture originated in China over 4,000 years ago when it was realized that soldiers wounded by arrows would recover from long-standing illnesses. Today, it is sterilized needles, not arrows, that are used. During treatment, the needles are inserted into your body (usually just a few millimetres) at specific sites chosen by the acupuncturist to stimulate the body's 'meridians' – channels which transmit your vital life energy known as 'chi'. When the flow of chi is blocked or in imbalance, illness results.

The primary principle in acupuncture is that of yin and yang, essentially the principle of the harmony of opposites. When our body's yin and yang elements are balanced, we are in a state of health and well-being, and it is impossible to experience ill-health.

The cycle of the five elements is the second major principle the Chinese use to assess body energy. The body's meridians all have a quality relating to one of the five elements: earth, metal, fire, wood or water. Here are the main meridians with their associated qualities:

Lung	metal	yin
Large intestine	metal	yang
Stomach	earth	yang
Spleen	earth	yin
Heart	fire	yin
Small intestine	fire	yang

Bladder	water	yang
Kidney	water	yin
Pericardium	fire	yin
Triple warmer	fire	yang
Gall bladder	wood	yang
Liver	wood	yin

A treatment for body and mind

Acupuncture works as a complete medical structure, and can therefore be of help in a wide range of cases, including addictions. It is thought that acupuncture can relieve emotional stress where traditional methods of counselling have failed. An individual may go with a physical problem and find the psychological one is also eased. Chinese medicine does not distinguish between physical and mental states. They are both an expression of chi, and the body's meridians are the focus of both mind and body. This approach lies at the heart of the harmonising aim of acupuncture.

"Since the beginning of Chinese medicine," says French acupuncturist Dr. Yves Requena, "Chinese physicians have approached physiology and psychological phenomena with the view that the two are not fundamentally different. The meridians are the junction of mind and body. They influence each other. The meridian is the hyphen in psycho-somatic."[415]

If you can afford it, acupuncture is an ideal preventive treatment. A visit every six weeks would be enough to maintain your body's energy flow and identify any possible future difficulties.

What happens

The practitioner will first talk to you and ask questions about any health problems. Diagnosis involves formulating a detailed family and medical history, along with a general picture of your lifestyle. An acupuncturist will try to establish which, if any, of your body's elements are out of balance and so may ask questions about responses to particular seasons and foods. He will listen to your voice and if, for example, he notices you are shouting, it may suggest there is a wood imbalance. The body's deep pulses, each relating to an organ system are taken several times during an examination. There are six on each wrist which can be read to establish the body's general state. The initial consultation may last about an hour.

You may take some of your clothes off (and may be asked to remove rings and jewellery too), and lie on the practitioner's table. Acupuncture needles are thin and flexible, and made of stainless steel. To prevent infection, new sterilized, disposable needles are used for each treatment.

Before insertion takes place, an acupuncturist cleans the area for treatment, massaging and slightly stretching the skin. The needles can vary in length, but are usually about five centimetres long: the shaft and the handle each measure about 25 millimetres, but only a small part is actually inserted. There'll be a prick as they are quickly inserted into the appropriate meridians, but the pain is not great and you may find the whole idea of being a human pincushion so bizarre that you break out laughing! Either that, or tears, because acupuncture is well-known for its swift ability to release the deepest of human emotions once the energies start to flow. So you may well find yourself sobbing your heart out, for no reason you can fathom! Don't worry. Either tears or the giggles are an excellent sign that energy is moving.

Variations in technique

The inserted needle will either be used to focus energy on a particular meridian, or to draw it away. They may be rotated, vibrated or manipulated for extra effect. You'll be told to concentrate on your breathing, and you'll stay like that, 'cooking', for half an hour or so. You may notice funny things starting to happen – your fingers or toes may twitch, a sudden deep ache may start. Just lie back, and observe. It'll be over soon!

Moxibustion is a slight variation of this method, in which a ball of the dried herb mugwort is placed on the handle of the inserted needle and set alight. The heat is thought to aid the stimulation process, although some practitioners see the herb as insignificant. Sometimes the needle will be inserted so that it touches the bone covering, or in such a way that it runs parallel to the skin's surface. This method is known as periostean acupuncture. For additional stimulation, a thread of knotted material may be put through the skin and pulled, or a salt solution injected into the area. Normally needles are inserted in any part of the body, but some practitioners may just use specific areas, so that, for example, a practitioner of reflexology might confine his treatment to the feet.

How to try it out

An acupuncturist will normally need to carry out a number of sessions before he or she can judge the amount needed to complete the treatment. The first consultation may cause only a slight response, but after about six, weekly treatments you should experience improvement. Then the sessions can be less and less frequent, perhaps having a top up every couple of months. This means that the whole process can take up to a year. Some NHS doctors and GPs have recently started to practise acupuncture, but a conventional doctor may not be the best person to understand all the great subtleties of this most ancient form of medicine.

It is best not to engage in sex or exercise, or have excessive amounts of food or alcohol either an hour before or after a session. If you experience any swelling, inflammation or tenderness, you should return to your acupuncturist as it could conceivably indicate an infection. There is also a slight chance of injury, either internally or to the nerves.

Three principal organizations are now trying to establish a common standard of acupuncture education and practice in the United Kingdom. They have jointly issued a code of ethics and produced a national register of acupuncturists which includes the names of qualified practitioners from all three societies. This can be obtained from any one of them; the addresses are in the Help section.

In 220 BC, a proclamation was made by the Emperor Houang-Ti, the Yellow Emperor. "I am disturbed by the amounts in taxes and dues that do not reach me on account of illness amongst the people. My wish is that we should no longer use medicine which poisons them, or ancient methods. I want those mysterious metal needles which direct energy, to be used instead." We may be around 2,000 years behind, but it looks as though we in the West may at last be catching up!

Chapter 65

What to expect from the Alexander Technique

~

Frederick Mathias Alexander (1869-1955) was an actor who one day found he could no longer perform after apparently inexplicably losing his voice. Conventional medicine, with its throat sprays, pills and potions, completely failed him. He was, therefore, faced with the task of healing himself – or not healing at all.

Over a period of ten years, he discovered that every movement he made was accompanied by a slight backward and downward jerk of his head, along with a raising of his chest and a hollowing of his back. Alexander recognized the knock-on effect this action brought about in his body and consciously went about trying to change the way he held himself. Eventually, by discovering the body's correct, natural posture, he healed himself, and formulated the Alexander Technique.

Alexander maintained that we learn to use our body wrongly through bad habits and lack of thought. He believed that we need to re-educate ourselves and consciously consider the way we act in all things. It is almost as if we are in charge of a machine for which no one has ever given us the instructions. What has happened is that we simply copy the people around us, establishing more and more unhelpful patterns of use as the years go by. The Alexander Technique aims to re-educate us about our bodies, and the way we use them.

It is important to realize that this method is not a matter of practising for five minutes each day. Rather, it is something to integrate into your lifestyle down to the smallest detail – so that it becomes the way you lift your coffee cup or sit on a chair.

The Alexander Technique can make an individual stronger and more at ease; and because bad posture often slows down circulation and impairs organ functioning, it has all sorts of implications for improved general health. People also frequently report a drastic change in their mental outlook, experiencing a wonderful sense of well-being. This can perhaps be attributed to the sense of emotional control that seems to accompany physical control, as well as to the release of tension that improved stature brings. A range of illnesses, including rheumatism, arthritis, respiratory problems, heart disorders and sexual problems are all thought to benefit from the technique. Performers worldwide have also experienced startling improvements in their working lives.

"It gives us all the things we have been looking for in a system of physical education; relief from strain due to maladjustment, and consequent improvement in physical and mental health . . . and, along with this, a general heightening of consciousness on all levels," wrote Aldous Huxley who recovered from a serious illness and chronic depression after discovering the Alexander Technique.

Test yourself

Notice how you use your body in daily life. When the 'phone rings, the chances are your whole body contracts and you jerk your head slightly backwards. To pick up the receiver, you probably use much more effort than is necessary. We repeat these ungraceful movements (compare them to the way animals move), in a zombie-like state, scarcely even aware that we are even moving! So first, start to become aware of how you really move. You can begin by carrying out these simple tests on yourself.

~ Sit in a chair and look around you, only moving your head from side to side. Then tilt it backwards to look at the ceiling, and then forwards to the floor. What can you feel? Is there tension in your neck? Does your body move as well? What is your breathing like?

~ Next, when you move your head upwards, make your body follow and see what difference it makes.

~ To discover whether you are holding tension in your jaw (a common problem), put your fingertips under your lips and your thumbs under your jaw. Relaxing all the jaw muscles, try to open and close it. If you find it difficult, you probably are storing tension.

What happens

You need to learn the Alexander Technique on a personal basis from a teacher (see the Help section for details on finding one) – it can't be learnt from a book. An Alexander teacher will give verbal instruction in body use, as well as using his or her hands to indicate any physical misuse. S/he will try to give you a better understanding of how you function so you can consciously attempt to make relevant changes. You will normally see an instructor on a one-to-one basis in a session which will last for between thirty and forty minutes. It is not necessary to remove any clothing, but do wear clothes that don't inhibit movement.

You will carry out activities such as walking, sitting and raising your arms, while the instructor 're-coordinates' you. S/he will point out any areas of tension so you can try to release them, as well as indicating when you are using unnecessary effort to carry out an action.

To benefit fully from classes, a course of around twenty or thirty sessions is recommended, although some results can be achieved from just a few. To begin with, two or three lessons a week is the ideal frequency. As you progress, they can be reduced to just one a week. Most people begin with a few lessons to find out how the technique and their particular teacher suits them. It is often possible to attend an introductory meeting or talk before committing yourself.

Try these exercises

~ Forward and back

Sitting down, move your head upwards and away from your body, with your torso following and your hips bending so that you lean forward. Practise doing this as often as you can – for example, when watching television.

~ Arms

Sitting, with arms by your sides, raise your arms over your head and then back down, first slowly and then quicker and quicker, noticing all the time how you move your head and body. With hands on the tops of your thighs, move your head up and away from your body, with your torso following. At the same time, move your hands down your thighs until they are straight and then raise them above your head. Bring them back down to your knees, to rest again at the tops of your thighs. Throughout, your arms should be lengthened and the rest of your body still. Normally, every time we move, we contract and tense our muscles. In using this movement in day-to-day actions, we can try to eliminate such tensing.

~ Walking

Walk up and down a room, trying to pinpoint any sources of tension and patterns of movement. Then, in a standing position, move your head forwards and upwards, putting your weight on your left foot. With your right knee bent, walk forward, your right leg first. Try to think of yourself as moving as a complete entity, and not as disjointed segments.

~ Legs

Stand with one hand on a table reaching your waist. Raise your right leg, with knee bent and try to balance, using the table for support if you need to, and noticing any tension or unnecessary movement. Then, move your head upwards, with your body following, and look around. Lift your right leg up, with the knee bent and try not to put all the weight into the left leg. Try carrying out this movement when walking up and down stairs.

~ FEET

Sitting down, with your feet apart, gently lift first one heel and then the other off the floor, noticing any unsmoothness. Move your head up and out and imagine you are lengthening your leg as you lift each heel up. When you lower it, continue to elongate your leg so that it is holding no tension.

~ KNEES

With your knees the same distance apart as your shoulders, stand with your feet parallel. Bend your knees until you can no longer see your feet, keeping your body upright; then straighten up again. Continue until you can establish possible areas for improvement. Then, apply the movement: push your head up with body following. Let go of the tension in your knees, legs and hip joints.

~ STANDING AND SITTING

Try standing up and sitting down. Take note of all the movements your body makes, and how they feel. Sit in a chair and then slowly stand up, turning your head and moving it upwards and forwards, so that you come diagonally off the chair. Repeat this several times, trying not to push yourself up.

When you sit down, it is important to continue with the upwards and outwards movement of the head, even though you are moving your body downwards. Don't allow yourself to just fall into the chair – control it.

~ RESTING

Lie down with your feet on the floor and knees bent. Your head should be resting on several paperback books, so that it is parallel to the floor. It is important that you feel comfortable. Lie with your eyes closed and breathe deeply, trying to relax your neck and noticing any sensations, tingling, tension or unusual temperature in your body. Try to do this for a few minutes each day.

Without the books beneath your head, try to expand your whole body. Experiment with rotating your head, making sure you are not holding tension in your body. Lift your arms, elongating them, so that each part in turn follows the initial movement of the hand and do the same with the legs.

The Alexander Technique can, and indeed should, be practised anywhere. It is not an isolated method, but a new way of moving. However, it will not be easy at first. If you always sit with your legs crossed, you will find it very difficult to sit with them uncrossed; it may feel uncomfortable, even unnatural. As a new approach, it will take some getting used to. But the rewards are ample compensation for your efforts!

Chapter 66
What to expect from aromatherapy

~

Your sense of smell is 10,000 times more sensitive than your sense of taste! Your body reacts twice as fast to smell as to pain! The incredible influence which this sense exerts over our mental and physical state is only now beginning to be realized.

This goes some way to explaining the power of aromatherapy, an ancient treatment using oils extracted from aromatic plants to heal and uplift. The wonderful thing about this therapy is that you can make up preparations to give you a personalized aroma, and heal yourself at the same time!

Aromatherapy has a remarkable history. Eucalyptus and lavender oil have been used for skin disorders and embalming for over 4,000 years in China and Egypt. In Britain during the plague, people carried nosegays as a defence against the disease. More recently, a French chemist during the World War I found that lavender oil could be used as a successful burn treatment. His research found that essential oils could penetrate the skin and actually reach the body's organs. In Japan, an aroma-releasing system has been introduced in offices in order to reduce tension and increase productivity.

Although it may be some time before we can experience lavender-scented offices in this country, it does look as though Britain is catching up. Aromatherapy is now practised in certain NHS hospitals as a massage aid. It is proving especially helpful in geriatric wards where each patient is given their own personal blend to keep by the bedside, and either inhale or use in the bath. The International Federation of Aromatherapists is encouraging such initiatives with the launch of its Aromatherapy-In-Care scheme.

Participating practitioners are offering their services on a voluntary basis to hospitals and medical centres within the NHS. The scheme is working particularly well with seriously ill and mentally handicapped patients, partly because of the unique relationship it encourages between individual and healer. The treatment also seems to have some effect with cancer patients, possibly due to stimulation of certain subtances the body needs to combat cancerous cells.

The applications are in fact endless. Labour pains can be reduced by massaging important muscles with lavender oil to relax them and then, during more advanced stages of labour, peppermint can be applied for stimulation. It has been found that women given such treatment need less anaesthetics as these oils have a painkilling effect. Aromatherapy oils have also been shown to have important anti-microbial activity, which (unlike conventional antibiotics) does not lead to the development of resistance in bacteria. Circulation can be increased, promoting the flow of oxygen and nutrients in the body, as well as encouraging the disposal of waste.

As natural balancers, essential oils can fight depression, improve concentration, increase energy. Latest research suggests that our bodies consist of electromagnetic fields which become disturbed through illness. Aromatherapists have always maintained that natural oils can affect these electrical patterns in the body.

How they work

Essential oils have a multiplicity of action because they are such complex substances. Just one oil may include hundreds of different compounds. It is almost impossible to isolate their characteristics as they work together as a composite whole. Similarly, in the body, when a particular smell enters the nostril the effect it has is multiform. The aroma will cause brain reaction, activate the limbic system (the centre for emotion and memory), the hypothalamus, the pituitary glands and the body's hormones. The implications are so wide-reaching that body temperature, appetite, sexual response and the subconscious can all be affected.

The oils used in aromatherapy may derive from the flowers, leaves, stems, roots or bark of a plant. They may come from the tiniest flower or the highest tree. They are harvested from all over the world: the island of Zanzibar produces clove, America peppermint and the Balkan mountains in Bulgaria the Damascus rose. The oil moves around the plant on both a daily and a seasonal basis, so that harvesting is often a complicated process. The jasmine flower only blooms for one day, taking eight million to make one kilogram of 'absolute' form. This is the main reason for the high prices of certain rare oils.

Using essential oils

Oils bought in concentrated form are very powerful and so always need to be diluted – either with water or a base oil. You or your aromatherapist can make up a blend unique to your individual needs. A trained aromatherapist can be seen as a sort of personal scientist, designing formulae for each patient which may change with each visit. S/he will take account of your personal smell preferences and your own body chemistry. S/he may even use hair colour, body shape and skin colour to decide on the combination which will best treat your condition. Chemical copies of these oils are sometimes used commercially in cosmetics and perfumes. Don't be fooled! Such products are much cheaper to produce, but do not contain any of the therapeutic qualities found in the natural form and prove useless for aromatherapy.

The method of application varies, but the oils are thought to enter the bloodstream more quickly by inhalation. Your aromatherapist may recommend a particular use, or simply suggest you follow the method which best suits you. If using a ready-made aromatherapist's blend, the necessary quantities will be explained to you. If, however, you are using an isolated essential oil, or blend of several essential oils, the amounts to use are as follows:

~ MASSAGE. Mix a couple of drops of essential oil into a vegetable base oil (about as much as will fill the palm of a cupped hand). The maximum is one drop of essential oil to 1 ml of base oil.

~ BATHS. Add five to ten drops of essential oil to a pre-run bath and swish in the water. Close all windows and doors.

~ SHOWERS. Wash as normal, then put a maximum of four drops of oil onto a wet flannel. Rub yourself as you stand under the shower, breathing deeply.

~ INHALATIONS. Add between two to three drops of oil to a bowl of steaming water. Put your head about ten inches away and cover with a towel. Breathe deeply with your eyes closed for one minute.

~ TISSUE. Put one drop on a handkerchief or tissue and simply inhale when required.

~ ROOM. Put one or two drops on a table lamp bulb, making sure the light is turned off and the oil doesn't run into the electrical fitting. The light can be turned on at any time, up to one week later, and the room will be filled with the smell of the oil. Or – place a couple of drops on a dry piece of cotton wool and put on a warm radiator. Or – put between one and nine drops into a bowl of boiling water. Close all the windows and doors and place the bowl anywhere in the room.

Do not take oils internally or use on a baby under 18 months. If you are pregnant or breastfeeding do not use the following: basil, cedarwood, clary sage, juniper, hyssop, marjoram, myrrh, pennyroyal, rosemary or sage.

Some essential oils for you to try

~ ANISEED. Used to help digestion, ease cramps and coughs. It has a fresh, slightly sweet smell.

~ BASIL. A sweet and spicy oil, perfect for trouble with insomnia.

~ BENZOIN. It is very warming with antiseptic properties, and therefore is useful for urinary infections and skin disorders.

~ CEDARWOOD. Try this for problems with oily skin and hair or dandruff.

~ CHAMOMILE. Very soothing, with an anti-inflammatory effect, useful in a wide range of conditions.

~ CLARY SAGE. This oilhas a strong spicy smell. It has a reputation for strengthening the nervous system. It has also been used to accelerate the contractions of childbirth.

~ GERANIUM. A sweet, fresh, cooling oil, useful for anxiety and depression.

~ GINGER. This oil improves circulation and can help to prevent colds and flu.

~ JASMINE. For an uplifting and stimulating effect.

~ LAVENDER. This oil has healing properties which make it perfect for burns, wounds and bites, or for nervous debility.

~ LEMON VERBENA. Use if mentally or physically exhausted or lethargic to lift your spirits.

~ MELISSA. Also known as lemon balm. Use for headaches, tension and general fatigue. Said to promote longivity.

~ PATCHOULI. Originally used as an aphrodisiac, patchouli is used to treat skin and scalp problems, and to stimulate the nervous system.

~ ROSEMARY. This oil stimulates the memory and all cerebral functions.

~ SAGE. Massage this oil into aching muscles or the temples of the over-worked.

~ TEA TREE. A 'new' oil with germicidal properties used for skin infections and viruses.

~ YLANG-YLANG. This oil has a beautiful aroma and a sedating effect.

When buying essential oils, it is best to choose the more expensive brands. It is not possible to produce these oils cheaply and the lower priced ones may cause irritations. Make sure you are buying 'pure essential oil'. You can tell if it has been diluted by putting a few drops on a piece of blotting paper. If it completely dissolves into the paper, it is the real thing. If, however, it leaves an oily mark, it is not the pure form. For all formulae use a clean, dry, dark bottle and store in a cool, dark place. You can obtain oils from health food shops or by mail order from the companies listed in the Help section.

Chapter 67

What to expect from Ayurvedic medicine

~

Ayurvedic medicine originated in India over 4,000 years ago. It regards illness as the result of an internal imbalance between three forces of nature that dominate your body and mind – vata, pitta and kapha.

If you'd like a more natural response to pain and ill health than the search and destroy mentality of modern, drug-dependent, conventional medicine, then perhaps you should look at Ayurveda.

Are you vata?

If you are high in vata, you are either very tall or very short. You probably have dark hair, dark eyes and like to stay very active. Vatas are creative, but are forever changing their minds. They eat frequently, but don't gain any weight. If you have a vata imbalance, you may suffer from arthritis, cracking joints or a nervous disorder.

Are you pitta?

Pitta types are of medium build, and gain or lose weight easily. They have light hair and eyes and like a cool, well-ventilated environment. They eat regularly and hate missing meals. Pitta types enjoy planning and are good leaders. They are opinionated and don't cope particularly well with stress. Pittas tend to get illnesses that make them hot – fevers, inflammations and rashes.

Are you kapha?

Kaphas are the biggest physically. They have large eyes and thick wavy hair. They are steady workers and are good at keeping organizations running smoothly. Kaphas love sleeping and hate exercise. If you have a kapha imbalance, you are prone to depression and nausea.

Ayurvedic medicine is a complete and sophisticated discipline, whose successes are now being slowly scientifically validated by Western doctors. "The Ayurvedic approach is more fundamental and radical than allopathic medicine," say Dr. Vasant Lad, director of the Ayurvedic Institute and Wellness Center in Albuquerque, New Mexico. "For example, Ayurveda never labels a disease as Chronic Fatigue Syndrome. We say it falls under the excess-pitta category. The treatment takes two to three months, then the patient shows marvellous results."[416]

To achieve good health, Ayurveda attempts to identify and correct imbalances of vata, pitta and kapha through a mixed approach which will often involve Ayurvedic medicines, meditation, herbs and, of course, diet.

But what is the right diet? Well, that depends on what type of imbalance you have: Ayurvedic medicine believes everyone has their own, unique, constitution and to achieve perfect health you need the kind of specially customized diet that an Ayurvedic doctor can draw up for you.

The consultation

An Ayurvedic consultation is private and will therefore cost for your first and for any subsequent treatments. If herbs are prescribed as part of your diet, these will involve a further cost. To find the name of a local practitioner, see the Help section.

When you visit an Ayurvedic practitioner, the first thing he or she will do is take your pulse. This will give the doctor an initial insight into your constitution. This will be followed by a more lengthy check-up – to fine-tune the diagnosis – which can take up to an hour. Then the doctor will be able to advise you on which foods to eat and which to avoid.

~ IF YOU'RE VATA. Because vata types are affected by the cold, they should eat plenty of warm, moist foods – soups, stews, cooked vegetables. Frozen foods and cold drinks should be avoided.

~ IF YOU'RE PITTA. On the other hand, as a pitta, you'll need foods that balance your erratic moods. Eat lots of fresh fruits, plenty of cool dairy products and dark, leafy vegetables. Avoid hot, spicy foods that can inflame your easily heated passions.

~ IF YOU'RE KAPHA. In this case, you should avoid wheat and dairy products. Concentrate instead on increasing your consumption of raw vegetables and light proteins like fresh beans.

Not many people fit cleanly into any one of these groups. You may fall between two – vata and pitta for example – and in these cases your dietary needs will be more complicated. What you need to eat for perfect health will vary according to the time of year. An Ayurvedic doctor will tailor your diet for each season.

If you are a vata-pitta, then you will be prescribed a vata diet for autumn and winter, and a pitta diet for spring and summer – logical if you think about it – because your vata half will need warming up when it's cold and your pitta half cooling down when it's hot.

Herbs

Herbs are used in Ayurvedic medicine to fine-tune the diet. The use of herbs is based on the same principle of balancing vata, pitta and kapha, but a further classification is used, that of taste.

- Sweet herbs reduce vata and pitta and also have a moistening effect. Liquorice would be used to cure a dry, hacking cough. Cardamom might be prescribed to cure constipation.
- Sour foods – vinegar, lemon and so on – reduce vata and are used to stimulate the appetite.
- Salty tastes are beneficial for vata and help maintain your mineral balance.
- Pungent spices, like peppercorns, garlic and chilies, stimulate the mind and are used to treat colds and 'flu.
- Bitter-tasting herbs are cool and good for treating fever and infection. Bitter herbs, such as hops or skullcap, reduce pitta and kapha.
- Astringent herbs, such as alfalfa and nettle, stop bleeding and heal sores. They reduce pitta and kapha.

You can buy Ayurvedic herbal cure-alls called Maharishi Amrit Kalash, made by the Maharishi Mahesh Yogi's Transcendental Meditation organization. These are rather expensive, and you may be better spending your money on a personal consultation with an Ayurvedic doctor.

Meditation

In Ayurveda, body and mind are inseparable; you can't have a healthy body without a healthy mind. Ayurvedic medicine believes that disease is the result of a mind that's out of balance and once you heal the mind, the body can heal itself. So for perfect health you need a perfectly healthy mind and meditation is the only way to achieve this.

Deepak Chopra, President of the Maharishi Ayurveda Association of America, says that meditation "prevents hypertension and heart disease, reduces depression and anxiety, slows ageing and unleashes untapped stores of creativity and intelligence".[417]

The Ayurvedic-Western combination

"There's no question that some good things have come out of Ayurveda," says Dr. John Canary, a consultant to the World Health Organization's traditional medicine programme.[418] Some practitioners of Ayurveda also use western medicine. Dr. John Peterson, an orthodox family GP who has also studied Ayurvedic medicine, says, "Using purely Ayurvedic appproaches, I've had success with heart disease, asthma, peptic ulcers, functional bowel disease, depression, insomnia, and a long, long list. But I will not hesitate to use Western drugs if the situation demands it."[419]

As is sadly usual with conventional medicine, studies are now being undertaken on animals to verify the claims of Ayurveda (the evidence of 4,000 years of human successes clearly isn't convincing enough). In one experiment involving rats who had been given breast cancer, it was found that Maharishi-4 (an Ayurvedic food supplement) was capable of suppressing cancer, and in 60 per cent of the rats, the tumours actually regressed.[420] This is certainly an impressive figure, but one wonders whether the world has really gained anything from this research which it didn't know beforehand.

In another experiment – this time on humans – it was found that Indian gooseberry (called 'amla') is capable of controlling cholesterol levels. "The supplement was given for a period of 28 days in the raw form," wrote the researchers. "Both normal and hypercholesterolaemic subjects showed a decrease in cholesterol levels. Two weeks after withdrawing the supplement, the total serum cholesterol levels of the hypercholesterolaemic subjects rose significantly almost to initial levels."[421]

When Margaret Thatcher was Prime Minister of Britain, it was strongly rumoured that she used Ayurveda to keep herself energetic, despite only having four hours' sleep a night. Uncharacteristically, Downing Street refused to comment when asked to confirm the story. But one conservative MP said: "If it is true that the prime minister does indulge in this, then it obviously works. She looks very good these days."[422] If Ayurveda can help a Prime Minister rule a nation, maybe it can work for you, too.

CHAPTER 68
WHAT TO EXPECT FROM BACH FLOWER REMEDIES

~

When you next have an emotional upset, experience a trying time or find yourself in a difficult state of mind, leave the gin in its bottle or the comforting cream cake in its wrapper. Instead, consider reaching for one of the thirty-eight Bach Flower Remedies!

Originally a bacteriologist, Dr. Edward Bach set up and ran a very successful orthodox medical practice in Harley Street. After taking early retirement from his practice, he moved to Wales in order to conduct research into the particular healing properties of flowers and trees. He discovered twelve (later expanded to thirty-eight) aqueous infusions which, he found, could successfully treat any negative state of mind. As a result, he published a small book, *The Twelve Healers*, which is still available (see the Help section).

Since the Bach Flower Remedies are specifically intended to treat disturbed emotional states, no claims are made that physical ailments can be treated with them. However, Dr. Bach believed that if the underlying emotional problem can be alleviated, there should be a corresponding improvement in the physical symptoms – "treat the person, not the disease; the cause, not the effect".

Preparation and dosage

The remedies are prepared by immersing the flowers of the plant concerned in a glass bowl with pure spring water, and leaving that to stand in full sunshine for a few hours. During this time the water becomes charged with the healing energies of the plant. This stock infusion is then preserved with brandy, bottled and sold. In this 'concentrated' form, the remedies will keep for ever. When they are needed, approximately two drops of the appropriate remedy are placed in a glass of water, and slowly sipped. The similarity is obvious between Bach Flower Remedies and homoeopathic treatments (see chapter 77).

The remedies are very safe to take. There is no risk of overdosage, of becoming dependent on them, or of their reacting with other orthodox medicines which you may be taking. They are even safe enough for babies, pregnant women, the elderly, animals and even plants!

The Bach Centre in Wallingford maintains that, from their own records, 75 per cent of people have been successfully treated, and they suggest that the remaining 25 per cent may consist of people who either had a problem which the prescriber did not accurately identify, or they may not have persevered with taking the treatment, or the person may not have had any real desire to get well.

Do it yourself!

The real joy of the Bach Flower Remedies is that they were originally conceived by Dr. Bach to be simple enough for self-prescription. It is *not* necessary to seek a consultation with a qualified (and expensive) 'doctor' – all the information is readily available to allow you to select the correct treatment for yourself, right from the start.

Bach intended the system to be used by ordinary individuals. Self-diagnosis is quite safe and simple to do. One has to select from thirty-eight remedies, those keyword (and related flowers) that most accurately reflect your own state of mind. Here is a list of the original Twelve Healers, and their associated keywords:

Flower	*Keywords*
Agrimony	Mental torture behind 'brave face'

Centaury	Weak-willed/subservient
Cerato	Seeks advice and confirmation from others
Chicory	Possessive – selfish
Clematis	Dreamers – lack of interest in present
Gentian	Discouragement – despondency
Impatiens	Impatience
Mimulus	Fear of known things
Rock rose	Terror
Scleranthus	Uncertainty – indecision
Vervain	Tenseness – hyper-anxiety
Water violet	Proud, aloof

The process of self-prescription is, in fact, a voyage of self-discovery. To begin with, it may seem as if almost all the keywords apply to your own state of mind. Further thought, and a little experimentation to find out which remedies work more effectively than others, will teach you more about your own state of mind. Although it is safe to take any number, it is unusual for more than six to be chosen. A change in the condition should be felt within a fortnight. If not, perhaps the diagnosis was inaccurate so try another remedy instead for another few days.

Many people like to have the Rescue Remedy to hand for use in emergency situations. It is the only combination remedy which Dr. Bach developed, and consists of five flower remedies – Impatiens, Star of Bethlehem, Cherry Plum, Rock Rose and Clematis. In emergencies, a few drops can be placed directly under the tongue. Rescue Remedy is particularly appropriate for situations of sudden shock, extreme anxiety or panic, stress, or terror. For example, going to the dentist, being involved in an accident, or suddenly learning bad news might all be situations where Rescue Remedy would be useful.

Bach Flower Remedies really work. In one sense, they are deeply revolutionary, because they put the 'patient' in the driving seat. Conventional medicine strives to separate the person from the disease. Bach Flower Remedies do precisely the opposite, and give *you* the tools to heal yourself. Their newness and ease of use (particularly when compared to other complementary disciplines, which take years of study to master) shouldn't fool you into thinking that they're not effective. If you have a real desire to get well (either emotionally or physically) and adhere to the principle of the mind-body link you should try them. It will cost you very little, produce no side effects and may well yield real benefits.

Chapter 69
What to Expect from Chiropractic

~

Four out of five people suffer back pain at some time in their lives. If you're one of them, consider this therapy.

Chiropractic – a complementary therapy using spinal manipulation without drugs or surgery – is too often viewed by the orthodox medical establishment as just another 'quack' therapy. This is grossly unjust, and narrow-minded, too. In a recent scientific report which appeared in no less an august publication than the *British Medical Journal*, it was found that not only is chiropractic effective, it is actually *more* effective than hospital treatment for back pain – and its effects last longer.

The study examined the progress of 741 patients aged 18–65 who were suffering from back pain. Each patient was randomly assigned treatment at either a chiropractic or hospital outpatient clinic in eleven centres across Britain. Then, the results of the treatment were compared. It was found that chiropractic treatment was uniformly more effective than hospital outpatient management, especially for patients with chronic or severe back pain.

The report also found that, if suitable patients were referred to chiropractors rather than to hospital, it could produce a reduction of up to 290,000 days in sick leave, saving potential losses in productivity of £13 million and £2.9 million in social security payments. In their conclusion, the scientists wrote: "For patients with low back pain in whom manipulation is not contraindicated chiropractic almost certainly confers worthwhile, long-term benefit in comparison with hospital outpatient management. The benefit is seen mainly in those with chronic or severe pain. Introducing chiropractic into NHS practice should be considered."[423]

This report echoed the findings of an inquiry which the New Zealand Government had published in 1979. After carrying out extensive research on chiropractic which included Australia, Canada, the US and the UK, it concluded: "By the end of the inquiry we found ourselves irresistibly and with complete unanimity drawn to the conclusion that modern chiropractic is a soundly-based and valuable branch of health care in a specialized area neglected by the medical profession."[424]

How it can help

Chiropractic originates from Hippocrates' belief that the spine is the root of all disease. Its founder, Daniel Palmer, a late 19th-century Canadian healer, suggested that problems with the spinal sections sometimes inhibited nerve movement which could be freed by manual adjustment. Although chiropractors frequently treat back pain, their view that the spine affects the body's general health means they take a holistic approach. Consequently, chiropractic can often successfully treat a wide range of disorders, including:

~ migraine
~ digestive problems
~ period pains
~ asthma
~ muscle conditions
~ arthritis
~ growing pains in children
~ sports injuries
~ sciatica and disc problems

What happens

You can be referred for chiropractic by your doctor, but currently it is not available on the NHS. As there are no standard charges the cost of treatment may vary considerably. On your first visit a case history is taken, you are examined, possibly X-rayed and a diagnosis is made. It may be decided that chiropractic cannot be carried out if, for example, there is evidence of bone crumbling, in which case another specialist will be recommended. If chiropractic is deemed to be appropriate, you will need an average of between six and ten sessions. Treatment normally involves application of sharp pressure to the joints, although there are many different methods of adjustment.

Reactions usually occur after the first or second treatment. Some patients feel worse before recovery begins, others experience a great improvement almost immediately. Forty per cent of patients report pain lasting between six and eight hours, normally after the first session. More unusually, some patients perspire heavily or suffer from trembling, chills or nausea. Such reactions should not cause alarm, although you should report them to your chiropractor.

You will also be told what preventive action you should take. For example, many of today's postural problems are caused by poor working conditions, so a patient might be advised to:

~ sit in a good supporting chair
~ use a desk of appropriate height
~ take a break every hour to stand and walk
~ relax wrists when typing

Patients will also be encouraged to exercise appropriately, but reminded to:

~ warm up sufficiently
~ build up gradually and rest if in pain
~ take gentle exercise such as swimming or walking

You will be told to make sure your bed is firm and not to lie on your stomach when sleeping. In other forms of treatment, back sufferers are often recommended bed rest, but chiropractors do not suggest this, believing that it inhibits healing and can weaken the muscles.

According to the British Chiropractic Association, there are many similarities between chiropractic and osteopathy (see chapter 86). Chiropractors are more likely to make direct adjustments to a specific part of the spine in a particular direction; osteopaths may use more massage or 'soft tissue' techniques. Also, chiropractors use X-rays in diagnosis considerably more than osteopaths.[425] While the Assocation points out that chiropractors are "often among the best equipped to identify a cancer at a very early stage in its development", their propensity to use X-rays may be of some concern, particularly since it has been estimated that up to 250 deaths from cancer each year may be caused by unnecessary X-ray examinations.[426]

If you do decide on chiropractic, bear in mind that there is no state registration for chiropractors in Britain. So make sure the one you choose belongs to The British Association of Chiropractors (see the address in the Help section). The Association's code of ethics regulates the chiropractor's procedure for examination and treatment. It also produces a range of useful leaflets on specific complaints.

Chapter 70

What to Expect from Colonic Irrigation

~

After heart disease, cancer of the colon is the second most common cause of death in the UK. Find out how to take care of your colon with a technique that is over 3,000 years old!

How clean is your colon? You may not know or even care, but watch out! A healthy bowel has been said by some to be the key to physical, mental and emotional well-being. If you allow your colon to become blocked with the waste of all the things you put into it, all sorts of diseases may result. The colon is the dustbin of our bodies, and it makes sense that sometimes it needs to be thoroughly cleaned out.

This is where colonic irrigation comes in. It is basically nothing more complicated or sinister than an internal bath to remove poisons, gases, faecal matter and mucus deposits. Sterilized equipment with an inlet and outlet attachment is used to flush filtered water through the rectum, into the colon and out again, carrying waste products with it.

The idea of colon cleansing is nothing new. It was certainly practised as far back as 1500 BC by the ancient Egyptians. Yogis in the Himalayas used a less sophisticated method of swallowing long strips of cloth and waiting for it to be excreted. In the Bible, Jesus talked of using a large trailing gourd as a means to inner cleanliness.

Colonic irrigation is better (and certainly more pleasant) than an enema because it treats the whole colon and, unlike regular use of laxatives, is not habit forming. The treatment actually works best as a complementary technique as it often increases the effectiveness of other, especially alternative, approaches. You may find it recommended as part of either traditional or naturopathic medicine.

What is the colon?

Also sometimes known as the large intestine, it is a tube one and a half metres long and six centimetres in diameter. As part of the digestive system, it absorbs nutrients and minerals from the foods we eat and tries to eliminate toxins and waste materials.

People who eat a lot of refined and processed foods, as well as those who smoke and drink large amounts of alcohol, can reap particular benefits from colonic irrigation. Our colons become so overloaded by today's unnatural diets that they are soon unable to function at an optimum level. Constipation is one of the most immediate results, followed by a drop in metabolism. We then not only become under-nourished, as our body is less able to absorb all the nutrients from the foods we are eating, but we become generally run down and more likely to develop all sorts of diseases. It has been estimated that four people out of every ten in the United Kingdom are regularly constipated, and in 20 per cent of the population, constipation is so severe that laxatives are used regularly. Furthermore, 77 per cent of the population only excrete between five and seven stools per week. On top of that, a further 8 per cent of people only pass three to four stools a week. That makes 85 per cent of us with slow bowel movements![427] It doesn't take much intelligence to see that, for many of us, ill-health may well begin in the colon.

When the colon is not able to do its job properly, our other eliminative organs, the skin, kidneys and lungs, become overloaded. Then, as all these eliminative systems begin to function poorly, wastes which should be excreted are reabsorbed into the bloodstream, thus causing 'alimentary toxaemia'.

In 1912 the Royal Society of Medicine produced a 380-page report which indicated the diseases for which alimentary toxaemia can be a contributing cause. Their list included:

~ gastric and duodenal ulcers
~ stomach cancer
~ cancer of the liver
~ intestinal catarrh
~ gases and colitis
~ appendicitis
~ blood pressure
~ headaches
~ irritability
~ sleep disorders
~ mental and physical depression
~ skin problems such as premature wrinkling
~ eczema
~ disorders of the uterus

~ breast cancer
~ bladder infections

The report concluded by saying: "to no other single cause is it possible to attribute one-tenth as many various and widely diverse disorders."

Detoxification

You may wonder whether there is a dietary way to clean a colon, but there really is no diet you can follow which will bring exactly the same results (although colonic hydrotherapists may suggest you follow a cleansing programme to accompany your treatment to maximize its effectiveness). This could involve adhering to a macrobiotic diet and avoiding all meat, sugar, alcohol, bread, dairy products and any processed foods. Acidophilus, which encourages the growth of good bacteria in the gut, may also be recommended (see chapter 52).

To find a qualified therapist in your area, contact the Colonic Irrigation Association (address in the Help section), which can give you a list of therapists who have trained with them.

What happens

During the initial consultation, the therapist will take your medical history and discuss any particular problems you may have. You will then be taken through the procedure and told what to expect during the actual session. After taking off your clothes, you will be given a gown to put on; it fastens down the back, rather like the gowns that surgeons wear. You will then get on to a comfortably cushioned table, lie back and let it all happen!

Don't worry, although it may strike you as a rather unusual procedure to allow a stranger to fit a speculum into your rear end, the process isn't painful. It's actually much less painful than having a conventional enema and a thoughtful colonicist will warm the speculum to body temperature. You'll next be aware of a gradual flushing feeling as the purified water starts to flow and do its work. If it's too hot or too cold, tell the colonicist and she'll adjust the temperature. There are in fact two methods for pushing the water through your body. The first, more gentle – and therefore more preferable – is the gravity-fed method in which the water enters by gravity. Other treatments use pressurized equipment to force the water into the body.

The key thing to remember is just to relax. On the first occasion, many people try to hold on to their bowel contents at all costs. Wrong. Let it all come out – that's what you're paying for! If you want to see what's disgorged, it can be arranged because the exit pipe is often transparent. You'll be surprised what you see! But it's probably better just to unwind and go with the flow!

Most sessions last between forty and fifty minutes. You'll gradually feel the water reaching higher and higher round your colon, and the colonicist may do some gentle massage to get things really moving. At the end, you'll feel a different person – light-headed, full of energy, and cleaned out!

The Colonic Irrigation Association recommends a course of six treatment sessions for best results, depending on your condition. When the necessary course is completed, it is suggested that you return every six months or so.

Chapter 71
What to expect from colour therapy

~

You walk out into bright sunlight and you instantly feel better, invigorated and more alive! In colour therapy not only sunlight, but also coloured light, is used to beneficially affect your well-being and health.

We are all sensitive to light. Light is part of the electromagnetic spectrum along with invisible radio waves, X-rays and microwaves. Colour is the visible light in the electromagnetic spectrum. Most other parts of the electromagnetic spectrum have scientifically-demonstrable effects on the human mind and body, both good and bad (for example, the damaging effects of X-ray radiation). Colour therapists simply suggest that the visible part of the spectrum can work on the mind and body, too.

Colour therapy proposes that, by altering the colours which surround us, we can alter our state of health. Certainly, light (or its absence) can have a demonstrable effect on the hypothalamus and the pineal and pituitary glands – and through them, on our mental and physical states of health.

Virtually every culture, religion and society throughout history has used colour and light in a variety of ways to treat the diseases and afflictions of their fellows. Colour therapy has grown out of this ancient and 'common sense' use of colour to enhance health and well-being.

What happens

At your first consultation with a colour therapist, your medical history is noted and your current state of health is discussed. The therapist will then observe your aura, the array of colours which they claim emanate naturally from all of us, but which few of us can observe.

Colour therapists do not consider the aura a psychic, clairvoyant or mystical phenomenon but a matter-of-fact part of the human condition which can be observed easily, with practice. It may be that the therapist you visit can see your aura by concentration alone, otherwise he or she may ask you to stand behind a Kilner screen. This consists of two sheets of glass which have a cyanine dye encapsulated between them. Kilner believed that the aura is an ultraviolet (non-visible light on the electromagnetic spectrum) phenomenon and proposed that his screen could enable even the untrained to observe the aura. In colour therapy it is used as both a psychological prop for the therapist and patient, and to help the therapist diagnose the patient's needs according to which colour or colours emanate and from which specific areas of the body.

Colour therapists believe that each organ, body part, emotion or mental state has a specific colour to which it responds. They determine your state of health by observing the colours which you project in your aura and then use colour to treat those aspects which seem lacking in health. After a thorough observation of the aura and a diagnosis of problems, your treatment can take various forms:

~ The use of sunlight focused on to a particular area of the body.

~ Advice on foods of a particular colour to be included in your diet. The chemicals which colour a food have specific actions within the body. Carotene, for instance, is present in orange foods such as carrots, pumpkin and sweet potatoes and is part of the vitamin A formula. Vitamin A is crucial to the health of skin, mucous membranes and to a variety of metabolic processes.

~ Drinking 'rainbow' water. In this remedy, water is poured into a coloured container which is then exposed to sunlight. On drinking the water you imbibe the energies imparted to the water by the colour of the container.

~ A meditation exercise, called colour breathing, requires you to imagine a specific colour as you breathe deeply and thoroughly. The colour may be imagined either bathing the whole body or directed on to a particular area of your body.
~ Coloured light (normally white light shone through coloured filters) is directed on to specific body parts or your whole body bathed in the colour. Sometimes the light is turned off and on in a rhythmical pattern as well.
~ You may be advised to wear or avoid certain colours of clothes as they filter the light which your body absorbs.

Colour yourself!

Colour therapy can be used alongside conventional medicine or other complementary therapies. Here are ten colours with potential to help you reach your optimum level of health and well-being. Choose which ones are most appropriate for your own personal needs:

RED: relates to the blood and circulation, state of vitality or debility, level of happiness or depression, the sexual organs, liver and lungs.

ORANGE: relates to the health of lungs and chest, the kidneys, pancreas, lower digestive tract, adrenal and thyroid glands, incidence of cramp and diabetes, quality of breast milk.

YELLOW: relates to the nervous system, health of the skin, stomach and upper digestive tract, the region of the solar plexus and the muscles; also to the incidence of asthma, migraine and diseases of the eyes.

GREEN: relates to emotional nervousness, incidence of headaches, the heart and circulatory problems such as angina, and to the pituitary gland.

TURQUOISE: relates to the health of skin and the acuteness of sight.

BLUE: relates to the incidence of fevers, bleeding and the states of irritability and anxiety.

INDIGO: relates to the senses of sight, hearing and smell, therefore the eyes, ears and nose and the whole head.

PURPLE: relates to mental and nervous equilibrium, incidence of neuralgia, arthritis and epilepsy; also to the level of blood pressure.

VIOLET: relates to the spleen, heart and sometimes the thyroid glands; also to the glandular and hormonal changes of pregnancy.

PINK: relates to incidence of insomnia, aggression, violence and hyperactivity; also to rhumatism and afflictions of the joints.

For the address of the International Association of Colour Healers, see the Help section.

Chapter 72

What to expect from crystal, gem and electro-crystal therapy

~

You are full of energy! You may not feel that way on a Monday morning, but you are! Crystal therapy aims to get your energies flowing again.

Your body's electrical energy field can be photographed by using a process called Kirlian photography. This technique involves placing your hand on top of a photographic plate, through which 25,000 volts of electricity is discharged (at a low current, so as not to electrocute you!). The result is a photograph of a darkened hand with a spectacular colour corona, which is said to be a magnification of the natural bioelectricity we all have. Kirlian photographers have demonstrated differences between the hand coronas of healthy people and sick people. The haloes of the latter tend to be indistinct, cloudy and blurry, while those of the former are sharp and bright.[428] From the photograph, it can be seen whether you have a harmonious flow and balance in your energy field (which means perfect health), or whether the flow is imbalanced, in which case you experience ill-health.

Crystal therapy aims to pinpoint any imbalance in energy, and treat both its causes and effects. You are probably already quite familiar with quartz crystal (think of all those quartz watches, clocks and radio alarms). It has the ability, as do all crystals, to produce an electrical output when mechanically stimulated, and vice versa. Silica, which quartz is made up of, has the ability to balance magnetic energy fields. It is this ability which gives gems and crystals their healing properties. They re-balance your body's energy fields when they become disrupted just prior to, or during, illness or disease.

What happens

At your first consultation the therapist will talk to you about your current and previous state of health and mind, and may note your past and present lifestyle and circumstances. You should use this opportunity to ask any questions you may have about the therapy and any aspects about which you are unclear.

The therapist will then work in one of two ways. S/he may take a hair sample and use this to help diagnose the problem, using an energy testing machine. This indicates where the imbalances in your body are. Or, the therapist may use a pendulum instead. For this you lie on a couch whilst the pendulum is held over your body by the therapist, who will then be able to pinpoint exactly where the imbalance is by watching the pendulum's movements.

Treatment addresses both the cause and effect of the illness. The outwardly 'visible' effect is treated by the direct application of the appropriate crystal over the area. Its naturally resonant qualities interact with the energy field in the specific area and start to re-balance it. The therapist may decide to use a stimulator like ruby or garnet, or you may need a tranquillizer like amethyst or sapphire, or yet again you may need a balancer like emerald or jade. The therapist will select the correct one according to your individual needs.

The direct application of crystals treats the symptom. But the cause also needs to be treated. This is done by using a gem elixir. It consists of water which has been energized by particular gems appropriate to your needs. It is similar to the 'rainbow' treatment in colour therapy and serves to work from the 'inside out'. It is the linch-pin in helping to remove the root cause of the problem.

Electro-crystal therapy

Electro-crystal therapy is slightly different, although it still harnesses the power of crystals which the ancient civilizations in Egypt, China and India all knew about. Developed by Harry Oldfield, in this therapy the diagnosis is first made by aiming high-energy, high-frequency radio signals at the patient. An analysis of the returning echo signal indicates which tissues are healthy and which are not. Once the problem areas have been pinpointed, treatment comes in the form of a tube containing crystals in a brine solution. This has high-frequency electrical waves pulsed through it, is aimed at the area to be treated, and then afterwards at the associated chakra (energy point).

Clearly, these areas are still way beyond the fringes of conventional medicine – which is not to say that they are ineffective. For further information about crystal therapy, contact the Institute of Crystal and Gem Therapies and the School of Electro-crystal Therapy (addresses in the Help section).

Chapter 73

What to expect from the Gerson therapy

~

You will undoubtedly have heard of diet therapies to fight cancer, but what do you know about the Gerson therapy? It's controversial, but its proponents believe it can work.

Dr. Max Gerson, the founder of the therapy, treated cancer patients in New York for over twenty years and in 1958 published a book detailing his theories and successful treatment of fifty patients, of which forty-eight had been initially diagnosed as 'terminal'. (For details of the book, see the Help section.) Gerson died in 1959. In his day, he was both vilified and eulogized. As far as the orthodox medical establishment were concerned, he made the unforgivable error of claiming, quite simply, that "there is an effective treatment for cancer, even in advanced cases", at a time when a diagnosis of cancer was invariably perceived as a death sentence. For Albert Schweitzer, however, Gerson was "one of the most eminent geniuses in the history of medicine. Many of his basic ideas," wrote Schweitzer, "have been adopted without having his name connected with them . . . those whom he has cured will not attest to the truth of his ideas."[429] So what is the truth behind this controversial man and his therapy?

Gerson believed that a healthy body has the natural ability to keep its cells functioning properly. His task, as he saw it, was to bring the body back to a natural state of health so that it could become capable of mounting a successful defence against proliferating cancer cells. According to Gerson, the key to achieving this is to support and strengthen the body's own oxidizing enzymes. "The ideal task of cancer therapy," he wrote, "is to restore the function of the oxidizing systems in the entire organism."[430] Gerson believed that it is the task of these oxidizing agents (which are generally thought to play a destructive role in the body – see chapter 9) to fight cancerous cells. His therapy aims to bring health by activating specific oxidizing enzymes using the following three methods:

~ Detoxifying the whole body.
~ Providing essential mineral contents in the potassium group.
~ Providing additional oxidizing enzymes.

What happens

Gerson's method of treatment evolved from clinical observations in which he discovered that what is most significant in cancer cases is the overall effect the disease has on the body. Bowel cancer, for example, does not solely affect one isolated part of the body – the whole system deteriorates. People with cancer have poor immuno-reactivity and damaged tissue throughout. All 'degenerative' diseases demand detoxification, according to Gerson. But since cancer patients have reduced stomach secretions and poorly functioning liver and pancreas, detoxification is a very delicate business. Fasting is not a good idea because their bodies are already too depleted in nutrients.

Instead, patients follow a strict and complicated diet which is low in sodium, high in potassium, vitamins, minerals and fluids, with fats and proteins severely restricted. It consists of food, juice and medication:

~ Three full meals are eaten every day. These are made up of fresh, raw, organic fruit and vegetables, rye bread and grains and a special soup. Only organic fruit and vegetables can be consumed – other produce does not contain the same quantities of all-important potassium and oxidizing enzymes.

All produce has to be fresh, not frozen, tinned, bottled or even smoked. Salt (including salt substitutes) is strictly forbidden, as are nicotine, alcohol, avocados, berries, any refined sugar, coffee, cream, fat, white flour, tea, tap water and soya bean products. A limited amount of raw sugar, honey and syrup is allowed.

In cooking, small amounts of certain herbs and larger quantities of garlic and parsley can be used. Vegetables should be washed thoroughly, even scrubbed; but never peeled or scraped. Then they are steamed in their own juices (without water) on a low heat until well cooked. Any equipment made of aluminium must not be used for cooking.

~ No less than thirteen glasses of fresh, raw juices are drunk daily. These are made from fresh organic fruit and vegetables immediately before consumption (so no nutrition is lost). Originally, Dr. Gerson insisted that the enzymatic fluids from calf's liver should also be used, freshly pressed. Today, this has been discontinued (because the animals' own state of health is now so poor), but some other animal-derived products are still used. Obviously, vegetarians or vegans will find this unacceptable.

~ Medication is prescribed, which may include:

- potassium compound
- thyroid hormone
- Lugol's solution (iodine and potassium iodide in water)
- injectable crude liver extract with B_{12}
- pancreatic enzymes
- enemas of coffee and/or chamomile tea

Since Gerson's death, additional ozone, hydrogen peroxide, intravenous GKI drip (of glucose, potassium or insulin), live cell therapy, castor oil and clay packs have been added to the prescription list.

It is a rigorous treatment, and many people feel they have had enough after a few weeks. They complain of nausea, headaches, vomiting, spasms and loss of appetite. Often these reactions are, according to Gerson, mistakenly described as physical rejection of the treatment, but what is in fact happening is a healthy response to the detoxification process. Nevertheless, this can be worrying.

There are also problems of isolation, and even depression, brought about by a totally new way of life. On a more practical level, it is important to consider the cost of the foods needed for this therapy, as well as the time needed to prepare them. As Gerson pointed out, others will offer to help, but too often this means they only prepare the juices in the morning and then again in the evening to fit around their working day. Unfortunately, this allows the vital enzymes to be destroyed and the treatment is rendered useless.

In Mexico, there is a clinic that takes in-patients for the Gerson therapy. The treatment normally takes between three and six weeks, with the patients continuing on the special diet at home for the next eighteen months or so. In-patient charges are approximately $2,400 per week, plus $400–$600 for laboratory tests and treatments. The hospital requires a $6,000-dollar deposit to cover the first two weeks of treatment.

Does the Gerson treatment work?

Conventional medicine says 'no'. In an extensive search of medical information sources, we have been unable to find any clear, independent and scientifically acceptable studies which prove the effectiveness of the Gerson therapy. In fact, most mentions of it are hostile. However, the absence of research does not necessarily indicate that the therapy is ineffective. In fact, there are several speculative papers which suggest ways in which the treatment *might* work.

One research paper states: "The high potassium, low sodium diet of the Gerson therapy has been observed experimentally to cure many cases of advanced cancer in man, but the reason was not clear." It goes on to speculate that "high potassium, low sodium environments can partially return damaged cell proteins to their normal undamaged configuration. Therefore, the damage in other tissues, induced by toxins and breakdown products from the cancer, is probably partly repaired by the Gerson therapy through this mechanism."[431]

Another hypothesis suggests that, because of its relatively high levels of carotene, vitamin C and potassium, the diet may boost resistance in several ways. One such could be to increase the body's production of aldosterone, a hormone secreted by the adrenal cortex, which might retard certain types of tumour.[432]

Yet another paper discusses experimental evidence showing that the Gerson diet can repair cells, and suggests that "the high potassium, low sodium Gerson diet, which increases tissue potassium concentrations and decreases tissue sodium concentrations, is a logical therapy for the tissue damage syndrome in cancer patients".[433]

A further scientific paper claims that: "Adjusting the diet may be useful when other types of therapy have not controlled the spread of the cancer. Reported results, using the Gerson diet, seem to support this hypothesis."[434] But these are isolated, theoretical papers. For the most part, scientific literature either ignores the Gerson therapy, or is disparaging of it.

There are, indeed, plenty of 'anecdotal' cases of remissions and cures in patients following the Gerson regime. Impressive though these are (particularly when told in the first person – how can you *not* believe someone who tells you their cancer has been cured by the therapy they chose?), it is important to state that these fall far short of clear scientific proof. The problem with anecdotes and case histories is that they are not compared to anything. "The lay public is not aware of the natural history of cancer," one professor of oncology told us. "Cancer is not an automatic death sentence. I have a number of patients' records in my files where the patient received absolutely no treatment at all, and they still lived a long time."[435] In other words, those people who were 'cured' by the Gerson therapy might have got better in any case.

When we spoke to the main cancer research organizations, it became clear that very few of them had any significant knowledge of the Gerson therapy. Most of them dismissed it as simply another unproven cancer cure. And here lies the central problem. Without clear scientific evidence, the Gerson therapy cannot be considered to be 'effective'.

Why don't proponents of the Gerson therapy produce such evidence, and settle the matter once and for all? Charlotte Gerson, daughter of its founder, says there are insurmountable problems in conducting the sort of randomized, double-blind trials which would convince sceptics.[436] Such a trial involves dividing a group of patients into two, one of which receives the treatment, and the other doesn't. Neither group should know whether they have been treated or not until after the experiment has ended. While such experiments are easy to conduct in the orthodox field (where a pill can either contain a drug or a placebo) they are impossible when, for example, the treatment involves consuming quantities of fresh juice and having coffee enemas. Even so, it should be possible to design a study, acceptable to orthodox scientists, which can prove the therapy's effectiveness.

"It is intellectually dishonest not to do so," a cancer specialist told us.[437] "What they should do is first define the outcome measures – the length of survival after treatment, say. Then you take a group of cancer sufferers, half of whom receive the alternative therapy, half of whom receive conventional treatment. And compare the results."

Such research may, of course, be published in the future. In the meantime, should you consider Gerson therapy? It is obviously a hard path to tread, and one which, for the moment at least, receives little encouragement from orthodox medicine. And the inclusion of animal products in the diet would make it repugnant for many. Another professor of oncology told us that he would adopt a 'flexible' attitude towards any of his patients who were considering it, but his first concern would be to ensure that the therapy didn't harm them. And he wouldn't wish them to discontinue conventional cancer therapy. If you are considering the Gerson treatment, bear these points in mind:

~ So far, no scientifically acceptable evidence has been produced that it is effective, despite many individual success stories.

~ The treatment may be expensive, and possibly too austere for a weakened system.

~ An open-minded orthodox doctor or cancer specialist is well worth finding to help and advise you. "We don't claim a monopoly on the truth," one specialist told us, "we're constantly being surprised."

Fundamentally, your own attitude towards your disease – and a burning desire for wellness – may be your best ally. Says one woman who successfully defeated breast cancer with self-administered Gerson therapy: "In fighting cancer, the most critical point is when you decide that you are going to survive. You need a focus for that desire to live, so you pick a therapy, orthodox or alternative, and you use it. But the most important thing is to believe that you will survive."[438]

Chapter 74

What to expect from Gestalt therapy

~

Gestalt therapy doesn't involve digging painfully into your deep past, and awakening painful memories. Instead, it involves learning how to feel your present experience, free of the anxious, distracting buzz of other concerns.

If you feel too stressed and fearful to enjoy life, Gestalt therapy can help. One of the gentlest sorts of psychotherapy, it aims to put you in touch with the here and now, by finding ways of completing the unfinished business of your life.

The theory

Gestalt therapy was devised and developed by Fritz Perls (a student of Wilhelm Reich with a mind of his own), who wanted to find ways of relating to patients with minimal professional routine. Every patient is different, and therapist and patient are essentially in an experiment together, in which they are finding out all they can about the patient's sensations, wants, actions, feelings and values.

As in Reichian therapy, it is assumed that emotional conflicts tend to be expressed and contained through skeletal and muscular armouring as well as in the formation of character. In Gestalt psychology, it is assumed that everyone has an inherent tendency to organize their perceptions on orderly principles, and to look for wholeness or completion ('gestalt' means 'whole').

Incompleted 'gestalts' persist disturbingly, and need to be settled before truly appreciative contact with the present can take place. This psychological 'unfinished business' will go on making itself felt in all kinds of ways – in aches and pains and knotted muscles, in twitches and itches, in feelings of panic, in distracted attention, in fantasies and dreams, in distance from the "here and now – until it is re-experienced and thus completed. The aim of therapy is to find out how to do that – and then to do it!"

The practice

~ 'I and thou.' You and the therapist are equal partners in an intimate relationship. Eye contact is vital, and you'll often be asked how you feel.

~ 'Here and now.' You'll be encouraged always to experience the present moment vividly. If you explore the past it'll be through feeling it again with fresh poignancy as part of now. Instead of dwelling on and nursing it, you'll learn to live through the past so that you can leave it behind. In this way you will eventually become centred in the here and now, a confident individual in full contact with your environment.

~ 'Not why, but how.' You're not trying to find out what went wrong in your forgotten past, you're trying to find out how to overcome fear and accept perpetual change. These are some of the means that Gestalt therapy offers to help you do this.

Action

~ You may be asked to enact important events in your life and live the feelings through to completion this time, without the risks those feelings had for you first time round.

~ You may be asked to speak without qualifications, or to say 'Yes' more often, which will encourage you to become aware of the possibilities for affirmation, and eventually to apply them outside the therapeutic situation.

Dreamwork

~ You may be asked to pay particular attention to your dreams and report them in as much detail as you can since they are the product of unfinished business. A particular twist of Gestalt therapy is the belief that every element in a dream is an aspect of self, cast out, so dreams can make you aware of important aspects of your self.

Fantasies

~ Your fantasies are an organic growth from your hopes and concerns, so you will probably be asked to pay close attention to them and report them in detail to the therapist, and together deal with their associated unfinished business. Because so much of this therapy consists in acting out, it is also highly suitable for use in groups – best thought of as collections of individuals, who will be treated as such.

Individual treatments are about £25 per hour, and you will be expected to commit yourself for some minimum number of sessions (perhaps as few as six), normally once a week. Most therapists will want you to make sure that you and they get on before starting, so will often give you a less costly first meeting. Group treatments tend to cost around £10 for about three hours once a week. Although you'll lose something in individual attention, you'll gain a close acquaintance with a lot of former strangers – and they with you – so close that you'll never need to put on any front with each other.

In Gestalt therapy you are treated first and foremost as an individual, and many possibilities may be pursued which are tailored to your own perceived needs. It's also comforting to remember that it is intended to provide a supportive environment for all those ways and means of sorting yourself out. Nothing you say or do will ever be greeted with stony silence, indifference or contempt – boosting your self-confidence is an important aim.

Chapter 75
What to Expect from Hand Healing

~

Learn how you can benefit from the healing partnership formed in one of the gentlest, and certainly one of the oldest, of all treatments.

If you have ever put your hand on the head of someone who was ill, or kissed a child better, you may have experienced some of the mystical power of hand healing. The phenomenon of healing is often dismissed, either because there is no real scientific explanation for it, or because of the religious connotations it often has. Ancient civilizations saw it differently. Illness was a temporary disharmony between the forces of nature or the gods, and hand healing was simply a restoration of balance. Five hundred years before Christ and his healing miracles, Indian texts described ways of channelling prana, the energy of the universe, with the use of touch.

Healing is sometimes called 'faith healing', a label sometimes applied derogatorily, with its overtones of evangelical and hysterical bogus. But 'faith' is not necessarily involved, as neither the patient nor the healer need to hold any religious convictions for the healing to be successful. The term 'spiritual healing' is rather more accurate, and covers most forms of hand healing. Spiritual healing is not necessarily mystical; in essence, it is simply about restoring one's 'spirit'. But many healers do claim that Christ, or some other divine force, is working through them.

Hand healing is sometimes also called 'contact' or 'touch healing'. The term 'the laying on of hands' normally denotes a specific practice carried out by the Church of England, taken from the method used by Jesus. Most healers believe in absent or distance healing, which involves a physical separation between the patient and healer. Usually the healer will concentrate on some item associated with the absent patient, such as a photograph or a piece of hair.

An accepted practice

The National Federation of Spiritual Healers was established in 1955. By 1959, some 1,500 hospitals permitted registered members of the organization into their wards. Today, healers are to be found in hospitals throughout the country. Your GP can even refer you to a healer, following the General Medical Council's decision in 1977 to lift its ban on doctors and healers working together. In New York University, therapeutic touch is taught as part of the nurses' MA and PhD courses and as a form of treatment is officially approved by New York's Commission for Mental Health.

Many healers are resistant to the idea of a spirit or religious presence working with them and prefer to describe it more in terms of 'energy transfer'. All healers work with the idea of universal energy, whether they call it love, god, chi or prana. Some work on the acupuncture model of meridians, or on the concept of chakras, but all hold to a broad-based approach of energy rebalancing to stimulate and harmonize the life force.

At the heart of the healing process lies a paradox. On the one hand, most healers will admit that the healing 'force' is an external one, and the healer is simply a vehicle for some greater energy which is channelled through the healer into the patient. In this sense, healing is something of an impersonal process.

On the other hand, the healer-patient relationship is usually crucial to success. As with any treatment, the 'personal chemistry' can make all the difference. Seen this way, the healing process works because of an empathy between the healer and the patient. It has even been suggested that this is the basic, underlying process by which many other therapies actually work.

The unknown power

We have all come across people who either uplift or drain us, simply through their presence. Healers are people who have a special ability in this area. It is thought that we all have this 'power' inside us to some extent, but healers can manifest it particularly strongly.

Does healing work? Many thousands of people would answer 'yes', although in the absence of effective scientific trials, orthodox medicine would take a different view. But in some ways, healing transcends conventional medicine. "Medical science can work wonders," says Dr. William Standish Reed, President of the Christian Medical Foundation. "Still, for many of the sick and dying it offers little, and we need to look in other directions as well. No one of faith would wish to rely on medical arguments for healing. Science may one day tell us much about its efficacy, though. We all know from the so-called placebo effect that a patient's beliefs can be marshalled to his benefit."[439]

Most of us are aware of the power of the placebo effect. This can be explained in terms of the mind's ability to bring about biochemical changes in the body just through suggestion and expectation. It is possible that healing, at least in part, relies on this principle. Some people define the process as the mind carrying out the actual healing, with the hands just acting as the link.

Occasionally, though, some interesting scientific work is conducted. Dr. William Braud at the Mind Science Foundation set up an experiment using cancerous cells, with startling results. A well-known healer, Matthew Manning, actually killed these cancerous cells by laying his hands on the flasks that contained them. It was found that those cells receiving the treatment had a 38 per cent higher death rate than those in the control group. Normally, Manning held the flasks for a twenty-minute period, but he achieved similarly strong results without even touching them, suggesting some mental influence was at work.[440]

What happens

The approach of healers varies considerably, but most follow a common procedure. In the first meeting, he or she will ask the reason for your visit. Then you will either sit in a chair or lie on a treatment table – you will not be asked to take off your clothes. Asking you to relax, the healer will explain how he or she is going to treat you and will then start work on your physical body or on the electromagnetic field (or aura) surrounding your body. The action is not massage or manipulation, although it may involve a very slight pushing motion. Some healers will talk as they work, possibly counselling you, others will remain silent. Time will be allowed for discussion of the session afterwards.

Your response during the treatment may range from sensations of heat, relaxation, calmness, tingling and coldness to discomfort; you may even have visual images of light and colour. Afterwards you may feel relaxed or regenerated, less in pain or more happy and some people will feel an immediate alleviation of symptoms. You may need a course of up to twenty treatments before you feel total benefit. Sessions normally last between twenty and forty minutes, although the first one may last up to an hour.

Are you a healer?

If you think you have healing influence yourself, either because of a compulsion or an overwhelming desire to help others, contact the National Federation of Spiritualist Healers, mentioned in the Help section. They offer a probationary scheme which involves working alongside an experienced healer and also run courses and seminars.

A significant point in favour of healing is that, since it does not conflict with any other medical treatment, you can receive healing at the same time as you may be receiving more orthodox treatment. You do not need any particular belief system, but you do need to be receptive rather than passive. It is also important to have an open mind and to be honest with yourself. You do not need to be ill or distressed to benefit from a healer, many people receive treatment as a kind of life maintenance.

To find a healer, see the addresses in the Help section. Do not continue with an individual you are not happy with; keep changing until you find the right one.

Chapter 76

What to expect from herbalism

~

Both humans and animals have always utilized nature's products to treat discomfort and illness – a cat chews grass to settle its stomach, you rub a dock leaf on your skin to alleviate a nettle sting – because they are effective. It is usually forgotten that the pharmaceutical industry has often relied on the herbalist for many of its most effective products. Rauwolfia, for example, is prescribed by Western doctors to lower blood pressure, and is an extract of the snakeroot plant, which has been used for centuries by Eastern herbalists. Similar stories can be told for hundreds of other natural plant medicines.

Modern herbalism has both encompassed and transcended the traditional folklore of the healing power of herbs to become a sophisticated system of patient care.

Of all the complementary therapies, herbalism can truly lay claim to having the oldest tradition; it is rooted deep in the primitive past and stems directly from the ancient lore of curative plants. If you wish to be treated by natural means, consider seeing a herbalist.

What it is

Medical herbalism is any treatment relying mainly on the use of plants and herbs to heal. It could even be said to include both aromatherapy and Bach Flower Remedies; strictly speaking it is the gathering and preparation of herbs to apply, in various ways, to heal disorders of mind and body.

Herbalists regard the plant as a whole organism in perfect, natural balance. They apply such natural organisms to the human organism which has fallen out of balance, in order to restore equilibrium and, consequently, good health. This is based on the premise that the body's 'vital force' is essentially self-correcting and that herbs can be used to support and nurture this energy where it is weakening. Indeed, herbalism can be described as the interface of human and plant energy fields. Herbalism is a holistic medicine in the same way that Naturopathy is. It treats the whole person and is not merely a collection of patent remedies designed to treat a range of symptoms. It encourages and enables the body to heal itself.

What happens

Initially, the herbalist will take your case history. They will be particularly concerned with, and ask questions about your:

~ allergies
~ diet
~ stress factors (harmony v tension)
~ spiritual and emotional life
~ bodily functions (digestion, bowels, etc.)
~ inner feeling (disturbance v tranquility)
~ regime and exercise
~ past health record

A physical examination will follow – a urine sample, blood pressure, pulse and temperature may all be taken.

Techniques of iridology and radionics (diagnosis based on the theory of electromagnetic energy flow) may be used too. Herbal treatment will be selected according to the main area of need. This will be related to the underlying cause of illness (not symptoms), termed the 'primary lesion'. The requisite herbs are applied in a number of ways:

~ Infusion. Boiling water applied to herbs, allowed to cool and infuse, then taken in the appropriate dose.

~ DECOCTION. The simmering of liquid containing herbs till it has reduced; again taken orally.
~ OINTMENT POULTICE. A hot application of herbs.
~ CONSERVE. A herbal syrup.

Enemas, baths, teas, tinctures, juices and powders may also be used. Naturally, great expertise is required to prepare and use herbs for effective healing, though the lay person can obtain an idea of the properties of various herbs by consulting Nicholas Culpeper's *Complete Herbal*, or a similar herb directory.

As well as the direct application of herbal remedies, the herbalist may also conduct a general 'lifestyle overhaul' involving diet and the correction of body functions through:
~ CHALLENGERS. Herbs that are used to provoke a protective response from the body; for example, using a diuretic such as dandelion (to make the kidneys produce more urine).
~ BODY-FUNCTION PROCESSORS. Herbs with a normalizing, supportive action; for example, hawthorn to increase blood flow.
~ ELIMINATORS. To get rid of refuse, clean out the body and improve circulation; for example, a purgative, aperient or laxative.

Modern drug companies synthesize herbs and plants to create concentrated and powerful drugs which often aggressively combat the symptoms of illness, and increase the likelihood of unwanted side effects. Herbalists believe their more subtle, sympathetic skills involve total plant chemistry and its complicated interaction with the patient. Only through the painstaking understanding of herbal properties and the root cause of human illnesses can a whole range of conditions, from migraines to asthma, be successfully dealt with. It is this natural healing which they believe offers a gentle path back to good health.

To consult a herbalist, contact the National Institute of Medical Herbalists (address in the Help section), which will provide information and the details of a local herbalist.

CHAPTER 77

WHAT TO EXPECT FROM HOMOEOPATHIC THERAPY

~

If you appreciate that inoculations, vaccinations and even 'hair of the dog' work, then you already appreciate homoeopathy.

Homoeopathy treats 'like with like', so if you are suffering from insomnia, a homoeopathic remedy will use a minute dose of a substance which, if taken in large quantities, would actually bring about sleeplessness! The small, and therefore completely safe, dosage has the effect of triggering the body's ability to heal itself. This was succinctly expressed in a saying attributed to the Delphic Oracle: "The Wounder Heals."

The other feature of homoeopathy which makes it radically different from conventional medicine is that it treats the whole person and not the symptoms. This fundamental difference has an important bearing on what you can expect from a consultation with a homoeopathic doctor. Conventional doctors tend to allow a set ten minutes per person, which is enough time to see the sore throat or aching leg and then to write out a standard prescription according to the symptoms.

A homoeopathic doctor, however, is likely to spend at least an hour with you during the initial consultation. In that hour the doctor aims to find out as much as possible about you, not your symptoms.

What happens

You will be asked about your family's health history, your own health history, your personality, what you like and dislike and so on until the homoeopath has built up a good profile of you.

By understanding what sort of person you are an appropriate remedy can be selected, most commonly in the form of a pill. Remember, though, that even if someone of the same age – or even of the same family – went with the same complaint, you may both receive totally different remedies, because it is you, the individual, who is being treated and *not* the symptomatic sore throat.

Homoeopathic pills were traditionally made from naturally-occurring substances, and they still form the basis of most treatments. However, the homoeopathic principle is also now being carried forward to deal with problems related to our contemporary lifestyles. For example, small doses of additives, colourants or preservatives are administered homoeopathically as a remedy for allergic reactions.

This all sounds and is wonderful – safe doses of treatments in minute amounts which trigger the body to heal itself! However, there are limitations. By the time a patient sees a homoeopathic doctor, irreversible changes may already have taken place. Orthodox medical treatment – such as surgery – may still be necessary to patch up the damage. Homoeopathy can still be used afterwards to help build up and maintain good health.

Under these circumstances, a revision of your lifestyle will also be advised so that you can eliminate those aspects which prevent the body from healing itself. Relaxation, an improved diet and environment all help support your body as it works its way back to health.

All this is explained at your consultation, as will be the need for patience. Acute illnesses do respond well to treatment if the patient's vitality is high. Chronic illnesses mean that your body has a lot of hard work to do, and so it will take longer for the remedies to be seen to take effect.

You can expect to feel that your symptoms are getting worse after you have started your treatment. Don't be alarmed! This 'healing crisis' is simply the remedy taking effect, and once this has passed you will be well on the way to full recovery. You may also experience a 'spring cleaning' effect on the body such as a runny nose or a rash. This, again, is all to be expected and the homoeopath will explain to you that it might happen, and stress that these new symptoms should not be treated. So don't feel tempted to take a proprietary cold remedy to stop the runny nose!

Theory and practice

As already mentioned (see chapter 63) there is scientific evidence to show that homoeopathy is indeed an effective medical treatment. To support this, a recent survey of NHS doctors in Britain revealed that there are at least 750,000 homeopathic consultations every year leading to prescriptions, most of them on the National Health Service.[441] The survey found that the most commonly treated ailments were respiratory disorders, arthritis, muscle and bone problems, and mental disorders, including anxiety and depression. This, perhaps, gives some clue as to those disorders which are most amenable to homeopathic treatment.

Modern homoeopathy was born with Samuel Hahnemann (1755). Known as the Father of Homoeopathy, Dr. Hahnemann became dissatisfied with the crude and often violent medicine of his day (which involved purging, cupping, leeching and bleeding, etc.). While translating the *Materia Medica* of the English physician William Cullen, into German, Hahnemann decided to experiment with Peruvian Bark (*Cinchona succirubra*, from which quinine is derived), which he'd just read about. Taking it himself, he was surprised to find that, in a healthy person, it produced all the symptoms of malaria, which it was actually intended to cure. Over several years, Hahnemann conducted more experiments with other drugs, and found that the effect was uniform. In a healthy person, a drug would produce the symptoms of the disease which in a sick person it was supposed to cure. This paradoxical effect became the cornerstone of his curative theory.

Following on from this, Hahnemann proposed that the 'potency' of a drug could actually be increased by diluting it. The more a drug is diluted, the more it is 'dematerialized' (becomes unrestrained by its physical and chemical nature) and its ultimate healing power is thus liberated. The first stage in the production of a homeopathic medicine is the production of a 'mother tincture'. Then follows a whole series of dilutions, producing ever-increasing potencies. The first dilution involves taking one part of the mother tincture and combining it with nine parts of water. This is then rhythmically succussed (shaken) for an exact time in order to fully potentize the liquid. The resulting dilution is known as 1X. Repeating the process (one part of 1X to nine of water) produces 2X, and so on. Reading the labels of homeopathic medicine you will often see 3X, 6X, 15X and 30X. Potencies referred to simply by a number (6), (30), etc., or with a C suffix (1C, 30C) are centesimal potencies – prepared in exactly the same way as above, but diluted with 99 parts of water.

Self-treatment

Although most health food shops stock a huge array of homeopathic medicines, self-treatment is not particularly easy. Remember, it is the person and not the symptom which is treated. So, by the time you have spent a considerable amount of money in the shop trying out different remedies, you would have been wiser to use the money on a full consultation instead and put yourself in the hands of a professional. But, since homeopathic remedies are never harmful, you can be sure that any experimentation you may indulge in will not hurt you. Here are some of the most common and usually effective homeopathic first-aid remedies. They should be bought in the 30 centesimal potency. Pills and ointment are often available, and may be used together.

Problem	*Remedy*
Bites and stings	Aconite
Bruises	Arnica, bellis perennis
Colds and chills	Aconite, gelsemium
Cramp	Aconite
Fracture	Arnica
Grazes	Calendula/hypericum ointment
Headache	Actaea rac.
Jet lag	Cocculus twice daily starting two days before journey
Nausea	Nux vomica
Shock	Arnica
Sunburn	Aconite, urtica ointment

It will be seen from the above very simplified table that arnica is a tremendously useful homeopathic remedy.

Just as Bach's Rescue Remedy should be in every home and handbag, so should arnica. In pill and ointment form, it is the remedy 'par excellence' for all cases of shock and injury, and to generally aid recovery.

So, where do you find homoeopathic doctors?

You may be surprised to hear that you do not have to be a private patient to receive homoeopathic treatment. There are some 600 NHS-registered homoeopathic doctors and, so long as you live within the catchment area of one of them, you can apply to transfer to their NHS list. There are also several homoeopathic hospitals around Britain which all operate under the NHS and to which you can be referred by your own doctor.

The address of the British Homeopathic Association, and other useful information, can be found in the Help section.

Chapter 78

What to expect from hydrotherapy

~

Do you dream of soaking for hours in the bath, uninterrupted, peaceful and relaxed? If you do, you're getting in touch with one of the therapeutic uses of water, known as hydrotherapy.

Father Sebastian Kneipp (1821-97) popularized the therapy which uses water either internally or externally to maintain health or treat disease. 'Dissolve, remove and strengthen' was how he defined its uses to:

~ Dissolve matter which contains disease.

~ Remove the diseased matter from the system.

~ Strengthen the body by restoring the cleansed blood to maximum circulation.

Taking the waters at spas has been popular since Roman times, and involves drinking the natural mineral water that comes from local underground springs. Today this is still an important aspect of hydrotherapy, and according to its mineral content can have a laxative, diuretic, phlegmagogic (phlegm producing), diaphoretic (perspiration inducing) or other specific effect. It helps dissolve toxins and restore vitality. Water-only fasts are also used to detoxify the body and colonic irrigation similarly helps remove toxic wastes by pumping water into the colon and then discharging it.

There are many external forms of hydrotherapy:

~ Hot baths. A 5–10 minute hot bath (36.5°–37°C/98–99°F) increases sweat gland efficiency, draws blood to the surface and affects hormone-producing glands, in particular the adrenal, to bring about a calming effect. Herbs can be added to the water as an infusion. For example, chamomile or valerian will help you relax further as you inhale their aromas.

~ Cold baths. Cold baths have an invigorating effect by drawing blood away from the surface, causing the blood pressure to rise and thereby stimulating circulation. Besides cold baths, cold wraps or packs are also used where, instead of taking a bath, your torso is wrapped in cold, soaked cotton. You then lie down, covered, and with a hot water bottle for a minimum of two hours.

~ Alternate baths. Alternate hot and cold baths have the effect of reducing inflammations, stimulating the circulation and encouraging lymphatic drainage to detoxify the body. A 'sitz' bath is used, which is similar to a hip-bath. You sit in a hot bath with your feet placed in bowls of cold water and then switch to a cold bath to sit with your feet in hot water. This is repeated several times.

~ Epsom salt baths. Magnesium sulphate is added to a hot bath. This makes you sweat profusely. You shower, have a rub down, are wrapped in towels to encourage more sweating, and then take a final shower.
~ Pressure hosing. A powerful water spray is directed at you from a distance of some 25 to 50 feet. The strong, controlled spray massages and invigorates you.
~ Needle sprays. Fine jets of cold and hot water spray your body to improve your circulation whilst also invigorating you.
~ Underwater massage. A highly pressurized jet of water massages your body as you lie relaxing in water. This is a widely used therapy which succeeds in massaging muscles far more rigorously as they fully relax with your weightless body.
~ Saunas. Sauna cabins produce a hot, dry atmosphere. They are normally communal although some have separate ones for men and women. As you sit in the heat, normally unclothed or with a towel wrapped around, your metabolic rate and blood pressure decrease, although some people may experience an increase in blood pressure. There is some physiological stress in coping with the extremely high temperatures in saunas (up to 100°C/212°F) and whilst many find them relaxing they are advisable only for people in good health. After the sauna you take a cold shower to stimulate the circulation and reduce further sweating out of impurities.
~ Turkish baths. These are similar to saunas but they have a higher humidity and are not so hot (45°C/104°F). Similarly they are not advisable if you have a health problem.

Hydrotherapy during a stay at a spa or hydro is a good way to relax, feel fully cleansed and very refreshed. Sensible eating, drinking, sleeping and other integrated exercise also help improve your sense of well-being during your stay. Closer to home, contact your local health clubs or gyms and find out what hydrotherapies they have available, then go ahead – splash out!

Chapter 79
What to expect from hypnotherapy

~

If you think hypnotherapy might help you, then it probably will.

Hypnosis creates a state of altered consciousness, when you are neither asleep nor fully awake. During this trance-like state you are in an increased state of suggestibility. This worries some people who think they will be made to do something embarrassing or even dangerous. The best way to avoid worrying about this is to find a qualified hypnotherapist in whom you can develop trust.

How it could help

There are many areas in which hypnosis is successfully used, either on its own or in conjunction with other therapies or medical treatments. These include:
~ asthma
~ childbirth
~ dentistry
~ dermatology
~ migraine
~ pain – alleviating or curing it
~ phobias
~ psychological disorders
~ smoking

~ stress-related symptoms
~ weight control

What happens

During the first session a hypnotist will want to find out about your particular problem, personal details and medical history. You can expect them to explain exactly what will happen, why and the course of treatment. You must take this opportunity to ask any questions, to clarify any areas of which you are unsure, and to satisfy yourself that you feel confident with your particular therapist. There may or may not be time after the consultation for you to be hypnotized. The therapist may decide to start treatment at the next session.

For the hypnosis itself, you will be seated in a relaxing easy chair or couch in a quiet room. Standing or sitting near you, the therapist will start to talk in a firm but monotonous voice, telling you to breathe deeply, slowly and evenly, and to relax your body. An object may be introduced into your line of vision. Suggestions are continually repeated that you are beginning to feel drowsy. Eventually, guided by the repetitious suggestions, you reach a trance-like state where you are neither asleep nor awake. You are hypnotized!

Therapy will then take one of two different forms:

~ SUGGESTION THERAPY. Suggestions are made to your subconscious in order to change certain automatic responses which you normally make when you are fully conscious. The responses which are changed are the ones which have been giving you the problem.

~ ANALYTIC THERAPY. Information is obtained from your subconscious in order to find out what is causing your problem. This could involve you being taken back to your early childhood (regression). Once the problem area has been found, the emotional block which is causing the problem can be released.

The hypnotist may make a post-hypnotic suggestion to you whilst you are hypnotized, as part of the treatment. The effect of this is to bring about a different reaction from you when a certain set of circumstances present themselves. For example, a post-hypnotic suggestion may be made to you that cigarettes taste awful. On waking, when you are offered a cigarette you will accept one and even light it, but you find that you do not like the taste and have to put it out.

Normally you are de-hypnotized at the end of the session, or woken at a post-hypnotically suggested word or gesture, or you may simply sleep it off.

Self-hypnosis

Self-hypnosis can also be taught to you by the hypnotist. This is especially useful in areas of stress or pain management. Self-hypnosis is safe since the hypnotist, in instructing you how to do it, will make safety post-hypnotic suggestions to you so that, for example, if a fire should break out you will instantly bring yourself out of the hypnotic state. The number of sessions you have will obviously vary according to your particular problem and your ability to respond. As an example, simple weight control is usually effective after five or six sessions.

You can be referred to a hypnotist by your doctor or you can contact one yourself. When you first contact them, tell them briefly what your problem is and judge for yourself as to whether you feel they are sympathetic or not. If not, contact someone else.

The downside

Is there any risk involved? Conventionally, hypnotherapists state that your subconscious will only accept suggestions or commands from the hypnotist if they do not conflict with your moral code or instinct for self-preservation. Therefore, you will not lose your identity, become a puppet-type figure in the hands of an exploitive therapist, nor will you reveal secrets if you do not wish. These reassurances may only be partly true. Anyone who has ever attended a display of stage hypnosis may have seen people behaving in precisely these ways. For example, we have watched as men have had both their cheeks pierced with knitting needles, we have seen women instructed to behave extremely intimately with complete strangers, and we have seen people ordered to remain completely rigid and motionless for several hours at a time. It is difficult to believe that all these people willingly accepted these forms of degradation.

The truth about hypnosis is that it involves the domination of one mind over another. This means that it could, for example, attract practitioners whose overriding motivation is the desire to achieve power over others. Such a person is likely to put their own gratification ahead of any benefit to their patient.

It is thus very important that you ascertain for yourself that your hypnotherapist's major priority is the welfare of his patient – you. Any indications that this is not the case – for example, a disinterest in your medical history, or indications of a contemptuous attitude – should be taken as warning signs.

Hypnotherapy is a valuable way to help you deal with problems which are concerned with the mind and the use of will-power. With the above proviso, it is safe, it can sometimes eliminate the need for drugs and it may empower you to successfully manage the problem yourself. For help finding a qualified hypnotherapist, see the Help section.

Chapter 80

What to expect from iridology

"You can tell a lot from a person's eyes!" A cliche, perhaps, but one which reflects the essence of iridology.

Iridologists believe they can tell a great deal about you and your health by studying the iris of your eye. Your bodily strengths and weaknesses, any health problems you may have had in the past, your propensity for future illnesses, and, most importantly, accurate diagnosis of your current health disorders may all be revealed by careful examination of your neuro-optic reflex.

Iridology differs fundamentally from other complementary approaches in that it is not a therapy or treatment, but a diagnostic tool. The eye has been used as a mirror to spot disease since ancient times, but the genesis of iridology can be pinpointed exactly. In the 19th century, a Hungarian, Ignatz von Peczely, noticed that an injured owl had a small spot on its iris which gradually cleared as the injury healed. Von Peczely used this incident as the basis for the first iris chart – a map of the iris where each 'zone' represents an area of the body.

The system is held to work because the various parts of the body are directly connected to tiny areas of the iris, via the autonomic nervous system. Today iridology has a complex and sophisticated chart with which to identify human health problems. Great skill and training are required to interpret such a map but, primarily, diagnosis is achieved through detailed examination of the iris, its structure, shape and colour, its zones, pattern irregularities and so on. Your iris is unique to you. It's like a genetic fingerprint, perfectly reflecting your health record: past, present and future. In this sense, it allows you – the whole person – to be treated. It is an holistic diagnosis.

A visit to an iridologist may be useful as a supplement to other forms of diagnosis, both conventional and complementary. Also, iridologists believe they can sometimes spot health problems a long time before they make themselves known through troubling symptoms. It could, therefore, be considered as an early warning device.

What happens

What should you expect? Don't worry, it's an interesting experience – and a safe, painless, non-invasive examination. The iridologist will use a light and strong magnifying glass to examine your iris from the side. Both eyes will be examined. This will take up to an hour as the light source can only be used intermittently on the eye and great accuracy and attention to detail are required in analysis. During examination many questions will be asked to develop a patient/consultant feedback and your case history will be noted.

A photograph of your iris will then be taken using special equipment and an enlargement produced which will be used to fine-tune the diagnosis. Such photos are beautiful reflections of you and your state of well-being. They are also a useful means of comparison. If a fresh picture is taken, say every year, treatment progress and your ongoing health record can be monitored. This is no substitute for 'eye to eye' examination, as direct examination yields the greatest information, but it is a complementary technique.

Interpretation and treatment

Iridology may identify the source of a whole range of medical problems from the simple (a migraine) to the highly complex (hypoglycaemia). This is because the markings of the iris reveal both weaknesses inherent since birth and problems which have developed in later life. Iridology will not, however, reveal infectious diseases, pregnancy, kidney or gall stones, or length of life.

After diagnosis, a course of action or treatment may be recommended. Usually, iridologists will have a range of complementary treatments and therapies at their fingertips. These may include naturopathy, acupuncture, colonic irrigation, shiatsu massage, reflexology, aromatherapy, hydrotherapy and so on. Herbal remedies and a dietary regime are also brought into play. For example, if the inner area of the iris shows an irregularity, a disorder of the digestive system may be identified and a programme of bowel cleansing and herbal detoxification may be implemented.

The iridologist will also identify health problems which they are not equipped to treat. This fact is openly acknowledged. In such instances, the patient will be referred to the proper source of treatment, whether this be in the form of conventional or alternative medicine. Iridology generally welcomes closer relations with, and greater collaboration from, doctors.

Currently there are only about fifty practising iridologists in the UK, but you can obtain details of one nearest to you from the National Council and Register of Iridologists (see the Help section).

Chapter 81
What to expect from kinesiology

~

Part diagnosis, part therapy, kinesiology aims to restore your internal balance by touching for health.

Originating from the Greek word meaning the study of motion, this form of treatment involves assessment of the body's movement in order to ascertain its mental, chemical and structural state. An experienced kinesiologist can give you a readout of your body's condition within thirty minutes. So, for example, if you are thinking of taking up a particular exercise, you can get a muscle test outlining any possible problem areas. Or, if you just feel generally that something is not quite right, an applied kinesiologist can try to find the answer. Touch For Health is a development of kinesiology, and aims to teach everyone simple and safe techniques for everyday use.

Kinesiology is based on the idea that structural, chemical and mental factors can all cause structural stress. Through examination of the body's structure these root causes can be diagnosed before they begin to affect us in more serious ways. This has all sorts of important implications. Often, for example, we may have an emotional problem we find difficult to discuss, or may not even be fully aware of. A kinesiologist may be able to pinpoint this underlying weakness by muscle examination.

Embracing the idea that the body never lies, kinesiology aims to act as a preventive treatment for a range of ailments. Growing children's posture can be corrected before any fault actually manifests itself. Parents can play their own role in this by looking for any lack of symmetry in their child's body and taking note of any physical complaint: there is no such thing as a growing pain. We often shrug off abnormalities as acceptable variations; kinesiologists maintain we, doctors included, must re-educate ourselves.

The energy to matter relationship

Assessment is based on the theory that all matter has an energy pattern, both cellular and general. This energy in other substances can affect our own bodily energy, often adversely. For example, if we eat something with an unusual pattern, such as a highly processed, synthetic food, our body may find it difficult to absorb. This can manifest itself in the form of a weak muscle. Normally, it is very difficult to ascertain our body's reaction to a substance unless it shows itself very violently, and then often the damage has been done. Kinesiology tries to give you the messages your body would love to scream out at you itself, such as: Don't give me any more caffeine; it's killing my adrenal glands!

Making use of the acupuncturist's system of meridians, kinesiologists suggest that temperature changes in specific places can indicate meridianal imbalance. Unlike acupuncturists, they only use this system for diagnosis and not for treatment. To find an imbalance, a patient's bodily temperature in particular spots may be measured, sometimes with a special instrument.

What happens

In the examination it is important to be as honest as possible. The chances are any secrets will show themselves anyway! Firstly, any possible imbalances will just be looked for, then points will be stimulated and your reaction noted: this is the beginning of the muscle testing procedure. The kinesiologist may use a tablet compound to discover a nutritional response by placing it on your tongue and then testing a weak muscle for strength. Different compounds may be administered until the muscle reacts with the strong response. Muscle testing will look for any structural cause of a body malfunctioning.

Energy imbalances are not only caused by chemicals in food. Our environment is full of chemicals to which we are constantly exposed. Emotion also has an important role to play. We may balk at the notion that a weak emotional state can in turn cause muscle weakness; but the mental affects the physical in all sorts of ways. When we are frightened, for example, we perspire, our heart beats faster and numerous other bodily changes take place.

Kinesiologists propose that if the endocrine system receives faulty messages, then inappropriate body responses may be the result. Calling these scrambled messages dysponesis, kinesiologists believe that they may result from feelings such as anger or grief. The thought process causing these feelings creates certain energy patterns which can influence the energy patterns of autonomic nerve signals and so cause a physical weakness. A patient suffering from such a condition will be instructed in exercises called nerve patterning procedures, which will help to correct the disorganization.

Building on the chiropractic technique of spinal manipulation, a kinesiologist will first carry out bone and muscle testing. Because any misalignment of vertebrae can have serious repercussions in other areas of the body, manipulation is used to treat such problems; and then the bones and muscles are immediately re-tested to discover if the manipulation has worked.

Kinesiologists have found that proprioceptors are a key to our body's condition. These tiny nerve cells communicate complex information about the environment to the responding bodily area and are found in the muscles, joints, skin and ears. It is thought that proprioceptors in the feet impart the sense of movement and position to the other parts of the body, so that imbalanced walking can confuse these nerves and cause damage. This has important implications when you realize that only ten per cent of the population walk equally on both feet. To look for possible imbalance yourself, check your shoes for even wear. They should wear down the same amount on each foot and evenly from side to side. Examine your feet for any corns or callouses. Numbness, pain and poor circulation in the leg or foot can also indicate a problem.

One must realize that the aim of kinesiology is mainly preventive; chronic illnesses such as cancer cannot be cured. When choosing a kinesiologist, make sure he or she is a graduate chiropractor. During a treatment session, they should explain their action, your bodily responses, give nutritional advice and try to correct any problems. For information and a list of registered practitioners see the Help section.

CHAPTER 82
WHAT TO EXPECT FROM MASSAGE

~

If you thought massage was just a euphemism for something you'd never dream of doing, you could be pleasantly surprised. It's a thoroughly respectable technique to be used for a range of problems, from indigestion to grief.

Therapeutic massage brings you many health-related benefits and uses one of our most natural healing instincts, touch. Mothers automatically touch a child's sore tummy or bruised knee. Touching is encouraged in couples who are experiencing problems with their relationship and studies show that children who are brought up in a touch-oriented family grow up healthier and happier.

Massage develops this concept of touch and, by applying various techniques, provides a means of deep relaxation. It can:

~ Improve circulation and energize you.
~ Aid digestion.
~ Help to eliminate toxic wastes.
~ Provide the psychological benefit of an increased sense of well-being.
~ Lower blood pressure.
~ Alleviate pain in arthritis and rheumatism.
~ Help cancer patients by reducing feelings of isolation.
~ Help with drug and alcohol rehabilitation by showing that there are other ways of feeling good.
~ Help slimmers, not by reducing weight or breaking down fat but by improving their sense of well-being, increasing energy and therefore making it easier to exercise.
~ Help insomniacs and migraine sufferers.
~ Help bereaved people through contact and providing a means of releasing pent-up emotions.

What happens

The massage should take place in a warm, quiet environment. Most masseuses prefer to work on a special massage table which is padded yet firm. Others work on the floor, with a padding of blankets for you to lie on. Beds are unsuitable because they are too soft.

If you are having a full massage, you will lie on the table undressed but covered with towels; only the area being massaged is uncovered.

The masseuse will start with effleurage: stroking movements using oil or talcum powder as a lubricant. Although there is no set sequence of working around the body, a typical one would be right foot and leg, left foot and leg, left hand and arm, right hand and arm, abdomen, back of legs and back, chest, face and head.

A whole body massage takes between sixty and ninety minutes. If that amount of time is not available it is best to concentrate on just one or two areas such as the back and shoulders or face and neck, rather than trying to rush through the whole sequence.

Besides effleurage, the following techniques are also used:

~ FRICTION: to open the pores, increase circulation to the skin's surface and to tone it up.
~ KNEADING AND RUBBING: to work on muscle tissue and stimulate blood supply.
~ HACKING: to relieve muscle congestion, strains and spasms.

The various techniques are used to either stimulate, strengthen or relax your body. The massage can be further enhanced with the use of scented oils from herbs, flowers or trees – in a similar way to aromatherapy. The oils can be used to affect your mood or help with a physical problem such as acne or ageing skin. For example, lavender oil has a calming effect, helps alleviate depression, and eases aches and pains as well as helping with wounds or inflamed insect bites.

A more specific massage technique called manual lymph drainage is used to help eliminate toxins from the body, for example in acne, eczema, fluid retention problems and sports injuries. It uses soft rhythmic movements which start closest to the torso and which are directed to the nearest lymph node, gradually working towards the extremities.

Related therapies

There are other specific therapeutic techniques which work on the same principle of touch and massage. It is worth trying several until you find the therapy which is right for you:

~ SHIATSU (see chapter 93). An oriental massage which uses pressure on the body's meridians of energy to help alleviate physical problems or to restore the body's energy balance.

~ REFLEXOLOGY (see chapter 90). Stimulation of reflex points on the feet which correspond to other parts of the body.

~ ROLFING (see chapter 92). A deep muscle massage which, although frequently painful, breaks down unnecessary connective tissue to free the posture and increase your sense of well-being.

~ DO-IN. A form of do-it-yourself shiatsu.

Massage has suffered from a slightly sleazy image in the past. Fortunately, with the growth in numbers of properly trained therapists (look for the ITEC Certificate in Swedish Massage), it is now being taken seriously again as people discover its truly therapeutic uses. You can find massage facilities in many health clubs and gyms. Some health food shops also have treatment rooms attached. So, forget its previously tainted image. Try a massage and you may be surprised to find out just how wonderful you can feel!

CHAPTER 83
WHAT TO EXPECT FROM MUSIC THERAPY

~

For most people listening to music is simply one of life's pleasures. For the music therapist, however, music is a powerful healing tool. It is claimed that music therapy (MT) can help children and adults who are physically and mentally handicapped; that it can be a therapy to elderly people who have become confused and isolated; and that other people, such as criminals and juvenile offenders, who may have very deep-rooted emotional problems, can come to express themselves and communicate more effectively. These are bold claims, but there's growing evidence that they are valid.

"And it came to pass, when the evil spirit from God was upon Saul, that David took an harp, and played with his hands so Saul was refreshed, and was well, and the evil spirit departed from him." *I Samuel 16:23*

The healing effects of playing and listening to music have long been known. The Arabs had a highly developed modal system of MT for treating maladies ranging from dementia to venereal disease!

Broadly speaking there are three interweaving strands or approaches to MT: the clinical, the recreational and the educational.

Clinical MT

This is by far the most important and radical use of MT. It forms a medical and psychological treatment for physical, mental and emotional disorders. Here MT is a therapeutic process in the truest sense in that the qualified music therapist will use their training in psychology, in counselling, in musical skills and in the understanding of the illness itself to effect a breakthrough in treatment.

This expertise is brought to bear on a variety of serious disorders ranging from children and adults who are educationally subnormal, to those with mental illness, and the severely physically handicapped. Many disorders and impairments leading to a physical, social and intellectual isolation; brain damage, depression, respiratory diseases, blindness, deafness, muscular dystrophy, and so on, can all respond in a positive way to MT. Listening to, or making, music will act as a stimulus to the patient, bringing them into greater contact with the outside world, with other people and with their own emotions.

Active participation in a musical group increases confidence and enhances the feeling of involvement. Solo efforts can, literally, give the patient a voice. Even passive MT eases the patient's tensions, relaxing them and freeing frustrations and emotional blockages.

The scientific evidence that MT is effective is growing all the time. "Music has the ability to dispel much of the fear and anxiety associated with facing the unknown alone," concluded one recent report into the use of music during surgery in hospitals. "As such it is an ideal support for patients undergoing surgery where a non-general anaesthetic is administered." This study questioned twenty-five patients, each of whom had had an operation performed on them which required a local, rather than a general, anaesthetic. Each one of them revealed positive support for the music that they listened to during their operation. Their remarks focused on the ability of the music, as a familiar personal and cultural medium, to ease their anxiety, to act as a distractor and to increase their threshold of pain."[442]

Perhaps it is not really surprising that music can help people to feel less stressful in hospital, but it is rather amazing to learn that music can play a part in the control of rheumatism and arthritis. In fact, several studies have now been published which indicate that MT can reduce pain and improve the quality of life of sufferers. In one study, eighty-six patients with rheumatoid arthritis were given 'emotional volitional training', a new treatment which comprises music therapy combined with group physical training. The scientists found that, after treatment, the doses of the patients' usual arthritis medication could be reduced by as much as 50 per cent; the patients' mental status was much improved; their ability to work increased; and the length of time they were hospitalized decreased.[443, 444]

People who have suffered a heart attack can also benefit from MT. After having a heart attack, a patient is often admitted to a coronary care unit. This, in itself, can be an extremely stressful event, and it is known that the amount of stress a patient has to cope with can affect their recovery. Another recent study aimed to find out whether MT could help to reduce this stress and, by doing so, improve the patient's chances of survival and recovery. Eighty patients, all recently admitted to a coronary care unit, were divided into two groups. One received MT, the other didn't. The study found: "After attending three sessions in two days, patient stress was evaluated by heart rates, temperatures, heart complications, and the patient's own feelings about their stress. Those patients who received music therapy had fewer cardiac complications, and thought that the therapy was beneficial for their condition. It is concluded that music and relaxation therapy are effective in reducing stress in patients and may aid in their prognosis and recovery."[445]

In summary, it seems as if MT has an important part to play in the healing process. Increasingly, orthodox medicine is willing to accept the benefits that MT can bring. In recent months, scientific papers have appeared in medical journals showing how MT can help in the treatment of an extremely wide range of diseases and afflictions, including breathing training and relaxation,[446] paediatric nursing,[447] dentistry,[448] the mentally handicapped,[449] severe head injury,[450] cancer pain control[451] and Alzheimer's disease.[452] MT is clearly here to stay.

Recreational MT

Recreational MT is now becoming available more widely, and is concerned primarily with the non-clinical uses of music. It ranges from music activity as a form of patient welfare in hospitals (it can combat institutionalization) to MT workshops for those seeking to overcome social problems like shyness, social embarrassment, anxiety or isolation. It is also plainly a way of releasing the stresses and frustrations of hectic modern life and a way of having fun with other people. Workshops involving communal singing, chanting, and humming foster and nurture a good, positive feeling about the self and lead to a spontaneous outburst of joyful energy.

By utilizing individual response to sound, music is used to reach hidden zones of consciousness, to create inner calmness, clarity and order. The psyche is tapped, self-understanding enhanced, a sense of community emphasized, harmony and creativity stimulated. Again, techniques will vary from therapist to therapist, student to student.

Educational MT

The approaches mentioned are, of course, learning situations. All therapy is educational, whether the patient or student is old or young, handicapped or able bodied, beginner or expert. Music therapy works at all levels, for the mentally handicapped or the jaded, ennui-ridden businessman or woman. In this instance MT can be utilized to assist personal development, with musical techniques used to develop imagination and communication ability. The slow learning child can be encouraged, the habitual young offender rehabilitated, all through nurturing creativity and teaching practical musical skills.

How does it work?

Dr. James Borling, head of the music therapy department at Radford University in the US, believes that "music reaches centres in the brain which are not reached by simple dialogue or rational thought. Music in and of itself is not a cure, but it is a catalyst."[453]

The main constituents of music – tone, pitch, note-duration, volume and colour – affect people in specific, individual ways. Response varies from person to person, depending on what is being listened to or the means of producing the sound. Some people will respond positively to a classical theme, others to Elvis. The therapist knows this and works on it.

The main aim is to encourage the affected person to communicate on a non-verbal level. A bridge is formed between the inner self and the real world. For example, a child with Lowes syndrome (who is silent and completely isolated from reality) may, with MT, gentle persuasion, and the therapist's persistence, start to bang a drum and create a rhythm. The language barrier is bypassed and a cathartic non-verbal communication achieved, on which further communication can be built.

Other disorders will respond to singing, dancing, tapping, clapping, playing an instrument, or merely passively listening to the beat of the music. Techniques will necessarily vary according to the depth of the problem and the nature of the individual being treated. The evidence suggests that MT can help most problems in some way. Private therapists will charge about £25 per session, but MT is sometimes available on the NHS. See the Help section for organizations which will send you more information, or which will locate a music therapist in your area.

Chapter 84
What to expect from naturopathy

~

Have you ever wished there was an approach to medicine based not on drugs and chemicals, nor on esoteric beliefs, but on the very nature of humankind? Naturopathy connects orthodox and unorthodox practices, with you as the vital link!

A growing number of individuals believe they have been failed by the conventional treatments of orthodox medicine. Should you be one of these, consider submitting your medical problem – be it physical or mental – to the natural healing methods of naturopathy.

Naturopathy (sometimes called nature cure) is a system of treating illness and maintaining health which goes back to ancient Greek times. Hippocrates originated the concept of the body's natural ability to heal itself. A regime of wholesome food, fresh air, exercise, sunshine and freedom from worry acted as the vehicle for this holistic self-regeneration.

However, it was between the world wars of the 20th century that naturopathy really took off, with the development of health spas where patients could take the 'cure' and rejuvenate the mind and body through hydrotherapy, diet, massage, osteopathy and other healing arts. Naturopathy's four basic principles were laid down at this time, and you will recognize Hippocrates' age-old tenet of self-healing among them.

~ Patient individuality
~ Treat causes not symptoms
~ Everybody has the innate power to heal him or herself
~ Treat the whole person, not merely the affected parts

Naturopathy today has moved on from its rather old-fashioned image of the 1930s. It argues that it is not an alternative medicine in the same way as, say, acupuncture or aromatherapy. Rather, it is the fundamental medicine that, fused with the twin precepts of diet and manipulation, releases our inner power to return to vibrant health. Naturopaths believe they can treat a whole range of disorders, from migraines to depression, back trouble to eczema, and even more serious diseases such as cancer, by attentive diagnosis, treating the whole person and stressing preventive techniques.

What happens

To start off you will receive an intensive introductory session, which may last up to two hours, and cost about £30. The naturopath will study your medical history, listen to your problems and find out the nature of your main complaint and any subsidiary complaints. This will include a thorough examination of the body, especially the spine.

Simultaneously, they will probably explain the concept of naturopathy as a system. Further sessions of shorter duration, for about £20, will involve the design of a strict diet regime plus use of techniques aimed at freeing the natural forces of the body. These then fight your ailments and promote well-being. The naturopath will feel for these forces to release them. This is often cathartic in itself and has been likened to letting it rip! However, this may also be difficult, as such forces are often blocked by factors such as:

~ Use of drugs, alcohol and tobacco
~ Hereditary factors
~ Environmental conditions usually to do with domestic and occupational circumstances
~ Bad diet

These blocks must be removed for the natural vitality of the body to flow and for self-repair to take place. The naturopath will use whatever tools they feel necessary or appropriate to achieve this, for naturopathy is an umbrella for many types of treatment: reflexology, homoeopathy, osteopathy, colonic irrigation, massage, herbalism and so on. These are all used at various times, depending on the problem.

The core of naturopathy

These individual treatments are in themselves regarded as transitional, or as back-ups to the main thrust of naturopathy, which is concern for the following key considerations:

~ DIET. The advocacy of natural foods such as fruits, nuts, cereals, vegetables and dairy produce, all processed as little as possible. Consumption of cooked, refined and concentrated foods must be reduced. A diet will be structured to the needs of the individual patient and may include fasting to remove impurities from the body and restore it to its natural state of balance. It is important to remove all the rubbish from the body, the accumulated store of poisons, like caffeine and additives, which have built up through eating the wrong foods.

~ BODY MANIPULATION. Balancing the nervous system and restructuring the spine. This can involve a range of treatments, from chiropractic through osteopathy to advanced sacro-occipital technique (SOT). Basically, the whole body, from brain to sacrum, the keystone of the pelvis, must be balanced to restore the human organism to all-round health.

The naturopath would expect the treatment to have fairly swift and dramatic results. Through basic natural healing and natural medicine, through regard of the whole person and the triangular relationship of the mental, physical and spiritual (emotional) factors, the body will be set on a true course to cure itself.

Does it work?

This is a difficult question to answer, because naturopathy may involve so many different techniques and disciplines. Orthodox medicine would argue that naturopathy has not been subject to the usual battery of scientific trials, and therefore cannot be deemed to be effective.

However, there are three good answers to this. First, thousands – perhaps millions – of people will vouch that naturopathy has worked for them, sometimes when conventional medicine has failed. This, by itself, does not constitute scientific proof of effectiveness, but it *is* strongly suggestive.

Secondly, orthodox medicine is altogether too eager to dismiss naturopathy, along with many other 'alternative' therapies, without giving them a fair trial. This is a deeply unscientific attitude, and smacks of prejudice. When we undertook a search of all the world's major medical publications, we found that naturopathy had been mentioned in less than 200 papers published since 1966 – a tiny, insignificant proportion of the total number of papers published. And many of those references were disparaging. What's worse, we could find no well-conducted, large-scale scientific trials to fully evaluate the potential of naturopathy.

Many eminent doctors would no doubt contend that it is not the responsibility of orthodox medicine to undertake scientific trials into the effectiveness of naturopathy. They would say (as they have said about many other complementary therapies) that it is up to the therapist to prove the effectiveness of his or her treatment. This is true – sometimes. For example, it is surely the responsibility of the Gerson Institute to prove that its therapy is all they say it is (see chapter 73). However, naturopathy is not comparable to the Gerson therapy, because it is not a fixed, prescribed course of treatment. Naturopathy is a flexible system of treatment which believes it provides the whole answer to health problems which have often been looked at in isolation by ordinary and alternative medicine. Essentially, it is an *approach* to treatment, rather than a prescription. And the treatment offered by one naturopath may be quite different to the treatment offered by another. Because of this, it is just not possible to evaluate 'naturopathy' and produce a meaningful answer. Actually, it would be rather like trying to evaluate 'Generals': some will be good commanders of their men, while others won't; some will employ good tactics sometimes, others won't. To get a useful answer, you have to be more specific.

The third, and most overwhelming, argument in favour of naturopathy is very often overlooked. Quite simply: over the past few years, modern medicine has (without anyone appearing to notice) quietly adopted a number of naturopathic practices, and called them its own. For years, naturopathic practitioners were urging their patients to eat less fat, and increase the amount of complex carbohydrates in their diets. For their pains, they were regarded as 'cranks'. This was at the time when conventional medical wisdom held that it was impossible for anyone to be well-nourished without copious quantities of meat and dairy produce in their diets. Slowly, we are learning the lesson that such a diet is the world's most lethal. Cancer, heart disease, arthritis, diabetes – all these occur much less frequently in people who follow a more nearly 'naturopathic' diet. Modern medicine now accepts this, but has singularly failed to give naturopathy credit. A similar lesson can be learned from orthodox medicine's adoption of other naturopathic tools such as chiropractic, (see chapter 69), and indeed, many of the other therapies mentioned in this book.

It seems as if orthodox medicine is prepared to accept, when necessary, that many of the healing tools used by naturopathy may, in fact, be effective. But it is still not prepared to accept that the underlying philososphy may also be valid. This is a shame, because in some ways, naturopathy is the missing link between the two warring philosophies of medicine. It is one you should consider trying, particularly if you have found other treatments ineffective and unsatisfactory.

To find a local naturopath, contact the organizations in the Help section. They will supply you with addresses of local practitioners and further information.

CHAPTER 85
WHAT TO EXPECT FROM ORTHOMOLECULAR THERAPY

~

It's a new science, ready to replace the outmoded ideas of 'old nutrition' according to Dr. Linus Pauling, winner of two Nobel prizes and inventor of orthomolecular medicine.

In the world of science, Dr. Linus Pauling holds a unique position. A controversial figure, he is revered and vilified in roughly equal amounts by doctors and scientists. In 1954 he won the Nobel prize for chemistry, in recognition of his pioneering work on the molecular structure of chemicals. In 1962 he again won a Nobel prize, this time for peace, in recognition of his campaigning work to ban the atmospheric testing of nuclear weapons by America, the USSR and Britain. At the time, the three superpowers maintained that there was absolutely no danger to the public from the radioactive fallout which their atomic explosions created. Difficult though it is for us to believe today, the American Atomic Energy Commission tried hard to convince Americans that atmospheric fallout was actually *good* for them. Citing evidence of studies on fruit flies, they put forward the view that radiation could bestow "more vigour, hardiness, resistance to disease, and better reproductive capacity".[454] In support of their position, they enlisted the help of Willard Libby, another Nobel laureate.

Pauling's response was typical of his careful, painstaking and often iconoclastic approach towards science. After a methodical analysis of the data Libby had produced to support his view that atmospheric fallout was 'safe', Pauling demonstrated that, on the evidence produced by Libby and the Atomic Energy Commission, the series of atomic test explosions then being proposed would result in 55,000 children being born with gross physical and mental defects, and more than 500,000 miscarriages, stillbirths and newborn deaths. Controversy erupted internationally and Pauling was at the centre of it. Having greatly angered the American authorities, he had his passport revoked and became the target of much official smearing and slander (*Life* magazine called his Nobel prize a 'weird insult from Norway'). Nevertheless, Pauling achieved his objective, and the atmospheric test ban treaty came into effect on the same day that he received his second Nobel prize.

In the world of science, Pauling has always been several steps ahead of the pack. For this, too, he has often had to endure much acrimonious criticism. Nevertheless, his ideas have almost always turned out to be correct. In the 1920s, his revolutionary theories concerning the three-dimensional structure of chemical molecules and their bonds (much opposed by 'orthodox' chemists at the time) essentially laid the foundations for modern chemistry. The molecular chemistry which is today taught in schools and universities owes much to Pauling's trailblazing work.

Many other major scientific achievements followed. He pioneered the understanding of protein structure, and explained the molecular basis of sickle-cell anaemia. He discovered the 'alpha helix' – the way in which polypeptide chains are arranged in proteins – and in 1953 he proposed the screw-like helix structure of the DNA molecule. This came tantalizingly close to the correct double-helix structure which Watson and Crick proposed the same year. (In his memoirs, James Watson tells of his great fear that Pauling would beat him to the discovery of the structure of DNA.) Banned from travelling (his passport was still revoked by the US State Department), Pauling was denied access to X-ray photographs of the DNA molecule, which would have completed his understanding of DNA's structure, thus winning him his third Nobel prize.

In 1983, after a lifetime of extraordinary scientific achievement, he was awarded the Priestley Medal, the highest honour of the American Chemical Society, in recognition of his stature as perhaps the world's leading chemist.

Today, ninety years old, Pauling is still busy, conducting research and stirring up controversy. His current work centres around his theory of orthomolecular medicine. "I have coined the term *orthomolecular medicine,*" says Pauling, "for the preservation of good health and the treatment of disease by varying the concentrations in the human body of substances that are normally present in the body and are required for health."[455] Pauling uses the word 'orthomolecular' to distinguish this sort of medicine from conventional drug treatment – which could be called 'toximolecular' medicine.

In fact, some forms of conventional medicine are also orthomolecular in their mode of action. Pauling cites the use of insulin to treat diabetes as one example. Insulin is a substance which is naturally present in the human body, although in the case of diabetics, not in sufficient quantity. When given additional insulin, a diabetic person can live a perfectly normal life. Similarly, orthomolecular medicine uses supplementation of other substances which are naturally found in the human body (usually vitamins) in order to bring about an optimum state of health.

Vitamins are, of course, vital for a healthy body, but Pauling maintains that the amounts necessary for disease-free robust good health are much larger than the officially-recommended daily allowances – often so much larger that they cannot be reasonably obtained from the present-day diet.

The orthomolecular way to health

Pauling recommends the following daily programme for adults:

~ Vitamin C – 6,000 to 18,000 milligrams

~ Vitamin E – 400, 800 or 1,600 IU

~ One or two Vitamin B complex tablets

~ Vitamin A – 25,000 IU

~ A general mineral supplement, including 100mg calcium, 18mg iron, 0.15mg iodine, 1mg copper, 25mg magnesium, 3mg manganese, 15mg zinc, 0.015mg molybdenum, 0.015mg chromium, 0.015mg selenium.

~ Very low sugar intake, plenty of water to drink, regular physical activity, moderate alcohol consumption, no cigarettes, and an avoidance of stress.

Does it work?

There are scientific studies to show that orthomolecular medicine is effective, and there are also scientific studies to show that orthomolecular medicine is not effective. And that's where the controversy lies!

Orthodox dieticians – the sort commonly found supervising those awful menus found too often in hospitals – are almost always suspicious of vitamin supplements. Very often, a dietician will tell you that people who buy vitamin pills are pouring their money straight down the drain. Some dieticians even believe that if an individual is satisfying their energy requirements (i.e. getting enough calories), then it is very difficult for them to be deficient in anything. This 'orthodox' point of view is rarely questioned or debated in public. In television, on the radio and in the newspapers, the opinion of the orthodox dietician or nutritionist is almost always accepted as being the ultimate voice of authority and therefore beyond criticism.

When the media examines the vitamins industry, which it does quite regularly, it usually follows a predictable, timeworn formula. One such 'exposé', typical of many, covered nearly half a page in a national newspaper. "People are being persuaded to buy huge quantities of dietary supplements such as zinc and vitamins," the article began, "in the mistaken belief that they are vital to their well-being."

Further in the article, a dietician was quoted as saying: "If people were eating a healthy diet with plenty of fruit, vegetables, lean meat, potatoes and bread, particularly wholemeal bread, they would be getting all the zinc, iron, vitamins and other minerals they need, without having to worry about the minute details."

And a nutritionist was quoted as saying: "If you are satisfying your energy requirements from ordinary food, it is quite hard to become deficient in anything."[456]

It would be all too easy to gain the casual impression from media reports that vitamin supplements are purchased and used by the gullible and the eccentric, and that the average diet provides all the nutrition we need. But this isn't the case. Two British government reports into the diets of schoolchildren and the elderly – two groups of the population who require particularly good nutrition – have revealed a worrying picture.

Looking first at the diets eaten by schoolchildren, the official evidence shows that:

~ More than 30 per cent of children between the ages of ten and eleven were getting less than the recommended daily allowance of vitamin A.

~ Among those aged between fourteen and fifteen, over 25 per cent were getting less than the recommended daily allowance of vitamin A.

~ Fifteen per cent of children between the ages of ten and eleven were getting less than the recommended daily allowance of riboflavin (a B group vitamin which is vital for normal growth and development).

~ Among those aged between fourteen and fifteen, over 25 per cent were getting less than the recommended daily allowance of riboflavin.

~ Eighty per cent of children between the ages of ten and eleven were getting less than the recommended daily allowance of iron (which prevents anaemia and is essential for haemoglobin production).

~ Among those aged between fourteen and fifteen, over 50 per cent were getting less than the recommended daily allowance of iron.[457]

Additionally, the survey revealed that many children also had low intakes of calcium (the building material for teeth and bones) and pyridoxine (another vital B group vitamin essential for normal brain function). Despite this troubling evidence, another government report (reviewing the state of the nation's health) casually stated that "schoolchildren in all regions and social classes were well nourished" and: "Most children had more than adequate nutrient intakes."[458]

A similar official survey also examined the dietary intakes of people aged over sixty-five years of age. The results were equally disturbing:

~ Over 50 per cent were getting less than the recommended daily allowance of vitamin A.

~ Over 60 per cent were getting less than the recommended daily allowance of riboflavin.

~ Over 40 per cent were getting less than the recommended daily allowance of vitamin C.

~ Over 80 per cent were getting less than the recommended daily allowance of pyridoxine.[459]

From this research, it is crystal clear that some people are not even meeting the very low officially-recommended nutritional targets, let alone coming close to the much higher figures suggested by orthomolecular medicine.

Notwithstanding this hard evidence of widespread inadequate nutrition, the orthodox viewpoint is the only one regularly given any credence by the media. 'Megadoses' of vitamins are almost always viewed with deep suspicion, or downright hostility. Rarely is any attempt made to question the prevailing wisdom that "vitamin supplements are a waste of money".

Ultimately, the two main objections to vitamin supplementation seem to be these. Firstly, the idea is repeated *ad nauseam* that people who take supplements are jeopardizing their health by 'overdosing' on vitamins. And secondly, because manufacturing and selling vitamins is a normal commercial operation, a subtle innuendo is often introduced which suggests that the manufacturers of vitamin supplements are somehow corrupt or, at the very least, unscrupulous. To illustrate the second point, newspaper 'exposés' regularly quote the size of the vitamin market (estimates vary, according to the article, but it is usually put between £50 and £100 million). The sheer size of the market is supposed to make us think that the manufacturers *must* be unethical.

In actual fact, the market is rather small, even accepting the higher estimate of £100 million. Compare it to the market for tobacco, for example, which is worth £8.5 billion in Britain alone – that's eighty-five times larger than the market for vitamin supplements![460] And tobacco is certainly more harmful to our health!

The other objection to vitamin supplementation concerns the possible adverse effects of overdosage. Linus Pauling is quick to point out that many physicians don't appreciate the difference between conventional medical drugs (which can be extremely toxic and have many unpleasant side effects) and vitamins. "It is easy to develop an exaggerated and unjustified fear of the toxicity of vitamins," he believes.

But can you hurt yourself by taking such large doses of vitamins? Many orthodox practitioners warn darkly about the "dangers of vitamin overdosage". Let's examine the major components of Pauling's daily regime, in relation to their toxic effects.

Vitamin C

~ At the top of the list comes vitamin C. Orthomolecular medicine believes that our bodies require much larger amounts of vitamin C than is normally found in our diets. In evolutionary terms, our bodies are certainly used to consuming far more vitamin C than we obtain from today's artificial foodstuffs. Our close cousin the gorilla, for example, requires four to five grams of vitamin C a day. Linus Pauling suggests a daily adult intake of between 6,000 and 18,000 milligrams (6 to 18 grams) of vitamin C. Even at the lower dose, this is still one hundred times greater than the officially recommended intakes in many countries, which were first determined many years ago, largely on the basis of the dose required to prevent scurvy in most people.

At this much higher dose, what side effects are there? The evidence shows that there are really very few indeed. Vitamin C (ascorbic acid) is almost always non-toxic. Since it is soluble in water, excess amounts will simply pass into your urine and be excreted. Rarely, adverse reactions have been reported, including nausea, vomiting, heartburn, abdominal cramps, diarrhoea, fatigue, flushing, headache, insomnia, or sleepiness. These can all be corrected, if they occur, simply by reducing the dose.

Pregnant women are perhaps a special case. Newborn babies have sometimes been found to suffer from scurvy if their mothers have taken very large doses of vitamin C while pregnant.[461] The reason for this is simply that the infant in the womb becomes accustomed to receiving high doses of vitamin C, which are suddenly discontinued following the baby's birth. A 'discontinuation' effect then ensues, until the baby adjusts to its new, lower intake of vitamin C. Although this effect can certainly occur, it is difficult to estimate just how serious a problem it really is. In adults, the same effect can also occur if someone who is taking large doses of vitamin C suddenly stops. "The discontinuation effect may not be very important for most people," Pauling believes, but as a safety precaution, he recommends gradually reducing the dose in stages rather than stopping abruptly (if, that is, you ever want to cut back on your vitamin C supplementation).

On the other hand, Pauling wisely points out that the dangers of not getting enough vitamin C during pregnancy are very real. Vitamin C is needed by both the mother and the growing baby – amongst other things, it is used to produce healthy bones, teeth and connective tissue in the developing infant. Conventional medicine certainly recognizes that a low level of vitamin C in the mother can jeopardize the baby's well-being, and most countries suggest that pregnant and lactating mothers increase their vitamin C consumption considerably. Pauling suggests that pregnant women should take about one gram (1000mg) of vitamin C a day.

It has been suggested that another possible side effect of large doses of vitamin C may be hyperoxaluria (high levels of oxalate in the urine), leading to stones being formed in the urinary tract. Again, it is hard to establish precisely how serious this potential problem really is. Certainly, a small minority of people have a genetic tendency to have high levels of oxalic acid in their bodies, and such people should consequently avoid eating food which has a high oxalate content (spinach and rhubarb are the two most common examples), and should probably also limit their intake of vitamin C. But the vast majority of people do not suffer from this genetic defect.

Other 'scares' relating to vitamin C consumption surface from time to time. Pauling deals with many of them in his landmark book, by patiently demonstrating that the underlying science is not correct.[462] For example, one report suggested that taking large doses of vitamin C acted to destroy vitamin B_{12} in food. Pauling examined the research evidence, and showed that the scientists making this claim were wrong – they used an inaccurate method of measuring the amount of B_{12} present in foodstuffs, which led them to produce erroneous results.

Turning to the positive side, Pauling and others have convincingly demonstrated that orthomolecular-sized doses of vitamin C can play a vital role in strengthening the body's natural defences. The most well-known example of the effective orthomolecular use of vitamin C concerns the common cold. "I believe that every person can protect himself or herself from the common cold," says Pauling. "Catching a cold and letting it run its course is a sign that you are not taking enough vitamin C."[463]

Numerous controlled scientific studies of vitamin C have indeed shown that it can prevent or reduce the severity of colds. Here are three chosen from many:

~ In Canada, scientists from the University of Toronto School of Hygiene set up two groups, consisting of over 400 people in each, who were randomly allocated a pill containing either 1,000mg (one gram) of vitamin C, or a placebo. Over four months, it was found that the group receiving the vitamin C were 30 per cent less likely to suffer from an incapacitating cold than the group receiving the placebo.

Forty per cent more of the vitamin C-takers stayed entirely free of all kinds of illness, including colds and 'flu, than the placebo-takers.[464]

~ A study of soldiers operating under Arctic conditions followed the same research format. Half of them received 1000 mg (one gram) of vitamin C a day, and half of them received a placebo. After four weeks of taking the pills, the experimenters found that those taking vitamin C had 68 per cent fewer days of illness compared to those taking the placebo.[465]

~ Orthomolecular medicine believes that colds can not only be prevented by taking large doses of vitamin C, but that they can also be cured with it – providing action is taken soon enough. This has been demonstrated in a very convincing study: 133 people with colds were treated with 1,000mg (one gram) of vitamin C six times a day (daily dose six grams). One group started treatment on the first day that cold symptoms were reported, a second group started treatment on the second day, and a third group started treatment on the third day. In addition to these three groups, a fourth 'control' group also received a placebo.

Every well-designed study must define its terms of 'failure' and 'success', and in this study 'failure' was defined as a cold which lasted 15 days or more, and which resulted in secondary bacterial infections. In both the placebo group (who consumed no vitamin C) and the third-day starters, the failure rate was high – about 40 per cent of each group developed colds which lasted 15 days or more, and which resulted in secondary bacterial infections. In the two-day starters, only 20 per cent of the group 'failed'. And for those who commenced vitamin C therapy on the first day of the cold, only 13 per cent went on to develop a full-blown cold. Similarly, the average number of days of illness was 3.9 for those taking vitamin C on the first day, 5.4 for those who started on the second day, and 9 days for those who didn't start treatment until the third day.[466]

Of course, there have also been studies which seem to show that vitamin C is of no use in the treatment or prevention of the cold. Such studies hit the headlines, in the medical press as well as more general newspapers, with the result that many doctors and ordinary people now believe that Pauling's theories have been discredited. But this simply is not the case.

Pauling has always given time and careful thought to any evidence which seems to contradict the orthomolecular theory of medicine. Often, he has subsequently demonstrated that the conclusions are, in point of fact, fallacious.

A study of students attending the University of Minnesota is often cited by critics of orthomolecular medicine to disprove the vitamin C hypothesis. The conclusion of the study of 400 students was, simply, that vitamin C was ineffective at preventing colds.[467] The study was published in 1942, and its findings were repeated, unchallenged, in professional journals, and by professional dieticians and nutritionists, for decades. However, once it had been published, no one had actually taken the trouble to critically review the study until Pauling did so. What he found was surprising. For a start, the scientists had only supplemented the students' diets with 200mg of vitamin C – a fraction of the dose which Pauling recommends. But even more startlingly – and contrary to the conclusion of the researchers – there *was* a reduction in colds suffered during the course of the experiment. Pauling found that the students who were given the placebo averaged 1.6 days away from studies because of colds. The students who received 200mg vitamin C a day only averaged 1.1 lost days – a reduction of 31 per cent. Quite simply, the wrong conclusions had been drawn from the data.

Although this one study was probably the most crucial in forming established medical opinion that "vitamin C can't treat the common cold", a great many other studies have subsequently been undertaken. The conclusions range from strongly positive to violently negative, with many shades of opinion in between. It is, indeed, difficult for both doctors and patients to make up their minds about the effectiveness of vitamin C, when the range of opinion is so broad.

From a survey of most of the studies, Pauling offers some basic conclusions of his own. The principal reason that some studies fail to show a positive effect is, Pauling believes, simply because the scientists controlling the experiment don't give their subjects enough vitamin C. Very few studies involve anything like the quantity of vitamin C which some orthomolecular specialists suggest for the treatment of colds. Some prescribe up to 15 grams, or even more.

Then there is the question of the way in which the results are assessed. We have already mentioned the 1942 study in which the same data revealed quite a different story when re-examined by Pauling. It is always important to carefully consider the evidence (rather than just accept the conclusion offered by the researchers), because the same data may be interpreted in quite different ways. For example, in a 1979 experiment, 674 US marine recruits were divided into two groups.[468] One received a placebo, the other received two grams of vitamin C a day for eight weeks. The conclusion of the report was that: "This study does not support the prophylactic use of vitamin C to prevent the common cold." The researchers based this conclusion on the fact that there was no difference between the two groups in the incidence or duration of colds, and the group taking vitamin C did not have fewer sick-call visits or training days lost. However, when they asked the recruits to describe how bad their colds really were, the vitamin C group rated their colds as being less severe. This was a double blind study, so no recruit knew whether they were taking vitamin C or a placebo. On a subjective basis, the group taking vitamin C were actually telling the scientists that they felt better than the other group. This, surely, is important evidence and shouldn't be dismissed. The fact that there were roughly the same number of colds in each group indicates perhaps that an eight-week study simply wasn't long enough to judge. If, after eight weeks, the vitamin C group rated their colds as being less severe, it is quite possible that, after six months or more, their resistance would have been built up to the extent that the difference in colds between the two groups could actually be measured.

Orthomolecular therapy is very different to orthodox medicine in one fundamental respect, which makes it very difficult to assess by conventionally-designed experiments. Orthomolecular medicine believes in what is termed 'biochemical individuality'. Simply, this means that different individuals will react in different ways to the same substance. Of course, this is true in conventional medicine, too, but in the case of orthomolecular therapy, it is likely to be even more pronounced. The reason for this is that orthomolecular therapy deals in natural substances which are *already* present in the human body. One person may already have a very high level of vitamin C in their system, another may be very deficient in it. A gram-sized dose given to each will be processed in quite different ways. One person may excrete as much as 40 per cent of the vitamin C they ingest within a few hours of taking it; others may excrete as little as two per cent.

Pauling points out that, based on experimental evidence, there is probably an eighty-fold variation in the individual requirements of vitamin C, ranging from 250mg a day up to 20 grams a day. Officially recommended daily allowances (30mg, 60mg or whatever) are far too simplistic a model for the diverse and complex human biochemical process. Obvious though this idea may seem, conventional medicine has traditionally avoided this approach, probably because the calculations and decisions involved quickly become frighteningly complex. Instead of a 'one-dose' approach for almost everyone, doctors would have to start from scratch with every patient, build up an individual biochemical profile, and prescribe for the patient, rather than for the disease. Two patients manifesting the same disease might therefore receive radically different therapy. This, for orthodox medicine, is near-heresy. And in any case, today's medicine usually adopts a Fordian, assembly-line approach to its patients – there just isn't time to waste 'getting to know you'.

Most conventional scientific trials today are conducted on a randomized, double blind basis. This means that neither the experimenter nor the subject know what substance they are taking until the trial is over and, most importantly, subjects are assigned to the test group or the control group on a random basis. After the experiment is over and the results have been collected, a statistical analysis is performed and, hopefully, a picture emerges of the effectiveness or otherwise of the drug. The whole point of such a trial is that it is uniformly random: no individual variation in individual treatment is admitted. This is, of course, diametrically opposed to the orthomolecular viewpoint of biochemical individuality.

To illustrate this point, let us assume that we are designing an experiment to assess the effectiveness of vitamin C in preventing the common cold. We select a group a people, who we consider to be all roughly the same (schoolchildren, soldiers, prisoners, and so on). Then we select a dose of vitamin C which, other research shows, has been effective in the past in reducing the numbers of colds in a population, say two grams. We divide the group into two, give half a placebo and half a vitamin C pill every day. At the end of the study (say, about eight weeks) we find that those people taking vitamin C actually had *more* colds than those not taking it! Our conclusion? Obviously, that taking vitamin C makes you *more* likely to suffer from a cold! But wait a moment. Within that 'randomly-selected' group of people taking vitamin C, there is a huge variation in biochemical individuality, which hasn't been allowed for in the design of our study. Within the group taking vitamin C, most people were (by orthomolecular standards, but not by those of conventional medicine) chronically short of vitamin C. For them, the correct dose would have been eight grams a day. But our conventionally-designed survey had no way of picking this up. Also within that group was a subgroup of people who were rather better nourished, and for whom two grams of vitamin C daily was indeed an effective dose. However, these positive results were simply swamped by the greater number of failures. By conventional standards, our experiment has been well conducted, but it has produced quite the wrong results.

Of course, this poses the question: What *is* the correct orthomolecular dose of vitamin C? Dr. Robert F. Cathcart, a physician who has treated many thousands of patients with vitamin C, believes that the correct dose needed to control a viral infection such as the common cold is that which just falls short of causing a loose, watery bowel movement.[469] The way to establish this is to increase the vitamin C dose until it acts as a laxative, then reduce it so that the stools firm up again. In most people, Dr. Cathcart believes, this dose will lie between 4 grams and 15 grams per twenty-four hours, but for those not normally in good health, it could conceivably be as high as 200 grams.

Pauling maintains that you will find out if you have taken enough vitamin C by the absence of any colds within a couple of months. If you do get the first signs of a cold, he suggests you take two 1,000 milligram tablets of ascorbic acid every hour until the symptoms disappear. You should be aware that, if the dose of vitamin C is abruptly stopped, the cold could return, even after a week.

Most public attention has focused on vitamin C and its ability to prevent and cure colds. It would be wrong, however, to simply to think of it as the 'anti-cold vitamin'.

Conventional medical science, although usually rather dismissive about vitamin C, quietly undertakes research into its properties. Here are some recent published findings:

~ High dosages of vitamins C and E have been given to patients with early Parkinson's disease, in an attempt to discover whether the progress of the disease could be slowed by these vitamins. The scientists found that, on average, the disease could be retarded by about two and a half years.[470]

~ A recent scientific experiment set out to determine whether vitamins C and E (both antioxidants) might be able to prevent cataracts of the eye from forming. The researchers compared one group of 175 people who suffered from cataracts with another group of 175 cataract-free people. They found that the people without cataracts used significantly more supplementary vitamins C and E than those with them. The results suggest that people who take these supplements reduce their risk of having cataracts by at least 50 per cent.[471]

~ Researchers in Spain have found that vitamin C can help patients with head and neck cancer who are treated with radiotherapy. A side-effect of radiotherapy when applied to these areas of the human body is that it can damage oral structures, but the researchers found that doses of vitamin C can protect against this effect.[472]

~ Hepatitis A is an infectious disease which can leave a sufferer feeling debilitated for months afterwards, and with an impaired immune system. By dividing a group of hepatitis patients into two groups, one of which received 300mg of vitamin C a day for two to three weeks, Russian researchers have established that vitamin C can boost the immune system and bolster resistance in people suffering from this disease.[473]

~ People who are operated on for stomach cancer often suffer from various post-operative complications. Another group of Russian researchers conducted a randomized study of 197 patients who had been operated on for this disease. They found that giving vitamin C to patients reduced the rate of post-operative complications from 30.9 per cent to 1.9 per cent.[474]

~ There is growing evidence that vitamin C can protect us against many cancers. Large-scale studies of the health of entire populations reveal that those groups who consume foods rich in vitamin C have less cancers, particularly those of the oesophagus and stomach, than populations whose intake of vitamin C is lower. It has also been found that cancer patients often have low levels of vitamin C in their bodies. Further, it has now been established that vitamin C interacts with various tumour-inducing substances (such as the N-nitroso compounds) to prevent the formation of tumours. All this accumulating evidence was reviewed in a paper published in 1986.[475] You may well wonder why the general public has not been adequately advised of this.

~ Another review paper, also published in 1986, describes how vitamin C can "ameliorate and sometimes completely block allergic and sensitivity reactions". People suffering from inflammatory, hypersensitivity, and 'autoimmune' conditions should take note of this.[476]

Vitamin E

Pauling suggests an intake of between 400 and 1,600 IU (International Units) of vitamin E a day. Again, this is considerably higher than the officially-recommended amount, which in many countries is round about the 10 IU level. Pauling believes that vitamins C and E work together in the human body to protect the blood vessels and other tissues against damage by oxidation. In particular, vitamin E is said to have a beneficial effect on the heart and the cardiovascular system generally. But what of the side effects?

Vitamin E is a fat-soluble vitamin (unlike vitamin C, which is water soluble). This means that it is not so quickly excreted in the urine, and is more likely to accumulate in body tissues over time. Although vitamin E was discovered in 1922, it has only been recognized as being essential to health as recently as 1968. Much of its precise biological function in the human body is still unknown.[477]

The body's own self-regulating systems work with vitamin E, as they do with many other nutrients, to control its absorption. Thus, if you consume very little vitamin E, your body will become quite efficient at absorbing the small amount available. Correspondingly, consuming larger amounts of vitamin E will result in a smaller percentage being absorbed. This is how the body naturally seeks to balance out the dietary extremes which our evolutionary ancestors had to cope with, and it is our natural way of avoiding side effects which could result from large doses.

According to the American Society of Hospital Pharmacists, "Vitamin E is usually nontoxic".[478] They advise, however, that large doses (by which they mean more than 300 IUs a day) can on rare occasions cause a range of symptoms, which may include: nausea, diarrhoea, intestinal cramps, fatigue, weakness, headache, blurred vision, rash, and a possible rise in serum cholesterol and triglycerides. All these symptoms are reversible (they will disappear after the dose has been reduced). Both conventional and orthomolecular medicine agree that our bodies' requirement for vitamin E increases in proportion to our intake of polyunsaturated fats. Pauling believes that a diet high in polyunsaturated fats can lead to brain and muscular lesions, and bring about the degeneration of blood vessels, and that additional vitamin E can protect against this. One of the best natural sources of vitamin E is wheat germ oil.

Although conventional medicine adopts much the same attitude towards vitamin E supplementation as it does towards any other vitamin (general scepticism mixed with warnings of 'overdoses'), many of the world's leading medical journals have published important research which confirms many of the claims made for vitamin E by orthomolecular practitioners. For example, much research clearly shows that higher doses of vitamin E can exercise a profound stimulatory effect over the entire immune system, and thus prevent or treat many illnesses and infections.[479, 480, 481] Other scientifically-tested aspects of the beneficial effects of vitamin E supplementation include:

~ A review paper published in 1990 summarized past research, and concluded that vitamin E supplementation is beneficial in two main ways. First, it enhances the function of the immune system. Second, it acts with other antioxidant nutrients, such as vitamin A and beta carotene, to scavenge for free radicals and thus enhance disease resistance.[482]

~ A Japanese study was published in 1989 which specifically examined the potential adverse effects of 'megadose' vitamin E supplementation. The researchers gave fourteen healthy college students 900 IU of vitamin E for twelve weeks. At the end of the period, the researchers wrote: "During the study, there were no changes in laboratory values for thyroid, liver, or kidney functions, and coagulation activity (including the vitamin K-dependent Hepaplastin test and PIVKA-II) or immunoglobulin levels. Healthy status continued without any abnormal symptoms, and without any subjective complaints on the questionnaire."[483]

~ A paper published in 1984 reviewed vitamin therapy generally, and although it considered that many of the claims made for vitamin supplementation consisted "mainly of uncontrolled clinical trials or anecdotal reports", the paper also admitted that evidence from properly-conducted, randomized double-blind trials "reveals a beneficial therapeutic effect of vitamin E in intermittent claudication and fibrocystic breast disease".[484] 'Intermittent claudication' is a medical term for a complex set of symptoms. The sufferer feels no pain in their limbs when at rest, but when they start to walk, the pain intensifies until walking becomes impossible. It is often an indication of the narrowing or blocking of the peripheral arteries. Pauling believes that vitamin E can certainly help control this sort of peripheral arterial disease, and that it can also help to prevent and control blood clots.

~ In a study conducted by the Imperial Cancer Research Fund in London between 1984 and 1988, levels of vitamins A and E were measured in blood samples from thirty women with cervical cancer, and compared to forty-five healthy women. The researchers found that the average level of vitamin E was lowest in those women with the most serious form of cancer, slightly higher in women with less advanced cancer, and highest in healthy women.[485] This in itself does not prove that a low level of vitamin E causes cancer, but – since we already know that vitamin E can bolster the immune system – the results are certainly suggestive. Only one previous study had been conducted into the relationship between cervical cancer and vitamin E, and it produced significantly similar results.

~ A very large-scale study of 36,265 adults in Finland has also produced highly significant evidence concerning the relationship between vitamin E and cancer. The study measured the vitamin E blood levels of all the participants at the start of the study. Eight years later, they measured the vitamin E blood levels of the 766 people who had developed cancer. The results showed that a low level of vitamin E is associated with a 1.5-fold greater risk of developing cancer. "It is concluded that dietary vitamin E can protect against some types of cancer," wrote the scientists.[486]

Vitamin B complex

Pauling suggests one or two vitamin B complex tablets should be taken every day. At this modest level of supplementation, it is most unlikely that any side-effects will be experienced. A word of advice: you should be aware that not all vitamin B complex pills do, in fact, contain all the important B-group vitamins. Here's a checklist to refer to when reading the labels, and deciding which one to buy:

Vitamin	*Also called*	*RDA**
B_1	Thiamine	1.0mg
B_2	Riboflavin	1.2mg
B_3	Niacin	13mg
B_5	Pantothenic Acid	4.0mg
B_6	Pyridoxine	2.0mg
B_9	Folic Acid	400mcg
B_{12}	Cyanocobalamin	3mcg
Biotin	Vitamin H	100mg

* Recommended daily allowances for an adult female, not pregnant or lactating, based on amounts suggested by the Food and Nutrition Boards of the US National Research Council.

Vitamin A

Vitamin A naturally exists in several different forms. Retinol, or pre-formed vitamin A, is the most active form, and is only found in certain tissues in animal products. Carotene, sometimes called provitamin A, is a substance which is the precursor to vitamin A proper, and is converted in the body to make vitamin A. Carotene is found in a wide variety of plant foods (most notably carrots, from which its name derives). Vitamin A is essential for bone growth, reproduction, and growth of the unborn baby, and a deficiency can result in night blindness.

The officially recommended adult daily intake of vitamin A in many countries is in the region of 5,000 IU (1,000 retinol equivalents). Pauling's suggestion (25,000 IU) is therefore five times the suggested intake.

The amount of vitamin A in Pauling's daily regime is certainly very high. The American Society of Hospital Pharmacists has reported that doses of 25,000 IU may do damage to babies while in the womb, although they do point out that "adequate and well-controlled studies in humans are not available", and that "further data are needed".[487] Nevertheless, it would be a sensible precaution for women, both before and during pregnancy, not to take such large doses. It is difficult to determine at precisely what dosage toxic effects of vitamin A consumption becomes apparent, but the American Society of Hospital Pharmacists reports that adult daily doses of 4,000 IU per kilogram of body weight, over a period of several months, could produce symptoms. People with poor liver function may be at greater risk of toxicity than healthy people. Reported symptoms of excessive vitamin A consumption may include: lethargy, irritability, depression or other mental changes, anorexia, nausea and vomiting, mild fever, excessive sweating, cracking of the skin, itching, brittle nails, falling hair, or orange colouring of the skin. They can be reversed by stopping or lowering the dose, and it has also been reported that taking Vitamin E (as Pauling proposes in his daily regime) can protect against the effects of vitamin A toxicity. And although Pauling doesn't suggest it, some of the possible toxicity of vitamin A supplementation could be mitigated by taking carotene, a plant pigment present in carrots and other vegetables, which can be converted in the human body to vitamin A (see chapter 9).

The positive effects of vitamin A are well known: it helps form and maintain healthy skin, hair, and mucous membranes, and it can help to build resistance to a number of respiratory infections. It has been used to treat a number of skin problems, including acne, and it can help to treat several eye disorders. But in addition to this, large doses (i.e. greater than the 5,000 IUs commonly suggested as the recommended daily allowance) have been shown to have a number of positive health effects. Here is a summary of recent research:

~ An ongoing study into the effect of high-dose vitamin A as a treatment for people suffering from lung cancer has produced some interesting interim findings. In the words of the researchers: "The clinical results available to date do well justify a continuation of the study." The daily dose was indeed very high – 300,000 IU daily for at least twelve months. Skin dryness and scaling were the most frequent side effects of such a large dose, affecting 60 per cent of all treated patients. Other symptoms such as indigestion, headache, nosebleeds and mild hair loss occurred in less than 10 per cent of the patients, and in any case were only temporary. The scientists concluded: "In our experience, high-dose retinol palmitate administration was a well-tolerated and safe treatment."[488]

~ Fishermen from Kerala, India, were the subjects of a recently-reported study, whose results are highly significant in proving the anti-cancer effect of vitamin A. The fishermen chewed tobacco containing betel 'quids', usage of which is strongly associated with mouth cancer. The first sign of mouth cancer is often the appearance of thick, white patches on the cheeks, gums or tongue, called leukoplakia. These pre-cancerous lesions are sometimes popularly referred to as 'smoker's mouth'. After being given vitamin A supplements for six months, 57 per cent of the fishermen had "complete remission of leukoplakias" – their pre-cancerous condition had been reversed. Beta carotene induced remission in 15 per cent. In addition, Vitamin A completely suppressed, and beta carotene suppressed by 50 per cent, the formation of *new* leukoplakia during the six-month trial. After the vitamin A or beta carotene had stopped being administered, the leukoplakias reappeared.[489]

~ A study of the blood cells of a 67-year-old leukaemia patient has confirmed that the regular administration of vitamin A (retinol palmitate) can decrease the proliferation of leukaemic cells. The researchers suggested that "the reduction in cell growth is the key phenomenon in the clearing of leukaemic cells".[490]

~ A review paper published in 1990 recorded that, "in a dozen case-control and cohort studies, high intake of fruits and vegetables containing carotenoids has been associated with a reduced risk of lung cancer". The same paper noted, however, that "little relation has been found between intake of preformed vitamin A and this disease". In other words, people who obtain their vitamin A as carotene (from plant sources) are less likely to contract lung cancer than those who obtain it directly as preformed vitamin A (retinol, from animal sources). "Available data thus strongly support the hypothesis that dietary carotenoids reduce the risk of lung cancer."[491] So should you follow Pauling's advice, and take 25,000 IU of vitamin A a day? On the one hand, there is clear evidence that vitamin A can protect against cancer. On the other, there are often-repeated warnings about overdoses. What should you do?

First, let's try to put the perceived danger in context. As Pauling astutely points out, a drug such as aspirin (widely considered to be 'safe') kills many more people each year than do vitamin overdoses (in fact, it is difficult to determine whether a vitamin 'overdose' has ever actually killed anyone). All the same, much recent publicity has been given to the 'perils' of vitamin A consumption. For example, *The Times* reported: "The Consumer Food Panel, set up by the Agriculture Ministry after criticism of its handling of outbreaks of listeria in soft cheese and salmonella in eggs . . . met last week in Norwich for two days and were told instantly of the discovery by government food specialists that excess vitamin A could be harmful to pregnant women."[492]

This is really extraordinary, because it suggests that some food specialists only recently became aware of the possible side effects of vitamin A. In actual fact, much of the concern over vitamin A's safety arose in the mid-1980s after it became evident that an anti-acne drug, which was chemically similar to retinol, could cause birth defects if taken during the early weeks of pregnancy. It rather seems as if food specialists, having singularly failed to take timely action over so many cases of food poisoning, were looking for a scapegoat substance so that they could be seen to be taking positive action, for a change.

We already know, from evidence such as that mentioned above, that a low beta carotene intake is associated with an increased risk of various cancers, including those of the lung, the stomach, the oesophagus and the cervix. Other preliminary research indicates that extra carotene may even be able to ward off heart attacks and other cardiac problems. So – leaving scares and panics aside – it seems to make sense to get as much of your vitamin A in its carotene form as you can. This means eating a diet which is very high in green and yellow vegetables, thus restricting or eliminating your need for supplementary vitamin A pills (retinol). Carotene from a natural source (such as carrot juice) is also more likely to contain a full range of co-factors, which may exercise a subtle but important influence over vitamin A's activity in the human body. And finally, research has established that abnormally high blood concentrations of vitamin A do not occur when you eat a natural carotene-rich diet, thus all but eliminating any theoretical risk of overdose.[493] Here are some particularly good sources of carotene:

~ Apricots
~ Broccoli
~ Carrots
~ Collard greens
~ Cress
~ Kale
~ Mangoes
~ Parsley
~ Peaches
~ Pumpkins
~ Spinach
~ Sweet Potatoes
~ Watercress

Several portions of these plant foods every day will provide you with an excellent supply of carotene, which your body can then process into vitamin A, and use as necessary. If you find it difficult to make regular meals with fresh ingredients such as these, seriously consider buying a juicer, and make your own freshly-prepared juice cocktails. Here is one of our favourite recipes:

2lb (1kg) fresh organic carrots
1 level tsp diced fresh ginger root
Half a cup Bonsoy soya milk

Juice the carrots and ginger, and mix with the soya milk and serve immediately. Guaranteed to turn anyone who thinks carrot juice is just for cranks into an instant convert! High in carotene, and a useful source of protein, too. You may want to vary the amount of ginger (its freshness can affect its strength quite considerably) – don't put too much in, it should just be there in the background as a subtle, hinted flavour. Also, don't use anything other than organic carrots. Those anaemic-looking objects sometimes found in supermarkets, all precisely the same length, are repulsive when juiced – they taste like soggy cardboard! Thanks to our friend Errol Shaker for this recipe.

The new nutrition

There is little doubt that conventional medicine is slowly starting to embrace many of Pauling's long-held beliefs, albeit somewhat grudgingly. You have just seen references to many scientific reports, published in respected medical journals all over the world, which confirm much of Pauling's orthomolecular thesis. It would be quite wrong, however, to think that, even at the age of ninety, Pauling has ceased to be a controversial figure. Currently, one of the most contentious areas of orthomolecular medicine (and one in which Pauling himself is closely involved) relates to its possible beneficial effect on the brain. In fact, Pauling believes that orthomolecular medicine's most important role may be in treating the brain. Since subtle chemical changes within the brain can have a dramatic effect on the rest of our bodies, and indeed on our entire lives, it is possible that this could be the most revolutionary application yet of orthomolecular medicine.

In 1981, a report was published in the *Proceedings of the National Academy of Sciences USA* concerning the orthomolecular treatment of mentally retarded children. One of the researchers had become interested in the subject following very positive results with one severely retarded seven-year-old boy. With an IQ of between 25 and 30, the boy was unable to speak and still wore nappies because he was incontinent. Then he was given the following total daily orthomolecular regime (divided into six doses):

Vitamin A palmitate	15,300 IU
Vitamin D (cholecalciferol)	300 IU
Thiamine mononitrate	300mg
Riboflavin	200mg
Niacinamide	750mg
Calcium pantothenate	490mg
Pyridoxine hydrochloride	350mg
Cobalamin	1mg
Folic acid	0.4mg
Vitamin C	1,500mg
Vitamin E (d-a-tocopheryl succinate)	600 IU
Magnesium (oxide)	300mg
Calcium (carbonate)	400mg
Zinc (oxide)	30mg
Manganese (gluconate)	3mg
Copper (gluconate)	1.75mg
Iron (ferrous fumarate)	7.5mg
Calcium phosphate ($CaHPO_4$)	37.5mg
Iodide (KI)	0.15mg

After two years the boy had progressed to an IQ of 90, was talking, reading and writing and attending school. The result of this dramatic study prompted the researchers to undertake further trials. They therefore devised a partially double-blind experiment with sixteen retarded children, whose initial IQs ranged between 17 and 70. For a period of eight months, they were given either nutritional supplements (as above, plus 30mg–120mg thyroid) or placebos. The first four months were double blind (i.e. neither the researchers nor the subjects knew who was taking the supplements or placebos). During this period, the five children who received supplements increased their average IQ by between 5.0 and 9.6 points. For the next four months, the subjects who had been given placebos in the first period also received supplements and they, too, showed an average IQ increase of at least 10.2 points, a highly significant gain. Four of the children had Down's syndrome, and three of them gained between 10 and 25 IQ points, and also showed physical changes toward normal. "Other evidence suggests that the supplement improved visual acuity in two children and increased growth rates," wrote the researchers. "These results support the hypothesis that mental retardations are in part genetotrophic in origin."[494] 'Genetotrophic' is a term the researchers used to describe a disease or syndrome in which "the genetic pattern of the afflicted individual requires an augmented supply of one or more nutrients such that when these nutrients are adequately supplied the disease is ameliorated".

Of course, to suggest that Down's syndrome and mental retardation can be helped through vitamin and mineral therapy is quite heretical. The research has been criticized as being 'flawed',[495] and several other studies have not repeated the findings. One study of fifteen children, aged between 7.5 and 63 months, reported that those children receiving supplementation failed to develop as quickly as those not receiving therapy.[496]

Down's syndrome is caused by an abnormality which results in cells containing three, rather than two, of chromosome number 21. This additional chromosome radically alters the sufferer's body chemistry, so that, for example, 50 per cent more than usual of many different kinds of enzymes are produced.[497] Sufferers are particularly prone to infections and autoimmune diseases, leukaemia, heart defects and, later, Alzheimer's disease. One scientific study examined twenty-eight Down's syndrome patients, and found that other, less obvious, health problems may also exist. For example, multiple food allergies can cause the malabsorption of essential vitamins and minerals (and may also precipitate severe autoimmune disease).[498] Several other scientific reports have also confirmed that Down's syndrome patients are at greater risk of vitamin and mineral deficiencies.[499, 500] Therefore, it is entirely feasible that the 'normal' recommended daily vitamin and mineral allowances as determined for the general population are totally inadequate for the much greater needs of Down's syndrome sufferers. This, in itself, is a strong argument for their regular and systematic treatment with orthomolecular therapy.

It has also been suggested that vitamin supplementation may be able to help children suffering from autism. In a questionnaire sent to 4,000 parents of autistic children, they were asked to rate the effectiveness of a variety of medical treatments for this disorder. The parents rated vitamin-mineral therapy way ahead of any conventional drug treatment. "High-dosage vitamin B_6 and magnesium received the highest ratings, with 8.5 of parents reporting behavioural improvement to every one reporting behavioural worsening," wrote the researchers. The second choice treatment was an orthodox drug, but only 1.8 of parents reported an improvement to each one reporting a worsening.[501]

We are, clearly, close to the frontiers of knowledge here. Orthomolecular medicine believes that it has a part to play in the treatment of mental retardation. Conventional medicine believes that since the cause is mostly genetic, the answer must also be genetic. When we spoke to several societies and others concerned with the welfare of the mentally handicapped, their answers were bland and diplomatic. "If a child isn't getting enough vitamins in his diet, then perhaps he should receive supplements," said one spokesman to us. "But we wouldn't like parents to think that they can treat Down's syndrome with vitamins." They're right, of course, to warn against false hope, but are they right to kill off hope completely? Especially when there *is* some evidence to indicate that orthomolecular therapy may help? As Pauling says, "Even a partial decrease in the severity of mental retardation can be very important."[502]

At the heart of the dichotomy between orthomolecular and 'toximolecular' medicine lies a philosophical divide. The conventionalists believe in prescribing tiny amounts of highly toxic drugs which often have a wide spectrum of unpleasant side effects. The orthomolecular practitioners, on the other hand, prescribe comparatively large amounts of natural substances whose toxicity is low and whose side effects are mild. A cynic would go further, and accuse conventional medicine of grossly failing its patients by being duped by the pharmaceutical companies into an ever-spiralling dependence on 'new' drugs, whose principal beneficial effects are on the drugs companies' profits. As an alternative to this, orthomolecular therapy certainly looks very enticing.

Although his ideas have always been mocked and derided by the conventional scientific community, time seems to be vindicating many of Pauling's theories. As one unnamed scientist recently said: "I think some of his current ideas are probably right. I just don't know which ones."

Chapter 86

What to expect from osteopathy

~

A worldwide treatment, developed over a hundred years ago and founded on the principles set out by Andrew Taylor Still, osteopathy emphasizes the structural and mechanical aspects of the body. Still maintained that correct bodily adjustment will maximize good health, believing that the body has built-in self-healing power.

If you thought osteopathy was simply an alternative back treatment, you could be missing out. Learn how it can successfully correct a range of health problems from breathing difficulties to headaches.

Osteopathy has certainly gained respect as a back treatment but it can also ease problems with joints, muscles, breathing, digestion, menstruation, allergies and headaches. The system's key theory is that many local disturbances are due to misplaced spinal vertebrae; once these vertebrae have been realigned, the body's self-healing system can take over again and the specific symptom will disappear. Sitting is one of the most stressful positions for your back, and a good osteopath will be able to offer you advice on the correct choice of chairs, too. Osteopaths would have far less work if people in sedentary jobs would consult them about their seating arrangements and work routines before the back-ache sets in!

Health stems from equilibrium

Based on the idea that good health is a question of proper equilibrium, osteopathy also takes into account influences on the patient such as environment, nutrition and childhood development. Most people are aware that if their occupation involves a great deal of sitting, they may be causing undue strain to their neck or back, but there are many other factors to be considered. For example, inherited characteristics also have an important role to play. It has been suggested that individuals with a thin, elongated bone structure are more likely to encounter structural difficulties.

Osteopathic lesions are of great significance. They can occur in joints and are caused by a yielding of the particular joint so that it becomes jammed within its normal range of movement. When this happens it will often not show up on an X-ray, which is why patients become frustrated with their GPs who rely so heavily on this aid to diagnosis. If a lesion appears in the lower back, it may eventually cut off circulation which can lead to disease. Lesions can cause trapped or inflamed nerves, as well as disc damage.

Cranial osteopathy is an advance on the original form, involving treatment of the head. It was discovered when a student of Still's noticed that the joints of the cranial bones actually allow some movement. If these bones become misaligned, they can restrict this gentle expansion and contraction, resulting in ill health. Sometimes such misalignment is caused by a blow on the head, or even from problems during birth. Cranial osteopathy corrects the problem by slight manipulation of the cranial bones.

What happens

The first appointment with an osteopath normally takes one hour, with subsequent visits lasting anything from fifteen to forty-five minutes. To begin with, the osteopath will take down a case history to make up a picture of a patient's life so that he can examine the inter-relationships between possible causes of the symptom. He may also give advice on correct diet, exercise, relaxation and posture. In this way, osteopathy differs from more traditional treatments, being very much individual – rather than disease-oriented.

First, osteopaths will note the way you walk into the room, because this, in itself, can reveal postural abnormalities and structural disorders. Then they will examine you in your underwear, sitting, lying and standing. They are particularly looking for 'somatic dysfunction', the name given to change or damage to the body's framework. This may be manifest through observations of your body's symmetry, mobility and tissue texture. At this stage, they may point out some interesting (and potentially harmful) symptoms which you may never have noticed before. For example, it could be that one shoulder hangs slightly lower than the other, or perhaps you stand with your hips at an uneven angle. All these things will be recorded. Then, closer examinations of certain areas may be made – using palpation (using the hands to detect problem areas) or X-rays. Blood pressure and urine tests may also be used in the diagnostic process. A number of techniques are used in actual treatment:

~ Osteopathic manipulative therapy (OMT) is used generally to restore movement in the musculo-skeletal system

~ High velocity thrusting is a form of spine cracking

~ Soft tissue technique is an action similar to massage applied to a specific area

~ Articulation technique involves stretching the tissue to promote fluid movement

~ Muscle energy technique employs movement of the joint to re-establish correct muscle alignment.

Finding an osteopath

Osteopaths work as independent practitioners, so a letter of referral is not needed. The cost varies but ask for a reduction if you are genuinely short of funds. If you cannot find someone who can make a recommendation, look in the Yellow Pages for an osteopath with the initials MRO, MBNOA or BSO, which are all recognized qualifications. Alternatively, you can write for a list of registered practitioners in your area, and for any other information, to the organizations mentioned in the Help section.

Chapter 87
What to expect from polarity therapy

~

Your body is part of a system of negative and positive forces and you can increase its harmony by creating equilibrium between its poles.

Polarity therapy works with the idea that our physical state is made up of opposing energy forces. Our body is seen as a powerhouse of electromagnetic forces, our good health depending on their equilibrium.

Founded by Dr. Stone – a chiropractor, osteopath and naturopath – polarity therapy uses therapeutic touch, diet, exercise and positive thinking to rebalance the fundamental energies in our body. Polarity therapists work with the energy of life, otherwise known as chi or prana. A polarity therapist does not treat a specific illness, but approaches its cause – an imbalance in the life energy – releasing blocks and healing, so it can flow freely again.

The polarity of your body

Your body's energy is thought to run in all directions: vertically and horizontally, and spiralling from top to bottom with the umbilicus as its centre. It runs through five channels which lie vertically in the body. Each relates to one of the five elements: ether, air, water, fire and earth. In this way they can be compared to the Chinese system of meridians. The notion of polarity springs from the idea that each area of our body is either positive or negative, as well as relating to one of the five elements. A polarity therapist will use this concept in treatment as well, so that the right hand is used for energizing and the left for relaxing. When two different polarities come together, new currents form. Disease and illness arises when the flow is altered. The balancing of this flow is the basis of all healing arts.

Diagnosis

The process used for diagnosis varies but it usually relies upon the five elements. Each, apart from ether, has a related astrological triad, a body part and a sun sign. For example, the earth element is connected with Taurus and the neck; Virgo and the bowels; Capricorn and the knees.

A session normally lasts for between fifteen and forty-five minutes. You will need to undress to your underwear and lie on a table, the floor or a bed where you will be covered with a sheet. The therapist will ask you to tell him if any areas are painful to touch. This gentle touching is used to distribute the energy and generally rebalance you. Your whole body will be worked on, including the head. Even the feet are treated, using the principles of reflexology, in which every part of the foot is taken to represent an area of the body.

In a session, the therapist first works at general rebalancing and then may go on to carry out specific manipulations. The hands are seen as human batteries, a tool for energy transmission, while the body is the centre of an electromagnetic force, attracting the energy it needs. A therapist uses his hands to change the body's poles: the ideal is a positive to negative force which creates a neutral pole. This can then be linked with any other contact point, using the law of polarity. The most stable points in the body are where positive and negative forces cross over, creating neutral areas. These are the navel, the chakras and a two-inch strip running right down the centre of the body.

What happens

During a treatment session, the therapist may advise you on diet. Food as the source of all life energy has an important role in polarity therapy. Each food has its own elemental nature. Solids relate to earth, liquids to water, gases to air, heat to fire, and ether corresponds to their look, smell and arrangement. Different foods can be prescribed to introduce more of an element needed by the body. For example, air, which relates to action, is particularly needed by nervous people who use up a lot of energy. This can be found in yeasts, fruits, nuts and dairy products. People with mental and physical disorders need the warmth and energy found in seeds, grains and beans. Green leaf vegetables, cucumbers, milk and sea food are water foods, appropriate for those with emotional problems. Fats, starches and sugars are earth products and useful for those with a physical disorder.

In general, natural foods are the best for any source of energy. Meats and flesh food hold negative energies of the pain and fear of the dying animal. In the same way, negative thinking affects the energy flow which can damage digestion and elimination and so cause disease. Thoughts in themselves are significant as energy vibrations. The power of positive thinking is such that it can create positive energy flow. If, on the other hand, we are ego-centred or clinging to our emotions, the flow is severed.

A polarity therapist may also advise you about polarity yoga, used to release and increase energy flow. It involves moving gently in all directions: as the body interacts with the earth's forces, it becomes charged with energy. Deep breathing also has a part to play as the air is such a powerful energy source. The therapist may also recommend you make use of the life force of the sun, exposing your body to it for about ten minutes every day. If you have a particular ailment, it may be helped by rubbing it in the sunshine.

Polarity therapy is a gentle, holistic treatment in the widest sense of the word. It is about the energy and healing force in our bodies, as well as in the people around us and in our environment. If you are attracted by the style and structure of this form of therapy, contact the Polarity Therapy Association (address in the Help section) for the name of a therapist in your area.

Chapter 88
What to expect from radionics

~

You've heard about mothers who, though at a distance from their children, know when they're in danger. Radionics harnesses the same psychic ability.

Radionics is "the utilization of an unusual energy or energies in devices to produce natural phenomenon or effects" (J. G. Gallimore).[503] Radionics as applied to health and healing is more properly known as radiesthesia (also called medical dowsing).

Radionics was first propounded at the turn of the 20th century by an American, Dr. Albert Abrams. If you have ever had a conventional medical check-up, you will probably be familiar with a technique known as percussion. By striking various parts of the body with short, sharp blows, it is possible for a skilled doctor to diagnose the health of the underlying body part according to the sound of the blow. For example, one percussive technique involves placing the middle finger of the left hand on a specific part of the body and sharply tapping it with the middle finger of the right hand. Although percussion is an orthodox technique, Abrams found that he could produce an 'unhealthy' percussion from a healthy person simply by placing another person's diseased tissue in contact with the healthy person.

From this surprising observation, Abrams suggested that the diseased tissue was sending out abnormal 'dull emanations' (or radio waves) which the healthy patient was unknowingly picking up. It is this assumption that radio waves were involved which gave radionics its name.

Subsequent experiments convinced Abrams he was onto something. He made the testing more rigorous. He placed various diseased tissues behind a screen. On the other side was a healthy subject who had a simple electrode connected to his forehead. The wire from this was, by Abrams' assistant, placed randomly over one or other of the diseased tissue samples. What Abrams found was that by then percussing the subject's abdomen and interpreting the response he could precisely determine which sample his assistant's wire was connected to.

Later Abrams found he did not even need to use tissue samples – blood spots on filter paper or even an object which they had touched would also produce the same remarkable results. But in order to help differentiate more specifically between different diseases, Abrams designed and constructed a box with variable resistance wiring inside it which could distinguish between the subtle differences in energy given off by different diseases from the 'witness' (the radionics term for the sample of material). Using this device, he found, for example, that cancer produced a 50 ohm resistance, while syphilis had a 55 ohm resistance.

In 1922, the Royal Society of Medicine received a scientific paper from Sir Thomas Horder, who had heard about Dr. Abrams' work and had investigated his 'boxes'. Much to Horder's surprise, the twenty-five subsequent trials which he carried out were all successful. The odds against this happening by chance is 1 in 33,554,432. The Society accepted the results presented in the paper, but did not sanction the practice of radionics – presumably because the report could not say how it all worked. Radionics soon generated great suspicion amongst many parts of established science, with the result that its practitioners were hounded by the law (Ruth Drown, who carried on Abrams' research after him, was gaoled for her work), and it is still illegal in many parts of America.

Into the ether

When asked to explain how it works, radionics practitioners will often refer to 'the ether'. Just as wires and cables carry electrical energy, so – they believe – the ether carries radionic energies. Here is an experiment which radionics practitioners cite to prove the existence of the ether:

Take a clear test tube and insert a piece of sterilized cotton, saturated with distilled water. Put a bean or pea in the initial stage of germination inside the tube and seal it carefully with a glass stopper and wax, making it absolutely air tight and moistureproof. Weigh the tube accurately. Wait for a week or two until the seed has sprouted, and weigh the test tube again. It will be seen that there is a considerable gain of weight, which simply cannot be explained by contemporary physical laws or theories. Radionics practitioners believe that the mysterious gain in weight is caused by the flowing of 'etheric forces' through the glass, to nurture the sprouting seed.[504]

What happens

Radionics (radiesthesia) involves analysing and treating your symptoms using a simple instrument in the hands of a skilled practitioner. The aim is to diagnose and then correct unbalanced etheric energy. Analysis and treatment are normally carried out at a distance from the patient or subject. All that is needed by the practitioner is a 'witness' from them – such as a piece of nail, blood spot or hair sample.

The radionics practitioner will place the witness in an instrument box and establish its frequency. Using this measurement, sometimes together with a written list of symptoms, an analysis is made. The best form of treatment is then established, normally by holding a pendulum over a table of treatments which is also linked to the witness. The remedy indicated by the pendulum is then administered either directly (it can be anything from colour or gem therapy to vitamin or homoeopathic treatment) or at a distance and transmitted by thought power.

Ideally, radionics should be practised by a medically trained person, otherwise an incorrect analysis could be made. It is important that the correct questions are asked, and that the results are accurately interpreted. Radionics cannot be adequately explained, yet it often seems to work. Its ability to analyse pre-disease states is certainly something which could be a great blessing to us all. For help with finding a practitioner, see the Help section.

CHAPTER 89
WHAT TO EXPECT FROM REBIRTHING

~

Is your past ruining your present? Rebirthing provides thousands with an effective means to replace their negative experiences with a positive self-image.

Rebirthing is a technique to help you relieve stress, anxiety and tension. Since it was developed in America in the 1960s by Sondra Ray, thousands of people in Britain have visited rebirthers every year. They find relief, not only from stress and emotional blockages, but also from stress-related illnesses such as asthma, skin disorders and circulatory problems. Rebirthing aims to break the stress cycle through controlled respiration, with a technique sometimes referred to as conscious connected breathing.

What happens

At the start of the session the rebirther will spend time talking with you about yourself, your life, and any emotional or physical problems you may be experiencing and wishing to resolve. You also have the opportunity here to ask any questions you may have about rebirthing, such as what role the rebirther will play during the session. The rebirther should talk you through what to expect and what you may experience.

If you are 'dry' rebirthing you will lie down on a mat, perhaps with music playing in the background. 'Wet' rebirthing is intended to simulate the womb experience and involves floating naked in warm water, face down with snorkel and nose clip. The rebirther supports you throughout and the experience is intended to help you surrender your ego in these womb-like surroundings as you follow the breathing cycle.

The breath of life

The breathing cycle begins with full and slow breathing, with no pauses between each inhalation and exhalation. After some time you start to breathe full and fast, and then fast and shallow. Through employing this breathing technique energy builds up and is used to focus on areas of emotional and physical tension. The aim is to use the energy to release the tensions along with negative, self-fulfilling, limiting thoughts and emotions which are affecting your life. After the fast and shallow breathing you either rest, or return to full and slow breathing. The rebirther will guide you as to what you should do. A breathing cycle can take approximately an hour to complete.

Rebirthers believe many problems in adult life are a result of childhood experiences. The rebirthing sessions help you focus on problem areas related to your past, to let them go, and to replace them with more positive beliefs about yourself and your life.

Sessions can be on a one-to-one basis or you can attend group sessions, some of which may be held over a weekend. As someone new to rebirthing, it may be more suitable for you to initially have individual sessions, where you can be sure that you have mastered the technique properly and where your progress is followed up in the next session. Normally ten to twelve weekly sessions of between one and three hours' duration are enough to learn the techniques involved and to resolve hidden inner conflicts and tensions. You can then use the techniques in your own time without the need for the rebirther to be present.

Initially, however, you need the rebirther there to help you:

~ Discover your own unique breathing rhythm
~ Keep it relaxed and controlled to avoid hyperventilation

~ Encourage and support you
~ Help you handle the unexpected reactions you may experience
~ Help you work through your inner conflicts as they arise

Different approaches

Different rebirthers run different kinds of session. Some use affirmations, some concentrate on birth and early childhood experiences and some concentrate on looking to develop the new you, devoid of emotional and physical stresses. It is best to ask a rebirther how they run their sessions and what they focus on. Choose one with whom you feel comfortable.

If you would like to experience a release from deep-seated tensions, stresses and anxieties, or you think rebirthing could help you with a physical complaint, contact the British Rebirth Society for further information and a list of practitioners near you. Details are in the Help section.

CHAPTER 90
WHAT TO EXPECT FROM REFLEXOLOGY

~

An immediate end to pain and tension! It will make you feel good all over, relaxed yet energized. Reflexology is the art of fingertip massage to release your energy blocks and your body's healing power.

Reflexology relieves specific symptoms and aims to bring general good health. Since all our energy channels, or meridians, end at the feet, reflexologists believe that massaging these 'reflex points' can treat the whole body.

Reflexology is sometimes called zone therapy, because the body is divided into areas or zones, each represented by a specific point in the foot. Dr. William Fitzgerald outlined five bodily zones on either side of the central meridian, making up the ten longitudinal zones. The first runs from the little finger, through the hand, arm and shoulder to the side of the neck. It follows up to the ear and the side of the head and then straight down to the little toe. The four other zones run in the same way from the other fingers to the toes. In this way, reflexology is based on principles similar to acupuncture. They differ in that reflexologists take the zones of the body, rather than the actual lines, as the areas to work on. In addition to these longitudinal zones, there are three transverse zones. This forms a complex network of zones in your body that can be transposed onto the feet, thus making a sort of grid system which relates to the whole body.

You don't have to subscribe to this theory to allow reflexology to work for you. Whether or not you believe in it, reflexology is still capable of stimulating your circulation and promoting marvellously deep relaxation. This, by itself, will help to restore your energy balance and so aid the body in its natural healing processes. In terms of reducing pain, reflexology may be a way of stimulating the release of endorphins, the pain-relieving substances in the brain.

What can reflexology treat?

Reflexology can benefit nearly all disorders. Even if you go for the treatment of just one symptom, all the reflex areas will be massaged, although, of course, specific attention will be paid to the problem area. Reflexologists categorize symptoms according to the part of the body in which they occur.

~ HEAD. Headaches, migraines, strokes, Parkinson's disease, multiple sclerosis and eye disorders all fall into this area. The root of the problem may be found in the neck, sinuses and eyes, with diet and hormonal factors also having an influence. As treatment takes account of both the symptom area and the underlying cause, pressure will be applied to the reflex point in the foot relating to the head as well as those corresponding to these connected areas.

~ MUSCULO-SKELETAL. This region includes any neck, hip and back problems, sciatica and arthritis. Although the exact nature of backache cannot be discovered through reflexology, the symptoms can certainly be relieved.

~ ENDOCRINE SYSTEM. Pituitary, thyroid, pancreatic, reproductive and gland disorders fall in this category.

~ RESPIRATORY SYSTEM. Asthma, bronchitis and emphysema are covered by this area. The direct reflexes involved may include the lungs and the bronchi, with the solar plexus and adrenal glands making up some of the associated reflexes.

~ HEART AND CIRCULATORY SYSTEM. Any patient with a heart condition is obviously vulnerable and so must be treated gently. Angina, high blood pressure and circulatory problems are all included in the heart reflex area.

~ LYMPHATIC SYSTEM. In cases of infection, breast lumps and shingles, the lymphatic reflexes, as well as the spleen may play a part.

~ DIGESTIVE SYSTEM. Digestive difficulties such as heartburn, flatulence and constipation, along with cases of hiatus hernia and allergies can all be eased by treatment of the reflex for this area.

~ URINARY SYSTEM. The reflex for this zone covers kidney and bladder disorders.

~ THE SKIN. Skin problems cover a wide range of disorders, including eczema, acne and rashes. They are often exacerbated by inappropriate diet, poor breathing and general tension.

What happens

Although reflexology is successful as a symptom-relieving treatment, perhaps its most important application is in terms of its preventive properties. Unlike traditional medicine, reflexology works on the less obvious, underlying problems within the body and therefore can treat disorders at a very early stage.

During the first treatment session a reflexologist will take a detailed account of your medical history. Then you will be asked to sit in a reclining chair. If such a chair is not used, you should have serious doubts about the professionalism of the practitioner. After taking off your shoes and socks, your whole lower leg should be supported.

In the examination, the texture, general appearance and temperature of your feet will be noted. Where there are any corns, scars, sores or swellings, pressure cannot be applied. In treatment, talcum powder may be used, but never oil. Although the amount of pressure applied will vary, it should not feel painful. Don't worry if you have ticklish feet – the movement is quite firm. The reflex points are tiny, so a reflexologist has to be very precise in his actions. First, he will act on the whole foot, little by little. This is both a diagnostic and healing process. If any tender areas are felt, they will be specifically worked on, possibly causing a slightly sharp sensation. Sometimes your feet will not respond at all if there is some sort of energy block, but a reflexologist will try to free this.

After treatment, your feet will probably feel warm because of the increased circulation. Your body may feel cold and even tired as it relaxes, although sometimes patients report a boost in energy. It is possible that, as a direct result of treatment, you could experience some specific symptoms. This is a healthy sign, indicating that the treatment has encouraged the release of harmful stresses and toxins. The reaction may take the form of increased bowel or urinary activity, cold-like symptoms, skin problems, or the manifestation of past disorders. This 'healing crisis' is a natural part of many complementary therapies (see, for example, homoeopathy).

Although you may feel dramatic effects after just one treatment, a course of about six weekly sessions is recommended for the optimum result. Each session will normally last about an hour, with around forty-five minutes for actual foot work.

Sometimes a reflexologist will show a patient how to continue treatment for a particular problem at home. Self-treatment is perfectly safe; even if you are not working the correct area, no harm can be done. The most important thing is not to press too hard. As a guide, use about the same amount of force as you would when pressing a doorbell. Do not use reflexology if you, or anyone you are treating, is pregnant, diabetic or has a heart or circulatory problem. You can actually buy so-called reflexology aids, but these are not really precise enough for specific point stimulation, they are better used simply to improve circulation.

Do-it-yourself reflexology

In self-treatment, it is often easier to work on the hands rather than the feet. But almost any area of the body can be worked on. Remember, if you feel soreness, it probably indicates a blockage. By rubbing it you can free any congestion. Any painful area should have pressure applied with the finger for seven seconds. If you experience a tingling in an unrelated area, it may suggest a connection between the two points. Work on each of these areas in turn with your first or middle finger, returning to any that bring particular results.

~ TENSION HEADACHE. Grab hold of clumps of your hair at the roots, pulling quickly for about thirty seconds each time. Tap head softly and briskly with loose fists relaxed at the wrists.

~ INSTANT ENERGY! The hollow at the bottom of your skull at the back of your head is called the *medulla oblongata*, and is a sort of dynamo, the centre of all bodily impulses. It has powerful significance. By applying pressure to this point, you can give yourself instant get-up-and-go energy.

~ HAND AND FOOT WORKOUT. Put your thumb in the middle of your palm, or the sole of your foot. Rotating and rolling the thumb gently, apply firm, even pressure. Do this five times before moving to another spot. Then work on every finger and toe, spending more time on any painful areas. The palm of the right hand has an energizing, positive force, while that on the left has a calming, negative influence. The opposite is true for the backs of the hands.

Points in the body are much more difficult to find and there are many more of them than in the hands and feet. If you feel pain at any point, massage along the whole meridian.

~ NAVEL TEST. Lie down and press all your fingers into your navel. If you can feel a throbbing pulse, hold for a count of seven and rotate. When the throbbing stops, the problem has gone. This method can be used as a test for any disorder, as well as an instantaneous means of pain relief.

~ EARS. Like the hands and feet, the ears contain hundreds of reflex points for the whole body. The state of the ear lobe can even be taken as an indication of general well-being. Apparently, if it is large and floppy, you are basically happy and healthy. Often when we feel uneasy, we fiddle around with our ears, perhaps unconsciously seeking some sort of relief. They can also be used for diagnosis. Temperature changes indicate tenderness.

To stimulate the ears, pinch them between the forefingers and thumbs. Starting at the top and, working on both at the same time, pinch and roll with your fingers, tugging upwards. After several times, your ears will begin to glow and tingle. Then pull and pinch your lobes. Finally, put your little fingers in your ears and rotate the fingers outwards in all directions.

~ TONGUE. The tongue is covered in reflex points which are divided into the ten body zones. The centre corresponds to the centre of the body. To stimulate, press the handle of a spoon onto the tongue, turning it. If you find a very painful area, try to locate the area of the body it relates to and massage it. Pressing the tongue is thought to relax the reproductive organs, so don't ever do this when pregnant. However, this means it can be very helpful in cases of menstrual pain.

~ TEETH. Push into your cheeks at the roots of your teeth and apply pressure, starting from the side to the middle of your mouth, first on the lower jaw, and then on the upper.

~ EYES. Problems can be caused by tightness around the eyes. Try to relax them by a little massage each day. Work under the eyes and on the bones above the eyebrows.

To find a reflexologist, contact The British Reflexology Association, whose details are in the Help section. They can provide a list of practitioners who have qualified from its official teaching body, The Bayly School of Reflexology. Always ask a reflexologist how long he trained for, and before embarking on treatment, establish the cost – a whole course could be expensive.

CHAPTER 91
WHAT TO EXPECT FROM REICHIAN THERAPY

~

If you favour a physical approach to emotional problems, Reichian therapy could provide you with a path to follow. Not recommended for the faint-hearted!

Do you feel out of balance, riddled with stress, or that you're not relating positively to the world? Are your energies trapped and not flowing properly? Are you unable to reach orgasm? Reichian therapy may be your answer. It's a form of body-centred psychotherapy which is frowned on by Freudians and the like for using touch rather than speech, and massage rather than analysis. They don't like the theory behind it either.

The theory

Wilhelm Reich was a famously wayward student of Freud's, who developed ideas about body energies which have more in common with the oriental idea of chi than with anything in the Western tradition. He held that a failure to dissipate sexual energy through orgasm would lead to neurosis, and that repression and psychological conflict are stored and made manifest in muscles and the skeleton as well as in the formation of character.

Each of us has a 'character armour' which we construct to protect us from feeling the *real* nature of our neuroses. It is a protective device which has the effect of 'freezing' our energies. Reich believed that it is necessary to break down this repressive armour so as to let the body energies flow harmoniously. But the armour is strong, and we hold on to it tenaciously – psychoanalysis alone isn't sufficient to penetrate it. What is needed is physical as well as intellectual therapy. So Reich evolved a system of massage and other forms of body contact, with the aim of dissolving the character armour and unblocking the life energies. In the process, neuroses are resolved, and orgasm is achieved.

In his later career, Reich focused on the idea of orgone, the cosmic energy which he believed powered the nervous system. He devised the orgone box in which patients were supposed to be cured of many ills, including cancer, by purportedly having their orgone levels raised. This, together with his uncompromising hostility to the Amercian medical authorities, resulted in his inhuman persecution and prosecution, the seizure and burning of his books and research papers, and finally, his death in jail.

What happens

The practice of Reichian therapy is generally one of two basic sorts, bioenergetics and biodynamics, both aiming to get the body's energies flowing well in order to put you in touch with yourself and the world.

~ Bioenergetics offers techniques for *breaking through* the armour. It involves exercises to shake out stress points, straighten posture and abandon your defences. It can have quite abrupt effects and may leave you feeling very vulnerable; this is fine so long as you're neither in an unpredictable relationship with someone, nor with a tendency towards paranoia. The method need not involve one-to-one encounters between therapist and patient, so it can be used for groups, which some people prefer. Make sure you're wearing loose, comfortable clothes if you try this.

~ Biodynamics offers techniques for *melting away* the armour. Body contact, stroking and massage are what you should expect from this form of Reichian therapy. If successful, it will gently, over several sessions, get your energies running smoothly, your stresses soothed and your defences lowered carefully, bit by bit. It is essentially a one-to-one form of therapy, and may involve taking most or all of your clothes off – so make sure you and your underwear are sweet and fresh if you go for biodynamic therapy!

The costs

One-to-one therapy will cost you about £20 for an hour – towards the low end of the tariff for individual psychotherapy. Groups will cost less. Biodynamic therapists expect that you'll want to go to them for at least six months; they may wish to carry on for years at the recommended frequency of one session a week. At the same frequency, bioenergetic therapists sometimes feel they are getting results in a matter of weeks.

There is no doubt that many of us, probably most of us, are hostage to the inner tensions we trap deep within our bodies, which cause us much unnecessary pain. Reichian therapy can help to get these energies to flow again. Many people will prefer to use the ancient techniques of Tai Chi for this end, but if you want individual treatment, and the unconventional philosophy seems appealing, then you'll probably find biodynamics to be most enjoyable. After all, with guaranteed attention and skilful stroking once a week, you may carry on with it for years! See the Help section for contacts.

CHAPTER 92
WHAT TO EXPECT FROM ROLFING

~

Would you welcome ten exhausting sessions of deep-acting physiotherapy to loosen up your tissues and rediscover your natural posture? If so, Rolfing could be for you.

Your recurrent back pain could be alleviated by the legacy bequeathed to natural therapies by Ida Rolf. An American biochemist who died in 1979, she understood that the body's bone and muscle structure is held in place by a web of connective tissue called fascia. When a muscle is put under strain, the fascia ligaments and tendons, for example, change shape to compensate. Thus, over time, the shape of the body changes permanently.

Rolfing would benefit everyone to some extent. However, because of its deep effect on the body, it is not recommended for sufferers from cancer, severe heart complaints, epilepsy or osteoporosis.

Many people with a backache visit an osteopath, who realigns the bone structure; but the tendons and ligaments can quickly pull it out of line again. A Rolfer realigns the entire body by working with her hands deep inside the connective tissue. The effects are intended to be both great and long-lasting.

The benefits

~ Posture improves. When the connective tissue is loosened, the body springs back into its most naturally balanced shape – erect. Stooped shoulders and knock knees are straightened; and people even find themselves taller.

~ Pains in the back, shoulder, knees and feet disappear. These pains are caused by muscle stress. The weight of the body falls in the wrong place, so muscles are forced to work harder. When the body's balance is restored, its weight falls evenly and naturally through the torso, legs and feet so that muscles are no longer stressed and pains evaporate.

~ General well-being improves. After Rolfing, people experience a lightness of movement and feelings of physical rightness unknown to them before. They also feel happier with the shape of their bodies and so feel more attractive.

What happens

Rolfing is a hands-on therapy like massage or osteopathy, but, unlike these, it follows a fixed format – a course, in fact – so every client's experience is more or less the same.

~ The Rolfing course consists of ten one- to two-hour sessions, held weekly or fortnightly. At each session the Rolfer works on different parts of the body. So the full benefits of the therapy are not felt until all ten sessions are complete.

~ The first session begins as an introduction. You'll be told exactly what the therapy consists of and what benefits you can expect. The Rolfer will ask about your health and about your reasons for visiting. She will then ask you to undress down to your underwear so she can photograph you for later comparison and show you where your problem areas lie.

~ Don't worry about 'cowboy' Rolfers. There are very few qualified people and all have received rigorous training at the Rolfing Institute in the USA or Germany.

The interactive procedure

~ After the preliminaries, you will be asked to lie down and the Rolfer will work over your body's superficial fascia, the stocking of tissue that lies just beneath your skin. As she works at areas of tension, you will feel the occasional moment of discomfort, but the final result is a feeling of lightness and ease.

~ You will be asked to join in as she works, with synchronized movements and breathing exercises. In fact the whole course relies on your active cooperation, so it is important that you want it to work. Homework plays an integral part. After the first session, for example, she may ask you to imagine a helium balloon pulling your head upwards as you walk – this gets you into the habit of walking tall.
~ The second and third sessions also concentrate on shallow tissue, but after that the serious work begins. If you're not happy, now is the time to drop out because from now on an interruption could leave vital areas of your body unbalanced. You'll be asked to make a definite commitment at this stage, and the Rolfer will not be held responsible if you break it. Payment is per session, so your only real commitment is to yourself.
~ Sessions four, five and six deal with the body's inner core. The Rolfer works deep inside the pelvic and abdominal musculature, as well as with the back and legs. Naturally, some intimate physical contact is required, but you should by now have developed a trusting relationship with the Rolfer. After session six, your body will have a balanced central structure and you'll experience new feelings of lightness and flexibility.
~ In these sessions you may experience moments of intense discomfort. You may also feel intense emotional release as deeply ingrained tensions are worked loose. It is at this point that the pains start to fade.
~ In the seventh session the head and neck are worked into a balanced position on the spine; in the final three your whole body will be reintegrated around its newly balanced spine and pelvic structure. Throughout, you will be given coaching in how best to move so as to preserve your body's new-found balance.
After the ten sessions the therapy is complete. The Rolfer will take your photograph to see the 'after' effect and give you movement exercises to take home. It may be worth an annual visit to keep your body in shape for the future – ask your Rolfer about this.

Finding a Rolfer

Even if there's nothing obviously wrong with you, it's well worth giving Rolfing a try. You can't help but benefit from the ease of movement and profound sense of physical well-being Rolfing brings. In Rolfing you are not so much a patient as an active participant. So it could be just the right treatment for people who want to take responsibility for their health into their own hands. Contacts are listed in the Help section.

CHAPTER 93
WHAT TO EXPECT FROM SHIATSU

~

Are you attracted to acupuncture, but frightened by the thought of needles? Or perhaps you would simply prefer something a little more sensuous? Shiatsu could be the answer.

Crudely described as acupuncture without the needles, shiatsu is based on the principle of meridians or energy lines, and uses many of the same pressure points as acupuncture and Chinese medicine. A shiatsu therapist, however, will use body pressure, not needles. Indeed, the term comes from the Japanese word for finger, *shi*, and pressure, *atsu*, and so is sometimes rather inaccurately known as acupressure. Shiatsu was introduced to Japan by Buddhist monks from China.

The five elements

Like acupuncture, shiatsu is based on ancient philosophical ideas on human existence which have permeated science, art, politics and religion in China for over 2,000 years. Again, everything is seen in relation to yin and yang and the five elements which correspond to different parts of the body. The heart is fire; the kidneys, water; the liver, wood; the spleen, earth, and the lungs, metal. Just as in acupuncture, the idea is to balance the chi, or life energy of the body, which is also present in the seasons, planets and all natural phenomena.

Shiatsu maintains that when we become ill this energy is disturbed, so that a symptom that presents itself will be related to a lack of energy flow. Shiatsu can help with a whole spectrum of disorders, but is of particular benefit in the case of headaches, fatigue, respiratory illnesses, tension, depression, bowel, back and arthritic problems. It also has an important preventive role to play, as an energy imbalance can be detected long before any symptom occurs. So it can be a good idea to visit a shiatsu practitioner even if you do not have any specific ailment. Not only is there the chance that you will nip an illness in the bud, but your circulation will be improved, the function of your organs regulated and you will certainly feel relaxed and rejuvenated.

As a Japanese form of contact therapy, shiatsu differs from traditional Western massage in that the fingers, along with elbows, knees, feet and the body, are used more than the palms of the hands. And of course it is much more than a slightly erotic experience; it is a means of rebalancing and rejuvenating the body's energies. Shiatsu has some elements in common with chiropractic and hand healing but is, of course, a healing system in its own right, useful for treating a wide range of complaints. Because of its reliance on physical contact, it can be particularly helpful for the elderly or very ill.

What happens

On the day of a shiatsu treatment, it is a good idea not to have a hot bath, drink any alcohol or eat for one hour before or after the session. Depending on the practitioner, you may need to strip to your pants. The rest of your body will then be covered with towels until she starts to work there. Some practitioners will allow you to wear *loose* clothing.

In a treatment session, a shiatsu practitioner will ask you about any specific ailments and about your lifestyle in general. She will observe your body in order to detect any energy imbalance and may take your pulse. Some practitioners employ *hara* diagnosis which involves palpation of the abdomen. All practitioners will use touch in the diagnostic process, feeling for areas which are either too full or too empty of energy.

During the treatment, you will become deeply relaxed. It is best not to talk; a good practitioner will not engage you in conversation – she should be far too busy to talk, in any case! You may either lie on the floor (on a futon) or on a special massage table. The massage table is probably rather easier to use, because it should have a face-sized hole cut in it which will hold your head while you are lying on your tummy, thus avoiding the need to twist your head to one side. Allow your tensions to drift away – you will probably sigh a lot to begin with, and may even find a release of emotional tension results in tears (or laughter). This is all to the good, since it shows that energy is flowing again.

After treatment, you should feel invigorated and relaxed. It is possible that you might feel slightly depressed or experience cold-like symptoms for twenty-four hours following the session. This is no cause for concern; it is simply a sign that negative toxins and emotions are working their way out of your body as a positive response to treatment.

Do-it-yourself shiatsu

Even if you decide not to go for a shiatsu treatment session, there are some simple and effective techniques you can use on yourself to relieve symptoms immediately and to lower your tension level instantly.

Always warm your hands first and take a deep breath, trying to relax so that you do not add any more negative energy. If you feel any significant pain, stop immediately. Consult a registered shiatsu practitioner first if you are pregnant or have high blood pressure. A good guide to the sort of pressure to use is to apply the same amount of force as you would to a doorbell. If an area hurts, you should hold it and rub, something we often do without thinking anyway.

~ HEADACHE. Put the thumb and first finger of your left hand on the web between the thumb and first finger of your right hand, about two centimetres into the hand. Feel around for a painful area by squeezing gently. Once you have found it, apply pressure for thirty seconds before swapping hands. Apart from your headache easing you will probably feel warmth in the massaged area, indicating relaxation.

~ NAUSEA. Put your finger on your inner forearm, about three centimetres away from the wrist and feel for the two tendons. Apply gentle but constant circular pressure in a clockwise direction to the area between the tendons for ten seconds. Then do the same with the other arm, repeating the action three times.

~ BACKACHE. Put the fingers of your left hand on the back of your right thigh, about half way down, where the muscles divide. At this point massage in a circular motion for thirty seconds, relax and repeat with the other leg.

~ FATIGUE. As mentioned earlier, shiatsu is not just a treatment for specific symptoms; it can be used to service the body. If you are feeling tired or a little tense, try this:

- Put your thumbs on the base of the skull, either side of the spinal column. Spread your fingers out on your head and massage for thirty seconds.
- Put your fingers on your crown, half-way between your eyebrows and the base of your skull and apply clockwise pressure for thirty seconds.
- Lie on your right hip with your left hand on your left buttock, about ten centimetres above your hip bone, and massage for thirty seconds.

Many of these techniques can be done anywhere – on the bus, at work or lying in bed. Next time you have a headache or think you are about to explode, don't reach for an aspirin or even a cigarette, look to your fingertips instead! The Shiatsu Society (address in the Help section) is an eclectic group coming from all approaches, whose registered members all have MRSS after their names. Ask them for more information about shiatsu, and details of practitioners in your area.

CHAPTER 94
WHAT TO EXPECT FROM YOGA

You can expect a lot from yoga. As a complete system of personal development it can improve health, bring a sense of well-being and change your whole attitude to life.

Some people maintain that yoga is not a pastime but a way of life. Although this is true in some ways, don't think you have to dedicate yourself to becoming a yogi to reap the benefits of this system.

Yoga, a Hindu discipline, began in India thousands of years ago and as such is probably the oldest structured form of self development. It is sometimes described as a complete science of life because it works on the balance of the mind, body and soul as well as the three forces – action, emotion and intellect.

The medical benefits of yoga are now – after many years – becoming well known in the West. There is hard scientific evidence to show that pranayama yoga can help to control asthma (thus reducing a patient's reliance on drugs of questionable safety).[505] An extremely thorough and well-conducted scientific trial has also shown that yoga can be just as effective in combating high blood pressure as taking anti-hypertensive drugs.[506] And, perhaps most exciting of all, researchers have found that a low-fat vegetarian diet combined with yoga relaxation for a year can actually reverse some of the damage done to the coronary arteries of people suffering from heart disease.[507] Further reported health benefits include alleviation of arthritic pain, chronic fatigue, asthma, weight loss, improved resistance to stress and reduced cholesterol and blood sugar levels.

The yoga postures (or asanas) exercise each part of the body, stretching and toning all the muscles, joints, spine and whole skeletal system as well as the internal organs. Because it helps to release mental and physical tension, practising yoga often results in a rise in energy levels. Other benefits include a sense of being revitalized and calm through the breathing exercises and greater clarity of mind due to positive thinking and meditation.

The word 'yoga' actually means 'to bind or attach' and its aim is to unite the self with a greater consciousness. True yogis believe in the illusory nature of what we perceive to be reality and hold that while the body and mind are only temporary, the spirit is eternal and passes on to new bodies.

In the West, the most well-known form of yoga is hatha yoga which consists of physical exercises for the body. Many people have tried hatha yoga a few times, and sometimes they have been disappointed by it. Invariably, the reason for this unfavourable reaction is a lack of skill on the part of the teacher. Too often, yoga is taught as if it were nothing more than a series of aerobic exercises. Sometimes, yoga classes can seem competitive, and the teacher too severe or uncaring. In this respect, yoga has become a victim of its own success. Because of the rapidly increasing popularity of yoga, a large number of people have set themselves up as teachers without sufficient knowledge or experience. If you have encountered such a teacher, it may be well worth trying to find another one (use the addresses in the Help section) who can offer you a more positive vision of yoga's true potential. And beware of large classes (especially common in evening classes) which will deprive you of the individual attention you really need. You may also want to reach out for one of the lesser-known types of yoga:

Karma yoga

Karma yoga is not a systemized form as such, but follows the principle of 'inaction in action' – that we should perform deeds without the 'self' manifesting itself. The idea is that in halting this pattern of behaviour we break the desire pattern and prevent karma. This underlying principle is in fact used in all forms of yoga.

Bhakti yoga

This is best suited to people with devotional and emotional natures. It normally involves silent worship of a particular object which should completely overwhelm the mind and heart. Two techniques – visualization and repetition of a mantra – are used in this worship. The idea here is that the love the individual has for externals is refined so that we can surrender the self. It was originally described as the most simple form of yoga and suited to all people.

Jnana yoga

This is the yoga of intellect and analysis. In this form, the individual uses the principle of discrimination to distinguish between the false and the eternal and to raise his consciousness.

Raja yoga

This is described as the 'royal path' because all yogis aim to reach this ultimate stage of complete mental and physical control.

There are eight steps, or limbs, in all the different forms, a progressive series of disciplines which lead ultimately to enlightenment:

~ YAMAS

The yamas are restraints, rather like the ten commandments, requiring one to refrain from violence, theft, lying, greed or sensuality.

~ NIYAMAS

The niyamas (or observances) are also in five parts, and aim for the fostering of positive qualities – purity, simplicity, contentment, repeated affirmation and sustained resolve.

~ ASANAS

The asanas are physical postures, carried out with ease in a comfortable position.

~ PRANAYAMA

Pranayama is the regulation of breathing in a quiet, rhythmic manner. This and the preceding step make up the sub-division of raja yoga known as hatha yoga.

~ PRATYAHARA

Pratyahara involves the deactivation of the senses with the aim of achieving concentration.

~ DHARANA AND DHYANA

Dharana and dhyara are states of intense meditation; in the first step an object of image is focused upon and interruptions accepted; in the second, the process is uninterrupted.

~ SAMADHI

The final stage, samadhi, is the attainment of ultimate union in which super-consciousness is reached.

This eight step structure is accepted by all qualified yoga teachers as the definitive frame of reference. Although it is possible to learn yoga from books, they are best used only as a form of reference. To do it properly, you really do need the guidance of a good teacher.

The yogic way of eating

As you become more knowledgeable about the philosophical basis of yoga, you will probably start to incorporate some of its principles into your everyday life. Yoga relies on five principles – proper relaxation, proper exercise, proper breathing, a correct diet and positive thinking and meditation. Diet – being the fuel which drives the rest of the body – is especially important. Only foods which the body can easily digest are eaten by yogis. Natural produce which is absorbed with minimum effort is seen as ideal, because it leaves the body light, but satisfied. Any refined, processed and preserved foods are regarded as denatured and avoided, because they get in the way of proper yoga practice. Meat, sugar, alcohol, certain dairy products, tobacco and overripe or stale substances are not eaten for this reason, and are labelled 'tamasic'.

'Rajasic' foods are also avoided – they tend to be very hot, bitter or salty – because they are believed to destroy the important balance of the body by over-stimulation. Coffee, tea, eggs and chocolate are all rajasic foods.

Instead, the emphasis is on 'sattvic' food which includes cereals, wholemeal bread, fresh fruit and vegetables, legumes, nuts and seeds. This food is seen as vital for nourishing the body and purifying the mind.

Yoga has well and truly hit the Western world. Certainly modern living with all its suffering, ignorance and constant striving could learn a lot from its theories. Looking into the way most of us live does beg the question – what are we searching for? If we incorporated some of the ideas of the yogis into our lives, perhaps it would help us to reach the realization that happiness and our true self are not 'found' or 'acquired', but rather 'come to terms with', by casting off externals. Yogis believe that we must accept the cycle of pleasure and pain and come to terms with the ultimate futility of our actions. They maintain that most of us live in a state of semi-hypnosis or 'maya' where we are not really aware of ourselves. Yoga ultimately aims to break that cycle.

The wonderful thing about yoga is that everyone can benefit – it is not just the preserve of the young and fit. Many pregnant women find practising yoga helps them in all sorts of ways, while the elderly and very young can also join in, within their capabilities. Because yoga brings fitness, youthfulness, relief from tension, better health and peace of mind, it is truly for everyone.

Book Three

SUPERHOME!

Chapter 95

Smart moves: how to take the heartache out of moving house

~

Even the nicest people can behave notoriously badly when it comes to buying or selling their dream home. If home is where your heart is, then moving house is like having a heart transplant: a bit risky, undoubtedly painful, and extremely expensive. But it needn't be that way. Here is our trauma-terminating manifesto for the homemaker of the third millennium.

We all have a horror story or two to tell about moving house. In our own case, we could mention the vendors who were so mean that when they moved out, they took all the light bulbs and even the toilet seat with them. Or the people who felt that the selling price we had agreed for their house was too low, so just before moving out, they smashed up the kitchen to prevent us from having the benefit of it. Or the 'gazumper' who, after agreeing a price for his house, accepted a higher offer just days before we were due to move in, thus making us homeless. We won't depress you with any more!

If you have ever been involved in buying or selling a home, then you will already be familiar with the worst side of human nature. Greed, deception, chicanery and betrayal – to move home is, almost by definition, to become either a victim or a wrongdoer, or perhaps a bit of both. But why do we behave like this? And what can be done to make the experience less unpleasant, and more civilized? After learning some painful lessons, we have some positive proposals to offer which should make life better for both buyer and seller.

~ More than bricks and mortgage. Generally, people behave with duplicity when buying or selling, not because they are inherently evil, but simply because they feel that is the way they *ought* to behave. Buying a property is the largest single investment most people ever make in their lives. Most of us feel intimidated by the size of the sums involved – tens or hundreds of thousands of pounds – and our fear of the loss of security which these large sums represent often makes us behave in an extremely aggressive way. Also, for most of us, moving home is a new and intimidating experience. Official figures show that, on average, most people stay in their houses between five and ten years, and thirty per cent of the population have been in the same house for fifteen years or more.[508] Since we have such little practice at buying and selling homes, it shouldn't be surprising if many of us behave rather amateurishly. But by far the biggest factor, we believe, affecting the behaviour of buyers and sellers is the subtle influence of television drama. In the 1980s and 1990s, glossy television series such as *Dallas*, *Dynasty* and others propagated values in which the super-wealthy were seen to achieve their fortune – and hold on to it – by dishonest, deceitful means. An entire generation came to appreciate the message that they had to "screw the other guy before he screws you". Greed was God, and it didn't matter how you made your money or who you hurt in the process. Otherwise honourable people actually began to believe that, if they hadn't employed extortion, coercion, fraud, deception and manipulation, they hadn't struck a good deal. In this, they were aided and abetted by an unholy alliance of unscrupulous estate agents, whose overriding concern was not the satisfaction or well-being of buyer and seller, but the swollen size of their own commissions.

Today, in the mid 1990s, the feeding frenzy is over, at least for the time being. A little sanity has come into the housing market and, with it, a growing appreciation that a home is something more than simply an over-priced pile of bricks and mortar.

Choosing a new home isn't just a high-stakes game of poker. Although the financial side is obviously one important part of moving house, it is not the *only* part. If you select a new home purely on the basis of striking 'a good deal', then you will almost certainly end up with the wrong place to live in. For example, apart from providing shelter from the elements, a real home should nourish your spirit, too. It is an increasingly-perceived truth that the price of a property often bears little relationship to the deeper qualities which turn it into a genuine home. Consider what a *real* home should be:

~ A SAFE HAVEN. What's the use in buying a tremendous 'investment opportunity' if you're not going to be happy there? The outside world is tough, dangerous, and stressful – and getting more so every day. Now, more than ever before, you need a safe haven – a cocoon – where you can truly relax, feel secure, and be restored. Many highly-priced properties lack this elementary, but essential, quality.

~ A PLACE TO THINK. Somewhere in your ideal home, there should be a small area reserved for thinking. It needs minimal facilities (maybe a power point and phone socket for computer connections to the outside world). But it must be capable of being isolated from the normal everyday chatter created by those living around you. Again, the price of a property is not an important factor in determining whether it can provide you with this essential facility – George Bernard Shaw, for example, found his own oasis of thought in a garden shed (which, incidentally, is where we do much of our work too).

~ A POSITIVE ATMOSPHERE. As soon as you cross the threshold, you can immediately sense whether a house has a good or bad atmosphere. You should never buy a property which your intuition tells you feels bad, no matter how tempting the 'deal'. A high price tag does not guarantee you a positive atmosphere – in fact, many expensively valued properties feel depressing and draining, precisely because they are tainted by the dark side of uncontrolled wealth. A good atmosphere will lift your spirits and refresh you when you need it most, whereas an unpleasant environment will only deplete your resilience and wear you down.

~ A WELCOMING NEIGHBOURHOOD. Again, people often foolishly pay exorbitant sums of money for what they believe to be a 'good address'. Estate agents emphasize the smartness of an area in their advertising copy, while neglecting to mention that many so-called 'fashionable' locations are, in fact, desperately lonesome. 'Rich man's ghettos' do indeed exist – they are soulless estates or blocks of flats, often ringed by security fencing or video cameras, and they lack any community feeling or spark of humanity. In such places, no one knows who their neighbours are or what they do; for all you know, your next-door neighbour could be a merchant banker or a mass murderer. Living in such places is rather like living in a numbered Swiss bank account. Real communities, on the other hand, are much harder to find, but far cheaper to buy into. They tend to have a good mixture of people of all ages, occupations and social classes, and there is a free and easy atmosphere which encourages, but does not force, mingling. Crime is lower, because the residents oversee each other's houses, and friends are easier to make and keep. Although most estate agents turn their noses up at properties in such areas (because prices here are reasonable and their commission is therefore lower), this is where you will find a house which you can truly make your home.

For these and many other reasons, it should be obvious that there is, in reality, very little connection between the asking price for a property and its true value to you as a home. Money is merely *one* measure of value – there are other, more important, human values which cannot be so easily enumerated on a surveyor's report or in the exaggerated sales literature produced by estate agents. Once you understand this, you will approach the whole process of home-finding in an entirely different – and more successful – way.

~ WINNING THE AGENCY GAME. Shopping for a new home is all too often a tedious and at times depressing business. The usual method is to register with several estate agents, who then send you to view properties which they want to sell. This works well for the estate agents, but not so well for you. At the initial interview, the agent will ask you a number of prying questions, whose sole purpose is to 'qualify' you as a sales prospect. To put it bluntly, he doesn't want to waste his time with you if you're not a 'hot' prospect. Resist playing this game! It is only designed to benefit the agent, not you. Here are some of the usual questions, kindly supplied to us by friendly 'moles' on the inside of the agency business, together with our suggested rejoinders.

~ "How much do you want to spend?"

His reason for asking: Although he may say he needs to know this in order to show you the 'right' properties, his real motive is to establish how far you can be pushed on price. If you give any indication of the price you'd be prepared to pay at this stage, it will work against you later on. For example, if you say you can go up to £150,000, then he's not going to show you properties costing £80,000. And if, later on, you make an offer on a property of £135,000, he'll already know that you are actually prepared to pay £15,000 more.

Suggested answer: "My funding is flexible. Just give me details of everything you have in the area." You may need to repeat this several times before he finally gets the message. Estate agents generally aren't used to their customers having the final word on anything.

~ "Have you sold your own property?"

His reason for asking: Two main reasons: Firstly, to establish whether he should be bothered with you (if you haven't sold your own house and say so, don't expect to be treated seriously). Secondly, he may be on the lookout for business, and suggest that you put your house on their books.

Suggested answer: "I'm ready to buy now. Show me the right property and I can proceed immediately." Again, repeat this little mantra several times until he gets the message. It is really none of his business whether you've sold your own property or not. And it is emphatically not a good idea to let the same agent act for you on both purchase and selling – it puts them in altogether too powerful a position. He may try to wheedle further details out of you by asking questions such as "have you exchanged contracts on your own sale?" or "when is completion?" The answer to these is a blunt "That's my lawyers concern, not yours." Don't worry about offending – you are, after all, the customer, and estate agents have very thick skins!

~ "Do you have a mortgage?"

His reason for asking: Two reasons: Firstly, to qualify you as a worthwhile prospective customer (and to give him an idea of your purchasing power). Secondly, to drum up mortgage business for his friends and associates.

Suggested answer: "My finance is not a problem. Just show me the right property." Your mortgage arrangements, if any, are none of his business. Your bank or building society, or a genuinely independent mortgage broker, can help you with finance – not an estate agent. Don't get side-tracked into a discussion of your own private financial arrangements – remember why you're there.

~ "How many bedrooms do you need?"

His reason for asking: By this time, you should be grateful that he's at least started to discuss your property requirements. This question, together with the previous

ones, is designed to make his job as easy as possible. So, for example, if you've told him you can spend £150,000 and want three bedrooms, he can go to his filing cabinet and pull out properties conforming to this criteria (actually, a sharp agent will show you properties costing just a little bit more – in the few minutes you've been talking, he's already made a shrewd judgement of the extent to which you can be pushed on price). The problem is that, although this way of doing things is tailor-made to suit the estate agent's office filing system, it is not really the way most people think about buying a home. 'Three bedrooms, £150,000' is the way a computer thinks, not a human being. The great danger is that you are simply being too restrictive in your criteria, and will therefore miss out on the more unusual and exceptional opportunities around. What about the recently-closed pub, with acres of space and a low asking price? Or two small and cheap terraced houses, both on the market and capable of being knocked into one splendid-sized house? 'Three bedrooms, £150,000' simply won't find these and many other exciting opportunities.
Suggested answer: "Show me everything you have in X area." The agent may well baulk at this prospect, because it could involve him producing a hundred or so sheets or paper. No matter! Glancing through this little pile will only take you a few minutes (ask to be left alone at a vacant desk if his attentions are too annoying while you do this). Also, it will give you a very good idea of properties available in the area concerned, and it will save you many hours or days of foot-slogging. When you eventually decide to view properties, try to visit them without the agent. Generally, they know no more about the property than the details you've already seen on the particulars, and their constant prying questions – and feeble sales pitches – can seriously affect your considered judgement of the property and the area.

Estate agents generally have a poor reputation, which is, on the whole, justified. If you are fortunate enough to find a real professional, who takes a genuine interest in helping you to satisfy your property requirements, then you are indeed lucky. Such a person will be able to offer much in the way of invaluable advice about the area and its good and bad points. But more commonly, estate agency staff tend to be young and thrusting, keen to make a deal, and sometimes not too concerned about the tactics they employ to achieve it.

Once you have decided upon a property, you would do well to exchange phone numbers with the vendor, and build a close relationship with them. Experience shows that you cannot always trust agents to accurately pass on messages, bids and offers, and other vital information. "We were appalled," say friends of ours, when we learnt that the agent had failed to pass on our offer to their client. Although we had bid more than the other people who were interested in the property, the agent had told their client that we had not made an offer. It was no coincidence that the other party had arranged their mortgage through the agent – thus increasing the agent's commission on the deal. We only learnt the full truth after we got in touch with the vendor, who was as horrified as we were." If you keep close to your vendor, and open up a direct line of communication with them, then you will reduce your chances of the purchase going sour.

Your quality of life

When contemplating purchase, ask yourself searching questions about how living in the property will affect you and your family's life. When you eventually sell, your buyer will be asking those same questions and the answers can make the difference between a quick sale and months of nagging uncertainty. Areas to watch are:
~ SAFETY – if you have children or pets, living on a busy road can be a constant worry.

~ NIGHT AND DAY – walk around the area at night. Do you feel safe? Is street lighting adequate? Consult the local paper and see if the neighbourhood is prone to burglary/mugging. Is there a neighbourhood watch scheme in evidence?
~ PEACE AND QUIET – check for noise disturbance, both inside and out. Are there any businesses like all-night garages/taxi services nearby that will be a 24-hour nuisance; do neighbours hold regular noisy parties and are adjoining properties well cared for or suffering from neglect? Inside, are bedrooms near to family rooms, thus making sleep difficult if someone's watching TV late?

Map out your route

Buy an Ordnance Survey map of prospective buying areas. Make a note of schools, libraries, colleges, parks, hospitals and police/fire stations. All are good selling points later, especially schools. Good schools boost property prices, so be aware of them, even if you have no kids of your own. Access to public transport and shops are priorities too. Once you've checked the maps, have a good look round, first by car, then on foot. Try the local shops and pubs, talk to locals and attend a local civic meeting to get a feel for the issues which dominate local life. You can hear of both advantages and disadvantages to moving into the area.

A case for restoration

Many people like to buy new or near-new houses and flats, on the basis that maintenance costs are lower. While this may be true, there are often hidden disadvantages, too. A brand new development can look enticing when first built, and the roses round the door of the show-house are still fresh. A year or two later, however, and the development can look very different – construction could still be continuing on the site, there may be arguments with the developer about repairs, and your neighbours will be very much an unknown quantity. Also, you will have paid the maximum price the developer could obtain, so (unless the economy is really booming) it could be several years before you can get your money back, should you wish to sell. For these and other reasons, it is well worth considering buying an older, perhaps even rather dilapidated, place – and restoring it. The advantages are: you will have absolute control over your own living environment (design it yourself!); you will get a bargain, and should do well when you sell; there may be grants available for certain parts of the restoration (see the addresses in the Help section for information); and you will have the satisfaction of 'recycling' a small, but personally important, part of our heritage.

Of course, you need to approach the task of restoring an older building with your eyes open. The basic cost of the building you choose is just the beginning. Obviously, the more decayed it is, the more work it'll take, and the more money it's likely to cost. If you've got lots of money and plan to supervise other people doing the work, then this may not be a problem for you. But for most of us, it's a crucial question.

If it's to be a holiday home, time won't matter quite so much, but do you really want to spend all your weekends and holidays for the next five years, slaving away? How soon could it at least be habitable? It's crucial to make a realistic estimate of what's going to be involved – and discuss it with other members of your family if it's going to affect them!

How good must the end result be?

Do you dream of having a house which has been so lovingly restored that every detail fits – matching tiles on the roof, quarry tiles on the floor, windows in period style? If you do, then you must be prepared for a long haul.

Finding the materials may in itself be a major task, and they're bound to cost a great deal when you do. You'll also need to be an expert joiner yourself, or pay for one – and they're, justifiably, very expensive. For tracking down materials and craftsmen it's well worth joining something like the Society for the Protection of Ancient Buildings, the Georgian Group, or the Victorian Society – many specialist craftsmen are members. See the Help section for their addresses.

Assessing the building

You've fallen in love with a house – should you go with your feelings? Assuming it fulfils all your basic criteria, just how much work and money will you have to pour in? Before you invest in a proper survey, there's a lot you can find out on your own. Take along a stepladder, a strong torch, a sharp knife, a fine screwdriver and a trowel and have a thorough poke around. Check the condition of window sills and frames, for example, by sticking in your screwdriver. Make yourself look with a seriously critical eye at the structure.

~ If the roof is sagging and full of gaps, go up into the loft and see how bad the damage is.

~ Is the house timber-framed, and damp?

~ If the walls are bulging or cracked, ask yourself why – is the whole house sliding down hill?

~ Are the foundations inadequate?

~ Are there trees near the house?

Any of these problems is likely to mean substantial work and expense – now may be the time to step back. If not, then it's time to get a surveyor in.

Getting a survey

If you need a mortgage, then a survey is essential. If you don't, it's just plain wisdom; you must remember, though, there's a lot they don't see in a normal inspection. To maximize the value of your report, you should go to the house first and help the surveyor in all possible ways.

~ All furniture should be pulled away from the walls.

~ Carpets should be rolled up.

~ Cellars should be emptied.

~ Lofts need to be easily reached, so take a ladder.

~ Make sure the water's turned on, too, so he can check that.

Even a satisfactory surveyor's report is no guarantee of a sound, rot-free structure. Nothing that's concealed behind cast iron or ogee guttering, rendering, pebbledash, hardboard, or fixtures and fittings, will be inspected. The more of these there are, the more likely you are to have hidden problems, especially in a leaky building.

You can have the survey supplemented by getting a report from a specialist firm on dry-rot, woodworm, damp, and wet-rot – this will normally be free. So make sure you go round the building with the specialist – he's quite likely to make informal comments which won't get into the report. Ask him about local services, how likely major works are, how long the work might be expected to take, how old he thinks the building is, what he knows about grants for the works needed.

Worst case scenarios

~ You find dry rot. This can be cured; but it lurks in dark places without ventilation, and it spreads rapidly through the structure, unseen by human eye, weakening everything. Even getting a specialist report can't guarantee it isn't creeping invisibly through your beloved house. Once it's been found, every centimetre of it must be exposed – which can mean ripping out and replacing anything from a few metres of rafter to a whole roof or floor. And you'll just have to pay the experts to come and deal with it, even if you put it all to rights yourself when they've killed the invading rot.

~ The cracks in the walls turn out to be getting steadily wider, and that means the foundations are going to have to be put right. This is usually an enormous job, needing major work to hold the house up while the digging goes on. Unless you're really a professional yourself, you'll need to bring in structural engineers. While the work goes on, the house will be completely uninhabitable – and it can last for months if it involves underpinning a large structure. If you've been able to get insurance on the building, then with any luck that will cover most of the cost, though probably not the first £500.

~ Whole walls that you hoped you could just patch, turn out to need total rebuilding. If this happens, then do check carefully to see whether they're load-bearing. Get advice if you're in any doubt: more than one person has had their home fall about their ears from over-optimism. If it's a vital part of the structure, then you'll have to put an alternative support in place while you do the work, and you may need to bring in a professional for this.

~ The roof, which you knew wasn't in wonderful shape, collapses under the new tiles you've been carefully putting into place. If you've got help, and you're a thoroughly competent carpenter, then you can probably do the basic work yourself. But it'll take weeks of solid work, months if you can only spare weekends; and you'll need to buy or hire scaffolding for the job.

Restoring a house to something like its former glory may bring you much grief, but in the long run it should bring you much joy – be patient! You'll be doing the rest of us a good turn, too, by saving a bit of the nation's treasure.

Go shopping at bargain time

Most people seek to move in spring. Yet that is when properties are at their spruced-up best, with prices to match, partly due to increased pressure from buyers. Instead, look for a real bargain in mid-winter when owners are huddled in front of their fires and properties look dreary, and the market is less active.

Time it right

Don't get caught up in a moving-house chain: you can waste massive amounts of time and money this way, to say nothing of the disappointment of finding your dream home only to have it snatched away from under your nose if your own sale falls through. Therefore, put all your effort into selling your own property first, before re-buying. This may entail leaving your own house before moving into another 'bought' one. However, the inconvenience of renting a property and storing your furniture for a time is often outweighed by being able to move quickly on your next purchase and, with the advantages of 'cash in hand', you can afford to shop around for a bargain, if necessary making several low offers on a 'take it or leave it' basis.

Indeed, during a stagnant period of house prices or when mortgage interest rates are prohibitive, it is well worth considering renting on a longer-term basis, as your money could earn more in a higher interest account than it will locked up in an unsaleable property in a dead market. Rents will have fallen, relative to mortgage payments, too, as desperate home-owners put their properties out to rent.

Everything is negotiable!

When you do find the house or flat you want, try not to regard it as the home of your dreams. This can be difficult, but it will avoid disappointment if another buyer beats you to the punch or if the seller withdraws; it will also lessen the chance of your paying too much for the place, or more than you had budgeted for, through over-enthusiasm. There's always another pebble on the sea-shore.

Even if you were shown the place initially through an estate agent, you should always establish contact with the vendor directly, before you make an offer through any agent. And it is important for you to sell yourself before you sell the deal. You may say, 'I'm not selling anything – I'm buying!' No. What you're doing is trying to persuade the seller to buy the deal you're offering (unless, of course, you're offering the full asking price – do you really have money to burn?). So start by visiting at least twice before you even hint that you're going to make an offer. This will raise expectations on the other side, and start to psychologically commit the vendor to you and this sale.

~ BE HUMBLE. Don't try any power negotiating tactics you may have seen on those American TV soap operas – that's strictly the stuff of fiction. Most deals go sour because one party acts in bad faith. Sharing a cup of coffee with your prospective vendor in the kitchen is the first step to establishing a successful and mutually-trusting business relationship.

~ BE FRIENDLY! Tell the vendor about you, your family, your personal circumstances, and all the reasons why you'd like to buy the house. Ask them in an honest, direct way whether they would be prepared to compromise on the price. At this stage, you'll get some feedback on the vendor's willingness to negotiate. As a guide, you could offer 10 to 20 per cent less than the asking price, but, of course, this does depend on the state of the market. Experience shows that in really tough economic times, people tend not to sell unless they really have to, and the market consequently dries up. In times like these, there is a good case to buy from people who *have* to sell for a living – builders and developers whose bank managers are about to foreclose on them have been known to agree to discounts of 50 per cent or even more for ready cash! If you are buying a new property, find out how many of the builder's houses remain unsold. Remember – the more unsold, the more potential there is for negotiating a cut-price deal.

~ Be patient. If the owner is offended by a 'derisory' offer, don't let his or her reaction affect your own emotional state. Stay cool. Set yourself a ceiling and, if you so wish, increase your offer. But in the final analysis, you must be prepared to walk away from the purchase without regrets.

The deal-breakers

Once you've agreed a price, you may think it's all over bar the shouting. Not so. You now have to deal with the professionals again – the estate agents and the lawyers. Sadly, many purchases fail at this point. Both professions have their own motives for exercising a negative influence. The agent may simply be incompetent, or he may advise the vendor to sell at a higher price to another bidder, or he may fail to pass on messages for his own devious reasons. As far as the lawyer is concerned, all too often he sees his role as one of trouble-spotter, rather than expediter or facilitator. Of course, if there are genuine legal problems, then you need to be warned of them, but there is a fine line between being a legal watchdog and artificially manufacturing a confrontation, which many lawyers don't seem to grasp. For example, one of our own house purchases nearly came to grief when a lawyer decided to take up the issue of whether the deeds to our new property allowed us to keep a boat in our back yard. Although he was a keen sailor, we certainly weren't, and in any case the yard was far to small for anything other than a rubber dinghy.

The longer the purchase takes, the more likelihood of complications. Although no one will admit it to you, it is usually possible for all the legal aspects to be completed in a few days, if you're willing to pay the price. Don't allow yourself to be fobbed off with 'eight weeks minimum for the search' – if necessary, go personally and do it yourself that very day.

The best way to prevent trouble at this stage is to keep your lines of communication with the vendors wide open. Don't lose contact with them at any point. If you do, you have no way of knowing whether their agent is conveying messages accurately between the two parties. Sometimes, the vendor's agent and the purchaser's lawyer will take an immediate dislike to each other. Although, theoretically, this shouldn't affect your purchase, in reality it will do. The agent will complain to his client that your lawyer is dragging his heels. The vendor will then start to lose faith in the sale, and may be persuaded to put the house back on the market again. To forestall all this, call your vendor each time you have any message from his lawyers or agents, just to check that what they've said is accurate. "We've heard from your agents today that . . . (whatever you've heard) . . . and I wanted to let you know that . . . (whatever you intend to do)."

The selling business

Selling a property is like buying, only in reverse. The first thirty to forty-five days that a house is on the market are crucial. This is usually when it's looking its best and the estate agent is keen to generate the most interest, contacting any prospective buyers on their mailing lists. If you price your home too high, you'll lose these early 'potential' buyers and have to hope for a 'straggler' instead. Selecting the best agent is never easy, but don't just fall for the one quoting the highest price, it doesn't mean you'll get it. Rely more on recommendations, reputation and knowledge of the local market.

If you want to have a go at selling it yourself, thus saving yourself a hefty agent's fee, first decide on your lowest acceptable price. You can still get some agents round to give a free property valuation to help you arrive at this figure. You may even need one later if you are unsuccessful. Boards, mailing shots, bulletin and notice boards, and newspapers/specialist magazines are all worth a try and be prepared for negative comments when showing potential buyers round. There's no sense in taking offence.

Selling psychology

The only facelift that most houses need is a thorough cleaning (don't forget the windows), a fresh lick of paint where necessary (don't tackle a job that's too big and which will leave you rushing it or half-way through it when the first potential buyer arrives) and minor landscaping (that means tidying up the garden). Pay special attention to the front entrance.

Most people buy on the basis of what they initially see, so keep the place tidy. In a slow market it's worth 'staging' your property, which can involve anything from storing furniture to make the place look bigger (but houses empty of contents are unattractive and are not good sellers) to displaying your finest objects such as grandma's set of bone china. Fresh cut flowers are worth the expenditure while the smell of fresh coffee or baking bread or cake is very seriously seductive.

~ Learn your script. Don't be embarrassed about this. You're not doing yourself or your potential purchasers any favours if you mumble something like: "er, well, just have a look round, and I'll be in the kitchen if you want me." In any case, don't let them out of your sight for their first two or three visits – how do you know they're not crooks?

~ Start in a relaxed, friendly manner. Shake hands, get their first names, take their coats. A few words about how long you've lived there, the high spots of the area, why regretfully you're thinking about moving (only 'thinking about' – don't give the impression that you're so desperate to move that you'll sell at any price). Then the room-by-room tour begins.

~ Point out each and every sales feature . . . the unique fireplace, the space-saving built-in cupboards, the mood lighting. Have a flattering photo of the place to give them. It is particularly impressive to offer to show them a copy of the survey you commissioned when you bought the place. Give them your phone number at the end of the tour, and invite them back for another look whenever they want. It's important they should feel at home right away, so keep it warm and friendly – a cup of coffee afterwards and a chat about their jobs will personalize the whole process.

~ There is a very simple way to deal with offers. When the place goes on the market decide what you want. Then set the price 10 per cent higher than that. Any offer even slightly less than your real price is rejected, politely but firmly. If you decide on £100,000 and a prospective purchaser offers £99,500, the answer must be 'no'. If they seriously want the place, they'll increase the offer. If they don't, then they were just wasting your time anyway. The big problem with accepting offers less than your real price is that it's a never-ending slippery slope: each time, you go a little bit further down (and you'll find your agent, if you have one, will push you hard to accept, it's his commission he's thinking about). Don't compromise!

Buying and selling at auction

Auctions have a mystique which puts many potential clients off, yet in certain circumstances they are an excellent medium for both buyers and sellers.

As a buyer, you can pick up a bargain, so long as you've really done your homework beforehand. Details of properties available at auction are sent out up to a month before day of sale, so if you are interested in one, thoroughly research your intended buy, then get a survey done, have a solicitor attend to details such as searches and speak to the auctioneer about estimated price. On the day of sale, if your bid is successful and over the reserve price (and remember, *don't* get carried away on the day), you are committed to buying and will need to pay a 10 per cent deposit then and there, and the rest within a month. The advantage of this is a quick move, though failure to get the property will mean loss of initial outlay.

You should consider selling at auction if you own an unusual property which is difficult to put a price on, if you're seeking a swift sale as a divorcing couple or trustee, and if you're moving to a new job in a far-off area. In a period of rapidly rising prices, a seller can sometimes do well by playing buyers off against each other through the medium of the auction.

Buying property abroad

A truly European housing market is ever closer with house purchase in France especially attractive through low prices. Finance for a home abroad can come from several sources: a second mortgage using the excess value of a domestic property to generate cash; or a loan taken out on the basis of the actual foreign property to be purchased. In the second instance this could be in sterling or local currency, with some experts recommending the latter as, barring a drastic fall in the foreign property market, a foreign currency loan remains smaller than the real property value, whereas a sterling loan can fluctuate according to the rate of foreign exchange.

In France, for example, it is simple to arrange a relatively cheap loan where the potential French lender will value the property and lend accordingly; surveys are not required as a basis for the loan (though, naturally, you may still wish to have one done). UCB, for example, offers franc-denominated loans.

Peseta loans are available in Spain where, for instance, the Abbey National has branches operating such facilities (more details in the Help section). For those wishing to stay with the certainty of sterling, again, there are facilities from UCB and Abbey National. Loans are raised on either the foreign or UK property. It is even possible to raise a loan in a third currency, but there are dangers if that currency, say the Swiss franc, rises against both sterling and the native currency.

Be absolutely certain that you really want the commitment of running two households (assuming you're going to keep your first home as well). A quick jaunt across the Channel for an idyllic French weekend sounds transcendentally blissful, but the reality can be ugly. Just getting there can take many precious hours out of a weekend. Then there are repairs, maintenance, mopping up a flooded cellar, burglaries. When it's good, it's really good, and when it's bad, it's perdition.

The leasehold trap

Owning a property on leasehold, that is where you, the 'home owner', have a lease (say of 99 years), but an extraneous landlord retains the full right of freehold, is a singularly unsatisfactory way to own any property. It means that the true freeholder possesses a great deal of control over the property you are living in, and in turn, the freeholder can appoint a 'managing agent' who will have little concern for you, but great interest in maximizing how much cash he can extract from you whilst you are living there. This often takes the form of excessive service and insurance charges and neglect of essential repairs (and prohibitive charges when they are done, even when, as is often the case, they are done badly by 'cowboys'). Yet this unsatisfactory method of property 'ownership' accounts for a vast proportion of property in London (mainly in the form of purpose-built flats and conversions) and elsewhere too.

In theory, the Landlord and Tenant Act of 1987 eased matters by allowing the leaseholder to buy the property freehold in certain circumstances and under protected conditions. For leaseholders, buying the freehold means gaining better management of their own property and, vitally, the extension of the existing lease. A lease with only a few years to run means that the property becomes a 'diminishing asset', unmortgageable and, virtually, unsaleable.

However, the reality is that leaseholders need much greater assistance, and further reform of the law, currently under consideration, is necessary. This should include the right to 'commonhold', i.e. the right of leaseholders to buy their property, in perpetuity; and for existing leaseholders to name their own managing agent so that they act for them.

In the meantime, however, you should take great care in buying leasehold, paying special attention to length of lease: don't be caught with the 'fag-end'. Satisfy yourself that the character and history of your freeholder and managing agent is adequate and that the place has a good history of repair, and get your lawyer to thoroughly check the lease's terms and conditions for you.

Get full value from your lawyer

Many people do not realise the full range of services available from solicitors, preferring instead to use them only for the basics of house conveyancing, such as searches and finalizing the contract. However, a *good* solicitor can help you with:

~ Objective mortgage advice and survey advice – if building work is recommended by your surveyor, your solicitor can negotiate who pays and incorporate details into the contract.

~ Leasehold problems (see above) and planning law – help regarding planning matters ranging from advice on whether land with your house can be released for building, whether your neighbour's ugly extension is permissible, to that new airport flight path going right over your house, some of the many factors affecting your house's value.

The M word

Most people will agree, a home of your own is an excellent investment. Having said that, the 'M' word or mortgage can affect one's life profoundly. The period of escalating interest rates between 1988 and the UK's entry into the European Exchange Rate Mechanism in October 1990 added up to mortgage misery – and real hardship – for hundreds of thousands of borrowers. It was a clear example of the impact of variable interest rates; with every new increase undermining over-stretched personal budgets.

Nevertheless, in the long run, our homes increase in value. And historically, mortgages usually account for a gradually-decreasing proportion of your overall income. But when you're buying for the first time, or if you're on the move, you need expert advice. These days, there are a bewildering array of mortgages on offer. So how do you choose between them, especially when the APR is much the same, wherever you look?

Repayment, endowment, pension linked . . .

~ A Repayment Mortgage is the traditional way of buying your home. It's basically a long-term loan. You pay interest on it and pay back the capital in stages, so that at the end of the term, you owe nothing, and the house is all yours. In today's uncertain economic climate, the repayment mortgage has one particular advantage: it is sometimes possible to extend the term of your loan, and therefore cut your monthly repayments, if you should get into financial difficulties.

~ Endowment Mortgages of one type or another have become the most popular way to borrow. You're taking on a package of two separate elements. First, there's the loan, on which you pay interest for the entire life of the mortgage. But you *don't* repay any of the capital. So if you're ten years into a £50,000 endowment mortgage, you still owe your lender the full amount, even though you've been making the monthly repayments.

At the same time as you agree to the mortgage, you also take out an endowment policy, which is effectively a regular savings plan. As the years go by, the value of the policy increases. At the end of the agreed term, you use the policy to pay off the mortgage in one lump sum – and hopefully, there's money left over, which is yours to spend as you please.

~ Pension Mortgages and Personal Equity Plan (PEP) Mortgages are a variation on Endowment Mortgages. The former can be extremely tax-efficient – although in most cases, the total monthly repayments are higher than other types of mortgage. With a PEP mortgage, the 'savings plan' element of your payments is invested in unit trusts or stocks and shares. This means you stand to end up with a larger lump sum than you'd expect from a straightforward endowment policy. A word of caution, however: this is by no means a risk-free investment, if the Stock Market plunges overnight, so does the value of your PEP.

~ Deferred Interest Mortgages were dreamed up by building societies and other mortgage lenders while interest rates were high. Their attraction? Lower monthly repayments, since as much as 30 per cent of the interest can be 'rolled up'. Naturally, there's a price to be paid for your short-term gain. Firstly, you end up owing more than you did at the outset: you'll find the debt increases, year by year, all the while a portion of the interest is being deferred. And secondly, your repayments go up, once a year, generally an annual increase of 10 per cent . . . so after three years, you're paying the standard monthly repayments. Are deferred interest mortgages a good idea? They can be, particularly if you expect your salary to increase significantly in the next few years. And, of course, if interest rates fall, the annual increase is easier to absorb.

~ Fixed Rate Mortgages can be a popular option when interest rates are high, since they offer you guaranteed stability. Nevertheless, they can also be something of a gamble. It would be heart-breaking if you locked yourself into a fixed rate 13 per cent mortgage for twenty-five years and interest rates dropped to seven per cent! But they're worth considering if the rate is fixed for, say, just three years.

~ Foreign Currency Mortgages. These are definitely not for the faint-of-heart. The attraction is simple enough – if interest rates in Europe, America or Japan are lower than in the UK your monthly repayments are going to be far lower. For example, a £100,000 loan at the UK rate of 14.5 per cent works out at £1,208 a month. The same loan in Deutschmarks, at 9.75 per cent, would cost you only £854 a month, a saving of £354.

But problems can arise if sterling falls sharply against foreign currencies, in which case you end up having to repay a great deal more than you borrowed, swallowing up the savings you'd made, and more besides. Now that the value of the pound is loosely tied to the major European currencies, this risk has been somewhat reduced. But the fact remains that these loans are a lot less safe than your average High Street lender's mortgage. Avoid them, unless you're already independently wealthy! And even then, remember you're taking a gamble.

Problems with the mortgage?

If you're not able to keep up the mortgage payments on your house – interest rates have risen, or you've been made redundant – it is worthwhile speaking to your bank or building society. You may not need to lose the house. For example, you could get a roll-back mortgage with reduced payments initially but more to pay back later. But this probably depends on your ability to increase your income in the future.

Another idea your bank manager may accept is deferring capital payments on the mortgage. Until you get another job, or interest rates go down you'll just be paying interest on the loan.

If you'll be able to keep up payments in future, but owe several months' back interest, you can ask for it to be added onto the capital you borrowed to buy the house.

Talk about your options with the Money Advice Centre and prepare a proposal for the bank manager before you meet him. He will be much more sympathetic if you've done your homework.

CHAPTER 96

DO YOU SINCERELY WANT TO BE RURAL?

~

Are you reaching the end of your tether? Can't cope with the air, street and noise pollution of daily life in the city? Does moving to the country seem the only sane solution? Going rural brings real benefits: cleaner air, more space for the children and animals, organic food from your own plot. Yet these and other enhancements to your lifestyle are only attained with careful planning.

One of the most significant population trends of our age is the move away from the urban jungle to the country. As life becomes more pressured, and less rewarding, in the cities, those who are able to relocate move away from the grime of the city to find peace in the country. Or so they think! Actually, it is rarely as simple as that. Country living can certainly be wonderful ('rush hour' in the country means sharing a back lane with a herd of cows returning to be milked), but it can also be an expensive and lonely nightmare. Go into it with your eyes open, knowing what to expect, and you will enjoy and profit from it. Fail to do so, and you're courting disaster.

After twenty years of country life, we decided to move in the opposite direction – from the isolated peace of rural Norfolk to the heart of London – quite a transition! And we've never regretted it. Many people couldn't understand why we made such a strange move, but to us, it made good sense. While we love the country, much of it is quite inaccessible to the ordinary person (unless you happen to own it). There is also far too much pollution, from farm sprays, agricultural run-off, and other agrochemicals. And in remote areas, simple tasks such as doing the shopping, taking the children to school, and commuting to work often consume much of the day's energy. In the city, everything is accessible (we've cheerfully done without a car for five years, and have never missed it) and friends are easier to make, too.

In this and the next chapter, we want to give you a clear, no-nonsense picture of what you should anticipate if you are interested in leading 'the good life'. And in chapter 99, we show you how to combine the convenience of urban living with a more natural, self-sufficient approach to your needs – perhaps the best of both worlds.

Spy out the land

First, three-quarters of Britain is still designated as rural, so where to go? House price, work possibilities, availability of schools, shops, hospitals, cinemas and theatres, all important facets of modern life, have to be reconnoitred before making hard and fast decisions. Local newspapers and estate agents supply useful advance data – not just the house prices but also salient facts about the infrastructure of the area.

Getting to know local people before you decide to become one, provides all kinds of pertinent preliminary information during the often neglected but always important, field research. This isn't always easy. In Norfolk, you weren't considered to be a 'local' until you'd lived there twenty years (so we just qualified before we left). Strangers asking prying questions in a small village will often be greeted with suspicion. In fact, the only two places where a stranger can rely on meeting people are the church and the pub (events at the village hall are for the locals, so don't gatecrash). So first write to the local vicar, telling him you are thinking of moving to the area, and ask him if you could possibly call on him for a few minutes for a chat. Most vicars are moved to a new parish every few years, so they know all about the problems of relocating and integrating into a new community, and will prove a treasure trove of valuable advice. At the pub, you may have to be more discreet. Make a couple of visits before you ask too many questions, so the landlord recognizes your face. If he proves friendly, he will introduce you to others who have already made the move, and who could share their experiences with you.

Rural emergencies

Wherever you choose to settle, one key difference between city and country is the climate. Cities, filled with bricks and bodies, are invariably warmer both in summer and winter, sometimes by as much as five degrees Celsius. The four seasons, especially winter, are a basic and inescapable fact of country life. Gales and blizzards can maroon your household and eliminate your power supply. Hedges – once a feature of the British rural landscape, now a rarity, thanks to the fatuous policies of the Ministry of Agriculture – always prevent the worst effects of snow drifts. In the first winter following the wholesale destruction of our village's hedges by a greedy farmer, the entire village was cut off for ten days. If you want to live by the sea, consider carefully the prospect of flooding. On the Norfolk coast, a life-threatening inundation happens, on average, every twenty years. Unless you've seen the after-effects of such a disaster, it is impossible to imagine. Entire houses can be picked up and deposited yards away. Massive concrete blocks (used as breakwaters) are tossed all over the place, often ending up some distance inland. And salt water gets everywhere – the cellar, the garden, the electricity supply, and the bedrooms. Less dramatic, but equally dangerous, is the slow but pernicious effect of coastal erosion, which has caused whole villages to disappear over the cliff face. Take all this into consideration when choosing a possible location. And plan for rural crises, hoarding food in bulk and, if budget permits, installing a generator to supply basic heating and lighting during an emergency.

Don't be a lone country-lover

Another universal fact of rural life is the variability of its attraction to different members of a household. The patch of land which appeals to mother with her green fingers may appal a teenaged child who is more concerned about how to attend the Madonna concert hundreds of miles away. Are you, as a parent, prepared to commit a larger part of your leisure to becoming a backroads taxi service for your own and other children?

Founding the homestead

If you have difficulty obtaining a mortgage on the rural retreat of your choice through conventional building societies, the Ecology Building Society, established in 1981, looks favourably on loans to those who want to start organic small holdings, rehabilitate a corn mill, live in a timber house or a croft, or otherwise defy the conventions (address in the Help section). For those seeking to convert a barn, remember that only listed barns can be converted to domestic use. Local Improvement Grants are usually available for properties built before 1961, but, from 1990, all such grants are subject to means testing.

While an extension or minor alteration to your property does not necessarily require planning permission, it will be subject to building regulations. This means that your 'olde worlde' cottage can only be re-created as an outer structure in its original design and materials. Building regulations now demand larger windows, they veto thatched roofs unless the straw is fire-lined and all cables are put in fire-proof conduits. Regulations will not allow walls of wattle and daub, that mixture of cow dung, straw and clay so much used in rural buildings before this century.

If you need manpower to help during a house renovation or in establishing a small business, whether it be a database or a guest house, enquire into the personnel situation well in advance of needing to hire. Are craftsmen available? If so, how much do they charge for their services? Bear in mind that young people in rural districts frequently migrate to the cities.

A place for the pets

Livestock, whether in the form of pets or for animal husbandry, is an established fact of rural life. If you own a dog or cat, be aware that under the 1980 Highways Act you can be prosecuted if they escape onto a public road. Farmers have the right to shoot dogs found on their land as they are considered a potential threat to their sheep or cattle, and poison (not all of it legal) is often put down for mice, rats, moles and other creatures considered to be pests. If you like animals, you will at some time be shocked by the callous way that farmers often treat their beasts and 'pets'. On a farm, every animal has a purpose. The cat is there to discourage rodents, and when it gets too old to work, it is often killed none too humanely. There's one country 'lore' which you can absolutely, utterly depend on, all the time: if you're an animal lover, the animals will get to hear about it. Before you know it, all the strays for miles around will be queuing up at your doorstep, and your home will become a menagerie!

Rural pollution versus urban pollution

Country living, foreseen as tranquil, can prove every bit as noisy as the city you fled. Tractors, low-flying jets from the nearby military site (many of Britain's 'beauty spots' have one), farm machinery, crow-scarers and clay-pigeon shoots all commonly serve to pollute the rural airwaves.

Agricultural or forestry buildings can appear almost overnight at the end of your garden, not always very pretty and especially repugnant if they blot out a vista. Planning permission is not required for buildings erected for farming and forestry use, so legal action is of no avail. A farmer also has the right to cut or remove his hedges, drop slurry from his tractor on the public highway and generally behave in a manner which, to ex-urbanites, can be distressing.

There is, however, a provision in law known as 'legal nuisance' protecting you from silage smells, tree roots, mists from farming insecticides and other threats to your quality of life. The local Environmental Health Officer is empowered to investigate all complaints of legal nuisance, so, if planning an appeal through this channel, it is worth keeping a log of events and, in many cases, providing immediate photographic evidence of the nuisance which afflicts you.

Take heart, too, from the Caravan Sites and Control Act of 1960, which requires planning permission for any landowner to establish a caravan site adjacent to your land. Planning permission, in this area at least, is very often withheld.

Your family and other animals

For those wishing to develop small-scale animal husbandry, goats, chickens and bees are the most viable ventures for beginners (see chapter 98). Investigate your options thoroughly, however. Nanny goats, for instance, lactate to a volume of around 4,000 litres. Are you sure you can use that quantity of milk? And bees must be hived with care, well away from children's play areas or neighbours' fences. Living with animals gives you new respect for them, which, not surprisingly, makes it harder to eat them. It is not uncommon for people to move to the country and rear, say, geese – intending to sell them at Christmas time. When slaughter time comes around, however, each goose has been given a name, and you're faced with the prospect of committing murder! It is probably best to restrict yourself to just one or two chickens, geese or ducks (farmers may give you their 'sickly' rejects if you ask them) who will give you an ample supply of eggs, in return for a safe home and an old age pension.

The woods, the fields and the wilderness

By far the greatest benefit of rural life is the sense of open landscape, apparently unoccupied. Remember, however, that in a country as densely populated as Britain, nearly every piece of apparent wilderness is owned by someone. If it is not a farmer, then it could be the Ministry of Defence, who utilize many heaths and moors as firing zones, or a city stockbroker, or a government agency. Many of the most beautiful regions are now designated Sites of Special Scientific Interest.

The only exceptions are the 8,000 commons and village greens registered under the 1965 Commons Registration Act. Land thus registered is designated as common land which cannot be cultivated, retained or used for anything but grazing and recreation. The Countryside Act of 1981 protects nearly all flora and fauna, whether found on private or common land.

Other access to the countryside is possible through the 225,000km of British footpaths. These are often illegally fenced off, ploughed or otherwise concealed by landowners. But if you possess the appropriate Ordnance Survey maps and know your rights, you cannot be accused of trespass. Footpaths are the right of all to enjoy; and quiet access on foot causes little damage to wildlife. Know, however, that most farmers hate footpath walkers, and be prepared for a prolonged and possibly nasty tussle with them.

For those who can budget for personal ownership of a small wood, prices in the south of England are around £6,000 per hectare. Half of Britain's 750,000 hectares of broadleaf trees come in packets of less than ten hectares, too small for forestry management. Coppicing your own wood provides timber for fencing and firewood and much-needed relief for the distant rain forests, cutting down on the need for timber imports. For useful addresses concerning woodland, see the Help section.

The rural dividend

Above all, the sense of space, of open roads and skies, of greeting people as individuals and not mere units of pressure, these are the unquantifiable but essential advantages of becoming 'sincerely rural' in your way of life. In the country, small is not only beautiful, it is also vital. As the organic gardener Lawrence D. Hills remarked: "I should like to die having found the answer to slugs." If you can sympathize with that, start your rural researches right away!

CHAPTER 97

YOUR COUNTRY HOME: TWENTY ESSENTIAL QUESTIONS TO ASK BEFORE BUYING

~

For some reason yet to be discovered, buying a place in the country turns normal, clear-thinking adults into dreamy, sentimental creatures, easy prey to the seductive charm of roses round the first doorstep they pass. Unless this tendency is carefully controlled, you could become your own worst enemy and end up buying a property that is actually a pile of problems. Here are twenty vital questions you should ask before you sign on the dotted line.

1) *What is access to the property like?*

Learn the answers to these important questions from the estate agent, your lawyer, or the local Land Office:

~ Is the land on which the access rests actually part of the property you intend to buy?

~ Or does the land belong to someone else, making the access a 'right of way' to your property?

~ Is the access shared, or are you sole user?

~ If shared, who else has use of it?

~ Who has responsibility, shared or otherwise, for maintaining the access and what is the cost?

2) *Is there enough privacy for you?*

No matter how pretty and perfect your intended property may be, you must make certain that it is private enough for you.

~ Can your immediate neighbours look into the house or overlook all of the garden?

~ Is the garden enclosed enough to keep out the prying eyes of passers-by?

~ Is there sufficient sound privacy between you and your neighbours?

3) *Are there any lands or parts common to your neighbours?*

A chat with the current owner and your lawyer will help you learn:

~ Is there any common land and to what use may you put it?

~ Are there common parts to the property itself? A semi-detached cottage, for instance, may have common walls and roof space. It is important that you learn precisely which aspects of the structure are common and what both your rights and your duties are towards them.

4) *What is the structural state of the property?*

You can tell much about the structure of a property by a careful first glance. If the roof sags, the windows and doors don't close properly and the rooms smell musty, you're probably in for some problems. Hire a structural surveyor to write a thorough assessment of the property. Among the most important details to learn are:

~ Is the house subsiding or moving?

~ Is there rising or penetrating damp and what measures can be taken to remedy this problem?

~ Is there dry or wet rot? How extensive is it?

~ Is the roof in good repair? If not, what needs to be done to it?

~ Are the windows effective and in good repair?

~ Is the wiring adequate and up to British Standards?

~ Is there any sign of lead piping in the water supply system?

~ Is there any sign of asbestos having been used in the building?

Learning the answers to these questions in particular will help you determine how much money you will need to spend to revive the property.

5) *What is the decorative state of the property?*

Although a surveyor will include comments on decoration in his or her report, you may learn most of what you want to know just by looking carefully. The state of decoration can indicate, in a general sense, how well the house has been cared for, though the main purpose in asking this question is to assess how much time and money you will need to spend to redecorate to your tastes and standards.

6) *Is the property connected to electricity and telephone?*

This question is very easy to answer, just by looking and asking. Don't ever take it for granted that either service is connected. Electricity supply, for instance, may be apparent in the house but be provided by a generator in the back garden rather than the mains service. While you're at it, you might as well ask if the house is connected to mains gas and also what the radio and television reception is like.

7) *What are the water and sewerage facilities?*

Mains water and sewerage are increasingly common in small villages, but isolated or very remote cottages will probably have their own septic tank and, possibly, their own well. Some places have no sewerage facilities and use chemical toilets instead of flush toilets (contact your council for Night Cart Soil Collection Service). There are usually grants available to help you connect with or install a sewerage system; the local council can advise on this as well as the procedure for connecting to mains water.

8) *What are the postal and other services like?*

Ask the current owner, and then ring the local post office to find out how often the post is delivered and whether it comes to your door or the end of your drive. Many rural places have a surprisingly good postal service – sometimes two deliveries a day. While you are at it, ask the current owner about other services available. Fruit, vegetable, milk and bread deliveries are all common in rural areas, as are newspaper and even laundry services! There might even be a mobile library service available.

9) *Is there a public transport service?*

Even if you never use public transport, find out if a service exists and what it consists of. Some areas enjoy a daily bus service connecting tiny hamlets and remote dwellings with the local towns. Visit the nearest tourist information office, ring the local bus companies and stop at the nearest train station. Get schedules for every service you feel might be of use to you and study them carefully. You'll be glad you did if ever your car breaks down.

10) *What is the local traffic like?*

Ask the locals if tractors and farm machinery use the lane nearest your property very much and, if so, at what time of year.

Drive round the lanes yourself and make note of the local businesses tucked away in those unlikely barns and cottages. Of especial significance are factories, riding schools, forges, craft shops and tea rooms. Each of these will add appreciably to the volume of traffic on the lanes near your intended property. Next stop should be your local council offices, where you can discuss traffic proposals (i.e. motorways or bypasses) with the transport and planning officer.

11) *Are the property boundaries clear and uncontested?*

Ask the current owner, have a good look at how the boundaries are marked, then compare this information with the deeds and plans to the property. Your lawyer will do a search as part of the normal conveyancing procedure, which includes checking that no disputes, lawsuits or other actions are under way relating to the property. Study the search report carefully to satisfy yourself that all is well.

12) *Are there any rights of way over the land?*

After asking the current owner, rely on the search (above) to turn up rights of way over your intended property. Sometimes there are rights of way which the current owner has genuinely forgotten because the right has not been used for many years. A farmer may have right of way over your land in order to gain access to one of his fields, or a public footpath might cross your land. If there are rights of way over your intended property, you should know about them and consider ways of accepting them.

~ Some rights of way might be moved from one part of your land to another, less intrusive part. Ask your local council if this is possible.

~ Consider a footpath, for instance, as an opportunity. Why not serve afternoon teas on the lawn for passing ramblers? Or sell the pottery or patchwork quilts you make all winter long?

13) *What rights and duties concern the water crossing the land?*

It may look like a ditch to you, but it is undoubtedly part of a well-planned and long-established network of waterways which keep the surrounding land in good shape for farming or grazing. Your local council, lawyer and water company will be able to inform you about your rights and duties concerning water that flows across your land.

~ You may have a duty to keep the ditch (or stream or river) clear of obstruction.

~ You are probably forbidden to divert the flow of water in any way (such as widening it to make a pond).

~ You may have rights which mean that the water will not be diverted off your land without your prior knowledge and opportunity to contest.

~ You may have to pay a small fee to the local water board for their role in maintaining any culverts, etc.

~ You can expect the water to be clean and can take legal action if it is polluted by a person or company further upstream from you.

~ Contact your local Environmental Health Officer in case of water-borne pollutants crossing your land. It is useful to have the name and number of this officer at hand in case of emergency.

14) *Is the property on an airport or RAF flight path?*

Ring the nearest RAF base and ask their public relations department to tell you the days of the week (and perhaps the time of day) when their men perform flight 'exercises' over your area.

15) *What are the local businesses?*

In this case, 'local' means anything from next door to ten miles away. Drive round the lanes, noting every roadside stand and signs of business you see. There are two reasons for this:

~ If you buy the property, you will want to know what is available nearby, whether it be fresh strawberries or a timber merchant.

~ You will want to know of businesses which will intrude upon your enjoyment of your new home. It is startling what the countryside can hide away in even its most idyllic spots – chicken batteries, nuclear power plants and chemical production works are among the most offensive to watch out for. So be thorough, drive down every lane!

16) *Who are your neighbours?*

Obviously you can't get to know everyone before you buy the property, but you can learn whether they have young children, whether the current owner gets along with them and even how sociable they tend to be. Talk to the vendor, then be bold and introduce yourself to a neighbour or two. They might not say much, but you should get an idea of whether or not it will take you twenty years to be accepted!

17) *Who is the nearest farmer?*

His attitudes on everything from conservation to crop spraying can seriously affect your life, whether you like it or not. Ask the current owner and any other locals you meet "what is he like?" and then just listen. Parts of the countryside are still painfully feudal, so if most of the local population is employed by the farmer, you won't hear too many complaints or candid comments. If, on the other hand, the locals are of mixed employment, you should get a fairly clear idea of what to expect from him. In particular:

~ His policies on tree and hedgerow management
~ His safe – or otherwise – use of chemicals
~ Whether or not he intrudes on other's land for hunting, fishing, shooting or other sporting activities
~ His general consideration for property other than his own
~ His adherence – or otherwise – to laws which are not necessarily in his favour, i.e. maintenance of public footpaths, planning zones and regulations, etc.

18) *What forms of pollution will you have to contend with?*

Sadly, there are many. It is a good idea to itemize them, so that you can compare one potential purchase with another. A few of concern are:

~ Water pollution from land run-off of crop fertilizers
~ Water pollution from industrial discharge
~ Noise pollution from aircraft, traffic or farm machinery
~ Electromagnetic pollution from overhead cables (pylons)
~ Radioactive pollution from nearby nuclear power plant
~ Lead pollution from use of lead pipes in old water system
~ Air pollution drift from use of crop sprays on nearby fields

19) *What do the nearby towns and villages have to offer?*

Take a Saturday off and drive through the nearby towns and villages, having teas and window shopping. You can discover, in this very pleasant way, what the people are like, how many of your needs the shops will supply and what schools are available.

20) *What are the policies and practices of your local council?*

Rural councils increasingly support rural development in the form of villages, small business enterprise and conservation. Visit your local council offices and talk to the information officer there. He or she will help you gain access to a variety of specialists who can advise you on many aspects of rural living.

Occasionally, a council will run very much on a 'government by the farmers, for the farmers' basis. Such councils may not be forthcoming with advice and you may find your way obstructed when you enquire about conservation, ecology and development issues. Best to learn the character of the local council before you buy, so that you can gauge how much heartache or happiness you will experience as a result of its input into your life.

If you go ahead and buy into the area, come away from your visit to council offices with a list of phone numbers and the *personal* names of the officers you think you will need to contact. For instance:
~ Economic Development Officer
~ Small Business Adviser (may liase with local banks)
~ Environmental Health Officer
~ Grants Officer
~ Library Services
~ Planning and Transportation Office
~ Emergency Services
~ Land Office

Chapter 98
How to set up your smallholding
~

If you're tired of living in the big city and want to make your own personal declaration of independence, you can do it by setting up a smallholding in the country. Here, we tell you how to plan the move, and help you decide whether running a smallholding is really the life for you.

A smallholding is a house and some land, usually less than fifty acres. The smallholder makes his living out of this land and property by running a small business – he is free to do as he pleases as long as he can make ends meet. This may be your idea of paradise; but be aware of the realities of modern smallholding. It is a 24 hours-a-day, 365 days-a-year job. The life is not simple and you will have to deal with all manner of bureaucracy. If things go wrong, it's you who suffers.

So bear these factors in mind and you won't fool yourself into a regrettable mistake.

Plan to get the right skills

The key to running a successful smallholding is planning. Everything should be prepared in the finest detail before you start. And the first thing to prepare is yourself. You will need:
~ Self-motivation
~ The ability and inclination to do physical work
~ A sense of economics

Does your background qualify you in these areas? If not, find ways to train and test yourself. When you're sure you're up to it personally, plan your business.

Plan to start the right business

A smallholding is a flexible venture. The only limits are your abilities and the need to make a living.

Don't be deceived by tradition and television. The small, self-sufficient farm is *not* a viable proposition. Large farms control the markets in staple products and you will never be able to compete.

If you want to go into agriculture, specialize. Look at the luxury market or ventures that have to be run on a small scale, like:
~ organic apple orchards
~ a 'pick your own' fruit business

What is *vitally* important is that you lift yourself out of competition with the big boys. You must develop an area of expertise which it will be very difficult for the prairie-farmers to copy more cheaply. Inevitably, this will involve you in some market research – what are consumers' changing patterns of taste? Which products are losing out, and which ones becoming more popular? Traditionally, farmers have never studied their markets, preferring, obstinately, to cajole governments into giving them subsidies to produce food which no one wants to buy. A genuine market-oriented approach will therefore stand a good chance of succeeding, simply because so few others have thought about doing it. In this, you should get as much help as you can from experts – a good starting point is your friendly bank manager. All banks have extensive knowledge of agriculture, and with a little prompting, you will be put in touch with your own bank's specialists in this field. Their advice is free, so get all you can out of them.

But you don't *have* to be a farmer. In fact, the unstable nature of agriculture makes it imperative that you plan some kind of alternative venture. If you already have marketable skills (secretarial work, vehicle repair, teaching) then make sure that they will be in demand locally, so that, in hard times, you can supplement your variable income.

Research the market

Investigate your market carefully, there may not even be one! Ask potential customers if they are interested. Use the local, national and trade press to identify the competition and obtain exact contemporary prices. Observe market trends. Is your product or service increasing or decreasing in popularity?

Work out exact costings for your business. With detailed knowledge you will be able to predict how much money you are going to make, and when. Include all your costs, not just the obvious ones. Don't forget:

~ Feed, medicines and transportation for animals
~ Equipment replacement, light and heat, maintenance

Don't guess – calculate; and don't be optimistic. Things are bound to go wrong to begin with. Take financial advice from your bank's small business adviser. He will find out if there are any small business grants you can apply for. If you are unemployed you can join the Enterprise Allowance Scheme. For details, contact your local Job Centre.

Research the location

Next, you must decide where to live and work. Your choice will be based on:

~ Where you want to live
~ Where your business is most likely to succeed
~ Where you can afford

The latter is the bottom line. Otherwise, it's up to you. Remember, the property you buy is extremely important as it will be both home and workplace.

When you have chosen an area that is suitable, look at as many properties as possible. Get an idea of the market and when you find a place you like, check it over carefully. Make sure that:

~ It feels right – and so does the local area. Talk to people in the area. Are they friendly?
~ There are no potential sources of annoyance in the vicinity, like a main road or rubbish dump.
~ The property is sound, particularly the walls and roof.
~ It and the land are suitable for your purposes. Make sure there are outbuildings if you need them. Building is expensive.

~ You add any repair work that needs doing to the financial plan. Avoid unplanned expenditure like the plague.

Plan financially

When you have selected and researched your specialization, you need to make a detailed financial plan. If you are looking for a loan or a mortgage you will not get one without proof that your business is well planned. Again, most banks can help you to prepare a good business plan (many have blank forms for you to fill in). Even if you are in the lucky position of not needing a loan, you should *still* prepare a business plan, because it will make you think about all areas of the business, especially those which you may be weakest in. Make sure you're up to the job. Read books on your business and, if possible, get some prior experience.

Go for advice

You are now ready to leave all behind and become a smallholder. But before you sign yourself into the property, bear the following points in mind:
~ If your business needs to start at a particular time of year, make sure you move at the right time! Otherwise you will be without an income longer than you can afford.
~ You may have to get a job to tide you over. Even if you dislike the idea, be practical. Look out for ways of using your skills in the area.
~ As a businessperson you will find yourself subject to new legal requirements. See the Help section at the end of the book to get advice on this.
~ You will have to pay business taxes and deal with VAT. Take a short course in business administration.
~ Life will be a lot easier if you have an accountant, so look into the local possibilities.
~ You will need comprehensive insurance cover in case of damage to your business or to others. See the Help section.
Now you know how to prepare to make the great escape. You should also know whether or not it's the life for you. Remember, planning makes perfect, so:
~ Decide on a business venture
~ Plan it, taking into account every eventuality. Then do it! You've only got one life, so live it the way you want to.

Chapter 99
How you can set up and run a self-reliant urban homestead

~

Do you ever feel city life is sterile and unrewarding? It's not surprising – so much of our lives seem to be run by other people! But don't despair – even in the city you can take control – by setting up a self-reliant urban homestead!

Living in a city or town it's easy to feel cut off from the natural world. Other people provide your energy, water and food. Different people deal with your waste. There's something missing! Being self-reliant is about taking steps to provide your own life-supporting necessities, and to do your own cleaning up. It's about living as a complete human being, in tune with nature and fully responsible for your own actions.

Follow the steps below and you will transform your home; it will become a self-reliant urban homestead. To go the whole way you'll need to be quite committed and determined, but many of the ideas are easy and don't require much effort. Also, while you'd need a house and some sort of garden to put the whole plan into action, separate schemes will work perfectly well in a flat, or even a bedsit.

Energy

Your first step towards self-reliance is to take control of your use of energy. You can not only slash your bills but also 'immunize' your home against power cuts – and do your bit for the environment as well, by using less commercially produced energy. Domestic heating uses vast quantities of fossil fuels – coal, oil and gas – both in their natural form and as electricity. By heating your home in the most efficient way possible, you are not only saving yourself money but helping to preserve fossil fuels and reduce emissions of gases responsible for the greenhouse effect. So it's in your best interests to heat your house efficiently and consider energy-saving alternatives.

~ Insulate your home and heat it efficiently. The roof, especially in old houses, lets a lot of heat out. So insulate the floor of your attic with lagging material available from DIY shops. In two to four years you'll have recovered the cost in reduced heating bills.

~ Windows mean wasted heat, especially if they're broken. So make sure they're in good repair and fit double-glazing, at least in rooms you heat regularly. 'Sealed units' (windows fitted with two layers of glass and a small space between them) are now available; so if you're buying new ones, get this type. The cost-recovery time for DIY double-glazing your sitting-room windows is about five to ten years.

~ Doors are even worse than windows, as they are often badly fitted, with gaps around them. You can draught-proof outside doors yourself very cheaply. Various materials are available from DIY shops; the cost-recovery time is less than a year.

~ Curtains or blinds add an extra layer of insulation to doors and windows. However, they must be covered at the top with a valance otherwise the hot air runs down behind them, is cooled when it comes into contact with door or window and comes out at the bottom as a cold draught.

~ The joins between windows and walls and between walls, floors and ceilings may need caulking and cavity-wall insulation. For details of materials, ask at your nearest DIY showroom.

~ Insulate your loft, hot-water tank and pipes carrying hot water.

~ Have a heating engineer check your boiler – if it's old and inefficient, a replacement will save you money in the long term. If in doubt, ask at your local gas or electricity showroom for advice on efficiency measures.

Next, use electricity as efficiently as possible. The new gas and electricity companies have a legal duty to advise you on home efficiency measures, so ask at your local High Street showroom. If they won't help, ask at your Citizens Advice Bureau for details of local energy efficiency schemes run by environmental or neighbourhood groups. Unfortunately, you can only get financial help with efficiency measures if you are claiming Income Support or Housing Benefit, but the measures are worth the expense even without a grant.

~ Control your heating with a clock thermostat.

~ Keep the heating on low and wear warmer clothing.

~ Only heat rooms you use regularly.

~ Make sure you can actually switch your radiators on and off.

~ Buy low-energy lightbulbs, such as those manufactured by Wotan and Phillips. These cost more than conventional lightbulbs, but will more than save the extra cost in electricity bills.

~ Make sure your cooker and fridge-freezer are only as big as they need to be. Remember, the bigger they are, the more energy they use.

~ Use your washing machine or dishwasher only as much as you need to. Save washing until you have a full load.

Now, why not consider producing your own energy! With advances in renewable energy technology, this is becoming an increasingly attractive option!

~ The World of Difference shop (see the Help section) sells the 'Marlec' wind generator. This uses a 30in wind turbine to charge a 12-volt battery, which is sufficient to supply domestic lighting needs. It is designed for the average suburban garden.

~ Solar power is widely used in sunny countries, and its potential for use in Britain is increasing. **Passive** solar heating simply uses the sun's direct heat. You need to build or adapt an extension or conservatory against a south-facing wall, so it has large windows and a floor of unpolished stone slabs. During the day the slabs soak up the sun's heat, which is released, and can be made to permeate the house at night by setting up a draught. During cold weather the sun room could be sealed off from the rest of the house.

Active solar heating systems use the sun's energy to heat water and create electricity. Unfortunately, the energy available in Britain is not sufficient for much more than swimming pool heating in the summer. However, it can be used in conjunction with a heat pump (see below). For information on solar heating and the technology currently available, see the Help section. These bodies will also be able to help you with other queries on energy efficiency and alternative energy sources.

~ The heat pump is a machine for extracting heat from low-heat sources and then concentrating it. In fact it works on the same principle as the refrigerator. The back of your fridge is always hot, because the cooling mechanism actually removes heat from inside and dumps it outside. A good heat pump delivers three units of heat for every unit of electricity used to run it. Possible low-heat sources include the air – as long as the air temperature is above about 4°C – the ground, or ground water; and heat from a solar collector. A ground source heat pump consists of a long plastic tube buried underground, through which a cold anti-freeze solution is pumped. The solution picks up heat from the earth and brings it inside, where it can be spread through a vent system. The heat produced is not as great as that from conventional central heating, so good insulation is imperative. Further information about heat pumps can be found in the Help section.

Water

After you've tackled the energy question, think about your water usage. We are well on the way to paying for domestic water consumption through water meters, so why not take the initiative *now* and become water-efficient! Here's how you can take steps to reduce your domestic water consumption:

~ One dripping tap will waste hundreds of gallons of water a year – so make sure all taps work properly. For the price of a new rubber washer, you could save gallons (and pounds).

~ A person having a shower uses on average between a half and two-thirds as much water as a person having a bath. Fitting a shower will save both water and energy.

~ A flow control device fitted to taps or showerhead will reduce water consumption by up to half. Ask your plumber or at a local bathroom shop for the Spearman Autoflow (taps) or the Nova (showerhead).

~ Use washing machines and dishwashers sparingly (see above).

~ Reduce the amount of water released each time you flush the toilet. Most cisterns release about five to eight gallons of water per flush; simply putting two or three bricks in the cistern will substantially reduce this figure!

~ There are many flush reduction systems on the market, including the Gold Ring variable flush attachment, which could save up to 30,000 gallons of water per year! For information, check with a plumber, bathroom shop or your local water supplier.

~ Use your 'greywater'. This is waste water from baths and sinks which presently ends up in the sewer along with 'blackwater' (from the toilet), but which could be diverted and used safely to irrigate your garden. You can simply scoop or siphon water from the bath and basin and carry it outside in a bucket. But a better arrangement is to disconnect the outflow pipe from the basin or sink and let the water drop directly into a bucket – which you can take outside when full.

~ The most ambitious solution is to modify your plumbing so the water flows directly from greywater sources to the garden. This will require compliance with environmental health legislation. For current regulations, consult your local council's Environmental Health Officer.

Rubbish

Use your rubbish creatively! Most of the refuse you throw in the dustbin has considerable value:

~ Composting is a means of turning most organic waste – food remnants other than meat and fish – into a highly nutritious growing medium for plants. It's a simple process whereby you put down alternate layers of waste and some dry material, like sawdust, then leave the resultant mass for about a year. You know composting is complete when the mass has become a kind of thick soil – and it smells sweet!

~ If you have a garden, you can create a compost heap. If you don't, you can use a large plastic dustbin instead. Preferably, build one pile while another is composting.

~ Certain kinds of organic waste – printed paper, glass, metals – can be recycled commercially. Collect these materials in separate bins then take them to your local recycling centre. Check in the phone book or at your Citizens Advice Bureau for details. In some areas environmental groups, companies or local councils organize collections of recyclable materials.

~ Deal with human waste at home. One of the most ambitious self-reliance projects you can undertake is to abandon the water-wasteful flush toilet! The composting toilet uses *no* water. Instead, excrement falls into a composting bin in which it is broken down into a harmless, dry solid. In some cases this can be put on the garden, but the main advantage is that one person's yearly input composts down to between one and two cubic feet of waste – which can be disposed of easily. Among the best models on the market are the Clivus Multrum, which can also handle kitchen waste, and the Bio-Loo. All models use electricity and require careful maintenance. For details of what to buy and where, contact The Centre for Alternative Technology (see the Help section).

Food

Put your garden to productive use. Even if the financial savings of growing your own food are not great, the satisfaction and pleasure of producing something useful yourself certainly will be.

~ You've already got two out of the three things plants need to grow; plentiful water (greywater) and good soil (compost). Sunlight is the third ingredient, so make sure the sunniest parts of your garden are for plants, not lawns or sheds.

~ Start small and simple. There are numerous gardening books available that will tell you what to plant, when and how to give your vegetables the best chance of success.

~ Be imaginative. If you want a hedge for privacy why not plant hazel or blackberry bushes – vines even? If you want a tree for shade, make it an apple or pear tree rather than a fir. If you want bedding plants to decorate the side of the house, plant strawberries rather than wallflowers. This way, your garden isn't just nice to look at, it's nice to eat too!

~ Build a greenhouse or conservatory. This should be south-facing, to make the most of the sun. It could be anything from a full-scale greenhouse to a broad window-ledge indoors. Even a sheet of glass propped against a wall will enable you to grow heat-loving plants like tomatoes.

~ A conservatory can be used for passive solar heating, if the floor is lined with stone slabs. These soak up the sun's heat, then release it again at night; by creating a draught through the house this heat can be used in lieu of central heating. Nothing could be more natural.

~ You can grow fruit and vegetables on a roof or terrace. Roof surfaces are not meant for walking on, so you should cover them with a wooden platform. This will also help spread the weight of pots and troughs full of earth.

~ Keep plants well nourished by growing them in a fifty-fifty mixture of soil and compost. They will grow bigger and produce more fruit if there is plenty of room for their roots. Always make sure water can drain out of pots easily; if water collects it causes root rot and other problems.

~ If you don't have any outdoor space don't despair! You can grow plants indoors too. Full spectrum light bulbs – available from DIY and lighting shops – can provide artificial sunlight.

If you put just a few of these ideas into action, you'll not only create a homestead in the middle of the city but you'll also consume less water and electricity, and produce a fraction of the waste you do now. So go on, start living!

CHAPTER 100

DIGGING IN: THE ADVANTAGES OF LIVING UNDERGROUND

~

Your heating bills have gone through the roof and your neighbour's hi-fi is giving you a headache: you want to move house but the options are old-fashioned and eco-unfriendly. As an environmental trail-blazer, isn't it time you took the radical way down – and went underground?

Building a subterranean dwelling is neither as daft nor as difficult as it sounds. Not only is it a practical way of saving on fuel costs and creating an individual, tailor-made living space, it's also environmentally and ecologically the most progressive way forward. Houses built partially or wholly underground require less use of dwindling stocks of fossil fuels, do not scar the landscape with concrete and provide ideal low-maintenance, high-privacy homes. We predict that underground housing will be the coming millennium's most fashionable – and most exciting – way of living.

"What got me interested in earth-sheltered homes?" says Dan Heim, who is currently building an underground home all by himself. "Well . . . a lot of it has to do with what I call the 'energy annuity' concept. I'm spending my money now (peak earning years) to build a home that costs a bit more than average per square foot, but which will provide me later with reduced energy and maintenance costs. Many people never stop to think about the alternatives to the typical above-ground dwelling . . . perhaps I did because of my training in Physics and Ecology. I am absolutely convinced that energy costs will dominate family budgets in the decades to come. Personally, I'd rather spend my money on other things."

How does he see the relative advantages and disadvantages of underground construction?

"First, it will be more expensive per square foot than a comparable above-ground dwelling. But then, I expected that and can accept the cost at this point. Second, and this could be a pro or con depending on individual tastes, it was very difficult to decide on the floor plan, what with constraints imposed by both geometry and building regulations. Third, and this is a definite advantage, the house attracts attention. Building inspectors, sub-contractors, delivery people, and passers-by are all fascinated by the concept. If I can get other people to see that there *are* some alternatives, then maybe the word will spread just a little faster that *you don't need to compromise lifestyle to be energy efficient!*

For far too many people the term 'energy efficient home' conveys images of woodburning stoves, kerosene lantern lighting, and occupants always wearing sweaters. I think this is changing . . . slowly. And it's because of efforts by people like us."

Take your choice

There are three main types of underground dwellings.

~ THE ELEVATIONAL MODEL: this is built on a sloping site or hill and has the advantage of windows on one or more of the exposed sides. These, coupled with roof skylights, are perfect as solar collection points, which, in turn, will provide solar energy. Naturally, south-facing is best.

~ THE FLAT SITE: built below ground on an even level, any light will be provided by a central courtyard or atrium with rooms radiating out around it.

~ THE PENETRATIONAL TYPE: again built on a flat site, but allowing light and air in through gaps which are left open and glassed over with domes or cupoli. Access can also be from around the edge of the building.

Where do you start?

At the moment, one specialist firm of architects, with experience of subterranean building, operates in the UK (see the Help section). Some conventional architects will be willing to draw up plans too. There is an even greater precedent for underground dwelling in the USA, and most of the useful books and reference materials are American (see the Help section). All these sources are well worth examining – after all, why not learn from and build upon other people's experience?

"I had been a practising architect for eleven years before I began to wonder if there was something less destructive than asphalt and concrete and 'toxic green' lawns," says underground architect Malcolm Wells. "The answer, of course, was all around me. The natural world teemed with examples. That the surface of the earth was meant for living plants, instead of dead buildings and asphalt, never got through to me until the environmental consciousness of the sixties unclogged my head. Rather than standing above Mother Nature, underground architecture lies in her arms."[509]

Your local planning department will consider any plans for an underground house in the same way it considers above-ground designs – that is, on individual merits. They will be concerned with design and overall appearance; location, including effects on nearby buildings; and access, including provision of services. They will be protective of the Green Belt, too. However, you should have few problems so long as you bear in mind the following:

~ Careful structural planning
~ Additional reinforcement, especially of the roof!
~ Extra waterproofing, light and ventilation

Difficult? It's worth it! When planning a subterranean house, consider the advantages.

Individuality and aesthetics

You can build the house any way you want to! You're starting from scratch and the finished product will be a unique statement about you, your personality and your positive intent regarding conservation. Underground there is less of a constraint on space and more scope for creating a multiplicity of rooms for different purposes and needs.

The house can be octagonal, circular, twin-storey or multi-level – it's all up to you and your imagination. There's a knock-on effect of enhancing the potential for interior design. You can create a dream house containing living sculpture, surrogate windows, spiral staircases, indoor pools and so on. Your imagination is the only limiting factor.

Energy-saving for both heating and cooling

The underground house is the house of the future. Research shows that, by building just one to two metres below ground, all the advantages of geothermic heat and earth insulation are gained. Amazingly, the average living-space temperature at this depth stabilizes to about 13°C without added heat from life activity. This increases with normal bodily activity and heat from light bulbs and cooking so that little extra heating through conventional means is needed, even in winter. Heating costs are slashed by up to two-thirds. More, even, by taking the natural next step.

This is to use the solar power available to subterranean designs of home; or the wind power you can obtain from having windmills on your roof! Just as in winter, such a house is warmer than its overground cousins, so in summer it's cooler, as temperature extremes are smoothed out. Vents can provide cross-ventilation and simultaneously, along with solar-powered exhaust fans, remove stale air and odours – and you can still open the windows!

Environmental harmony

By building below ground level, minimum damage is done to surface habitats. The roof area above the house can be re-greened. The landscape, the trees, remain virtually untouched so that you hardly know the house is there. It is visually an environmental dream with the lowest of low profiles. You live close to, and in harmony with, nature. Whole villages and towns, even shopping malls, can be built which barely ruffle the surface of the countryside. A sharp contrast to ugly suburban sprawl and the endless search for fresh fields to build upon and urbanize.

Land grabbing

You can build beneath the cheapest, most unattractive and least desirable land. It doesn't matter, you'll be underneath! You can also be close to noisy roads, schools, factories, etc. You won't hear a thing below ground. Marginal building land is brought within the scope of subterranean dwellers. Where there is existing overcrowding, such as in most cities, new areas for building are opened up.

Peace and quiet

In an underground house you can't be overlooked; complete privacy is assured. You can take advantage of the natural soundproofing of a troglodyte dwelling. Soil dampens down noise to the extent that an unprecedented tranquillity reigns; and you bask undisturbed amid perfect acoustics.

Low maintenance costs

The wind, the rain and the extremes of heat and cold take a considerable toll on our surface dwellings. You have only to think of the gales of recent years and the havoc wreaked on exposed houses, let alone the steady ingress of the elements and the damaging expansion and contraction of house materials, to appreciate the benefits of burrowing down.

Sub-surface living means not having to strip away the peeling veneer of the home to repaint every few years. The whole weathering process is reduced to a minimum; stresses and strains are reduced; maintenance to exposed areas like windows and skylights is low-level and easy-access. Plumbing, contained within the cocoon of the earth's natural warmth, is at low risk to freezing and bursts.

Security and stability

Underground homes, like caves, have a feel of permanence about them. With proper design and construction their life expectancy is virtually infinite. They are particularly resistant to burglars because there are fewer direct access points. Home security is easier and the mainly concrete construction is less of a fire risk and has greater resistance to insects and infestation.

The greenhouse effect?

The land above your private burrow is released for the growing of fruit and vegetables. Surface dwellings cover substantial areas of ground which you can use, instead, to create the garden of your dreams above your house.

It is a common misapprehension that underground homes are dark. This is not so. Living with an exposed or roofed-over central atrium, there are no shaded, dark or difficult corners – all areas receive the same glorious sunshine. Inside, the light and heat enhanced by skylights and south-facing windows can be used to create exotic conservatories packed with tropical plants.

Modern cave dwelling fulfils the desire to return to Mother Earth, fused with the practicality of a warm, protective cocoon and your own design for living. It can be the starting point for a whole new eco-harmonic way of life. Aligned to the meridians of south and north, your house is a sundial, a latter-day, sub-surface Stonehenge, where careful planning will enable you to watch the sun rise and set upon an aesthetic, environmentally benign, warm and cosy earth shelter.

Going underground makes sound economic and ecological sense. The future lies under your feet!

MAKING YOUR SUPERHOME

CHAPTER 101

FENG SHUI: THE ART OF LIVING IN HARMONY WITH NATURE

~

Do you have a favourite armchair? Is there a room in your house which somehow doesn't feel quite right? Have you ever lived in an 'unlucky' house, or immediately felt at home the first time you've entered a building? All these are examples of feng shui in action.

Literally, feng shui means 'wind and water'. Perhaps it is best described as a philosophy, although it has all the makings of a quasi-religion. In fact, feng shui evolved from one of the ancient Chinese religions – Taoism – which glorifies the natural world, and maintains that humans should act according to nature's laws, and reflect its inner harmony. Good harmony brings health, wealth, good luck, and long life, while lack of harmony brings nothing but unmitigated disaster. "Today's superstition may be tomorrow's science," says Lin Yun, who is one of the best-known feng shui practitioners in the West. "Our life and destiny are closely interwoven with the workings of the universe and nature."[510] A wise person will work with, not against, these natural laws, and so bring great happiness to every aspect of his or her life.

As the third millennium dawns on our troubled planet, we are all searching for something. Our environment becomes dirtier, more violent, more stressful. Our lives become more frantic, more manic, more pressured. It becomes harder to relax, unwind and escape from the madness of the material world. What we're really looking for is a way of living that's in harmony with nature. And that's what Feng Shui can offer.

Yin, yang and chi

The Chinese hold that the universe and everything in it is made up of yin and yang. These are opposite, but not conflicting, forces; each depending on the other. Yin, for example, is dark, female and passive; while yang is light, male and active. Houses, too, consist of these elements, so that if an individual wants to be balanced in himself or herself, he or she must first ensure that the balance of the house is correct. Similarly, chi – the life force of both the earth and people – is also to be found in houses. An acupuncturist will base his treatment on restoring the balance of yin and yang and the flow of chi in a patient's body. A practitioner of feng shui will do the same thing, for a building.

In the West, such a practitioner is sometimes called a geomancer: perhaps best described as a combination of priest, psychiatrist and interior designer. A feng shui practitioner such as Lin Yun will study for years before becoming proficient in his art. Most practitioners would say they are simply using a sense which we all possess, but have usually failed to develop. Indeed, we do seem to have lost some of the magical relationship with our natural environment, to the extent that it has almost vanished entirely from urban existence.

A question of balance

When we alter the landscape without any thought for the existing energy patterns, we can easily damage the state of chi. Roads, buildings, doors, windows and furniture can all affect the energy flow, for good or bad, depending on their location with respect to the natural forces of chi. In ancient China, feng shui practitioners had to be consulted before any construction went ahead, acting as a sort of archaic planning permission. Today, the Hong Kong government always asks the advice of geomancers before proceeding with development plans, and many other major corporations employ a feng shui man to bring them commercial good fortune. Estate agents in some parts of America are making sales at the nod of the head of a geomancer, and Chinese businessmen base the movements of whole corporations on the words of their feng shui guides. The Hong Kong and Shanghai Bank, for example, consulted a feng shui expert to determine a propitious date for the opening of its new headquarters. In Singapore, the Hyatt Regency hotel carried out extensive renovations to its front entrance after a practitioner determined that the hotel suffered from bad feng shui (the solution was to place the front doors at an angle to the street and to remove a water fountain). And the Hong Kong Land Company, the colony's most prominent property firm, employ feng shui experts to examine their building plans before committing themselves to expensive developments. In fact, it is said that the extraordinary rise of Hong Kong, from a tiny harbour town to a massive commercial centre, is due to the positioning of the Governor's mansion, which is in a perfect spot, high above the financial district.

On the other hand, bad feng shui can cause a wide range of disasters. To this day, many people still attribute the sudden and unexplained death, from brain swelling in 1973, of Kung Fu film star Bruce Lee to his living in a house with bad feng shui.

How to improve your chi

Clearly, urban living cannot accommodate all the principles of feng shui. It just isn't possible for us all to live near rivers and trees, for example. However, the basic rules still apply, and can be simply adapted to accommodate modern architecture. Feng shui experts are still hard to find in the West, but that needn't prevent you from starting to rebalance your house and change your destiny yourself! All you need to do is bear in mind some general principles which apply to geography, streets, houses and gardens right through to the positioning of your stove. Here are some fundamental guidelines, which you should use as the basis for developing your own intuition:

~ The best shape for a house is the simplest – either square, rectangular or even circular. Irregular shapes block the flow of chi, and so should be avoided. For the best feng shui, a building should face south and the kitchen east or west. If possible, a building's entrance should face the sea (since water is a symbol of prosperity) and should be protected from the north (where storms originate). Your home is a microcosm, your own little universe. It is important to maintain a garden (no matter how small) because this is your link with nature and the elements and so is vital to develop your own sense of chi.

~ Windows and doors are thought to act as chi regulators. If there are too many, or they are out of proportion to the house, chi will become unbalanced. The front door is particularly important. It should open into a wide, light room and certainly not directly onto a wall. If necessary, hang a mirror on the offending wall to brighten and enlarge the room and dispel any negative energy. Most of us prefer the entrances of our house to be shielded from the road. This makes feng shui sense – access should not be direct as money can too easily flow out! If your main entrance looks directly onto the road, move it to a side door. Slanted doors are particularly ominous – straighten them with a curtain. Windows should not slide up and down to open, but open outwards to create good career prospects. If you work from home, make sure that the door to your office does not face the entrance to your house building. If it does, money will flow out the doorway.

~ Consider your bedroom and kitchen carefully, as they have the greatest significance. It is best not to have the kitchen too close to the front door as it will encourage callers to come round just for something to eat! The Chinese word for food is the same as for wealth, hence the importance of the kitchen for good fortune. Particularly significant is the oven, which must have space around it for chi to circulate. When you stand at the stove, you should be able to see the whole kitchen: again, use mirrors if you cannot change the place of your oven.

~ Furniture has a big part to play in the creation of positive chi. Probably the most important piece is your bed. Position it so it is diagonally opposite the door, so you can see anyone coming in. If this isn't possible, use a mirror. Do not have any big items of furniture near the base of your bed, for they may block chi. If it is a marital bed, make it a rounded one – it will hopefully make for an equally smooth marriage!

~ Next time you decide to move your bed, consider what you most want out of life. If you crave fame, put the foot of your bed to the south; put it north for good business, east for happiness and west for fame for your future generations. A marital bed should be shielded from evil spirits for a couple to be fertile; therefore, there should only be one or two entrances into the bedroom.

~ The bedroom should not be located over an empty but enclosed space (such as a storeroom or a garage). Such spaces do not permit the chi to flow freely, and a stagnant area of dead chi may be created underneath your bed, leading to psychological and eventually physical illness.

~ Perhaps the single most important factor in feng shui is water. As a metaphor for the coming and going of money, its careful use can greatly increase your good fortune. Any source should not be either stagnant, indicating dead chi, or too fast-flowing, indicating overwhelming chi. In some situations water can be a bad sign. If, for example, you have a stream in your garden, it will carry away all your money. If water is too near your house, its chi can literally knock the energy out of it. Similarly, if it is too far away, the house will get none of its positive effects. Don't worry though, you do not have to move your garden pond. If it is too distant, use mirrors to bring it nearer; and if too close, put a winding pathway from the house to the pond, to give the illusion of distance.

~ If you want to rid your house of any evil forces, put a fish tank, preferably bubbling, with six black fish in your hallway. If they die, don't worry; they have simply absorbed all the negative influences in your house!

~ If you have a number of electronic devices (such as television sets, home computers, etc.) at home (or at work), they should be arranged on a clear, straight chi path, rather than haphazardly around the house. This will reinforce, rather than disrupt, the natural energy flow.

~ We all know the benefits of oxygen-giving plants, but according to feng shui, they also create positive chi energy. Trees on a roadside in front of a house will protect it from the negative chi of the traffic and pollution, although they should not be too near the main entrance, where they may inhibit the flow of chi into the house.

~ As we have seen, mirrors can remedy a number of ills. They have an important harmonizing effect, balancing out any chi disorientation. The Chinese have always used them literally to deflect evil spirits and demons. They are often placed in tombs as protection for the dead, and even police stations use mirrors to create positive forces. Mirrors can expand a room and are also useful in deflecting evil spirits. Light – the more the better – helps, too, as does the colour red.

Feng shui is impossible to prove or disprove by Western scientific analysis. It is rather like trying to grasp a handful of sand – the harder you squeeze it, the more it escapes you. But it is a peaceful, mystical art, which, at the very least, encourages us to give more thought and consideration to the often-brutalized environment that we all create and live in. And maybe – just maybe – your health, wealth and happiness could depend on it!

A prediction: by the turn of the millennium, our homes will have become bunkers. In case you hadn't noticed, those streets outside are getting meaner all the time. And as life outside gets steadily tougher, so we'll spend longer periods in the safety of our new, multi-purpose homes. No longer merely a place to rest your head for a few hours, your new-style home will be a place where you can work, be entertained, have your groceries delivered, educate your children, get fit, have a gourmet meal . . . there will even be a place where you can live out your wildest and darkest fantasies. All these things will happen far sooner than most people suspect. In 10,000 years of human civilization, the role of the home has never changed so quickly as it is today. As the 'age of the bunker' dawns, we present you with one hundred best ways to brighten up your bunker – without having to go to the expense and inconvenience of moving. Sounds like a gilded cage? That all depends on what you make of it.

CHAPTER 102

THE BUNKER HUNTER'S COMPANION: ONE HUNDRED BEST WAYS TO IMPROVE YOUR HOME WITHOUT MOVING

~

Once, not so long ago, a home was simply base-camp. You went there to eat and sleep, in the in-between times when you weren't working or going out. Now, all that is changing. The bunker generation are stay-at-homes. We're going out less and less, turning inwards for our entertainment, looking to our own microcosmic little worlds to keep us safe and sane. The figures tell it all. In 1955, every person in the United Kingdom averaged two trips to the cinema every month. Today, it's one and a half visits per year. At the same time, 30 per cent of the population hire a video cassette to watch at home every week. In 1984, we spent twenty-three hours a week watching television. Today, it's over twenty-six hours, and growing.[511]

The role of the home is clearly being transformed. It is no longer a functional four-walled box with a roof – instead, it is becoming our own highly-controllable universe, a place of enablement rather than containment. As we demand more dimensions from our home life, so the infrastructure has to change radically. In the new millennium, the keywords will be *space* and *flexibility*. Space, because it is the medium of change, the manifestation of latent potential. Increasingly, you will envisage your home as a shell made up of the outer walls, ground floor and roof – the canvas upon which you will repeatedly construct, deconstruct, and reconstruct your dream home. Flexible, because perfection is a state of flux, never fixed. Fixtures will be temporary, the only hard and fast rule will be that there are no hard and fast fittings. So mix and match from the ideas that follow – and when you've done that, mix and match again!

Space, the final frontier

In the next millennium, we will all become expert interior decorators. We will know all the tricks to transform our homes from spacious palaces to cosy little cottages, and back again. Today, you can create more space – or rather, create the illusion of more space – by using new colours and patterns to change a room's perceived size and shape like this:

~ Pale coloured walls seem *further away*. Misty yellow, powder blue, cream – all these colours will allow the eye to drift off into the distance, and so help smaller rooms to appear more spacious.

~ Rich colours make walls seem *nearer*. Rocket reds, royal blues, egg-yolk yellows can all bring objects closer. Why would you want to do this? Simply, to add contrast and give added depth of field. For example, a room uniformly painted cream will, by itself, seem flat. But pick out a few key features in the mid-distance – for example, an archway or a beam – in a rich yellow, and you've suddenly added drama, and emphasized the extreme distance of the paler colour.

~ Horizontal stripes make a wall seem *wider*. Your eye can't help following the line all the way along, stressing the long, flowing lines of the wall and adding length to your room.

~ Vertical stripes make it seem *taller*. Your eye runs from floor to ceiling, the lines accentuating every centimetre of the distance.

~ A dark ceiling appears *lower*. Use this trick to make cold rooms with high ceilings more cosy.
~ A large pattern *fills* a room. A bold repeating pattern (like a Greek or Aztec design, for example) can make a large room seem dramatically smaller. But be careful of appearing to make small rooms seem even more undersized!
~ A small pattern makes the room seem *bigger*, the opposite of the above. A small pattern deceives the eye and the brain into thinking there are an infinite number of patterns, thus creating the impression that the room is of greater dimensions than it really is.
~ White makes a room seem airier and more *spacious*.
~ Pale colours are fine for a sunny room; a gloomy room needs bright colours.
If redecorating isn't enough to give you what you want, the next step would be to consider structural change. Demolition and building work require considerable expertise, so get an expert to do it if you're not happy about doing it yourself. The best way to find a good builder is by recommendation from a friend. You may also need official approval for your plans. If you are doing conversion or building work, inside or out, you need to obtain Building Regulation Approval. This is to ensure your property remains safe and fit to live in. If the work involves external structural change or a change of use of your property, you need planning permission. For information on these matters, contact your local council. Now for some stimulating ideas:
~ Combine your sitting and dining rooms to create a roomy open-plan living area. With this larger area, you are now free to experiment with your use of space at your leisure – you need never live in the same room for more than a few months!
~ Knock out the ceiling to create a two-storey room (but get expert structural advice first). The effect will be very dramatic. Use the extra openness to feature sensational lighting, sculptures, and suspended works of art. Or re-create your own concert hall – the shape and height of the ceiling will determine the room's acoustics.
~ Go even further, and knock out the attic floor and use the shape of the roof to dramatic effect. Expose the roof beams. Install skylights, to suffuse your house with natural, energy-saving light during the day, and to provide a glimpse of the universe at night.
~ Use the space available in a high-ceilinged room by building a bed platform. You can build it on stilts or attach it to the supporting beams.
~ Construct a gallery. This would work particularly well in an open-plan living area, offering some seclusion for work, games and hobbies.
~ Alter windows and outside doors. Put in French windows and a patio to make your sitting room brighter and to appear to bring your garden into the house.
~ Put in a dormer window and construct a window seat to fit it.
~ Build or upgrade a fireplace. A good fire makes a sitting room, so if you have a chimney, use it. If not, you could build one against an outside wall. A fireplace can also be used as a decorative centre-piece of a room, with a stainless-steel chimney rising through the centre of the house to the roof.
~ Convert part of your house into an independent flat to house older children, relatives or a lodger.
~ Soundproof a room (details from DIY stores) so children can do what they like without disturbing you.
~ Convert unused space to living accommodation or a work area.
~ Build a conservatory against a south-facing wall. In summer this becomes a sun room – a warm place to relax and grow plants.

~ Raise your roof. You can remove the roof, build an extra floor, then replace it.
~ Build a roof garden, balcony or terrace. Partially enclose it with trellis-work and plants to make it feel private but accessible.
~ Roof over part of your garden – build a colonnade even – so you can be outside and in at the same time.
~ Landscape your garden. Build a rockery, dig a pond, plant trees, grow vegetables. Plant a beech or privet hedge for privacy.
~ Build a summerhouse, outhouse, workshop or even a small second house for visitors, relatives, etc. You don't have to stop there. You could adapt your home to your own interests by, for example, building a telescope station on the roof. Or building a sauna and gym room. Or installing a recording studio or dark room.
Rooms can be also be partitioned without recourse to major structural work:
~ Divide off a work or wardrobe corner with a freestanding screen.
~ Construct a wooden partition which is attached to the wall and can be folded back when the full room space is needed.
~ Add or remove partition walls or dividing doors to alter the size and shape of rooms.

Reclaim that space!

There is a huge amount of unused space in even the minutest of homes. Your next step should be to reclaim this 'dead' space, and put it to good use again. Needing more room is often one of the reasons to uproot; and just think how expensive that is! Changing your attitude, having a rigorous and regular overhaul of what you've collected and taking a new look at storage possibilities can all help. Without realizing it, we have all been sucked into, and play, the game of consumerism to a greater or lesser extent. Take a moment to think about what you have bought over the last year or so. Could a change of attitude have prevented you buying at least some of the things which you are probably now wondering how to store? Next time, ask yourself if you really need to buy it.
~ Could you borrow or hire it?
~ Think about starting a shared ownership scheme with your neighbours for infrequently-used items, which will help save you money and reduce storage problems.
~ Display that collection of thimbles, stamps, shoe-horns or coins, instead of keeping it locked away in valuable storage space.
~ Put an absolute ban on buying new toiletries and cosmetics until all the half-used old ones are gone.
~ Keeping bits and pieces which might come in useful is a good idea if you have the space. If not, it might be cheaper to recycle those bits elsewhere, rather than hoard them. Use the charity shops, hospitals and other needy causes to recycle clothes and goods you no longer need. Make a firm promise to turn out your wardrobe every January 1st, ruthlessly discarding *anything* you haven't worn in the last twelve months. Many other people will be grateful to receive your unworn clothing.
~ Natural fibre clothes that are too far gone to be worn again can be put on the compost heap. If you don't have one, ask your neighbours and find out who has.
~ Recycling workshops rejuvenate old household electrical wares. Find out from your local council where your nearest one is. If there isn't one, lobby them for one.
~ Use old clothes for upholstery stuffing and re-use: make cushions, draught excluders, patchwork quilts, cleaning cloths and handkerchiefs.

~ Recycle those magazines and papers. Cut out anything of great importance, then send them to the local hospital, surgery and old folk's home, or council recycling depot.

~ Send foreign coins and petrol tokens from holidays to charities who can cash them in. See the Help section for information.

~ Copy out your favourite recipes and then you can recycle the book. If you have a great many press clippings, consider having them microfilmed (check your Yellow Pages for microfilm services). You can then dispose of the originals, and use the microfilm readers in your local library when you need to refer to them (or you can buy a small, cheap, second-hand microfilm reader from an office equipment company). If you want to go very hi-tech, you can equip your home computer with a scanner and optical character recognition software, and 'read' all your clippings into your computer, so that they are accessible at the press of a key.

~ Help others by thinking carefully about what you buy them for Christmas and other occasions: perhaps some home-made produce like chocolates or special preserves would be better than the umpteenth salt and pepper set, or other piece of 'giftware'.

~ Buy a shopping bag and stop amassing all those plastic carriers. A simple idea, really, but very, very important! Not only will it prevent you from being smothered in useless plastic bags, but it can also greatly reduce the amount of excess packaging around.

~ Take part in a car boot sale. This has the dual advantage of freeing your storage space for really important items, and giving the benefit to others of those artefacts which have ceased to be useful to you.

Now, here are some suggestions for finding new storage space. The secret is to organize your things well and also to use your eyes. Wherever there is an unused surface there is the potential for storage. Look inside and out, up and down, under and over. Try to look at your rooms in a new storage potential light:

~ Look up! Make your rooms two-tier. Build sleeping or work station platforms. Install hanging shelves, racks, baskets in kitchens, bathrooms and work areas. Use the space above doors for shelving and cupboards.

~ Use the dead space at the tops of stairs for cupboards and shelving. Once you start looking, you'll be amazed to see how inefficient the design of the average house is in the allocation of useful space.

~ Exposed joists in basements or garages provide opportunities for combined storage and insulation. Make boxes to fit between the joists and mount them on hinges so that they swing down to open.

~ Look around! Walls often have recesses where you can install shelves or cupboards. Investigate boarded-up chimney space, too. Buy or make radiator covers to provide extra shelf space. Investigate wall racks for hanging and hooking difficult-to-store items like bicycles, sports gear and cleaning equipment.

~ Make drawers two-tier and install a second tray. Use the inside of cupboard doors and install storage racks. Similarly, look at the underside of shelves and cupboards – just look at all that space! Fix runners and install drawers.

The front of a sink also has a certain amount of space, enough for a drop-down front in which to store kitchen gloves and scourers. Baskets on the backs of doors will hold untidy bits and pieces.

~ Look down! Beds often have room for plastic storage bags underneath. All that space under your bed is generally completely wasted. So build your bed into the floor and use the underneath for storage. Or buy a bed with storage space already built in.

~ Double-usage often makes unexpected space. Use a trunk as a coffee table. Make covers for blankets and use them as floor cushions. Build a window seat and use it for storage too. Start seeing double!

~ Make space underground. Build garden bunkers and garage cellars. Apply all the principles above to your basement.

~ Look out! Outside, build sheds and a lean-to to store items which are less sensitive to changes of weather.

You have a garage. You keep your car in it. Instead of taking these facts for granted, pause for just a moment and consider the following. Congestion on the roads is a nightmare. Cars are becoming almost obsolete in some towns and cities where parking is a real problem. Pollution from cars is too high and land is at an all time premium. Consider for another moment becoming car-less. Think of how much you really need your car . . . It may not be all that much. If you don't use your car very much, think of how much it is costing you to keep it on the road and of all the opportunities you are missing for using the garage-space for other, perhaps more profitable things which you are yearning to do. In cities, especially, car-substitutes are easy to find – public transport, taxis, even walking! We evicted our car five years ago, and haven't missed it once! In fact, we've saved appreciable amounts of money.

~ An average garage is about 24 cubic metres. That is a considerable amount of space and there are a multitude of things you can start to use it for. First, phone your local town hall or visit the Citizens Advice Bureau to find out if there are any regulations related to changing the use of garage space. It is best to find out about these before you start generating ideas and making plans so that you can bear them in mind as you go along. Also, if you are a leaseholder or tenant check the lease for any restrictions on its use. If there are, contact the freeholder and tell him what your ideas are. He may be open to negotiation once he knows what you want to do.

~ Once you've evicted your car, don't just pile all your household junk into the garage, and forget about it! Here are some suggestions to start you thinking about what you would *really* like to do. Heating, decorating, floor covering and perhaps a few minor modifications, depending on what you have in mind, may be all that is needed to turn a dull garage into the most exciting room in the house!

~ Family use. The most obvious use for this newly acquired space is to allow members of the family to expand and develop their hobbies or interests. But before you allow it to become a model railway haven or astronomical observatory, consider whether you could build on top of it? And if so, could you then rent it out? Suddenly, your former garage could be a very productive member of the household. Also consider:

- A solarium or sauna
- A gym
- A store for homegrown or homemade produce
- Could it be the start of a local co-operative?
- An office or workspace
- A potting shed
- Why not use the roof to install solar panels, and save on your electricity bills?
- A safe play area
- A family quiet area or retreat
- Creative space especially for making a mess
- A library

~ Business or hobbies. Perhaps you would like:

- A photographic studio

- An artist's studio, which could be hired out
- A potter's studio
- Beer or wine making
- Housing or breeding animals
- Herb and flower drying and arranging
- Craft oriented ideas – renovating antiques, carpentry, metalwork
- Secretarial business
- Printing
- Music studio
- Hire it out as storage space
- Mechanic's workshop
- It may even be possible to convert it into a shop

~ Ideas to benefit the community:

- Community meeting space for local groups
- Desktop publishing and print shop
- Nursery
- Art gallery for local artists
- Workspace for local theatre groups
- Small viewing theatre
- Kiddies' theatre
- Animal sanctuary
- Collection point for recyclable material
- An opportunity for you to start an interest group and provide the ready-made meeting place
- Music practice space
- Recording studio – video or audio

Some of these ideas may require planning permission and observance of certain health and safety requirements. Contact your council's planning department when you have a clear idea of what you would like to do and ask about any specific regulations of which you should be aware.

Once you start to think about your family's needs, your community and your own interests it is easy to brainstorm with more ideas. Realizing you have that extra space could be just what you needed to significantly reduce family tensions, or to turn that favourite hobby into a working business. Or if you were wondering how you could become more involved with your local community, this could be the ideal starting point. And of course, if the garage is on your own land you could always simply knock it down and grow your own vegetables there instead! Evict your car, start brainstorming and use that space!

Kitchen know-how

~ Upgrade your kitchen. The last two decades have been heralded as a time of disintegrating social structures and the breakdown of family life. One of the consequences of this sad trend has been to diminish the relative importance of the kitchen in the design of the home. Kitchens became small, cupboard-like affairs, often grimly utilitarian, and very claustrophobic to be in for anything more than a few minutes. In America, some apartments were even built with no kitchens at all. Bunkering will dramatically reverse all that. In the coming millennium social trends, which are beginning to develop now, will mean that the kitchen will become a larger, more important room in the house. It will be a place where the family can meet, have their meals, do their homework and catch up with the gossip. The kitchen will be the warmest and friendliest room in the house, and you can start this process in your own kitchen now! If you have a small kitchen, consider expanding the room into an adjoining area – a few extra square feet can make all the difference. If your kitchen is next to your living room, seriously consider knocking the two rooms into one super-large, super-comfortable kitchen! In the winter, there's nothing nicer than snuggling down with a book, or curling up in front of the television, with a steaming pot of soup smelling enticing on the stove in the background. And in the summer, an old armchair at one end of the kitchen can provide you with shade and relaxation on long, lazy summer days. And when friends call, there's nowhere better to entertain them than at the real heart of your welcoming home (people feel immediately relaxed and comfortable in a kitchen – just think about all the shy people who end up in the kitchen at parties!)

~ Carefully plan your super-kitchen before you start work. If space allows, make sure you have a large central work table. And remember that the type of food you eat very much determines how your kitchen looks. Over the past few years there has been a great rise in convenience and frozen foods, which meant the redesigning of kitchens to allow space for large freezers and microwave ovens. But now, people are becoming more concerned with what goes into their food, and 'instant' food is correspondingly losing its appeal. Also, more people are discovering that many wholesome, natural recipes are just as quick and convenient to make as their processed equivalents. This will, in turn, have an effect on kitchen design and appliances. Although microwave ovens can sometimes save time (but not always – many vegetables are just as quick to steam or sauté), there is a growing feeling that cooking with them is somehow less 'real' than more traditional methods, as well as concerns as to what the process does to the nutritional value of the food. So if you are planning to replace your cooker, consider going for a high-speed oven and hob – that way you can combine speed, convenience and healthy eating.

~ Make more room in your kitchen to store fresh food. Turn cupboards that used to store tins into fruit and vegetable racks. If you are buying a fridge or freezer, get a combined model that has more fridge space than freezer to keep fresh, perishable items.

~ Build recycling in. Recycling has considerably grown in public awareness over the past few years, and the bunker-home of the future will be designed with recycling very much in mind. Around 80 per cent of your dustbin contents can be recycled, but at the moment most household waste is dumped in the ground. As more and more of our landfill areas are being filled up, we are literally running out of places to dispose of waste. Also, of course, the world's resources are rapidly being depleted. Note that the average family uses six trees' worth of paper, 508 kilograms of metal and 410 kilograms of plastic every year. Recycling saves money, creates jobs and preserves our environment. It might be too late tomorrow; the time to act is now.

Do you recall how, when recycling first became fashionable, people were caught up in a frenzy of keeping all their newspapers, bottles, glass and aluminium cans? All this was done with the best of intentions, but it soon became clear that recycling your household waste could easily become a full-time job. People got fed up with having piles of rubbish around the home, and those carefully sorted heaps started to end up back in the dustbin with all the other household waste. But recycling is still a vital part of our care for the environment and practical realistic ways of being able to re-use valuable materials must be found.

~ Avoid waste in the first place. The first step you need to take is to minimize the amount of potential waste you take home with you.

~ Buy milk in reusable glass bottles, not cartons.

~ Take your own bags when shopping.
~ Buy products with the minimum of packaging – it makes up 70 per cent of our rubbish: and don't forget to voice your concern to your local supermarket manager.
~ Buy recycled products whenever possible, including toilet roll made from recycled paper.
Today, some of the more avant-garde kitchen designers are turning their attention to recycling, and specifically designing waste-free kitchens. One idea – which you could imitate – is to have a work surface with separate uncovered holes at one end. Each hole is for one type of re-usable waste. As the aluminium packing or glass jar gets used, it is simply deposited into the correct hole, where it falls into a receptacle ready for collection and recycling. Another interesting idea is the 'drawer' which crushes cans. You put the aluminum can in the drawer which, when shut, crunches it into a small block – and gone are the carrier bags full of sticky cans!
~ Have at least three bins – one for general waste and the two others for reusable material. You will have to decide which types of waste you will collect. The most common types are aluminium, paper and glass. Bear in mind your family's lifestyle before deciding. Also find out what recycling facilities there are near you, there is no point saving up all your aluminium if the nearest place you can get rid of it is fifty miles away. If space is at a premium in your kitchen then keep your recycling bins outside.
~ ALUMINIUM. Over half of the 20 billion cans we use every year in the UK are aluminium. These can all be recycled to save up to 95 per cent of the energy used in production. It seems crazy, then, that we only recycle a tiny one per cent, especially when these cans are a potential source of revenue. If you belong to a charity or fund-raising group, or are involved with a school association, why not set up your own scheme and create some funds? The Aluminium Can Recycling Association (ACRA) will pay you 40-60p per kg (about 50 cans). All you need to do is make sure the cans are aluminium by testing the side (not the top) with a magnet. If they do *not* hold, they are aluminium. Then just crush them and put them in a bag. See the Help section for the addresses to contact.

If you do not want to set up your own scheme, write to ACRA for details of current initiatives near you, or contact Save-A-Can. Sponsored by British Steel Tinplate, Save-A-Can has set up can-banks in supermarkets and public car parks. They provide the skips and the council concerned provides free storage depots, inspection and vehicle loading. Save-A-Can keeps the metal and donates £8.00 to a charity of the council's choice for every tonne collected. All cans, including those used for pet food, can be recycled. Just rinse and squash them and put them in your nearest skip (but do not squash aerosol cans).
~ PAPER. Newspapers make up one-fifth of all household waste, but at the moment most of the recycled source comes from unsold shop papers. Local councils are in fact collecting less waste paper now than they did in the 1970s, but attempts are being made to set up paper banks in car parks and shopping centres. Old newspapers, magazines, books, cardboard boxes, washing powder packets and toilet tubes can all be used. Make sure you take off any plastic or polystyrene and do not put in any plastic bags.
~ GLASS. Every year, we put five billion glass bottles and jars in the bin. Unlike other materials, glass can be recycled forever without any quality deterioration. It also saves on oil resources because recycled glass melts at a lower temperature than the raw material. In addition, the countryside is spared some ravaging as there is then no need to quarry sand and limestone.

Try to take any returnables back to the shop and put out used, rinsed milk bottles. Make use of your nearest bottle bank. If it means a journey, get together with neighbours to take it in turns. Currently, six million people use bottle banks, and 90 per cent of the population would like to see more of them. This will only happen if you use existing banks and encourage others to do the same. If there isn't one near you, pester your council. When using a bottle bank:

- Check that you have separated bottles according to their colour
- Only recycle glass bottles
- Do not recycle returnable bottles
- Remove tops and caps

~ OIL. It is illegal to pour used motor oil down the drain and doing so carries a possible hefty fine of £2,000. This is because if just one gallon of oil gets into our rivers, streams or ponds, the effects on animal and plant life can be disastrous. Many recycling centres are now accepting oil, so ask your local council.

~ PLASTICS. Plastic products take more out of our environment than any other material. Keep your use of plastic to a minimum and reuse as much of it yourself as you possibly can. Plastic is one of the most difficult materials to recycle. It is the cause of a great deal of harm to the environment, and its production is resource-wasteful. So buy as many products as you can in refillable containers – these are becoming more widely available, particularly for cleaning products.

Attempts are now being made to produce fully degradable plastic materials, and research is being conducted to see whether plastics can be recovered from domestic waste. Kerbside collection programmes for plastics, and plastic bottle banks at supermarkets, car parks and council amenity sites, are also being planned.

~ Contact the British Plastics Federation (address in the Help section) and ask them what progress is being made to these ends. Suggest to your local council that they should establish plastic bottle banks.

Low-stress living

A vital ingredient of tomorrow's bunker-home is an effective means of reducing stress. When you come home, you want to get right away from the frenzy of the world outside. You should leave the stresses, threats and anxieties of street and workplace on your threshold, and step inside to a tranquil haven. These simple steps can make your home more serene:

~ At least one piece of really comfy furniture is a must – something which invites you to flop out on it, and lives up to its promise when you do. The way things are arranged can make a big difference to your comfort too. Unless everything is set up to be as convenient for your needs and habits as possible, you're living with avoidable discomfort. Check your home to see if there are a few easy changes you could make to improve the convenience of your life. For example, if your phone won't reach your favourite chair, it's cheap and practical to fit an extension lead yourself.

~ Be aware that the textures and inside surfaces of your home can add to, or detract from, your relaxation. Avoid harsh, shiny, super-smooth surfaces – while they may look attractive in glossy television commercials, they're hell to live with, and difficult to maintain in a pristine condition. Instead, go for the subtle textures of natural substances like wood and stone – these materials will soothe the soul as well as the eye, and will allow you more latitude if your cleaning routine gets disrupted. Choose fabrics which welcome you when you come home, like soft velvets and velours, rather than cold plastics or bold patterns – you want to be stroked, not assaulted, each time you open the front door.

~ Choose kind colours. As with textures, the point is to go for what soothes rather than disturbs. That doesn't mean you shouldn't have strong colours, but it does mean you should avoid violent ones like lime green or vermilion except in small quantities; and do watch out for clashes – they can have a profoundly disturbing effect (see chapter 104).

~ Select soothing sounds. Nothing is more conducive to serenity than the undisturbed enjoyment of a piece of favourite music. But few of us can afford the time to regularly stop what we're doing to sit down and enjoy a favourite symphony or rock concert. So instead, consider playing ambient music. Sometimes called 'New Age' music, this style of gentle musical background is intended to drift into and out of your consciousness, fading away when you're concentrating on something, and gently re-emerging to relax and soothe you when necessary. Or, you may like to have a purely natural soundtrack as the backing to your everyday life – ocean waves, for example, or the spectacular sounds of a tropical rain forest. All these new sounds are now becoming widely available (for some main sources, see the Help section). Some of our personal favourites include music by Andreas Vollenweider (usually dramatic and uplifting) and Schawkie Roth (lyrical, gentle flute and ocean sounds). But you can go further, still. It is now possible to buy New Age music with an embedded, subliminal message. For example, a Relaxation tape we regularly use contains these affirmations: "I am relaxed", "I feel light and free", "I am free of tension", "I am content", and "My thoughts are as gentle as a soft, summer breeze". Make no mistake – a well-produced subliminal cassette can indeed have a powerful effect.

"I had just landed in California," reports Peter Cox, "after a particularly long and gruelling flight from London. It was ten o'clock at night and I needed to sleep if I was going to be fresh next day, but my body clock was telling me it was only two in the afternoon. By chance, I saw a subliminal Relaxation tape for sale. I bought it, played it on my personal hi-fi, and in a few minutes was in the deepest sleep you could imagine. It was comparable to taking a heavy sleeping pill except, of course, there were no side effects. Since then I've used subliminal tapes for similar purposes, and have become a firm believer in their power to affect us on a deep, subconscious level."

~ Sweet smells soothe. The natural perfume of scented plants can reach deep into the pleasure areas of your brain, and instantly achieve a profound change of mood. A good pot-pourri expertly conserves those scents, and a couple of bowls in the hall will make home-coming a pleasure. Use beeswax on your wooden furniture and it'll smell gorgeous too. Other sources of good smells are cedar wood or sandalwood: a ball among your clothes will give them a delicious scent. Many people also appreciate essential oils and incense. Whatever you do, don't use so-called 'air-fresheners', these chemical cocktails often smell revolting.

~ Plants lighten the pressure. Having growing things around definitely reduces stress. Tending to any living thing does you good, and a plant takes minimal care – so long as it has enough light and the right amount of food and water. Yucca plants, cacti, and umbrella plants are probably the least trouble; spring flowers, especially hyacinths, have the most potent perfumes. Many herbs are pretty as well as tasty; ivy and other creepers will climb indoors as well as out and could even make a leafy bower over your bed. A beautiful, flowing palm will add grace and elegance to any indoor space.

~ Let technology take the tension. Not all technological products are stress-inducing, although too many seem to be designed with the sole purpose of increasing the number of neurotic people in the world. But you will find that a telephone answering machine will allow you to handle calls at a time which is convenient to you, and in the order that you determine. Make sure that the one you buy will allow you to monitor calls as they are received, so that you can pick up the phone and speak live to your caller whenever necessary. Also, make sure that it has a volume control which can be turned down to zero. If the internal speaker can't be turned completely down, it means that the amplified callers' voices will boom all through your house, thus negating the very point of having an answering machine. There is nothing more infuriating than to be awoken in the middle of the night by the amplified voice of a drunk dialling a wrong number, or by a long-lost Australian acquaintance who's forgotten about the difference in time-zones. You don't have to lie in your opening message "I'm not in right now . . ."), nor should you record your phone number (this prevents random nuisance callers from noting the number they've haphazardly dialled). Just say: "Hello, this is my message line, please leave your name, number and message after the beep."

Manage your time wisely

No matter how wonderful your home, you will never enjoy it if you lack the time to do so. In our parents' generation, 'housework' was paradoxically seen as something which was unimportant, because it lacked social status, yet was never-ending. A woman's place was in the home, and a woman's work was never done. Just how many intelligent women went quietly crazy while trying to keep a perpetual shine on the decorative horse brasses it is impossible to estimate.

Today, home managers tend to fall into two distinct categories: the slobs (who have totally opted-out) and the fanatics (who compulsively take after their mothers). Slobs end up on a Friday evening trying to concoct a meal out of a tube of tomato purée, a jar of pickled onions and a slice of stale bread, while standing on their ironing pile. Fanatics spend Friday evenings doing ten useful things with an empty toothpaste tube. It needn't be like this. It only takes a little planning to run an efficient and, above all, relaxed home. The requirements of an average household can be divided into six categories and there are simple ways to save time and money within each:

~ Little and often is the key. Don't allow mess to accumulate and don't spring clean every day.

~ Have a place for everything. You won't waste time looking for it and you avoid those shelves and drawers which bulge with unidentifiable clutter.

~ Clean the bath, sink and lavatory after use at least once a day. This will only take a couple of minutes, and prevent much harder work later on. If you can, draw up a weekly rota of shared duties on which this is listed.

~ Particularly in a large family, laundry can take on a life of its own. Ironing piles seem to breed in the night and your newest item of clothing mysteriously disappears in the tumble dryer. There are ways to keep it all under control and make sure that you don't spend your mornings frantically searching for a sock to match the one you have on.

- Always sort clothes into wash types.
- Check all pockets before washing.
- Wash often in small loads. It will put less strain on your washing machine.
- If you don't have a tumble dryer, hang shirts to dry on a hanger. They'll be easier to iron.
- With tumble-dried clothes, take them out slightly wet and iron as soon as possible.
- Sort out socks and stockings, match pairs and throw away or mend those with holes.

- Keep your ironing pile to a minimum; if you have got to have one, fold the clothes carefully. It will save you time when you do get to iron them.
- Make sure your ironing board has a good thick pad on it. You'd be surprised how much difference it makes.
- Invest in a good steam iron, it will be worth it.

~ The rule for professional chefs in the kitchen is 'wash as you go'. It is so much easier to rinse a pan immediately after use, rather than let it sit and congeal overnight. And psychologically, no one feels like doing the washing up after a meal, whereas it's hardly noticed if you do it during food preparation. If you can't do this, at least put cooking pots in to soak before you serve the meal – they'll be so much easier to wash up.

~ Stack dishes and wash up in a sensible order. First glasses, then mugs, plates, cutlery, serving dishes, pots.

~ Make sure you give kitchen surfaces a wipe after washing up.

~ Clear up spills immediately.

~ Put aside half an hour each day for special attention to one room and give it a quick clean. You'll find your heavy cleaning reduces rapidly.

~ When leaving a room take anything that doesn't belong there away with you.

~ Employ outside services when possible. A regular window cleaner is relatively cheap and saves a very time-consuming job. A really heavy-duty, two or three times a year professional 'spring clean' (including carpet shampooing, floor, wall, tile and ceiling cleaning and penetrating all the 'hardest-to-reach' areas) will be well worth the money, and will allow you to do the bare minimum in between times.

Cooking

Cooking can be an unavoidable chore. Wholesome and appetizing food is vital for a healthy lifestyle. However, inspiration can often fail after a long day or faced with an apparently bare larder. A little thought and preparation will enable you to enjoy cooking a varied diet without having to spend hours in the kitchen.

~ Plan major meals of the week just before you make up your shopping list; so you'll have the ingredients and won't waste time trying to find something to cook.

~ When cooking storable meals, make double quantities and freeze them for quick midweek suppers.

~ Gather all ingredients together before starting to cook so you don't waste time rummaging through cupboards for what you need.

~ Keep everyone else out of the kitchen to allow you to get on with cooking quickly and efficiently.

~ Buy as much as possible in bulk, monthly or weekly. It saves money and shopping time.

~ Dry up! Buy dried beans and pulses instead of their canned equivalents – they represent much, much better value for money, and they will keep indefinitely. One cup of beans, lentils or peas measured dry makes about four average servings. These inexpensive foods are rich in fibre and come in a range of varieties – black beans, lima beans, lentils of all sorts and colours, aduki beans and chickpeas. If you can, buy these products from wholefood shops which re-package their own supplies from bulk purchases, because you'll get a better price (and probably higher quality, often organic) than supermarkets or 'bijou' health food shops.

~ Do not try to combine food shopping with a major clothes shopping expedition. It never works and whichever way round you do it, you'll be hauling bags around the streets.

~ Always have the ingredients for a quick emergency meal when unexpected guests arrive. Our suggestion: become a pasta specialist. There are so many different types of pasta available in supermarkets now that you don't have to restrict yourself to anaemic-looking spaghetti (spaghetti is actually rather difficult to cook outstandingly, unless you're Italian – and poorly-cooked spaghetti probably puts more people off pasta than anything else). We use stoneground, 100 per cent whole-wheat large pasta shells. They are very easy to cook, are extremely tolerant of amateur cooks (even your teenage son can manage it) and are very nutritious. Above all, pasta is quick to cook, will store indefinitely and, being one of the all-time classic dishes, is universally popular. Here are our three easiest, most successful rave recipes for the new wave of bunker people:

Cooked Whole Wheat Pasta

Serves 1
Calories per serving: 205

Ingredients

55g (2oz) whole wheat pasta of your choice
Water

Method

Bring a large pot of water to a hard boil and add the pasta to it. Boil the pasta for 5–15 minutes, depending on the size and type of pasta you are cooking (check the packet for recommended times). The water should cover the pasta at all times. Stir the cooking pasta gently from time to time to prevent sticking. Alternatively, some people add a little oil to the water to prevent sticking. Test the pasta by chewing one piece. It should be easy to bite, but not soggy or doughy. Drain immediately and serve hot with a sauce. To serve cold, drain and immediately rinse under cold water.

Pesto would be our first choice for a first-class, simple sauce. Pasta with pesto sauce is served at almost all Italian restaurants, and the basic pesto sauce can be bought in jars in supermarkets, health food shops and 'delis'. Since it is oil-based, it will keep for extraordinarily long periods – again, good for an 'emergency' situation. Pesto sauce is itself quite rich (containing pine nuts, basil and olive oil), but it has such an intense flavour that you hardly need to do any more than show it to the pasta to obtain a beautiful, spectacular aroma. A great choice for eating out, and just as good if you're intending to curl up at home in front of the video, with a glass of chianti!

Colourful Pasta Salad

Serves 4
Calories per serving: 144

Ingredients

225g (8oz) whole wheat pasta shells
1 × 340g (12oz) tin sweetcorn
1 large green pepper, finely chopped
2 large carrots, peeled and shredded
30ml (2 tbsp) chives *or* 2 spring onions, finely chopped
15g (½oz) fresh parsley, chopped

Method

Cook the pasta until just tender, drain well and allow to cool. Mix the sweet-corn, pepper, carrot and chives together in a large salad bowl. Stir in most of the chopped parsley as well. When the pasta has cooled, stir it into the salad also, along with a dressing of your choice. Sprinkle the remaining parsley over the tossed salad and serve immediately or chill for one hour before serving. Allow 20 minutes, excluding time to chill.

This superb salad is ideal for spring or summer days when it's inappropriate to serve a hot dish. Again, it is highly flexible, and will withstand any extra ingredients or flavourings you happen to have available and can throw at it!

Baked Pasta Shells In Creamy Tomato Sauce

Serves 4
Calories per serving: 275

Ingredients

225g (8oz) wholewheat pasta shells
225g (1/2lb) onions
3–6 cloves of garlic (optional)
10ml (2 tsp) soya oil
140g (5oz) tomato purée
2.5ml (1/2tsp) each of dried basil, parsley, oregano and ground black pepper
350ml (12 fl oz) low-fat milk *or* soya milk
350ml (12 fl oz) water

Method

Weigh the pasta and place in a deep casserole. Chop the onion and garlic and sauté in the hot oil. Remove from the heat and add the tomato purée, herbs and pepper. Stir well, gradually adding the soya milk and water. Pour the sauce over the pasta shells and bake at 180°C/350°F/Gas Mark 4 for 45 minutes. Serve immediately.

This is a superb dish for a chilly autumn or winter's day. It requires the most basic of ingredients yet produces a rich, classical dish. Like the previous recipes, it is suitable for vegetarians or vegans.

Shopping without dropping

Bunker people are going to be expertly efficient shoppers – they'll have to be. But currently, food and grocery shopping can be one of the most frustrating and unpleasant of household tasks. Unorganized shopping is also extremely wasteful as you inevitably come home with unwanted items, only to find you forgot the one thing you went out to buy. Therefore, always have a shopping list. Keep a pad in the kitchen and note down when you run out of an item, this will form the basis of your shopping list.

There are countless variations on the traditional shopping list, ranging from the wipe-clean slate on the kitchen wall, which can be easily updated, to the hand-held computer (such as the Psion), which can actually go shopping with you, add up all the prices, and save you money when the check-out operator incorrectly enters your purchases (this happens surprisingly often – if you can't run to the complexities of a hand-held computer, at least consider taking a simple calculator with you to check your bills). Use whichever method you're happiest with. What is most important, however, is that you use *some* method to arrange your shopping in an orderly and organized way. Because today, shopping is war.

Most families now spend a large proportion of their household budget, and free time, in the multi-product supermarket or hypermarket. They appear clinical, clean, cheap, efficient and totally honest. In fact, beneath their bright, smiling exterior lurks an awesome selling machine geared up to induce you to buy, buy, buy. Everything in the modern supermarket from layout to logo, sound to smell, taste to touch, is designed to make you purchase – even if you didn't intend buying in the first place. You entered the store to buy a bag of sugar, you leave with a full trolley and an empty wallet. Why? Consider the tactics they employ against you:

- Lighting. Red light is used in meat displays, green in fruit and vegetables. This exaggerates the succulence of even the most anaemic and unappetizing produce. The overall white fluorescent light of the store emphasizes the fresh, clean and efficient atmosphere.
- Sound and smell. Unpleasant, intrusive sound is kept to the minimum. Air conditioning or equipment noise is silenced by soothing mood music to relax you into a state of pliable consumption. Bargain bulletins over the in-store tannoy exhort you to buy. The seductive aroma of baking bread stimulates impulse sales; test tastings of cheeses, wines and cooked meats are yet another weapon in the sales armoury.
- Colour and texture. Dark wood trim and decor conveys a rustic, traditional illusion – a strong appeal to the desire for a country kitchen packed with tasty, country produce.
- Meat and fish is regularly enlivened with a fine spray to keep its glistening texture. Topmost pieces are put to the bottom when they take on that curled and jaded look.
- Layout. Products are displayed to maximize customer flow; the more you see, the more you will buy. Essential items are kept far apart to ensure that you wander all over the shop. Old stock is always pushed to the front, the fresh, new goods put to the back of the shelf. While you wait interminably in the checkout queue – where did that time go that you were supposed to be saving? – your kids will pillage the choc bars placed there specifically for their attention.

None of these techniques is illegal, of course, and you can't blame the shopkeepers for wanting to sell their produce. However, these tactics are clearly designed to benefit the shopkeeper – not you, the customer. This is why a well-organized shopping list is imperative if you are to save your own time, money and sanity.

~ Know your rights. As bunker-dwellers we are, more than ever before, extremely dependent on other people to provide us with goods and services. From home-delivery pizzas to mobile car valeting services, the clear future trend is for the suppliers of goods and services to visit us at home, rather than make us waste our valuable free time calling upon them. And as we become increasingly dependent on others to provide satisfactory goods and services, so it is ever more important that we know how to enforce our rights. It is an inescapable truth that, sooner or later, someone will fail to provide you with the quality of service that you require, or that something you've bought for your home will go wrong. When this happens, it is absolutely crucial that you know how to complain effectively, and how to get satisfaction. If you don't know your rights, and don't go about exercising them properly, you are losing money, wasting time, and adding unnecessary stress to your precious free time.

But what precisely are your rights? Obviously, you need to know these to get anywhere. When you, the consumer, buy an item or use a service, you have entered into a contract with the seller or provider of that service. Indeed, under the Supply of Goods and Services Act 1982, the law says that under that contract the goods supplied must be:

~ Of merchantable quality – they must be reasonably fit for their purpose and for common, everyday usage.

~ As described – they must match any written, or oral, description made of them by the seller.

~ Fit for their specific purpose – they must do what the shop says they will do.

If any of these regulations, the Big Three, have been breached, then the buyer-seller contract has been broken and you have the right of redress. These rules also apply to hired goods and services (such as dry cleaners, hairdressers, etc.) with the additional demands that a *service* must also be provided:

~ WITH REASONABLE CARE AND SKILL – there must be an acceptable standard of workmanship.

~ WITHIN A REASONABLE TIME – this can have been previously agreed upon.

~ FOR A REASONABLE PRICE – where no advance price was fixed.

So how do you complain? Follow these simple steps. Be persistent and firm, but don't lose your temper.

1) Stop using the item immediately and do not delay in returning it to the point of sale.
2) Return it to the shop taking receipts/proof of purchase, if possible.
3) Do not deal with the nearest shop assistant – request to see the manager or owner.
4) Calmly explain the problem. If the goods fail to meet any of the Big Three you have the right of a refund (or compensation if the goods damaged your property); and you do *not* have to accept a credit note. Quote the Supply of Goods and Services Act 1982, if necessary, to prove you are aware of your rights. Remember: stick to the facts and stay cool. If things don't get sorted out immediately to your satisfaction, what should you do then?

~ Getting serious. Find out the name, address and phone number of the most senior person in the organization. This could be the owner, if it's a small shop, or the managing director, if it's a chain. The information will usually be on shop literature – or try the phone book. Write a letter of complaint *even if you have already complained in person without success*. Keep it simple, state all the facts, and enclose photocopies of receipts, documentation, etc. Send it by recorded delivery and keep a copy, it will be useful later. You can also complain by phone, but do keep a note of what's said and when, and to whom. In this and all subsequent stages, it is essential for you to keep an accurate and detailed account of your dealings with them. Don't skimp on the paperwork!

~ No progress? Do not give up! Professional consumer advisers recommend the 'incremental approach'. Persistence is the key to success. So *continue* to make a nuisance of yourself. Don't lose your temper, but do carry on writing and phoning. It has even been known for a person standing outside the shop with a placard explaining their complaint to bring results – but is the aggravation worth it when more considered methods will bring equal results?

~ Still no joy? Don't give up! If the shop or firm belongs to a trading association contact the relevant one with the details of your complaint and copies of all correspondence. You should be able to get the address from your local Citizens Advice Bureau or council Trading Standards Department. Trading associations have Codes of Practice and guidance on how members should deal with customers. They can bring pressure to bear on recalcitrant members.

Also try contacting a consumer adviser at your local council Consumer Protection or Trading Standards Department – details in your local phone book or from the Citizens Advice Bureau. They are experienced in consumer complaints and will give you help and advice. They can also bring additional pressure to bear by writing on your behalf and mediating between you and the trader.

The dispute may well be settled by this stage. Occasionally, extra effort on your behalf is required. But don't despair! If you honestly believe you're in the right and have a genuine grievance you *will* win out – in the end!

~ The final thrust. If your opponent is in a trading association which has a Code of Practice as mentioned above, it may contain an independent arbitration scheme. If it has, use it! Both sides can put their case to an independent arbitrator, who will decide who is in the right, based on the facts.

If there is no trading association, take your case to court. You may feel it is easier not to bother; or you may feel intimidated by the idea of legal action. Do *not* be daunted. It is now easy to take a small claim to court – they are there for the consumer and do not involve lawyers. You will need a court application form, which is obtainable from your local county court office – consult the phone book under 'Court'. Your local Trading Standards Department can help you to fill it in.

If your claim is less than £500 it is officially called a 'small claim' and will be settled by a quick and easy court arbitration. Larger and more complex claims will require a solicitor. Again, your consumer adviser will point you in the right direction. There are also free information leaflets available from the county courts on these subjects. Help is always available, so do not give up. You *can* win!

Four exceptions to the general rule

~ Gas, Electricity, Water, Phone, Post, British Rail: There are watchdog bodies who will look into your complaint. Their addresses will be on your quarterly bills or in the phone book (except for British Rail, where the procedure is shown on notices displayed in railway stations).

~ Private sales: The Big Three rules apply when you buy from a trader. Only the *As Described* rule applies for private sales.

~ Secondhand goods: The Big Three rules do apply, but you must accept the negative aspects that come with secondhand items. So be careful!

~ Auctions: Auction rooms may decline responsibility for faulty goods; they should, however, inform you of this, so check beforehand.

CHAPTER 103

THE BLAZING TRUTH ABOUT YOUR HOME LIGHTING

~

Natural sunlight

Many of us spend up to 16 hours a day under artificial lighting. Choosing the wrong type of light may give you headaches, depression or even panic attacks. Here's a briefing on the different types of lighting available, and their advantages and disadvantages.

Don't forget the oldest, most natural form of all lighting – the sun. When moving house, or when having structural work carried out, give a moment's thought to the possibility of bringing more sunlight into your home. This could mean opening up another window or rooflight, or even using large mirrors, cleverly positioned, to reflect the glow of the morning or evening sun. Apart from saving on energy costs, you'll also be getting more healthy sunlight, which is good for your body. These days, mainly because of the diminishing ozone layer, we tend to think of the sun as a rather dangerous source of cancer-causing radiation. But the fact is that, if you deprive yourself of natural sunlight, you put your health on the line. Your body uses sunlight in a variety of ways:

~ To help you fight off colds, tiredness and depression.

~ To produce and absorb certain vitamins and minerals. We all know that calcium builds strong, healthy teeth and bones, but in order to absorb calcium your body needs vitamin D, which is produced by your skin during exposure to sunlight. About ten minutes of sun exposure a day will be sufficient to manufacture vitamin D. More than that will not increase the amount of vitamin D you make, and will raise your risk of skin cancer.

~ Direct sunlight can also stop your body producing the hormones which has been linked to Seasonal Affective Disorder – SAD syndrome (see chapter 45).
~ A lack of natural sunlight has been linked with obesity, hyperactivity and even cancer.
Far from being a substitute for sunlight, recent research suggests that artificial lighting can actually damage your health, causing illnesses as wide-ranging as impotence, depression, blindness, headaches and eyestrain. Artificial lighting comes under four main headings – vapour, fluorescent, full spectrum and incandescent. Some kinds of artificial lighting are considerably better than others. But which should you choose?

Low-energy vapour lights

Vapour lights, of which sodium and mercury are the most common, are used primarily for outdoor lighting – street and security lights – where high-quality light is not vital. But because of their energy efficiency, they are sometimes used for indoor lighting, and this is where the problems start to arise.

The light produced by sodium vapour lights is, of all artificial lighting, the furthest from natural sunlight. Remember studying rainbows at school? Sunlight is made up of all the colours of the rainbow, in more or less equal amounts. But sodium vapour lights are dominated by the yellow and green portions.

When sodium vapour lights were introduced into schools in the United States, children complained of nausea, headaches, dizziness and eyestrain. Although scientists cannot explain why this negative health effect should happen, you'd be wise to avoid installing high-pressure, low-energy vapour lighting anywhere indoors.

Fluorescent lighting

Fluorescent tubes were supposed to be the miracle, energy-efficient alternative to ordinary lightbulbs. And they are certainly much cheaper to run – unlike ordinary incandescent bulbs, they generate very little unwanted heat, and so waste little energy. They give off a bright light and the tubes last much longer than old-fashioned bulbs. But fluorescent tubes have several drawbacks, as well.

The installation of fluorescent lights in schools and factories has regularly brought a flood of complaints from workers and schoolchildren. Health problems which seem to be associated with this type of lighting include nausea, eyestrain, headaches, depression and even panic attacks (see chapters 47 and 126).

Scientists have been unable to establish exactly why fluorescents should appear to cause these problems. What they do know is that fluorescent lights flicker on and off at a very rapid rate – sixty times per second – and also that they generate radio waves and an audible hum. These phenomena may affect certain sensitive people. The German government has tacitly admitted that fluorescent lighting could be dangerous to your health by banning it from hospitals and doctors' surgeries.

Skin cancer

Even more worryingly, a 1982 paper in the medical journal *The Lancet* reported how an Australian scientific study had established a significant connection between exposure to fluorescent lighting and melanoma – skin cancer.[512] The report was largely ignored at the time it was published, and some subsequent research has not confirmed the same relationship. However, other research has indeed confirmed that exposure to fluorescent lighting can increase the risk of skin cancer – specifically, that fluorescent lighting might aid in the development of cancers which were originally caused by other factors.[513]

Babies

A further problem concerning fluorescent lighting has recently been revealed. In 1988, the *People's Medical Society Newsletter* reported on the "devastating effects of harsh fluorescent lights on the delicate eyes of premature babies".[514]

When fluorescent lights are used in nurseries for premature babies, they can literally cause blindness. The People's Medical Society estimates that up to 2,500 premature infants are being blinded by excessive light in the intensive care nursery each year. A newborn baby's eyes may receive more than eleven times the amount of irradiation recognized as the industrial danger limit for adult workers, causing 'retinopathy of prematurity', or ROP.

This entirely preventable cause of blindness is now the subject of a Turn Off the Lights campaign in America, which aims to bring this scandal to the public's attention. However, many medical professionals deny that the problem exists – possibly because, in this era of litigation, they don't want to admit that they've been making a huge mistake for years (for more information about ROP, see the Help section). The problem could be solved by:

~ Replacing fluorescent lights in the intensive care nursery with incandescent bulbs.
~ Fitting babies with isolettes and protective side shields.
~ Turning off the lights at night so that babies experience a natural light and dark cycle.

Work

While it's usually easy enough to get rid of the fluorescent lighting in your home, how can you safeguard your health if it's installed in your office?

The answer, quite simply, is not to turn it on! While your boss may balk at the cost of replacing all the office fluorescent lights, he or she should be happy to give you a non-fluorescent desk lamp. Rely on *natural sunlight* as much as possible, then *turn on the desk lamp!*

Desk lamps have other advantages. Like a stage spotlight, a desk lamp can direct and pinpoint your attention. And because it gives very direct, strong light, it will help you avoid eyestrain.

Full spectrum

Full spectrum lighting is the very latest technological development in lighting. It's a kind of fluorescent light which is designed to mimic both the visible and ultraviolet (UV) light radiated by the sun. It's artificially generated sunlight.

But as we know, the same ultraviolet light that helps you manufacture vitamin D can also give you skin cancer if you get too much of it. The question is whether working eight or more hours a day under full spectrum lighting, which includes ultraviolet light, is too great a risk.

Opinions vary as to the answer. Predictably, the makers of full spectrum lighting argue that the risk of over-exposure is almost non-existent because their lights are designed to minimize the emission of ultraviolet radiation. However, figures in the brochure of one of the biggest full spectrum lighting manufacturers show that their lights actually emit rather *more* dangerous ultraviolet radiation than is present in sunlight.

Apart from the risk of skin cancer, another possible danger is that of damage to your eyes. When you work in an office, full spectrum artificial sunlight reflects off the paper on your desk and up into your eyes. When you read, your eyes are wide open and your retinas are fully exposed to the ultraviolet radiation. This sort of exposure could cause serious damage.

Most of the major lighting manufacturers don't sell full spectrum lighting, probably because of the possible risks and liabilities involved. Although we can't be certain that all forms of full spectrum lighting are dangerous, personally, we wouldn't take the risk.

Incandescent

'Incandescent' literally means glowing with heat. Incandescent light is generated by an electric current being passed through a carbon or tungsten filament. Ordinary light bulbs fall into this category. Incandescent lights have several advantages over fluorescent lights: they don't flicker, they don't hum and they don't produce any radio waves. They also emit very low levels of UV light.

The disadvantage is that such lights give off considerable amounts of heat as well as light, and so they are not energy efficient – in fact, they probably use up more energy in heat than light. On the other hand, the bulbs are very cheap to buy and replace. But because of energy inefficiency and the short life of incandescent bulbs, the cost to the environment is not so low. Furthermore, the quality of light is not ideal – especially when compared to sunlight.

Quartz halogen

The quartz halogen light is becoming increasingly popular. Basically, it's an incandescent bulb, filled with a highly reactive halogen gas (usually iodine). The bulb is made from quartz, because the gas generates enough heat to melt glass.

Quartz halogen bulbs give off a very intense light. They are popular as floodlights and headlights. While the light given off is visually pleasant (unlike fluorescents, for example), it's not much better quality than normal incandescent bulbs.

Chromalux

Probably the best indoor light currently available is chromalux. It radiates 28 per cent less heat than normal incandescent bulbs, it emits light similar to the visible spectrum of sunlight, and it emits a safe level of ultraviolet light. And the cost is low – one bulb usually lasts over five times as long as a conventional incandescent bulb. It's still not quite as good as natural sunlight, but it's the best artificial substitute there currently is. It's been manufactured by the Lumiram Corporation in Finland since 1960.

Chapter 104
What colour can do to your mental state

~

Manipulating the colour of your home and working environments can provide the key to enhancing both your physical and mental sense of well-being, and may help to create ease and harmony in your life.

Industry and commerce increasingly realize the importance of colour in the workplace, and many companies use colour schemes to create just the right level of stimulation and repose for the people who work for them.

Colouring your mood

Colour is visible light and, as such, occupies just one small part of the spectrum of electromagnetic waves. Colours are produced by light waves of varying lengths. These light waves are interpreted as colour by an interplay between your eyes and your brain, and a person with good colour-sight (i.e. not colour blind) can enjoy hundreds of subtle shades of colour in their life. Although there are theories under study which propose that light, and therefore colour, can actually penetrate bone and muscle tissue, the use of colour to manipulate mood and general well-being is generally based on the effect of light striking the retina. When this happens an immediate change in brain function and hormone production occurs. In broad terms, these changes range from stimulating to relaxing. It is no wonder then that colour in clothing and environment is considered so important to most people.

Colour codes

Colour is often divided into categories of bright, cool and warm.

~ Bright colours are commonly associated with children or with people and places that appear cheerful and energetic. They are stimulating and tend to arouse autonomic functions such as heart and respiratory rates.

~ Cool colours are linked with quiet concentration, repose and mental calm. They are non-stimulating and can subdue.

~ Warm colours are uplifting both physically and mentally, but do not provoke or over-stimulate, as would bright colours.

These are only broad guidelines, however, as there are hundreds of hues and shades of colour. So let us look at ten colours in more detail so that you may begin using colour to manipulate your mood at home and work.

~ *White* is a fresh colour which creates an atmosphere of simplicity. Too much of it can give the appearance of a cold, antiseptic environment, so be certain to warm it with natural wood, bright or pastel colours and plenty of pattern and texture in your furnishings. In the workplace, white is usually considered too harsh: it contributes to eye strain and loss of concentration. Used with care, white allows you to feel the innocence and *joie de vivre* that lingers in even the most jaded of us.

~ *Red* is a stimulating colour which can therefore counter depression, sloth and reticence. However, it is not recommended for those who are anxious or aggressive as it would only exaggerate these characteristics. A red room will help you to feel outgoing, vigorous and ambitious, so it may be a perfect antidote to the shy and self-effacing. This may explain why it is regularly used in children's environments. If you really like red, be certain to use it with a light hand as it can promote crudeness, ruthlessness and impulsiveness. Red is strong, optimistic and uncomplicated – a definite stimulant.

~ *Blue* is a very soothing, calming colour, good for places where you wish to create a retreat from the world. It promotes deliberation, introspection and duty and is therefore an excellent colour for clubrooms, offices and studies; it is also restful to the eyes. It is a good colour for babies' rooms as it helps promote sleep. Blue reduces blood pressure and creates a mood of serenity, emotional control and compassion.

~ *Pink* has a calming, even soporific, effect which has been used to good effect in the treatment of violent people. In Britain and the United States, pink cells are used to calm aggressive people being held in detention centres.[515] After just ten to thirty minutes in a pink cell, the detainees are reported to become peaceful and sometimes fall asleep. For non-violent people, this warm colour creates a mood of love, affection and gentleness.

~ *Orange* creates a mood of flamboyance and camaraderie. In the work place it promotes curiosity, fearlessness, and restless inquiry. This invigorating colour should therefore be used with considered restraint to ensure that its benefits are not overdone. You could soften it by choosing a more apricot shade of orange.

~ *Yellow* is the colour of happiness. It is a good colour for schoolrooms, studies and busy offices as it inspires wisdom, imagination and mental acuity and adventurousness. Yellow is often liked by clear and precise thinkers. A golden shade of yellow has a more soothing effect.

~ *Green* is the colour of harmony, hope and peace. It is not recommended for places of work or study except in its very pale, very cool forms. For waiting rooms and small sitting rooms, however, it creates a mood of renewal, gentleness and a sense of 'everything's all right'. A very pale, washed-out green is often used in institutions such as hospitals and schools. Here the benefits of green are meant to combine with the non-disruptive coolness of the shade selected. Fortunately, more and more of these institutions are choosing new and stronger colours to achieve a more definite environment.

~ *Purple* creates a very grand and flamboyant atmosphere just perfect for the extrovert in you. It has its solemn and fastidious effect as well, as implied in the decor and garments of church and monarch. But purple is really a colour of extremes, either exhilaration or depression, and it should therefore be wielded with a light hand. Its softer shades, such as lavender and mauve, create a mood of aloofness and aspiration.

~ *Brown* is a perfect companion to white. Its mood of solidity, stamina and patience combines extremely well with the innocence and purity of white. As in so many simple settings where wood floors and exposed beams soften the all-white glare of walls and ceiling, brown gently introduces the ideas of work, duty and dependability. Too much brown in your environment may induce you to reject change and to tend towards inertia and paranoia.

~ *Grey* is an excellent colour for workplaces, desk tops and VDU screens. It creates an attitude of caution, composure and a measured expenditure of energy. It is also easy on the eyes and therefore prevents fatigue. You should not be concerned that grey is synonymous with dullness, however. Simply mix a little purple or blue into your very grey paint to add the qualities of those colours to your environment.

Colour design

Here are a few basic guidelines for designing the colour scheme of your home or workplace.

~ Decide on the intended use of the room and the level of activity it will invite. This will help you determine which colour to paint it. Red, for instance, is rarely conducive to a room meant for peaceful retreat from the world. On the other hand, it may be just the colour for the corridor or playroom – both areas of great activity.

~ Remember, there are hundreds of different shades of colour to choose from. If you really like red but can't face living with a very strong version of it, try a shade that tends toward the pink, apricot or peach. The colour charts available from paint and interior design companies will help set you on your way.

~ Always use rather less of the colour than you at first imagine you would like. This will prevent you overdoing a colour to the point of it becoming a nuisance or an eyesore. Use items of furniture or decoration to highlight the colour instead and allow the rest of your colour scheme to remain a contrast or background to the prominent colour.

~ White and light-coloured ceilings lift the room space and help reflect natural light.

~ Offices, libraries and schoolrooms are often painted in cool, neutral colours such as grey, pale blues and pale greens. These colours help reduce fatigue and eye-strain and can promote concentration. Try using brighter shades of the same colours on end walls to keep you relaxed and concentrated even when looking up from your work. White and very deep or bright colours cause distraction in these settings.

~ Bright colours should be used to mark hazards, first aid and fire equipment, and all safety and precautionary measures.

CHAPTER 105
SOMETHING'S IN THE AIR: IONIZERS AND AIR PURIFIERS

~

You can live for months without exercise. You can live for weeks without food. But if you're denied the air you breathe for more than four minutes, your brain will die. Air is the essence of existence, yet we rarely think of it as the number one human nutrient, which it is. In fact, the air that you breathe – in your home, in your office, and outside – is far from clean and in many instances is actually damaging your health.

On Thursday, 4th December 1952, a slow-moving anticyclone came to a halt over London, trapping smoke from domestic fires in the lower atmosphere. The resulting chemical smog killed 4,000 people.

Today, the air quality in many British, European and North American cities is still a public disgrace. Friends of the Earth estimate that over 10 million people in the UK are at risk from contaminated air. Those especially vulnerable are young children, the elderly, pregnant women; and those with respiratory illnesses such as asthma, hay fever, bronchitis, angina and emphysema.

The World Health Organization sets guidelines for maximum levels of certain major pollutants – among them, sulphur dioxide, carbon monoxide, ozone and nitrogen dioxide. But these limits are regularly exceeded. For example, the WHO recommends that the amount of carbon monoxide in the air we breathe shouldn't exceed more than 10 milligrams per cubic metre over an eight-hour period. Yet official British figures show that, during the three-month period of 1 October to 31 December 1988, this limit was exceeded on twenty-four days in London. The highest reading was almost double the WHO guideline.

When asked to comment on stark facts such as these, officials usually have a pack of lies ready and waiting to be dealt. Often, the first move is to disparage the WHO guidelines. "They're just suggested amounts," runs the official line, "with a wide safety margin built in."

That's a lie. The WHO guidelines do not include a "wide safety margin". Says WHO:

"When populations are exposed to air pollutant levels above the Air Quality Guideline, adverse health effects may occur. In any population, a number of people will be especially sensitive to a given pollutant. Young children and the aged are likely to be more sensitive, as are people with pre-existing lung disease and/or cardiovascular disease. People who exercise or work outdoors will increase the inhaled dose and, hence, be at increased potential risk . . . the majority of Europeans are frequently exposed to ozone concentrations exceeding the Air Quality Guideline values. *Since the Air Quality Guideline value incorporates little or no margin of protection* (our italics), widespread acute effects of the respiratory tract may be caused. The frequent and repetitive nature of ozone exposure might contribute to the irreversible decline of lung function as well as to structural lung damage."[516]

Another ever more barefaced lie is to simply tell the population that the air quality is 'good' when, in fact, it is not. Here's how they do it. The WHO guideline limit for eight-hour exposure to ozone is 50–60 parts per billion (ppb). But the British government's own definition of 'good' air quality is set at 50–100 ppb. By fiddling with the figures like this, official bulletins can describe the air quality as 'good' when, in fact, the ozone levels breach WHO guidelines.

It would be comforting to be able to write that you can simply cure the problem of air pollution by sitting indoors, buying an air purifier and switching it on until the problem has passed. Unfortunately, you can't. Air pollution is an insidious problem which can't be solved like that. And it has many dimensions. Did you know, for example, that sulphur dioxide, which is primarily generated by the burning of fossil fuels at power stations, combines with other chemical pollutants to form acid rain in the atmosphere. Acid rain is mainly sulphuric acid, a highly corrosive chemical, capable of causing a wide range of illnesses. Asthmatics are obviously particularly vulnerable to this type of assault on their already-sensitive airways, and it is probably no coincidence that deaths from asthma have soared by 50 per cent in the past ten years in many Western countries.[517]

When acid rain falls to earth, it leaches out toxic metals from the soil – such as arsenic, aluminum, cadmium, lead, and mercury – and introduces them into the water supply, thus posing a further grave threat to human health.[518] But that's not the end of it. Now, scientists have found that acid rain plays an important part in the spread of cancer. Frank Garland, Chief of Occupational Medicine at the Naval Health Research Centre, and Cedric Garland, Director of Epidemiology at the University of California, San Diego, have found that atmospheric acid rain can absorb certain wavelengths of light, which are essential for the human body to manufacture vitamin D. Remember vitamin D plays a vital part in helping the body fight off cancer. "We can get vitamin D from the diet, but the main place we get it is from the sun," says Cedric Garland. "What we found is that sulphur dioxide absorbs light in the very part of the spectrum that vitamin D is produced."[519]

The bad news goes on and on. We haven't yet mentioned the effects of other pollutants, such as nitrogen dioxide and the cancer-causing substances emitted by vehicle exhausts. And in case you're still hoping that you can hide away from all this, safe in your bunker, think again. Most people spend about 70 per cent of their time indoors, but quality of air inside is little better, with build-ups of formaldehyde, benzene, trichloroethylene (TCE) and more ozone, from building materials, furnishings and office equipment. That's before you even consider lesser, but still harmful, nuisances such as dust, dirt, smells, and pollen.

But let's pause here, before we get too depressed! There is *some* positive action you can take now, to exert a benefical influence on both existing conditions and those which will prevail in the next millennium:

~ Reconsider your use of the car. Although switching to unleaded fuel certainly reduces the amount of lead in the air, it does nothing to reduce other pollutants. The next step is to fit a dual oxidation-reduction catalytic converter, which can decrease your emission of hydrocarbons, carbon monoxide, and nitrogen oxide. However, cities such as smog-bound Los Angeles and Tokyo are finding that, despite tough emission controls, attempts to make cars 'cleaner' have largely been disappointing. Ultimately, the only answer is to remove the source of the pollution. If you live in a city with adequate public transport, perhaps you could get rid of your car completely. Since we 'abolished' our car a few years ago, we calculate we've saved several thousand pounds, with zero inconvenience. Public transport, taxis, shared shopping trips and an occasional hired car (once or twice a year) completely fulfil our transport needs. Two additional benefits: the stress of sitting behind the wheel in rush hour is gone forever (who needs more stress these days?), and the added personal pollution of continually breathing in the exhaust from the car in front is gone, too.

~ Support clean air campaigns both locally and nationally. The Friends of the Earth (address in the Help section) run a campaign for cleaner air, and inform the media when pollution levels exceed WHO guidelines. Contact them to see what you can do to help them.

~ Stricter Europe-wide controls on air pollution are essential, together with an impartial and accurate monitoring service, and stiff penalties for polluters. Write to your MP, MEP and the Secretary of State for the Environment and ask what firm proposals they have in this regard.

But what can you personally do to improve the quality of the air you breathe? Should you consider buying an ionizer or air purifier?

Ionizers

There are basically two types of air pollutants: particulate matter and molecular pollutants. Particulates include dust, pollen and tobacco smoke (smoke is actually composed of millions of microscopic particles that can be isolated and trapped by some filter systems). Molecular pollutants, on the other hand, are substances such as carbon monoxide and nitrogen oxide, and are very difficult for domestic ionizers, air filters or purifiers to eliminate.

The manufacturers of ionizers are, traditionally, prone to make rather excessive claims on behalf of the products they sell. There is, however, evidence to suggest that ionizers, cheap both in initial price and running costs, will provide somewhat fresher and cleaner air for you and your family to breathe indoors. Ionizers work on the principle that negative ions not only have a 'tonic effect' on the nervous system, but also clear the air of dust particles, smoke, pollen and smells.

Negative ions exist in plentiful numbers in nature. They are produced by the continual, electrical re-charging of particles by the action of the sun, wind, rain and lightning. They are particularly in evidence on mountain tops, near sea, river and waterfall, after thunderstorms and in your own shower! That's why ionizers are sometimes claimed to be invigorating, and able to improve your mood. It has been claimed that the presence of negative ions can regulate the body's production of serotonin, a chemical present in the brain, which helps control moods. We have seen no clear scientific evidence to justify this assertion.

Ionizers work by giving a negative charge to airborne particles, which then drift to grounded surfaces such as walls and ceilings, where they stick. Unless the ionizer is combined with a fan and a filter of some type, the particles tend to be attracted to walls and other nearby surfaces, causing noticeable staining.

Manufacturers claim that their products can benefit a range of ailments from allergies and hay fever, asthma, sinusitis and bronchitis to colds and migraines; they also claim benefits for animals and plants too.

Ionizers do indeed appear to have a positive role to play in regenerating the stale, tobacco-ridden air of homes, to alleviate the negative effects of office equipment, like VDUs and photocopiers, and to ionize your car. When used in conjunction with air filters, which sift the air for tiny pollutants (some models combine both features in one unit), they may provide a partial answer to your indoor air pollution.

Air purifiers

There are three basic types of air purifiers available: conventional air cleaners, purifiers with an air-freshener stage, and purifiers which also incorporate ionizers.

Air purifiers use a small fan to draw the contaminated air through a woven fabric filter, usually followed by an activated charcoal filter, which strains out the larger elements in the air, like dust particles, smoke and pollen. Some systems follow this with an air-freshener step, where the air passes through a wire mesh coated with tiny crystals of lemon-lime air freshener or some other fragrance. Finally, some versions also incorporate a negative ion generating stage before the air is recycled into the room. Here's what ionizers/air purifiers can and can't do:

~ If you suffer from allergies, a combined ionizer/air purifier may work for you, although the evidence is not conclusive. The problem is that larger particles of dust and other material which you may be allergic to will quickly settle on the floor, beyond the reach of the purifier.

~ If you live or work among machines which give out positively-charged ions (such as television sets, monitors, VDU screens) and suffer from persistent headaches, try using an ionizer for a period. There are many individual reports of dramatic improvements under such conditions.

~ Most air purifiers can do a good job of removing tobacco smoke from the air, thereby reducing eye, nose, and throat irritation. However, they may not remove the actual smell of smoke so effectively – the molecules are too small to be filtered out.

~ Most domestic air purifiers won't be able to tackle the threat posed by dangerous gases such as carbon monoxide, oxides of sulphur and nitrogen, and ozone.

Plant power

The best solution, we feel, is to use a combined air purifier/ionizer (a larger fan-driven model is best, see the Help section for a manufacturer), together with liberal use of household plants. As we've previously seen (chapter 59) certain houseplants can filter your domestic atmosphere very efficiently. A two-year study by NASA scientists concluded that common house plants such as spider plants (*Chlorophytum elatum*), English ivy (*Hedera helix*) and indoor chrysanthemums can remove a number of dangerous toxins from the air, including TCE, benzene and formaldehyde.

But how many plants should you use? A NASA environmental research scientist, B. C. Wolverton, says: "If you have an office or a home that isn't making you sick but is a wee bit stuffy, then put a dozen or more plants in there. But if you're having symptoms of sick building syndrome, or if someone in there smokes, go ahead and put plants in, but supplement them with a high-efficiency filter."[520] Wolverton has himself designed just such a filter, which takes the revolutionary approach of using several plants' root systems as the means by which to 'scrub' the air. Using a fan, fifty cubic feet of air can be cleaned every minute, by drawing it through the plants' roots. Unlike other carbon-filter systems, it doesn't need to be changed because the roots and the bacteria which live there actually consume the pollutants as their food source. For more information about this radically new system of air treatment, contact the Foliage for Clean Air Council (details in the Help section).

You Must Be Choking! A Guide To Air Quality Standards

Next time they tell you the air quality is 'good', be suspicious. Find out the actual measurements, and see if they exceed the WHO guidelines below:

Sulphur Dioxide	350 μg per cubic metre for 1-hour exposure
	125 μg per cubic metre for 24-hour exposure
	50 μg per cubic metre for 1 year's exposure
Carbon Monoxide	30 mg per cubic metre for 1-hour exposure
	10 mg per cubic metre for 8-hour exposure

Ozone	150-200 μg per cubic metre for 1-hour exposure (76–100 parts per billion)
	100-120 μg per cubic metre for 8-hour exposure (50–60 parts per billion)
Nitrogen Dioxide	400 μg per cubic metre for 1-hour exposure
	150 μg per cubic metre for 24-hour exposure

Note: the abbreviation 'μg' means 'microgram'. You will sometimes see it abbreviated to 'mcg'. A microgram is one-millionth of a gram. It is 1,000 times smaller than a milligram (mg).

Chapter 106

How to turn your garden into a nature reserve

~

One of the most beautiful and rewarding things you can do with your garden is to share it with Mother Nature. Wherever you live, and whatever your garden's size – from 'postage stamp' patio to country estate – you can make a real difference by turning it into your very own nature reserve. At last, here's something positive and practical you can do to give nature a chance to fight back.

The traditional, formal suburban garden is dead – literally. With chemicals to kill off the weeds, more chemicals to eliminate pests, and even more chemicals to ensure that the remaining plants grow to a correct size, there's very little that's either natural or life-enhancing about it. The over riding objective is to maintain a controlled mix and match of colour, shape and height, and to achieve it, you have to engage in ruthless toxic warfare.

In a garden nature reserve, the rules for success are very different. Here, you must choose your plants for their potential to harbour wildlife, rather than for their exotic or visual appeal alone. You must aim to create opportunities for a very broad range of wildlife to become established in your plot of land. And you must kick the chemical dependency habit!

This does not mean that your garden will become a tangle of thorn and grass, nor that you will have to forgo the pleasures of patios, formal beds and tidy lawns. You can still have these things, but, with careful planning, you can create them from plants that will also provide much needed links in the eco-cycle which naturally exists between plant, insect, mammal, amphibian and bird life.

How to plan your nature reserve

Planning your wildlife garden should be undertaken in three stages.

~ First, make a precise and detailed record of your garden as it exists at the present. (You may repeat this stage two or three times in the course of one year for a really complete garden plan.) Take a notepad and sheet of graph paper into your garden and draw a rough plan of the garden; then wander slowly round and draw in each shrub, tree and bush to fill out the picture. Make additional notes about the state of the soil, any rotting logs, piles of moulding leaves or mounds of rubble. You might also note any obvious health problems that a tree or shrub is suffering, any birds nesting or any preponderance of bulbs, insects or fungi. In short, notice and record everything that you observe about your garden. This is an immensely pleasurable job, one that you could reasonably expect to take a whole day – depending on the size of your garden and how long you dawdle in the sunlight!

~ Secondly, identify the plant and wildlife species you have observed in your garden. For this fascinating task, allow spare hours in the evenings, early mornings and weekends, as it cannot be hurried. Some birds and insects, for instance, only make their appearance at a certain time of day and, if you don't ever notice their presence, you may inadvertently destroy their habitat when you begin to modify your garden. So take your time, and enjoy learning all you can about the life already flourishing in your garden.

~ The last step in planning your nature reserve is to use the following rules of wildlife gardening in order to decide what to add and what to take away from your garden:

- Give priority to native plants as they *always* support more wildlife than imported or exotic species of plant.
- Aim to create a variety of wild environments to provide habitats for a diverse range of flora and fauna. This means planning your garden to include pond or marsh, woody border, grassy wild 'meadow' and a rough bank of herbs and flowers.
- Work with nature, not against her. Excessive tidiness almost always interrupts the process of growth and decay which is so important to the life cycles of other creatures. So, for instance, leave rotting logs to provide homes for new insects, unusual fungi, toads and newts. This rule also means you should aim to garden organically using the techniques and materials which help you manage your garden, but do not destroy wildlife in the process. (See also chapter 107.)

With these rules in mind, begin the exciting job of creating your new garden, one teeming with wildlife and full of the scents, colour, visual texture and overall beauty that you desire. (See the Help section at the end of this book for a list of where to find native seeds, plants and trees, wildlife and wild garden literature and organic gardening supplies.)

Trees, shrubs and woodland

Don't start chopping down trees just yet! Work with the plants which have arrived in your garden of their own accord as your first step in creating natural habitats. Many city gardens, for example, contain self-seeded buddleia bushes or elder. Buddleia, with a common name of 'butterfly bush', attracts butterflies. The elder may look a bit ordinary and spindly, but its bark attracts birds which feed off insects gathered in the lichened surface. Its blossom, in May, attracts bees and its berries, in September, delight the smartly plumaged tits and finches. The elder, like the buddleia, thrives in relatively poor-quality soil and in sunny or shady areas. It is versatile as well as unassuming and makes an excellent start to any woodland site. In fact, if you haven't got an elder in your garden, dig up a self-seeded specimen from waste ground and give it a home.

If you do have a surfeit of trees or shrubs in your garden, you may decide to fell one or two of them to provide space for an adjacent tree or shrub to thrive. Just be certain that you use the cleared material somewhere else in the garden: compost it or pile it into a special 'rotting wood' corner to attract those toads, newts and insects mentioned above.

When you have the space and opportunity, plant native trees or shrubs. These include oak, alder, birch, ash, hawthorn, lime and beech – the list could go on and on. Of course, you might not have room for a full-sized beech tree, for instance, but you could plant a beech hedge instead. Using woody plants in this way enables you to create a woodland habitat without the acres of land commonly associated with trees of this sort.

Holly, laurel, privet, yew, bramble, dog rose and hazel are examples of other plants that will form an attractive, tight hedge which also provides homes for hundreds of species of wildlife. Once established, a hedge of this sort will surprise you with beautiful flowers, evening scents and a chance to observe nesting birds.

When planting trees and shrubs, observe these basic guidelines:
~ Plant from October to March.
~ Check the plant for signs of mildew, disease or dry roots and select another specimen if any of these are present.
~ Soak the roots while you dig a hole large enough to include compost and the fully spread roots of the tree or shrub.
~ Plant the tree/or shrub, staking it if necessary. Firm the soil around it, water it well and mulch the area around it.
~ Tie the tree to the stake (if using one) and add a rabbit guard to young, succulent saplings.

The woodland canopy you create from a combination of trees, shrubs and hedges will provide shade and areas of dappled light. This is the natural, preferred habitat of woodland plants such as lungwort, oxlip, bluebells, wild garlic, dog violet, ground ivy, sweet cicely and herb robert. The presence of such plants provides the ground cover you need to encourage shy forms of wildlife such as toads, newts, warblers and grass snakes. The tops of trees and high hedges provide good cover for rooks, pigeons and the commoner raptors such as sparrowhawks and kestrels, all of which live and breed quite comfortably in cities.

Moors, meadows and lawns

Moors and meadows are favourite habitats for many of our prettiest butterflies and small reptiles. They are rich with colour and nurture rare and endangered species of flowers, insects and birds.

You can create a moor or meadowland habitat even in a standard-sized suburban garden:
~ Starting with an existing lawn, grow wildflowers from seed, pot them and then plant them out. Do not continue to feed your lawn as this will only encourage your hybrid lawn grasses to grow. A wild meadow develops better with reduced soil fertility.
~ Starting with a bare piece of ground, first clear the soil: pull up weeds when they reach maturity but have not yet gone to seed and plant potatoes or pumpkin in the area for one year. These will slightly reduce the fertility of the soil, enabling the successful growth of a wildflower meadow.
~ Alternatively, replace the topsoil with subsoil. This means digging! This method will enable you to plant your meadow immediately, however.
~ Then, scatter a mixture of coarse grass and wildflower seed (see Help section) and keep it well watered.
~ Learn to leave the lawn unmown until mid-June (for a spring meadow) or from late September (for a summer meadow). This allows the meadow herbs and flowers you have planted to bloom, the insects to colonize, the bees to flourish and the birds to nest and feed in your meadow. When it has passed its flowering period, you may roughly mow it and use it as you would any other lawn.

Once established, you may wish to add boulders and moorland plants such as scabious and heathers. These will draw lizards and grass snakes, attracted to basking in open sunlight. Or plant your moorland with bulbs, such as the delicately formed and scented wild daffodils – division ten in the catalogues. And remember that bulbs are self-propagating, so what begins as a self-conscious patch can spread to become a lush carpet of colour.

Pond and bog

A watery area can be created in even a very small corner of your garden. It will attract aquatic insects such as the water flea and water boatman which feed off algae and help keep your water oxygenated and clean. A pond or boggy area also attracts frogs and toads. They are only likely to spawn, however, if parts of your pond or bog are secluded, offering cover from crows, jays or magpies, which are all common visitors to urban or suburban gardens and love to feed on the wildlife you have worked so hard to welcome. Larger pond-loving birds like the coot may decide to nest on the fringe of your pond, if it is big enough.

Your pond may be an old stone sink or a fully fledged pond lined with concrete, clay, plastic or fibreglass. If you make a lined pond, remember these simple guidelines:

~ Site your pond in full sunlight, away from overhanging trees whose leaves will clog it up in autumn.

~ Ensure that your pond is at least one metre deep at its deepest point. This will allow pond creatures to survive even if the pond freezes over in winter.

~ Gradually slope the pond edges so that there is a broad area of shallow water. This will guarantee that marsh and waterside plant species will thrive and will also enable animals to climb easily in and out of the pool.

~ Create variety even round the edges of your pond: let one part act as a beach by spreading sand and gravel; let grass grow wild up to one edge to give cover to birds; pile rocks along one corner to give homes and basking opportunities to newts; and let one corner remain very boggy and wet so that you can grow a variety of marsh plants.

~ When you have filled your pond, add one or two bucketsful of water and sludge from a nearby, well-established pond. This simple step will immediately change your pond from a new and sterile environment to one inhabited with hundreds of pond dwellers who will waste no time in making your pond their home. In spring, add a jar or two of frog spawn from a friend's pond to introduce frogs to your pond and garden. (Do not collect from the wild, please.)

~ Select plants you wish to grow in your pond and along its edges (see the Help section for list of suppliers), choosing native plants, of course. Some plants may need to be kept contained so that they do not overgrow; simply plant them in buckets and embed those in the soil.

You may forgo having a pond in favour of a small bog or marsh. For this, select an area in shade or semi-shade and spread a shallow pit with plastic liner. Cover with earth and add plenty of water before planting it with a selection of marsh-loving plants. The insects, birds and animals which thrive in a bog will follow in a very short time.

Borders

You will want your pond, meadow and woodland to somehow fit together so that your garden is pleasing as a whole – traditional border flowers are ideal for this purpose. These should, again, be native varieties and not the exotic or hybrid sort you might be familiar with. Remember, the point is to attract as much wildlife as possible while still creating a garden which will delight you. Plant your border areas with herbs, early- and late-flowering bulbs, poppy, mallow, calendulas, native roses, sunflowers and daisies. These plants all attract insects and therefore birds; many are scented as well as handsome and some of the herbs are useful in the home and kitchen.

As with all aspects of wildlife gardening, don't be too eager to tidy up your border: seedheads, for instance, may be lunch to a visiting bird!

Walls and derelict corners

The rock garden which has become so popular in recent years has its origins in the natural deterioration of old stone walls. As they crumbled and bowed they became colonized by insects and small animals eager to make good use of the shelter they provided. Wild herbs and flowers would soon establish in the silted cracks and crevices, attracting more insects and animals.

Whether you build a rocky corner in your garden, or simply leave the mound of rubble which has been considered an eyesore until now, you will invite more species of wildlife into your garden. Bees and hedgehogs are two examples of creatures who love this sort of habitat. Make sure there is a bit of soil in and around the rocks or rubble, then add a few plants such as stonecrop, houseleek, rockrose and one of the many so-called Mediterranean herbs such as thyme, hyssop, sage, mint and rosemary.

Bird life

Once you have planned your wildlife garden you may realize that there are still one or two species of bird who are not yet attracted to nest or feed in your garden. You can remedy this by providing bird boxes and feeding tables that will suit them.

~ A nesting box must be sited high enough off the ground (minimum of two metres) to make it safe from ground predators. If you have cats to contend with, protect nests by placing a ruff of chicken wire about a foot below the box.

~ Ensure that you have made or purchased the correct type of box for the bird you wish to attract. There are many different box designs, but two basic designs will get you started and suit a great variety of birds: an 'open nest' box will suit birds such as robins and wagtails; a 'hole nester' box will suit tits and nuthatches, for instance.

~ The entrance to a hole nester box must offer the bird a clear flight path in and out of the box. No other tree, for example, should be directly in front of the mouth of the nesting box. An open box may be positioned in dense foliage or in open summer houses or sheds.

~ Clean the nesting boxes once each year, in January, with boiling hot water.

Once nesting is under way, give the site a wide berth. Your presence can frighten away timid birds like tits, nuthatches and warblers – use binoculars to observe them instead. If birds are nesting in your hedge, trim it only sparingly, leaving as much ivy, honeysuckle or periwinkle as you can. Wrens, in particular, are very shy and favour nesting in dense thickets of ivy, holly or laurel.

Once you have attracted birds to your garden they will want to stay as long as the cover and food are there for them. To keep the welcome mat out all winter, erect a bird table.

~ Position it in a fairly open area of your garden, not too close to trees and shrubs, which enable cats to attack feeding birds. Cats and squirrels can also be deterred by placing a ruff of chicken wire about a foot below the table.

~ The table should be secured about five feet above ground level.

~ Bird feeders that hang from the eaves of your house allow you to watch birds from close quarters, but they should be positioned rather closer to the window (about twelve inches) than you might at first assume. This will prevent the birds from flying into the window at high speed and injuring or killing themselves. Hanging a net curtain will also help prevent this sort of accident.

~ If you feed the birds, be consistent and provide good food and clean water all winter long. Good foods include seeds, fruits, berries and fatty foods such as coconut or cheese. Water should be placed in a broad, shallow bird bath.

Insects

Insects provide food for the birds, toads and frogs that live in your garden as well as help in the process of breaking down garden debris such as compost, old wood and rotten logs. By and large, you should aim to encourage a wide range of insects in your garden.

~ Ants build their hills in the pulpy fibrous material of rotting wood. Their presence attracts both the splendidly-marked green and the spotted woodpeckers, now returning to the town garden from the beleaguered countryside.

~ Butterflies are attracted by the Buddleia bush, Michaelmas daisies, Lunaria (honesty), mint and valerian. Moths love flowering sage, hyssop and nicotiana.

~ Bees are attracted to undisturbed sites such as rock piles or mounds of rotting wood and feed from nectar-rich plants such as honeysuckle, snapdragon, hollyhock, borage, lemon balm, crocus and mallow. Bees are fascinating to observe and will not disturb you if you do not interfere with them. They are in great need of a welcome as their country habitats are rapidly disappearing and they are victim to the widespread, heavy use of herbicides and pesticides.

~ Worms are a gardener's friend and, hopefully, you will find them working on your compost heap before too long. You may gather a few from a friend's garden if you don't see signs of any in yours.

~ Beetles and centipedes may seem creepy to you, but they do good work in the garden. They both feed off slugs, for instance, and contribute to the breakdown of garden debris.

~ Unwelcome 'bugs' such as aphids and slugs are the usual reason given for gardeners using toxic sprays and chemicals. However, by welcoming their natural predators and with a little 'companion planting' (see chapter 107) you may keep the problem under control. Slugs, for instance, are a favourite food to hedgehogs, frogs, toads and some birds.

Bats

An established wildlife garden might well attract bats all by itself; you can encourage them to settle in your garden, however, by leaving hollow trees or by installing bat boxes. These are similar to bird boxes in that they allow the bat to roost in places where a natural habitat does not (yet!) exist. (See the Help section for further information on making and purchasing bat boxes.)

Bats are voracious feeders, eating thousands of tiny insects each evening. They do no harm to humans, despite the many myths and fairytales involving them. Neither do they harm property. In fact, it is illegal to interfere with a bat in any way, especially if it is roosting in your property. If you are concerned by their presence, contact the Nature Conservancy Council or The Bat Project (see Help section), who will assist you and give you further information on how to help prevent the rapid decline in bat colonies.

Hedgehogs

These noisy creatures love to scour your garden at night in search of tasty slugs to eat. Of course, they do drink saucers of milk placed outside the back door, but you will be doing them a greater service if you leave secluded corners in a jumble of leaves and leafy branches. Alternatively, you may build a hibernation box in a quiet corner of the garden and hope that your hedgehog will raise a family. (See the Help section for details.)

Patience breeds pleasure!

Your wildlife garden will give you pleasure from the moment you begin to plan it, but it will be of a different sort to the pleasure felt managing a more formal garden. If you can cultivate patience, as well as plants, you will be privileged to observe nature at work through hundreds of different life forms. Be prepared to sit still and silent while animals, accustomed to quiet, wild places, adjust to you. Then will come that moment when the garden stirs around you. You are there but the wildlife ignores you. Few pleasures in wildlife gardening are more fulfilling.

Chapter 107

Being nicer to Mother Nature: a gentler way with pests

~

With no chemicals around, why wasn't there a worm in the fruit of Eden? Just give Nature a chance and she will return your infested garden to good health without poisoning the planet!

Pests are creatures with whom we co-exist (and sometimes co-habit!) with a great deal of reluctance and antipathy. In home or garden, pests are those creatures which we believe are unhygienic, dangerous or damaging to property. They include a huge number of insects and some mammals: flies, wasps and bees, aphids, mice, rats, slugs and even birds. In recent decades a huge industry has sprung up to deal with our aversion to so-called pests – an industry based largely on killing the offending creatures. It seems that for every pest or combination of pests we encounter, there is a pesticide, insecticide, dusting powder or spray of some sort that will eliminate the problem.

Elimination usually means death, but what kills one species usually has a profound effect on other, close-to-hand, species – including humans. There are several hundred household and garden pest products on the market, most of them containing powerful chemical ingredients which will upset the natural order of wildlife, and many which will pose a threat to you and your children's health. Pest control products may, for instance:

~ Cause irritation or allergic reaction, including headache, cold symptoms, rashes, sore eyes and throat.

~ Be very poisonous. In fact, some are fatal to humans and/or their pets. Most of these products contain warnings on the label, but not everyone reads labels thoroughly. There are also, for instance, many cases of a spray used in one garden drifting to neighbouring gardens and poisoning the unsuspecting people, plants and wildlife there.

~ Cause cancer, genetic mutation or birth defects in humans and animals. Studies to prove such effects take years and years to conduct and much secrecy and controversy surrounds them. Meanwhile, many suspect products are still on the market.

~ Kill wildlife that is not considered a pest. Harmless insects, birds, plantlife and pets are often killed in the wake of a pest control product being used against one particular creature. This slaughter greatly upsets the natural balance of wildlife in the garden and can lead to greater pest problems than before. (See the Help section for who to contact for more detailed information.)

There are steps you can take now to greatly curtail or eliminate the use of dangerous pest control products in your home and garden.

Physical barriers

~ Ensure doors and windows are well fitting. Mice often just walk into your house through an open door or window in spring or winter; so keeping the doors and windows closed is a simple answer to a potential problem.
~ Fit insect screens on windows and adopt the American use of screen doors in front of solid doors. These let the light and air through, but nothing else. You might hang bead or plastic strip curtains in open doorways instead. These will reduce flying visitors though not necessarily walking ones.
~ In the garden, chicken wire fencing may help to reduce visitations by moles and rabbits. Dig a trench twelve to eighteen inches deep around your garden and embed the chicken wire in it, leaving the remaining width of fencing to stretch between posts above ground. Fill the trench and tightly pack the earth around the buried fencing. This will prevent the creatures gaining access by digging or walking.

Hygiene

~ Vacuum upholstery, bedding and carpets regularly, working right up to the skirting boards. This simple precaution helps reduce the number of insect eggs tucked away in folds, creases and crevices.
~ Clean clothes or bedding to be stored, then wrap them in plastic or paper along with strongly scented spice or herbal sachets.
~ Be prompt and efficient with clearing away your rubbish. Keep dustbins well covered and securely tie any refuse sacks. This is standard practice to reduce the incidence of flies, mice and rats.
~ Store loose food in plastic or glass containers in a cool, dry place to prevent infestation by insects such as flies, beetles, silverfish and moths.
~ Don't treat your compost bin as a rubbish tip. Follow the rules of good composting and don't allow any bacon rind or other fatty or fleshy foods which will attract rats and flies. Paper and very woody twigs and branches will also slow the decaying process and should be kept out of your compost bin.

Catch, don't kill!

There are many ways of catching pests and setting them free again outside.
~ Place a glass over insects and then gently slide a postcard underneath. You can then carry them outside without having killed or touched them.
~ Buy a spider catcher, a long-handled, specially designed dustpan to help you catch creepy-crawlies even when they're high up. You'll find the address in the Help section.
~ Buy a mousetrap which doesn't kill – usually available from pet shops. The mouse can then be set free outside.

Deter and repel

The kindest and most gentle way to deal with pests is to deter and repel them. Quite simply, to make them want to go elsewhere instead! These methods are also the safest for you and yours, and they quickly and easily become part of your routine of cleaning, gardening and general housekeeping.

For the home

~ Ants can be deterred by keeping sweet substances well cleaned and covered – no gooey drips of jam on the cupboard, for instance. If you have a nest of ants or a seasonal caravan of them through your sitting room, place ammonia-soaked cotton wool or bunches of the herb wormwood at their point of entry to your house.

~ Add sachets of lavender, rose petals, cedar wood chips or a blend of cloves, cinnamon and allspice to drawers, cupboards and stored clothing to deter moths, flies and other insects.

~ Hang bunches of lavender in doorways or windows to deter flies and grow rue, basil, tansy and mints, especially pennyroyal, in window boxes or in tubs by doors.

~ Use netting and protective clothing as a first resort when dealing with mosquitoes. Avoid using commercial repellents which contain Diethyltoluamide (DEET) as this substance can be absorbed through the skin and may cause toxic reaction, especially in children.[521] Instead, use citronella and pennyroyal herbal products, such as the citronella soap available from Oxfam.

~ The smell of peppermint, turpentine or cats usually deters mice and rats. Peppermint is easy to grow in your garden or windowsill. Turpentine should be kept well out of reach of children or pets and is usually poured on to cotton wool and placed in the mouth of a mouse hole or rat run. While cats usually deter mice and rats, they also kill them, so be prepared to face a few carcasses. Sonic pest repellers, said to deter mice, rats and moles, are available for purchase, see the Help section for details.

~ Bats are a protected species and it is illegal to try to evict them from their roost, even if it happens to be your attic. In fact, bats should never be considered pests in the first place: they do no damage to people or property, their droppings do not cause damage or offence and they help to control insect pests in your garden. You may encourage and safeguard bats in your vicinity by avoiding the use of chemical pesticides and timber treatment and by hanging bat boxes in trees and on the outside of sheds (see chapter 106 and the Help section).

In the garden

~ Adopt companion planting techniques. This ancient form of pest control relies on the idea of mutual benefit when planning your planting scheme in orchard, flower, herb or vegetable patch. For example:

- The roots of African, French or Mexican marigolds excrete the same chemical compound as pyrethrum – a widely used pesticide. Eelworms, wireworms, millipedes and other root-eating pests are brought under control when you plant a ring of marigolds around your vegetables, or plant them in amongst your vegetables.
- Garlic planted near roses helps to prevent black spot and aphids. Onions should be planted in rows alternate to rows of carrots to prevent carrot root flies on the carrots and onion root flies on the onions!
- Nasturtiums have a strong essence which aphids and white fly find obnoxious. Their root excretions deter root lice and strengthen neighbouring plants' resistance too. Grow them in amongst your tomatoes and fruit trees. (See the Help section for further information on companion planting.)

~ Every pest has its natural predator and you may find that pest control is best achieved by encouraging these predators to thrive in your garden. Your garden will become an attraction for these natural predators when you stop using chemicals that kill them or the insects they feed upon.

- Birds eat slugs, caterpillars and a variety of insects. Allow plenty of leaf cover for nesting and ensure feeding opportunities such as leaving seedheads intact for birds to eat.
- Bats eat up to half their own weight in insects each night. Encourage them by hanging a bat box (see the Help section for details).

- Hedgehogs eat slugs, beetles and other insect pests. Leave a rough and tumble corner of your garden for them to nest in, or build a hibernation box (see the Help section).
- Toads and frogs eat insects. Patches of long grass, piles of rotting wood and a pond are attractive to them.
- Ants may be a nuisance in the home, but they should be welcome in the garden. They feed on aphids and tree-dwelling insects. They nest in old wood or under rocks.
- Ladybirds are voracious consumers of aphids and no healthy garden should be without them. They live in orchards, shrubbery and meadow-like grasses. Stop spraying pesticides to encourage these mini pest controllers, or collect some from a friend's garden.

~ Regularly change the varieties of annual flowers and vegetables you grow and practise crop rotation to create a 'pest-resistant' garden.

~ Adopt organic gardening methods; these aim to work with nature, not against her. You may have to wait a year or two to achieve a natural balance of pests and predators, but your garden will become a productive haven for a huge variety of wildlife.

CHAPTER 108
GROWING AND KEEPING GOOD NEIGHBOURS

~

If you can't stand your neighbour, you're not alone. According to a recent study, one-quarter of people living in Britain's cities feel the same way, and the number of neighbourly disputes has skyrocketed over the last ten years.[522] In fact, difficult neighbourly relations can rapidly lead to living under siege-like conditions. But before things get that bad, there are many things you can do to make life with the person living on the other side of your wall more amicable.

A neighbour is "a dweller next door, especially regarded as one who should be friendly or as having claim on others' friendliness", according to the Oxford English Dictionary. That would be fine, except that we rarely have any choice in choosing our neighbours. Like our family, they are just there – for us to get on with, or not, as the case may be. And if you don't make an effort to get on with them, then life can end up being hell. All those endless petty jealousies and arguments that only seem to happen between neighbours rarely ever lead to any changes in conduct. Instead, a sort of cold war seems to ensue and the aggrieved party is left feeling even more frustrated and bent on revenge.

Count your neighbours as assets

If you do decide you want to be on speaking, rather than screaming, terms with your neighbour, you are half-way there. Coldly calculating the benefits you could reap from the relationship can help you on your way. When things start becoming difficult, remind yourself that you are dealing with a potential babysitter/plant-waterer/sugar-lender. You may feel uncomfortable about this, but the strength of communities in other parts of the world is only forged out of necessity, because survival relies on inter-dependency, just as, during the war, basic human need bred an incredible system of co-operation and moral support.

Many people bemoan the lack of any real community as it used to exist, but this can only come gradually from individual action. A change in attitude on your part may prompt others to follow, and who knows, it could be the start of something big! The ideal situation in most people's eyes would be the creation of some sort of informal support system. The significance of this should not be underestimated; such a structure could save someone's life, either emotionally or literally.

Organize for neighbourliness

Various schemes under the names Home, Neighbourhood or Community Watch have been set up in an attempt to encourage a community spirit and to provide some mutual protection (see chapter 115). Their primary aim is to reduce crime, while playing a secondary role in encouraging individuals to become good neighbours generally. Suspicious behaviour and other relevant information is reported by members to a co-ordinator, who then acts as a representative and reports back to the police.

What is it about such initiatives that makes so many of us squirm? Perhaps we resent the perpetuation of that old theory of loving thy neighbour, or simply that it just seems such a busy-body, middle-class thing to do. But these schemes do actually reduce fear and crime, as well as helping to foster good relationships. There are now 74,000 Neighbourhood Watch schemes in this country, with more than one in six households participating. If you do not have one in your area, why not set one up?

Even if you do not feel Neighbourhood Watch schemes are for you, there are a number of local and national bodies that can offer advice on improving the community generally. You'll find these in the Help section at the end of the book.

We like music, our neighbours like noise

Obviously, even with the existence of these groups, disputes continue, with noise ranking as the major cause. People have been known to kill over this matter, so take some measures to ensure it doesn't come to that! Firstly, make sure your home is properly insulated. A survey has shown that 20 per cent of the population are bothered by noise, primarily because of poor insulation.[523] In Scotland, new occupation of a house or flat is actually forbidden until it has passed an acoustic insulation test.

The Noise Abatement Society can offer advice on soundproofing your home. It is a voluntary, non-profit-making organization aiming to eliminate unnecessary noise from all sources. Ear defenders, which reduce noise by up to 40 decibels, are also available from them. See the Help section for details, and also see chapter 109.

Assuming you have noisy neighbours, how should you deal with the problem? A loud, late-night party once a year is probably excusable. And if, one night, you hear serious screaming and shouting, then you should call the police. But what do you do when you're robbed of your sleep night after night?

It's logical to begin by having a quiet word with them. Tempting though it might be to bang on the door and give them a piece of your mind, resist! It won't stop the noise nuisance (they may even turn the hi-fi up just to spite you) and relations between you will go from bad to worse. So, instead of starting a feud, start a dialogue. You are most likely to achieve good results by choosing a more neutral moment – leave it until the next day, if you can. Provided you're assertive yet polite, an appeal to be a good neighbour may be all that's needed, especially if they were unaware that they were disturbing you. If the thought of confrontation is off-putting, you could always write them a note. Tell them:

~ The last thing you want to do is spoil their fun.
~ You value their friendship and want to keep them as good neighbours.
~ You do need to get some sleep because work is very demanding at the moment for you.
~ Offer to tell them when you're going to be away so they can party as loud and as long as they want to (and could they water your plants, please?).

The right approach will almost always work, and is by far the best way to sort things out. There are other, more formal, steps that you can take, outlined below. But do understand that once you call in outside assistance (the police, for example), then relations between you will become permanently impaired. Think carefully before doing this – one day, you just may need their goodwill very badly indeed.

~ If polite, personal appeals for moderation are contemptuously rejected, then obtain a Citizens Advice Bureau or a solicitor's letter detailing the action you are prepared to take.
~ If appropriate, complain to the culprit's landlord, but be aware that this can lead to eviction. Alternatively, notify your local authority's housing department, which has powers to deal with noise from fixed premises.
~ Notify the police.
~ Ask the Environmental Health Department for an officer to come to your home and measure the decibel rate of the noise.

If nothing is resolved, an abatement order can be imposed. If this isn't complied with, prosecution will follow. A maximum fine of £2,000 can be imposed on the first or subsequent offence and £50 for each day the offence continues after conviction. Sometimes damages can be claimed, or compensation, if the value of the house has decreased because of the problem.

That's the heavy way of doing business. Now, here's an alternative way. On the day after a particularly noisy event, call round and speak to the head of the household (let's be frank – speak to the woman of the house – women are almost always more level-headed about these matters than men, and are far less likely to become territorially aggressive). Explain that you're taking up the flute, and you hope that your playing won't become a nuisance to them. Emphasize that, should they ever find your playing at all disturbing, they shouldn't hesitate to call or phone, and you'll stop immediately. While giving your most sincere smile, stress that you don't want to cause them any inconvenience at all. Whether you do, in fact, take up the flute is up to you. Next time you see them, repeat the performance – anxiously ask them whether they've been bothered by your playing. Slowly, they'll start to understand that their neighbour is a caring person. And consciences will start to prick.

Know your rights

It is worth making yourself familiar with your legal rights, as they affect you and your neighbours. You could save yourself face and money, and maybe even foster a good relationship with your neighbour.

The title deed and/or lease to your property will stipulate the rights and duties of the owner/occupier. For example, they will clearly state who holds responsibility for repair. The deeds are normally held by the mortgager – either a bank or building society.

There are a number of other very common neighbour disputes which can usually be resolved quickly and painlessly with the correct approach. Try to make sure of your legal position before launching into any premature attack.

Boundaries

Disagreements over boundaries can normally be settled by referring to the deeds or lease of a property. These should provide you with conclusive information. However, if the boundaries are not defined, there are certain common rules to follow. For example:

~ A flat owner's property includes the external walls.
~ A fence belongs to the person owning the garden containing the upright posts.
~ Walls of semi-detached or terraced houses are divided vertically down the middle and repairs are at joint expense.

Animals

Owners of livestock and unusual pets are liable for any damage they cause. But this doesn't apply to domestic animals. The property owner who is being troubled by animals should make his own arrangements to keep them off his land. To do this, he is permitted to use any reasonable material.

Barriers

If the barrier belongs to one owner, he can use it in whatever way he likes, and as long as it is safe is not obliged to repair it. The non-owning neighbour must seek permission before using the barrier.

Planning permission is not required to erect a wall or fence as long as it is less than one metre in height.

Trees

An overhanging tree signifies a trespass. The neighbour should be asked to trim the branches and, if he refuses, you may trim them yourself, although the branches and any fruit must be returned to the owner. If a tree causes any damage, the owner is responsible.

Shared amenities

The person with responsiblity and rights of use will be stipulated in the title deeds or leases. Sometimes rights to use another's property are given, for example to receive gas deliveries.

'Ancient lights' allows an individual who has enjoyed a certain amount of light for twenty years to continue doing so. This only applies to light into windows of a building. So if your neighbour's extension blocks your sunbathing, there is nothing you can do. You have no general right to privacy.

Bonfires

If a bonfire is dangerous, you have the right to tackle it. Your rights may be affected by stipulations in the title deeds or lease, or by bye-laws. If a bonfire is smelly or particularly smoky, it may constitute a legal nuisance.

Conciliation

This year, the Islington Neighbourhood Disputes Centre in London was set up to act as a mediation service in cases of community disagreement. Funded by the Department of the Environment, the centre joins twenty others established since 1983. The idea is to offer a kind of 'marriage guidance counselling' service for neighbours to prevent the need for legal action. Trained mediators visit each party and listen to their grievances. Then a session is arranged during which each person can express himself, uninterrupted. A written agreement may then be drawn up which each party agrees to adhere to. However, this is not legally binding and the Centre's role is not to offer legal advice. Hopefully, this will become part of a standard national service. It certainly seems to be working at present, and the scheme has a 90 per cent success rate. It could be worth suggesting to your local council that they establish a similar scheme.

Chapter 109

What you can do about a noise nuisance

~

If someone makes an unprovoked physical attack on you, you have a right to defend yourself, by force if necessary. But if you're subject to an assault on your eardrums – what can you do?

People who complain about noise have traditionally been regarded as spoilsports and killjoys – busy-bodies who want to stop other people from having a good party, listening to pop music or enjoying an invigorating domestic squabble. But times are changing. Noise pollution is today recognized as an important environmental issue in its own right. After all, you *do* have an inalienable right to peace and quiet in your own home! And the scientific evidence clearly shows that, far from being a trivial annoyance, noise can have seriously hazardous effects on the state of your health:

~ When exposed to inescapable loud noise, experiments show that humans soon lapse into helpless despair and then clinical depression. Eventually, they don't even try to turn off the noise any more. Life becomes passive and seems not worth living.[524]

~ Excessive noise can drive your blood pressure up, making you a candidate for strokes and heart disease.[525]

~ We now know enough about noise to say with certainty that sound levels of 85 decibels or more with exposures of eight hours a day will produce permanent hearing loss.[526]

This is the sort of noise which might be experienced at work in factories or other noisy environments.

~ Noise which is 'uncontrollable' seems to have a particularly strange effect on us. Scientists have found that exactly the same noise can have very different physical effects, depending on whether we are able to control it (i.e. switch it on and off) or not. Women exposed to uncontrollable noise produce more of the hormone oxytocin, which makes the uterus contract in childbirth, and also makes milk flow from the mammary glands. Exposure to uncontrollable noise also produces a worsening of mood, together with memory lapses.[527]

~ A study of the noise effects of living near London's Heathrow airport, one of the busiest in the world, has shown that the greater your level of exposure to aircraft noise, the greater are your chances of being admitted to a psychiatric hospital.[528]

~ Further research now under way suggests that the adverse effects of noise may include lowering your overall ability to concentrate and perform basic everyday tasks; it may make you forgetful; it could be responsible for a whole range of sleep-related disorders; and it may even have a part to play in the development of heart disease.[529]

That's the bad news. But there's no point suffering in silence – unless you want to risk your temper and your health. So here's how to take positive steps to combat a noise nuisance.

Call the experts

To start with, it's probably best to consult your local council's Environmental Health department. It's their job to investigate all complaints – about neighbours and other sources of noise. And you will undoubtedly receive a sympathetic hearing.

Having said that, when environmental health officers are asked to investigate a noise complaint, the critical point on which they must make a judgement is whether the noise amounts to a *statutory nuisance*.

Your word is not good enough – because what may cause extreme annoyance to one person may be hardly heard by another. There is no fixed level of noise which constitutes a statutory nuisance. So the environmental heath officer has to consider what would be the reaction of an average, reasonable person to the noise, taking into account not only its loudness, but also such factors as when, how often and for how long the noise occurs.

If the official is satisfied that you have grounds for complaint, and informal approaches fail, the council serves a notice on the person causing the noise. And if this doesn't work, court action follows.

The maximum penalty, under the Control of Pollution Act 1974, is a £2,000 fine plus a daily £50 penalty if the noise continues.

Frankly, it is rare for individuals to be prosecuted, although the threat of being taken to court is often enough to make them more considerate.

What next? If all else fails, there are three further courses of action you can take. Firstly, you're entitled to complain directly to a magistrate's court and apply for a summons to be issued. Secondly, you can also take civil action, by seeking an injunction. This may be expensive, unless you qualify for legal aid, but if you are successful, you can apply for damages.

But probably the most practical course of action is to improve the soundproofing of your own home (see "Practical noise reduction steps" following).

Here's how to deal with other major sources of noise pollution.

Businesses

Your local authority is more likely to institute a prosecution when there's noise nuisance from a factory, building site, late-night pub or disco. London's Westminster Council, for example, has a specialist noise team, available to investigate complaints seven days a week. It also encourages contractors to join its 'Considerate Builders Scheme'. Why not suggest that your own local authority follows suit? You can also write to the local paper, or phone your nearest radio station. This can be extremely effective; no one wants bad publicity.

Work

Don't allow your employers to risk your health and your hearing. *You are at risk if you work in a place where the level of noise forces you to shout to make yourself heard.* But you are protected by the Health and Safety at Work Act 1974, which requires your company to take practical steps to ensure employees are not exposed to dangerous noise. If there's a problem, contact your trade union or ask the Health and Safety Executive to intervene.

Planes

Complaints about noise from aircraft taking off and landing at most major airports can be made at any time (see the Help section for some phone numbers), and the governing aviation authority is also duty bound to investigate your written complaints, too. Complaints about military aircraft can be made to your local air force station, as well as the Ministry of Defence, who will also consider claims for compensation (addresses in the Help section).

Roads

If a new road or railway line is being constructed, you could be entitled to a grant for double glazing. Your local council will advise. Such schemes are usually given the go-ahead only after a public enquiry and you have the right to object on any grounds, including noise intrusion. There's no need to be a lone voice. Form a local action group. When it comes to effective protesting, there is strength in numbers.

Burglar alarms

How often have you been driven to distraction by the incessant ringing of a burglar alarm? There are over one million false alarms every year. When you hear one, contact the police right away – the alarm may have gone off for real. The registered key-holder will be contacted and requested to restore tranquillity to the neighbourhood. Although often this is easier said than done, since the key-holder is under no obligation to do so. Be wary of taking the law into your own hands: one desperate restaurateur who did so, attacking the offending alarm with a hammer and chisel, was taken to court and accused of criminal damage! Moreover, he was found guilty – but the magistrates clearly sympathized with his predicament, and gave him an absolute discharge, the next best thing to being found 'not guilty'.

Car alarms

The havoc wreaked by the siren wail of theft alarms installed in cars has reached such a level that many places are now introducing legislation to control this most unpleasant and distracting noise nuisance. Car alarms are usually triggered by a change in air pressure, so an over-sensitive one can be set off simply by the buzzing of a fly or the passing of another car. First, check with your local police – there may be recent legislation which allows them to cut the alarm off or even tow the car away. Again, don't take the law into your own hands, much as you may be tempted to: a fine for criminal damage can be considerable, and you'll get a criminal record too. Most alarms have an automatic cut-out, which stops the noise after a few minutes. Sometimes, however, they can go on for hours. So if the police can't or won't do anything, consider:

~ Swathing the car in old blankets. This will reduce the noise to some extent, and will be quite a surprise for the owner when he returns.

~ Leaving a sharp note to the owner under the wiper.

~ If the car is parked on private property without permission, the owner of the property may have the car removed.

~ An extraordinary number of drivers never bother to check that all their doors are locked, so check to see if any of the doors (or the boot of a hatchback) are unlocked and, if so, whether you can switch the alarm off.

~ Using their radio links and computer network, the police can find the name and address of the registered owner of a car in a matter of seconds. If asked nicely, a friendly police person may identify the owner like this, and if their workplace or home is nearby, pay them a visit.

Personal stereos

Equally widespread, and equally irritating, is the noise caused by personal stereos, which can cause intense annoyance to a captive audience on a bus or tube train. In London, the local authority is doing its bit, by fixing 'Keep Your Personal Stereo *Personal*!' notices on the underground trains. But don't just sit there, exchanging long-suffering glances with your fellow passengers . . . take the initiative and *complain.*

Wallpaper music

What about that dreadful wallpaper music that now seems to be an indispensable part of all shops, restaurants, pubs and hotels? Britain's Noise Abatement Society, the first national noise protest group set up in 1959 with Sir John Betjeman and T. S. Eliot as founder members, can help you out here. They produce postcards which bear the message

> *'I am a supporter of a citizen's group which is fighting painful and dangerous noise. I am leaving your establishment because your music is TOO LOUD, and I am advising my friends to do the same. Your establishment will be boycotted until you reduce the noise to an acceptable level, or better still stop the noise altogether.'*

There's space for you to leave your name and address, encouraging the offender to act upon your complaint. The Noise Abatement Society also sells ear defenders and a booklet which shows you how to improve the soundproofing of your home.

That mysterious hum

Finally, if you suffer from a strange buzzing, throbbing or humming sound, but can't tell where it's coming from, don't panic – you may not be imagining it. For some time, scientists have tried to track down the source. Recent work makes it seem likely that it could be coming from powerful microwave or radar transmitters, or possibly from high-pressure gas pipelines. Not everyone suffers from it. One theory has it that radar energy coming from nearby transmitters may directly stimulate the hair cells in the inner ear, causing a strange humming sound which is impossible for the hearer to pinpoint. Indeed, Britain's Ministry of Defence concluded in a recently-published research document: "*It is possible to hear the modulation frequency of pulsed microwave transmissions. The mechanism for this phenomenon is a small localized temperature rise in the head causing a pressure wave which reaches the cochlea.'*[530] In other words, part of your brain heats up a little bit, causing the sound receptors in your inner ear to register a noise.

At the moment, it is not known what other health hazards might be associated with this phenomenon. But if you suffer from this strange and distressing problem, it would certainly be worthwhile to investigate whether you're in close range of any microwave or radar transmitters, and if so, move – or at the very least, tell your local media, who will almost certainly be interested in investigating the source of this mystery (show them this page from *Superliving!* to get them going!).

Practical noise reduction steps

Noise is generally defined as unwanted sound, but you need to remember that the term is subjective. What is noise to one is pleasure to another. We are all victims of noise pollution, but many of us are also noise culprits, with our mixers, car alarms, burglar alarms, mowers and chain-saws. Remember, too, that noise is not only airborne sound waves, but also vibration, known as impact noise. That low-frequency thud coming from a local workshop's diesel generator could be reduced if the machine were installed in a basement with thick walls and a concrete floor.

Local authorities are empowered to designate Noise Abatement Zones within their area of control. This is a move aimed at regulating long-term noise coming from industrial premises. The local authority also has the right to scan the plans which might be in development for that new motorway link or shopping-centre in your area. It can investigate your query or complaint about noise levels arising from such large-scale developments.

Racket while you work

Noise at work, whether in office or factory, is often a major contributing factor to stress. Much can be done in an open-plan office where distracting voices leak into your cubicle. By careful use of angled screens and sound-absorbent fittings you make significant reductions in noise. Try thick carpets and curtains, shelved walls lined with heavy paper and impact pads under typewriters or other vibrating equipment.

Many machine tools produce decibel levels well above the safety limit. Under the Health and Safety at Work Act 1974, employers must safeguard the hearing of their employees. Rubber or plastic ear plugs must be issued to comply with these regulations. The Department of the Environment issues codes of practice which detail statutory noise levels from all forms of machinery. See the Help section on where to get these.

Noise outside

The most common noise pollution most of us experience outside comes from traffic, whether road-bound or airborne. Double or triple glazing may be necessary; but in severe cases of multi-directional noise problems caused by speeding trucks or low-flying jets, the Department of Transport is the ultimate authority to contact. See the Help section for details. The Department also issues regulations regarding levels of airport and aircraft noise under the terms of the Air Navigation Act (Noise Certification) Order 1984. Night flying of the noisier jets is already restricted.

Noise and property

Take the noise factor seriously when considering your house purchase. Noise not only pollutes, but can lower the value of your prospective property. Try to visit it at different times in order to ascertain the variations in noise levels from day to day and hour to hour. Note any possible sites which you suspect of producing noise – that factory on the corner or ghetto-blaster three doors down. Noise pollution demands assiduous field research.

~ Whether you are the recipient of other people's noise or the culprit, you will need to take steps once inside your home to diminish noise levels by providing absorbent and insulating surfaces in lofts and on walls, floors and ceilings.

~ Wall-to-wall carpets, cork or rubberized tiles, solid doors and thick curtains all provide absorption when applied to floors and walls.

~ Ceilings can be lined with acoustic tiles of polystyrene or dropped to a lower room height. Lower ceilings, lined with mineral wool, reduce the many indoor sound waves that reach you multi-directionally in the form of reverberation. Outdoors, sound is usually unidirectional, travelling out unimpeded from the sound source.

~ To achieve a drastic reduction in either impact or airborne sound, a floating floor may be required. The surface is first screeded in concrete. A layer of mineral wool is laid on the screed and joists laid un-nailed across this insulated base. The free joists minimize vibrations. Floorboards are then secured to the joists, forming a raft.

~ If your walls are letting sound out, attention to stud walls is worth considering. Stud partition walls are prone to amplify sound – the plasterboard panels nailed to the stud frame act like speakers. So use thick fibreglass quilting to fill in between the studs. Above all, cover all chinks in doors, window frames and skirting-boards. Pad any clanking or squeaking pipes and pad the feet of your piano since the sound waves it emits are impacted as well as airborne. A piano or typewriter being struck sets up vibration.

~ For specialized problems consult the Noise Abatement Society, which offers advice free of charge on many aspects of noise pollution and will guide you in your quest for acoustic well-being. Find the address in the Help section and, meanwhile, get going with the mineral wool and the stud wall.

Chapter 110

The harmless house: your cardinal checklist for safety

~

Gas

A gas leak can be extremely hazardous – an explosion could harm not just your household but others too. You have a legal duty to inform your local gas service centre if you think there is a leak. Turn off your mains gas supply until the leak has been investigated and stopped. Stop using any appliance you think is dangerous. Leave installations and servicing to the experts.

~ For your own safety, don't mix DIY activities and gas.

~ Be particularly careful with second-hand appliances.

~ Ensure all appliances are serviced regularly.

~ Ensure all appliances have an adequate supply of fresh air to remove dangerous fumes.

~ If you smell gas, put out cigarettes, matches, and all flames. Don't use *any* electric switch, even a doorbell. If the lights are on, leave them on. Open doors and windows. Turn off the mains supply. Call the Gas service centre (in your phone book under Gas).

It is bizarre to realize that, although our homes are where most of us feel safest, that is precisely where most accidents actually happen. The evidence shows that almost all accidents are preventable – is *your* house or flat as safe as you think? Take a few moments now to run through this quick checklist, noting any weak spots in your home and dealing with them immediately.

Electricity

Electricity can also be dangerous – the current running through an ordinary plug socket is enough to kill.

~ Make sure all plugs are in good condition and fitted with the correct fuse.

~ Always use the correct fuse wire in your fuse box. Otherwise an electrical fault could become a fire.

~ Only fiddle with wiring if you know exactly what you're doing – and always turn off the electricity first.

~ With any DIY activity, make sure you don't damage a power cable. This could lead to a shock or fire.

~ Make sure all cables are short, properly connected (no masking tape!) and, wherever possible, attached to the wall.

~ Keep electrical appliances away from water. Only electric shavers should be allowed in the bathroom. A wet hand on a light switch could mean a shock, so use pull cords in the bathroom or have the light switch outside the door.

Glass

Glass is a major source of injury, particularly to children, so:

~ Fit safety glass in doors and low windows.

~ If that's not possible, stick a transparent plastic sheet to the existing glass. This will minimize the damage if the glass is broken.

~ Remember, smoked or patterned glass is no stronger than the ordinary kind.

Child hazards

Children will eat anything, touch anything, fall into or out of anything and get to places you would never have dreamed of. The points below are particularly aimed at

families with children, but everybody will benefit from thinking about them, too:
~ Take a child's eye view of your home (get down on your hands and knees) – it may trigger you to notice dangers an adult would normally miss.
~ When a baby isn't in its cot, keep it on the floor. A bouncing baby chair, for example, can easily bounce off a table.
~ Make sure there's nothing lying around for a baby or small child to choke on.
~ Take a safety tour of your house. Carry this list with you and go into every room, checking off each point. In every room, check that:

- Carpets are firmly attached to the floor, and free from frayed edges and bumps that might make someone trip. Uncarpeted floors are not slippery.
- Electric and phone cables aren't lying around for people to trip over.
- Pictures and mirrors are *securely* attached to the wall – especially if they're heavy.
- Heavy or breakable ornaments can't be pulled off tables, etc. by small children.
- Good lighting is vital, particularly on the stairs. There should be switches at both ends of corridors and staircases.
- Stairs should be in good condition, especially if carpeted. If the carpet is worn, turn it upside down so the worn parts are on the vertical face of the steps.
- Don't leave objects on the stairs. Tell your kids this is not a place for toys to be left.
- Fit a gate at the top of the stairs to protect small children. If you have a landing with banisters make sure the gate keeps them off it – banisters are great for climbing on.
- Remember, banisters and stair rails are for support, so make sure they're up to the job.

The sitting room. This is a heavily-used room, so you need to keep a watchful eye on its condition:

- All fires should be surrounded by a guard. Babies love things that glow, so make sure the guard is baby-proof.
- Don't hang or lean anything on fire guards.
- Keep flammable materials (like curtains) well away from fires.
- If you have a balcony, keep the door to it locked, with the key out of the lock.
- Keep your drinks cabinet locked or on a high shelf. Even a small amount of alcohol can kill or badly injure a child.
- Be very careful with hot drinks and food. Don't leave your coffee in a precarious position or try to drink it while holding a baby. A sudden movement could result in a nasty scald.

The kitchen. This is the scene of most domestic accidents:

- Be careful with sharp implements. Keep knives and scissors on a rack on the wall.
- When using the stove, turn pan handles inwards, so they can't be grabbed from below. If possible, get a pan guard.
- *Never* leave anything unattended on the stove. Especially if there is a child in the kitchen.
- Try to make sure you have a work surface next to the stove, so you don't have to carry hot pans across the kitchen.
- Have oven gloves readily accessible for handling anything hot.
- Your kettle should be in a secure place, with no dangling flex to tempt children. Remember, the water in a kettle is still scalding hot half an hour

after it has boiled, and accidents with kettles inflict horrific injuries on little children every year.

- Never leave a hot iron unattended. And when you've finished with it, put it away immediately. A dangling flex is again to be avoided, since a child could grab it without you noticing.

~ Poisonous substances like bleach should be kept well out of children's reach, always in their original container. Check where and how you keep:

- caustic soda
- bleach
- lavatory cleaner/disinfectant
- weed killer/insecticides/rat poison
- petrol/paraffin/turps
- paint stripper
- meths (methylated spirits)
- glue – especially super glue

Bedrooms:

- A bedside lamp is a must, especially for old people. If you have a baby, a dim light left on constantly will enable you to move around safely and easily.
- A cot should have narrow spaces between its bars, so there's no chance of a baby getting its head stuck. It should be equipped with a firm mattress but no pillow – pillows can suffocate.
- Windows in children's rooms should be fitted with safety catches (available from DIY stores) or, if necessary, bars that can be removed by an adult in case of emergency. The same applies to all potentially dangerous windows.

The bathroom:

- Remember – no electrical appliances apart from electric shavers.
- The bath should be fitted with handles or a non-slip mat, especially if old people use it.
- *Never* leave small children in the bath unattended, even for the briefest moment. They can drown in an inch of water in the time it took for you to get a towel.
- Put the cold water in first, and test the water before putting a child in it.
- Make sure your water heater is properly maintained and well ventilated. Check with your local gas or electricity service centre or a heating engineer.
- Use a bath mat to ensure the floor doesn't become wet and slippery.
- Whether you keep medicines and pills in the bathroom or not always ensure children can't get hold of them. Preferably, buy them in child-proof containers and keep them locked in a cabinet.

The attic/cellar. These are usually the least well-maintained rooms in any house:

- Check that the stairs or ladder are sturdy, well lit and child-proof.
- Make sure the room itself is well lit, with a switch outside.
- If you use your attic make sure you can move around without falling through the floor! Preferably, have a proper floor put in.

The garage/shed. Another little-maintained area:

- Check what's in there. You should anticipate your child's curiosity by making sure anything dangerous is well out of reach.
- Use only sturdily-built shelves for storage.
- Apply the same rules for electrical safety and lighting as you would in the house.
- Only keep petrol, paraffin, etc. in small quantities and away from children.

- o Never get underneath your car unless you either have a properly-constructed inspection pit or you use ramps or a tripod axle stand.

The garden:

- o Make sure that small children can't get out into the road. Install a gate, and make it child-proof.
- o Any water – swimming pool, pond, etc. must be covered or netted, and inaccessible to children.
- o Check for poisonous plants, like foxglove, horse chestnut, laburnum or privet. If there are some, make sure children know not to eat them.
- o Don't leave potentially dangerous garden implements lying around.
- o Take care with lawnmowers. Always maintain them properly and wear stout shoes to avoid accidents. If you have an electric mower, use a residual current device (ask at your local garden machinery shop) and be careful not to damage the cable.

If you check and act on all the points on the above, your house will be a safer place. But don't forget to consider fire safety too – see chapter 117. For further help and information on safety in the home see the Help section.

Remember, the two most valuable safety measures are:

~ vigilance
~ commonsense

CHAPTER 111

YOUR SUPERHOME'S ABSOLUTELY ESSENTIAL SURVIVAL INSTRUCTIONS

~

Would you know what to do if an electrical fire melted a central heating pipe and flooded the fuse box? Find out about your essential preparations for the unforeseeable – before it happens.

Every time you fly, the stewards and stewardesses give you a basic course of safety instructions. Do the same in your home – use the following Survival Instructions as the basis for a yearly family teach-in about safety.

Who's on call?

Jot down the following emergency telephone numbers, copy it, hang one copy next to the telephone, and give one copy to each member of the family:

Builder ....
Central heating engineer ....
Doctor ....
Electrician ....
Electricity emergency number ....
Family ....
....
Fire brigade local station ....
Gas emergency number ....
Glazier ....
Insurance company ....
Local council environmental health and engineer's department ....
Locksmith ....

Neighbours ....

Odd-job man ....

Plumber ....

Police local station ....

RSPCA ....

Solicitor ....

Taxi ....

Vet ....

Water emergency number ....

If you don't already know any repair people, ask neighbours and friends for recommendations. Otherwise look through the Yellow Pages or your local paper and select those who belong to a professional body. Or you can contact the organizations in the Help section for names of local members. Include service numbers for specific equipment; for example, the washing machine.

Start preparing the rest of your essential tool kit now. Some things you will need to buy, some things you will need to do:

Accidents

Contact the Royal Society for the Prevention of Accidents (ROSPA) for information about preventing accidents in the home.

Fires

Have a family teach-in about what to do if a fire breaks out. Walk around the house and decide between you how you would reach safety. Play some games to have everyone practice walking in the dark – a fire may happen at night and fuse the lights or create too much smoke to allow you to see. Establish fire safety rules, like unplugging televisions and closing all doors and windows at night. See chapter 117 and its Help section for more details.

Gas

Does everyone know what to do – and what not to do – if they smell gas? If not, now is the time. Contact your local Gas Area administration or showroom for full printed details.

You can make a summary of these and stick it inside the door of a shed or out-house. This is because an unnoticed build-up of gas is most likely to occur when you are out; and one thing you must not do in these circumstances is switch on a light. If you smell gas on entering and know the rules are pinned up outside, there's a good chance you'll go to read them there and prevent yourself from blowing up your own home! The basic essentials follow.

~ Turn off the main gas tap if you can safely get to it.

~ Open windows.

~ Get out.

~ Phone the gas emergency number or 999 from a neighbour's or a call box. Using your own phone *could* set off an explosion.

Electricity

Make sure you and everyone in your family knows where the fuse box is, how to throw the mains switch and how to reset or change fuses. Gather together all instruction manuals and booklets. Put them in a cupboard close to the fuse box or some other suitable place. Make sure everyone knows where they are.

~ Have a family teach-in now on how to change a fuse in a plug.
~ Establish electricity safety rules.
~ Keep a torch, candles and matches near the fuse box along with a set of fuse wire, a selection of plug fuses and insulating tape.

Flooding

Make sure everyone knows where the mains stopcock is and how to turn it off. You all need to know this *now*!

Familiarize yourself with the layout of your attic. Put boards down to allow normal walking instead of balancing on the joists. Keep some plastic sheeting, even one or two plastic carrier bags, near the entrance for ready use along with a torch, pipe repair tape (in the Sellotape range) and all-weather repair tape (also in the Sellotape range).

Have a teach-in about what to do in case of a flood, including where to switch off the mains water supply, switching off central heating and perforating a sagging waterlogged ceiling.

If flooding from a nearby river is a potential hazard, make special preparations like sandbags, wellington boots and even an inflatable dinghy. Remember that boats can easily float away, so be sure to keep yours moored to a point at least two metres above the likely flood level and accessible from an upstairs window.

For washing machines, read your instruction manual now. Most say what to do in the event of it flooding. Pipe repair tape can deal with the problem in the short term.

Be prepared for burst pipes by establishing a frozen pipe precaution routine. This will include putting the plugs in sinks and basins and having pipe repair tape on hand.

First aid

Enrol at least one member of the family on a first-aid course. Your local branch of the St John Ambulance Brigade runs these regularly.
~ Assemble a first-aid kit that holds the following items:

First-aid book
Scissors
Thermometer
Safety pins
Tweezers
Cotton wool
Sterile eye pad
2 × 5 cm. crêpe bandages
2 × 7.5 cm. crêpe bandages
2 × PFA (perforated film absorbent) dressings
5 sterile gauze dressings
Small pack of paper tissues
Packet of plasters
Adhesive dressing strip

~ In the medicine chest, make sure you have all the following:

Paracetamol tablets
Antiseptic cream
Calamine lotion
Indigestion mixture or tablets
Kaolin mixture for diarrhoea
Bach rescue remedy

Arnica 30X pilules and cream

Blockages

There's normally space to make a purpose-built cupboard in the side of a panelled bath. Store the following kit in the bathroom or lavatory:

washing soda
sink plunger
waste pipe clearing wire
toilet plunger
caustic soda

Read the instructions on the chemicals carefully. It's a good idea to paste a list of their principal dangers on the inside of the cupboard door.

Broken windows

~ Keep some board for boarding up until repair is possible.
~ Learn how to replace a pane of glass.

Burglary

See chapter 116.

Evacuation

Having to leave your home unexpectedly for a long period of time, or even just overnight, can catch you completely unawares. Pack a basic evacuation bag *now*. Assume you may never see your home again and, to add to the usual pyjamas and toothbrush, which will immediately spring to mind when the time comes, put in the following items :

Passport
Address book
Prescribed medication
Birth certificate and other important documents
Small personal and family mementos
£50 note (or highest single denomination)
Pack of cards
Small torch
Small first-aid kit
Travel sewing kit
Sanitary protection
Plastic mac
Hand towel
A one-metre square cotton scarf
Small radio

If some of these items are in frequent use, list them on a large piece of cardboard and keep that list in the bag so you can immediately get them, without being flustered. Most importantly, agree a Meeting Place for you and the rest of your family to rendezvous in the event of your being separated. Do this *now* – before you ever think it will become necessary.

Food

Have enough dry and tinned food stocked to be able to make at least three meals without heat.

Locks

Take that spare set of keys to the neighbour now. Collect all household and personal keys together, label them and hang them all together, preferably in a lockable key cabinet.

Get some graphite from a hardware shop to pour into jammed locks.

Subsidence

Check your house insurance policy *now* to make sure it covers you for subsidence. If not, change it immediately.

Basic tool kit

Put the following tools together in a sturdy box, and keep it handy:

Chisel
Drill (hand or electrical)
Goggles
Gloves: rubber and garden
Hammer
Nails and screws – a selection of sizes
Pencil
Pliers
Scissors
Screwdrivers: electrical, cross-head and medium
Spanner: adjustable
Tape-measure
Trimming knife
Tenon saw
Wire cutters and strippers

Include the following spares and supplies additional to those already mentioned:

Clean white cloth
Fuses and fuse wire
Glue
Glasspaper
Insulating tape
Masking tape
Oils: machine and penetrating
String
Washers

Now you've developed a frame of mind to foresee survival needs and adapt to them with what you've got. And that frame of mind is the most valuable tool of all.

Chapter 112
How to be a mean-streets survivor!

~

Why do you live here, anyway?

Take a moment to consider this question seriously. If you don't have a good reason to live in the city, perhaps you shouldn't. After all, the best way of avoiding those mean streets is simply not having to walk down them.

London's population is currently 20 per cent below its maximum and falling; also in numerical decline are New York, Hamburg, Paris, Chicago and Birmingham, to name but five. More dramatic still are population migrations from cities like Liverpool and Detroit. People are leaving the cities in droves and the reasons are obvious when the acute level of urban decline is considered. You can see it all around.

There's no shame in leaving the city behind for a greener future in the country (but remember – you won't find Utopia there either – see chapter 96 for some down-to-earth advice about the reality of country living). If you decide to stay, make sure you've got genuinely good reasons for doing so. And, most important of all, make sure you have the stamina and fight (because fight it is) needed to survive and prosper. Living in a great city is like riding a wild horse: do it well and it will take you where you want to go, but lose control and you'll be trampled underfoot.

So – we live in the city because we want to be part of it and profit from it. The glittering, shining city still exerts its spell over the young, the upwardly mobile, the fashionable and the quick-witted; like moths dancing round a candle flame. Where else but the metropolis can you see a different film, play or concert every night of the week? Where else for top sports, splendid parks, unparalleled art galleries and museums? And although they say that cities are the loneliest of places, it is also true that you can meet people and make friends more easily here than perhaps any other place on earth. Everyone should try city life, once.

City streets are mean, and getting meaner. London is a classic example. Its streets are filthy, its air polluted, the noise intolerable; its transport system is in chaos, with awesome road-traffic congestion and under-financed, expensive and overcrowded public transport. And yet, millions of us choose to live there – ourselves included. Obviously, there must be compensations to make it all worthwhile. But just as obviously, there are risks – which you must know about, and know how to handle.

Fight the blight!

Architect Rowan Moore says, with absolute accuracy, "the design of the city was always its weakest point." Certainly the buildings where you live and work shape the way you think and feel – everyone knows this, except city planners and architects! Bad planning and poor design adversely affect your quality of life. It doesn't require Prince Charles' education to appreciate that cities of unremitting concrete, steel and glass are soulless and alienating. Who needs more mega-building projects and runaway developments which have no relevance to the real needs of people, their neighbourhoods and the environment generally? What people really want is local shopping parades and parks, not giant malls, out-of-town superstores and windswept, artificial 'piazzas'.

This, more than any other aspect of city life, seems utterly beyond the control of the average city dweller. We're just not used to being part of the decision-making process as it relates to our environment. 'They' control it – we have to live with the consequences.

Wrong. City planners are paid to listen to, and consult, their citizens. The fact that only a minority of citizens ever get involved in public consultations about architecture and planning makes us believe that we're not entitled to. But the fact is, all over the world, when people act together to preserve and enhance their cityscapes, they can and do succeed.

For example, through the Pratt Center for Community and Environmental Development extensive areas of derelict Brooklyn and the Bronx have been rehabilitated. In Philadelphia, the Foundation for Architecture "gives people the opportunity to comment on the way their city looks, and leads on to popular concern for more fundamental issues". But it's up to you to take the initiative.

People want work and shops near their homes so they don't have to travel across the city (de-centralization); they want less high-density building so they can move about and breathe; they want gardens, parks and open spaces; community and sports centres to occupy their kids; lighting to illuminate dark streets, and pavements maintained to prevent the old and unwary tripping and injuring themselves; ramps and easier building access for the disabled and people with prams; they want ecological balance, not blind destruction through planners' bulldozers. Greater involvement in planning should extend to building too. Use of environmentally friendly materials, elimination of 'concrete cancer' and utilization of the latest energy-saving technology.

~ Get to know your city planners – before they threaten to build a six-lane highway through your neighbourhood. Make friends with them. Invite them to speak locally, so they know you, your neighbourhood, and your concerns. A good understanding between planners and people is your best insurance policy against mindless city hall bureaucracy.

~ Get involved! You know what is good for your city neighbourhood. Organize (or play a part in) a local community or residents' association; your investment of time will be well rewarded. Such a group doesn't have to be stuffy and old fashioned, nor a vigilante mission; merely a representative bunch of local people wishing to improve their environment. Civic pride can start with your yard or window box and end with building a community centre or alternative technology park.

Co-housing: your next good idea

Co-housing is a form of housing which, at the moment, is unknown in the United Kingdom, but which has achieved enormous popularity in Denmark and Scandinavia. It's a system that takes into account not only people's need for privacy but their need for community as well, a way of building not just houses and flats but villages. Sympathetically imported into this country, it could do much to cure many of the present woes afflicting our cities' mean streets. Maybe it's your next good idea?

A co-housing community can be composed of anything from two to eighty households, though the optimum number is between fifteen and forty. The essence of a community is that it combines private houses and/or flats with shared gardens, walkways and a Common House – the centre of the community. Thus inhabitants get the best of both worlds; community living without loss of privacy or independence.

Co-housing is inherently flexible, but all existing communities share the following features:

~ Planning as a group for the group. Communities are planned and their construction or conversion overseen by the people who are going to inhabit them. This not only means communities are made to measure but also that people get used to each other and to the idea of group responsibility before they move in.

~ Deliberate, thoughtful design of a community. For example:

- o Roads are replaced by pedestrian walkways or squares, so adults and children can come and go easily and safely.

- Living areas, particularly the kitchen, are placed at the front of the house, so people can easily see each other when they want to. More private rooms are placed out of sight at the back.
- Houses have semi-private front gardens or porches where people can sit and chat to passers-by.
- The shared Common House may contain a dining room, TV room, laundry or crêche. In general, facilities can be acquired for the community that one family could never house or afford. Properly placed where people pass it constantly, the Common House becomes the centre of community life. But there are plenty of other opportunities, including shared workshops, garden equipment or computers.

Most communities have:

~ A monthly discussion meeting.

~ Committees dealing with particular projects or an issue like fire safety.

~ Rotas for communal chores.

All but the smallest communities are designed to cope with a changing population. Houses and flats vary in size and price so as not to exclude the family of six or the single student, the rich or the poor, and buildings are designed to facilitate the addition and removal of rooms by partition. New people can be integrated quickly, thanks to the sympathetic, human-scale design of the co-housing development.

Apart from these common features co-housing communities are infinitely varied. For example, they can be urban or rural; some are purpose-built, others are converted from disused buildings or adapted from failed housing projects – even tower blocks. And the benefits are wide-ranging:

~ You have friends who are neighbours and neighbours who are friends. No need to worry about babysitters. And you can work from home without feeling cut off from the world.

~ Your children can play safely outdoors with the other kids and have access to a range of games and activities you could never provide yourself.

~ The option of being able to eat communally means less time spent on chores and more relaxing or doing other things.

~ You have access to people with a range of skills, interests and possessions you can swap, to the benefit of all.

~ You only need to buy or rent a small space, but have the access to the facilities of a mansion.

Of course, co-housing won't suit everyone. But for many, it could provide a wonderful alternative to the grim, soulless existence many of us presently face in the city. The concept of co-housing has yet to become established in this country, which means setting up a fully-fledged co-housing project would be hard work. However, if you feel you could be a pioneer, see the Help section for more information.

Transport: get street-wise!

In terms of pollution, noise, dirt, danger and congestion, the car is the behemoth of the modern city. In British cities it consumes all before it as the government champions its cause to the detriment of the public transport system. The Department of Transport's policy of 'freedom of choice' is, in reality, a free-for-all, with the poor city-dweller getting to their destination as best they can. That means surmounting the problems of super-jammed roads, inadequate bus timetables, and overcrowded, antiquated and under-invested rail/tube networks. The motorist, poor lonely soul in his metal box, goes to hell at a snail's pace: in London, horse and carriage transport in the year 1900 was faster than the average car speed in the 1990s.

Over a quarter of a million people are involved in traffic accidents every year – of these, 5,373 die and 63,158 are injured seriously. The motor car has an unnatural appetite for the very young and the very old – 43,041 children and 36,553 elderly people were its victims for the last recorded year.[531] Presently, thirty-nine in every hundred people own cars – estimated by over-zealous motor companies to double before market saturation is reached – so, without firm action, the situation can only deteriorate further.[532]

What can we do to protect ourselves from the onslaught of the automobile? There are several possibilities:

~ Support the Grand Plan. Huge and powerful lobbies oppose, for purely self-interested reasons, the introduction of a sane transport strategy for all. If we want a solution, it's up to each one of us to lend his or her support to the few small voices of reason on the other side. A starting point is to greatly reduce the number of cars entering the city. This can be achieved by introduction of a toll or road-user's charge; an experiment already successfully tried in Oslo. Not only would many drivers be deterred and damage to roads and the environment lessened, but the cash collected can be used to improve public transport.

The lessons of the King's Cross tube and Clapham rail disasters are that you, the urban traveller, deserve better than shoddy, dangerous and expensive public transport. Many cities, like Manchester and Bristol, are already investing in alternatives such as the light-railway. These updates of the old tram are a cheaper, safer, more efficient way of moving large numbers of people from A to B. A model like the Briway Transit System, essentially an electric tramcar, can run at 85mph but minimizes noise and pollution, and is being considered for use by Southampton. Several organizations are currently trying to introduce some sanity into the car-crazy world of the inner city. Get in touch with them, and offer your support (addresses in the Help section).

Travel at low-risk times

~ You should realize that certain times of the day – and certain days of the week – are more risky than others. Sunday is the lowest risk of all (only 11.2 per cent of all accidents happen then). Monday (13.7), Tuesday (13.8), Wednesday (14), Thursday (15.3) and Saturday (14.7) are all somewhat higher, and Friday is lethal – with 17.3 per cent of all accidents happening on that unlucky day.[533]

As far as time of day is concerned, we have produced a computer analysis of official government road accident figures which, when plotted graphically, reveals some very interesting trends.[534] You can see from the graph that there are four basic patterns, corresponding to the Monday to Thursday period, Friday, Saturday and Sunday. If you can time your journeys to avoid the peaks on the graph, you'll considerably reduce your risk of having an accident.

~ During the Monday to Thursday period, especially risky times to travel (or to be a pedestrian) are in the morning during the hour beginning 8am, and later in the day, round about 5pm.

~ On Fridays, the 8am period is again particularly risky, but the afternoon high-risk period is more prolonged, between 4 and 6pm.

~ On Saturdays, the 8am peak is absent. Instead, the risk gradually climbs all morning, until the day's riskiest time to travel occurs during the hour beginning midday. The risk doesn't drop appreciably again until 8 o'clock at night. Note the 'mini-peaks' on both Friday and Saturday after 11pm.

~ On Sunday, there is again a slow build throughout the morning, but the hour of highest risk is later than Saturday – 3pm.

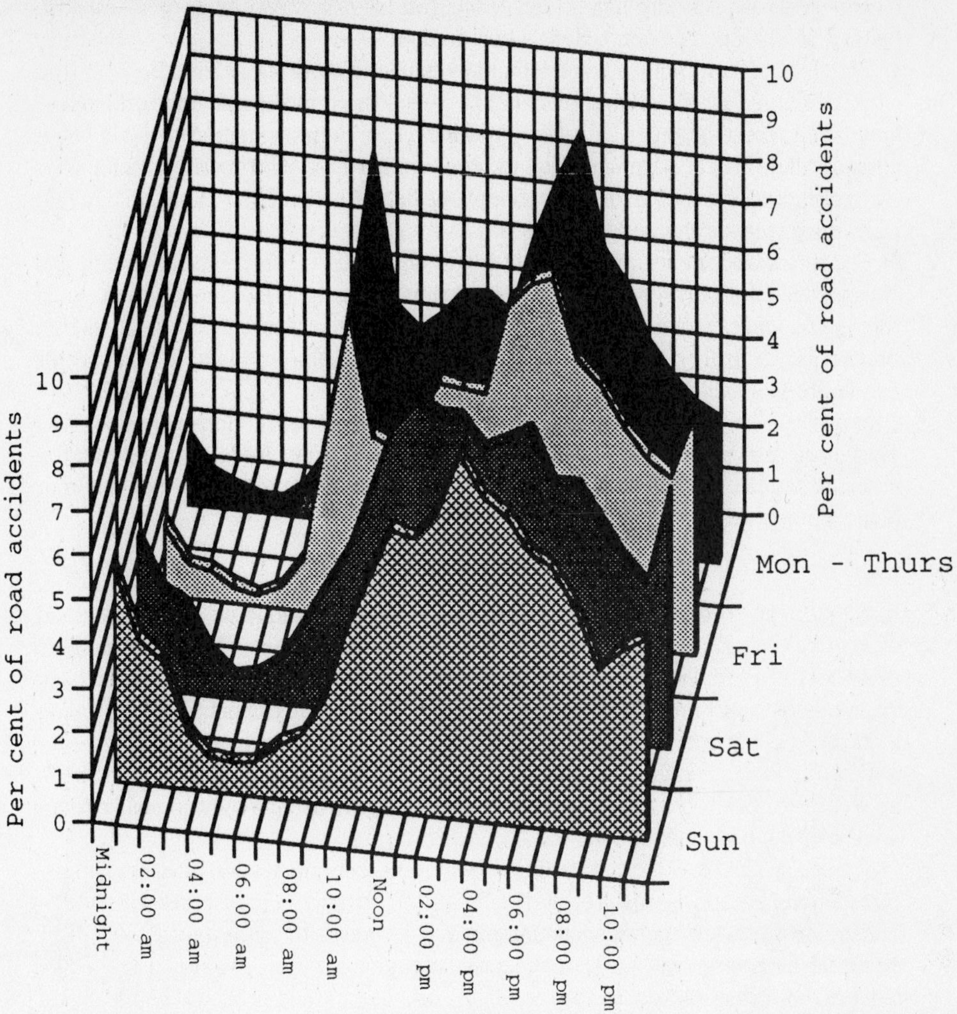

~ Be different. If the majority drives to work, try walking or cycling. Use large-scale maps to plan your transport strategy; get to know every alley and short-cut which you can use but cars can't. Go against the flow – use flexible time at work to travel at unconventional times.

~ Split long, regular journeys into smaller sections which are faster and more dependable (for example, take the tube to the central city area, then bicycle the last 2 dense miles). Schedule meetings unconventionally – breakfast at 7.30am is easier to get to before the rush starts and the meeting will be a shorter and more productive one. Or, instead of that long, expensive business lunch, instead arrange to have afternoon tea at a smart hotel (much cheaper, quicker, and it doesn't make you feel bloated for the rest of the day!). Use travelling time productively: a portable phone, a notebook and a pocket recorder will all boost your personal productivity and generally lower stress and frustration.

Become a home telecommuter

One of the best ways to avoid being exposed to the noise, filth, danger and general rottenness of the city's mean streets is simply not to use them so much. We're not suggesting that you become a hermit in your bunker. However, eliminating the daily commute to the office or workplace will drastically cut down on your exposure to the worst side of city living, and leave you free to travel when you want to, instead of when you have to. Here's how to do it:

The first telecommuters were women – unable to work away from home – who were employed by the computer industry. Since then, more and more employers have seen the advantages of telecommuting. A modem connected to your home computer lets you send information to other computers, and receive data for your own computer, through an ordinary telephone line. With a modem, you can be a full-time office worker and never have to leave your house!

The financial benefits are obvious: huge savings in office rentals, heating and cleaning bills. Employees can enjoy home-made coffee, healthier lunches and, since there is no longer any need to commute, more free time. And research shows that productivity actually increases – people working from home are doing at least 30 per cent more work than those who opt to stay at the office.

Journalists have been telecommuting for years: without the interruptions of an office, you can get a lot more writing done in a lot less time. And if you find that the soothing tones of Tchaikovsky's 1812 Overture help you work, you can play it at high volumes without complaints from your office-mate!

How to start

In Sunderland, redundant shipyard workers have found jobs as secretaries and office workers for London businesses – without leaving the North. Managers dictate letters and documents over the phone, they are typed up and shunted back via modems and come up through the office printer in London. And with the increase in electronic documents, most filing can be done electronically.

In the Orkneys, children are being taught by a telecommuter. Their blackboard is an electronic 'whiteboard' – scribbled on by someone using a light pencil, twenty miles away in Kirkwall.

These are just examples. Any job in computers, communication or information – salespeople, estate agents, teachers, computer programmers, secretaries, data-entry clerks, travel agents, accountants and lawyers, to name but a few – is a potential telecommuter candidate. The rule of thumb is this: if you spend more than half your working day staring at the office computer, you'd probably be better off doing it at home.

If telecommuting appeals, then why not get in touch with one of the companies who are receptive to the idea? ICI, Rank Xerox, British Telecom, and the Civil Service are some of the bigger employers introducing telecommuting as an enlightened option for their staff. Obviously which company you choose to approach depends upon what skills and experience you have.

How to sell it to your boss

If you think you could telecommute in your present job, then speak to your boss. You may be surprised how receptive she or he is to the idea, once you explain the advantages. They may be particularly receptive if you are pregnant or moving house, and the only other option is quitting your job. They might even lend you the computer you used when you worked at the office. Like all things, it'll need presenting properly. Here are the main advantages to your company:

~ Greater productivity. It stands to reason that if you have fewer interruptions (and office life is full of them!) you'll get more done. Companies who have implemented a telecommuting programme have reported 15–30 per cent gains in productivity.[535]. Job satisfaction also increases because the frustrations and time-wasting of traditional commuting is ended. And happy employees are productive employees!

~ Better communication. No one will ever complain of not being able to find you any more! If someone wants to leave you a memo, all they have to do is drop it into your electronic mail box, and you've got it. Also, being plugged into your company's online world means that everyone can connect with everyone else much more efficiently. If you want last July's sales figures, you've got them instantly. If you want the most recent comments on the marketing plan you're working on, you've got it at the click of a key. It makes no difference whether the person you're working for is five or 5,000 miles away – you can still communicate faster than the blink of an eye.

~ Happier workers. Telecommuting is an attractive way of working for many people. It makes it easier to attract and keep productive people. Relocation nightmares become a thing of the past. Maternity leave is no big deal. The semi-retired can still contribute. The home-bound or disabled can work as productively as anyone else.

~ Cheaper office costs. Your company doesn't need to move into larger offices – save the money they'd spend and put it towards a telecommuting programme!

Crime and violence

From mugging to urban riots, city dwellers walk a thin line between survival and going under. Serious crime is spiralling by 10 per cent in London every year – that's violence against the person, and sexual assault. Couple this with the lowest detection rate in the UK and it's enough to concern any citizen. We all need to learn and adopt a few simple survival principles:

~ Don't be an obvious target – walk tall, don't hunch; and, according to Chicago crime prevention lore, establish brief eye contact with potential assailants before moving confidently on your way.

~ Alcohol slows reactions: take a cab home or stay with friends when 'under the influence'.

~ At night avoid using bank cash machines; other danger zones are airports (as you fly off, so do your bags), public toilets and car parks. Listening to a personal stereo while jogging/walking makes warning sounds of attack inaudible.

~ Carry some cash: a mugger can extract more severe retribution if you have no money on you; better to lose £20 than your life!

The Adam Smith Institute recommends the privatization of streets, with private security patrols paid for by residents, and traffic kept out of bounds by secure gates. One alternative to this rather drastic measure is to form a Neighbourhood Watch scheme (see chapter 115) and strengthen community bonds.

~ Learn the basics of urban self-defence, and make sure your close ones know them too (see chapter 113).

Despite having many an obituary prematurely penned, the indications are that the city will continue to survive – and perhaps even thrive. Whether or not *you* survive with it depends on your ability to adapt, chameleon-like, to the constantly changing challenges your metropolis throws at you.

Urban life is an often reviled concept, yet today's crop of kids living in Chipping Sodbury, Cambridge, Massachusetts or Choshi are more likely to want to move to London, New York and Tokyo than their urban counterparts are to make the return trip! The real answer to improving cities is to generate greater social and collective responsibility for what takes place in them. The concept of civic pride may have fallen out of fashion in the last few decades, but we predict it will return again, sooner rather than later. Humans need cities, and cities need humans. So get out there, get with it and create the city of your dreams!

Chapter 113
Keeping your nearest and dearest safe on the streets

~

Well-tried methods will help you most in facing this age-old problem.

You, your family and your neighbours all have the right to feel safe and secure on the streets. Sensible precautions taught at an early age will become second nature to your children – perhaps their best insurance policy.

Make a positive start

Caring parents realize quite instinctively that children can be at risk and automatically take sensible precautions on their behalf. Their difficulty is in alerting children to potential dangers without making them frightened, fearful and over-anxious. There are two ways in which you can do this, instead of simply burdening them with lots of don'ts.

~ The first is to encourage a sense of independence. In this way a child grows up without being fearful and without being intimidated by people whom they sense are behaving in a threatening way. Instead, they would seek help, scream or run away to the nearest place where there is safety in numbers, whatever seems appropriate.

There is a paradox in that parents tell their children that they should always listen to grown-ups and do what they say. Yet children need to know that sometimes they shouldn't. The golden rule which runs alongside this is, of course: don't talk to strangers – ever.

~ The second way to help children's safety is to encourage and develop a sense of trust in your relationship. They must be able to tell you if they are frightened by what someone has said or done to them. And they must also feel that they will be believed. If they can tell you straight away about worrying situations, you may be able to take quick, pre-emptive action.

With teenagers, convene security negotiations

As children reach their teenage years and their yearning for independence grows stronger, you still need to make them aware of their own safety and get them to take responsibility for it.

A list of negative don'ts will tend to provoke an equally negative reaction from them. There are two ways in which a more positive approach can be taken.

~ Agree with them on one or two basic ground rules. For example: they will always let you know where they are and what time they expect to be back. Agree to do the same with them, to let them know where you are and what time you will be back. Another ground rule may be that if they're out with friends and miss the last bus or train, they should always take a taxi home. Give them one or two numbers or business cards of reputable taxi firms. If they don't have enough money for the fare, tell them that *you* will pay the driver.

~ Openly discuss with them what they will do to protect themselves in a threatening situation. Wait until you see a report in the newspaper of a handbag snatch or something similar, and use that as a starting point for discussion. Points should include putting safety of yourself above concern for your property – let the thieves have the handbag. Similarly, prepare them to seek help from others if they feel worried or threatened. Discuss how they could best defend themselves – using an umbrella or keys, for instance. Foresee how to avoid potentially dangerous situations – don't take short cuts or accept lifts from someone you don't know.

~ This can all be backed up by positive action like attending self-defence classes and by getting them to encourage their friends to join too. Buy them a screech alarm and encourage them to be aware and alert whenever they are out.

Foreseen is forearmed

Women, too, can think of attending self-defence classes and make use of discussions. Talk to friends about what they would do in a threatening situation. You need to think about it beforehand so that if it happens, you are to some extent prepared.

If you have already discussed with friends what to do when you suspect someone is following you, you will already be prepared to take some positive action if the situation arises. Friends may also have their own ideas about self-defence: from pepper pots and umbrellas to screech alarms and flat shoes for running away.

Safety in old age

With the elderly, always stress the safety of the person. Muggings worry elderly people. Talk with them about how they must let bags or money go should someone attack them. Wearing shoulder bags across the body and carrying a personal alarm are things you can talk about too. They should be able to feel secure when they go out and being aware of a few simple points will help.

~ Make them feel happy and confident about telephoning for help or assistance if they feel at all worried. Talk to them about who else they can call on as well. Reassure them about contacting the police. Older people don't like making a fuss. Reassure them, repeatedly if necessary, that safety is not fuss.

~ They need to feel confident and secure and some need lots of reassurance about their safety. Their homes can be checked by the Crime Prevention Officer from your local police station and made secure. Grants may be available to do this from your council, through the housing department. Again, one or two simple ground rules can be established, such as never opening the door unless the chain is on, and never letting anyone in without identification. It is also a good idea to talk to their neighbours. Make sure they know there is an elderly person at that address and ask for their help in keeping a look-out for them. Encourage the community spirit – most people welcome the opportunity.

A dozen do's for street safety

~ Avoid short cuts.
~ Walk on the pavement which faces oncoming traffic to avoid kerb crawlers.
~ Keep your hands out of your pockets to be free and at the ready.
~ Have your keys ready to let yourself in – or to help defend yourself.
~ Use taxis where you can, especially at night – the expense is worth it for your safety.
~ If someone attempts to snatch your bag, be prepared to give it up.
~ Sit in train or tube compartments which aren't empty.
~ On solo car journeys, check the back seat before you get in and, once in, stay in.
~ If someone tries to get you to stop for help, carry on to the nearest call box and phone for help from there.

~ Park in well-lit places.
~ Walk purposefully.
~ Buy a personal alarm.

CHAPTER 114
HOW YOU SHOULD HANDLE AN OBSCENE PHONE CALL

~

People who make obscene calls are on a power trip. If you take charge of the situation, all their weird pleasure has gone!

Do you see obscene phone calls as an insignificant problem? If you're a man, do you dismiss them as a female issue? Incredibly, neither British Telecom nor Scotland Yard hold statistics on this much-underestimated abuse; indeed, estimates revealing its true scale have only recently become available.

One terrified victim of persistent obscene calls saw moving house as the only solution. She reasoned that if she changed her number, the frustrated caller would find her address in the phone book and come to her home. The telecommunications watchdog, OFTEL, estimates that ten million such calls were made to women in 1989 and around five million to men.

You are the first line of defence

Support from all angles is becoming increasingly available, but you can do a lot to protect yourself. Take the following steps and you might well end up beating the caller on your own.

~ When you receive an obscene call, replace the receiver gently without giving any reaction which could encourage future calls.
~ If you can remain calm enough, place the receiver on its side and go into another room until the call is over.
~ If you are repeatedly troubled, get an answering machine. It will disconcert the caller and protect you from direct abuse. You can still take other calls if you pick up the receiver as a message is being left.
~ Pretend the line is so bad you can't hear the caller. 'You've got a twelve-inch what?' may unnerve the caller enough to discourage him.
~ Never give your number to incoming callers. If the caller asks, 'what number is this?', ask what number he wants.
~ Don't put your forename in any directory if you are a woman.
~ Avoid being gender-specific when placing advertisements.

Official confusion

There is a very real problem of categorization in this area which even BT appears confused about. Obscene calls are often put under the umbrella of 'nuisance' calls, which greatly understates the fear they cause. BT now seems to have rejected the phrase, but is indecisive about the alternative. Its advisory leaflet, originally entitled *Nuisance Callers*, is now called *Offensive Callers*, but may soon be changed to *Menacing Callers*.

OFTEL's definition of 'unwelcome sexually suggestive or unwelcome sexually threatening calls' is probably the most useful. The important thing is that some definition is agreed on so that remedies can be developed.

Official action

BT representatives, the police, consumer groups and victims are now banding together to find a common approach to the problem. The aim is to consolidate efforts from all these sources in order to actually reduce the number of obscene calls. A national help-line is also being launched shortly.

As part of this initiative, a bureau dedicated to this purpose was established in June 1990 in Canterbury. Serving BT users in the region, this specialist customer care unit receives reports of obscene calls and advises on possible action. A computer will record complaints for the first time and cross-reference them in an attempt to identify persistent callers. The bureau hopes that lessons learned from this pilot project will be applied throughout the UK, possibly resulting in more bureaux in other areas. It is also possible that Victim Support, a national body which gives back-up to victims of crime such as burglary and rape, may also start to work with BT's bureau to offer more help to victims.

In the meantime, whilst the authorities are working out what they can do, your best approach is to take obscene calls as a serious issue but don't over-dramatize their impact on you. Remember that in nearly every case the caller is just another boring old obscene phone-caller trying their luck on someone they don't know. Getting angry only plays into their hands. Hang up calmly and, if they persist, go for help.

Chapter 115

How to set up and run a Neighbourhood Watch scheme

~

Your car has been broken in to and a house across the street has been burgled. It's time to act – form a Neighbourhood Watch scheme!

When you barely even know your own next-door neighbours, yet you've lived in the street for several years and you realize that you're all feeling like the isolated victims of petty crime, it's time to stop criticizing and start organizing.

Whether you live in a built-up urban area or a small rural village, crime is a distressing reality. You can easily feel powerless in the face of increasing burglary, vandalism, and theft. But it is easier in the long run to take strong positive action and set up a Neighbourhood Watch scheme.

Isolation breeds resignation

Why bother? Be realistic! The police cannot tackle the scale of present-day crime on their own. If you want a safe home, a safe neighbourhood, you must first take action yourself. It may seem hard to start with, especially in the face of apathy; and it is tempting not to bother. But if you don't, no one else will, and things will stay the same. You have the power to change all that. Form a scheme and the situation will improve. Not only will crime go down, but you and your neighbours will feel safer and happier. Plus you will actually get to meet, and form friendships with, the people who live beside you.

The power of neighbourhood watch

There are now over 74,000 Watch schemes in this country and crime rates fall dramatically in areas where they operate.

How do they do it? It is a collective way of fighting crime through the local community; that is, by the co-operation of you and your neighbours. It utilizes the special knowledge that you have of your own area. It works by:

~ Making vigilance the key.

~ Keeping a watch on neighbours' homes and the neighbourhood in general.

~ Reporting anything suspicious to the police so that criminal activity is highlighted and criminals deterred.
~ Securing your own home and property in accordance with police advice.
~ Marking your own property with your postcode using invisible markers.

Setting up the scheme

First, contact your local Crime Prevention Officer (CPO). He will give you advice, information and encouragement every step of the way. If in doubt at any time, then call your CPO. It is the CPO's job to help you; and he or she is experienced in the correct methods to pursue for success.

Now is the moment to go public! Canvass support in your street or block of flats. Knock on doors and talk to your neighbours. You will be amazed at the interest: they are as worried about crime as you are but did not know how to act. They will receive your initiative with open arms.

Arrange a meeting of as many neighbours as possible. This is not as difficult as it sounds! Contact your local council, library, and Citizens Advice Bureau. They will suggest a venue such as a hall – the police themselves may even provide one. Liaise with your local CPO, who will attend. You can then run off a simple, single information sheet like this example, photocopy it, and put it through every door in the street.

WORRIED ABOUT LOCAL CRIME?
INTERESTED IN FORMING A NEIGHBOURHOOD WATCH SCHEME?
WANT TO MEET OTHER INTERESTED PEOPLE?
DATE, TIME, VENUE OF MEETING
LOCAL POLICE IN ATTENDANCE

What next? At the meeting the CPO will explain all the details of the scheme, answer any questions and help your group elect one or more watch co-ordinators. They will act as a contact point between police and the scheme. It is not a difficult or particularly time-consuming role and you will already be finding the start of a community spirit which will give the scheme impetus. Each co-ordinator, will be able to obtain support from other existing watch co-ordinators, who will be able to provide the benefits of their own experience.

The benefits of professional support

In some districts an Area Watch co-ordinator will already exist who oversees all the existing watch schemes in that area. This can be of great help.

The CPO will provide posters, and property-marking stickers and Watch stickers to put in windows. He will also provide equipment with which you can security-mark your property. Police estimate that hundreds of thousands of pounds' worth of the stolen property which they recover could be returned if only it had been security-marked. Most importantly, the CPO will give you up-to-date information on crime in your area and how to prevent it.

At this stage the CPO will willingly visit any members to discuss specific aspects of their home security. You must also contact your local council to arrange for a Neighbourhood Watch plaque to be erected in the street.

Keeping the scheme running

Once the first meeting is over, the members need to act to maintain interest in the scheme. You can do this by:

~ STARTING A NEWSLETTER. Within the group there is bound to be someone with access to photocopying facilities. If not, use the library, Citizens Advice Bureau, or try the CPO. A regular information sheet will sustain interest. In it can be local news, meeting times, security advice, and the latest information on crime prevention.

~ FUND-RAISING. This is not always essential, but some schemes have arranged sponsors, such as security firms, to provide funds. Indeed, it is a good idea to try to organize a small but regular financial contribution from scheme members, even 50p per week, to cover any small costs which might be incurred.

~ ARRANGING SOCIAL MEETINGS. You will find that you get to know your neighbours and a new level of trust and interest in the neighbourhood will be built up. Arrange meetings fortnightly or monthly to sustain and generate co-operation. You can rotate the venue using your own homes.

~ ENCOURAGING RELATED INITIATIVES. For example, contacting the local council to get better street lighting and fight vandalism, or organizing special provision for houses left empty during holidays. You can also foster community relations through keeping an eye on the elderly or running a small disco for kids in the neighbourhood. There is a knock-on effect from these efforts in that they draw people closer together and help them realize that they are not alone with their problems. Crime is a shared, community problem, with a community solution.

Practical results

Once the scheme is under-way, you will immediately notice a change. People in the neighbourhood will be more acquainted with each other, there will be a friendlier atmosphere in the street and, most important of all, you will notice the number of local crimes falling.

For example, in one area of Bedford in 1984 there were seventy-eight burglaries. After a Neighbourhood Watch scheme had been running for three years, there were just six per year. In one rural area of Bristol, there was a 30 per cent drop in crime; while on a council estate in urban Gateshead, petty crime fell by 10 per cent during a period in which crime increased by 40 per cent in nearby areas without schemes. There is no reason why a positive, enthusiastically-run scheme in your neighbourhood should not have comparable results. It just needs you to sow the seeds.

CHAPTER 116
WHAT TO DO AFTER A BURGLARY

~

Your home has been violated. A stranger has handled your most intimate possessions; but don't despair, get going! You can do a lot to put things right.

You return home after a hard day, your mind still on work. It takes a second for you to notice that the front door is slightly open. Had you left it unlocked that morning? Surely not. And then you notice the damaged door frame. You've been burgled.

If this scene greets you, don't go in and run the risk of disturbing the burglars. Instead, go to a neighbour or a phone box and call the police.

What the police will do

When you do go inside, the golden rule is to touch nothing, not even the light switches, which may have useful fingerprints on them.

Once the police arrive, events take their own course to some extent. The uniformed police officer will ask you a number of questions.

~ What is missing?
~ Can you provide descriptions or photos of valuables?
~ What time did you leave that day?
~ When did you get home?

The officer will be looking for evidence: footprints or marks for example. If there are a number of clues they will contact the Scene of Crimes Officer, who will visit, but not necessarily on the same day, to take fingerprints and collect details of any other evidence.

Meanwhile, there are other practicalities with which the police also try to help. If a window or door has been made insecure, they normally have an emergency repairs help number for you to contact. Being used to this sort of emergency, the repairers are usually very quick to respond to your call, sometimes within the hour. Keep invoices from any work you have done in a safe place. You will need to send copies of them to your insurers later.

So, the police have left and you are boarded up securely, what then?

In terms of police involvement, once the burglary has been reported, they will write to you confirming the details of your report. This letter is important because on it will be a reference number. You will need to quote this on your insurance claims form, so keep it in a safe place along with the invoices from the emergency repairs. They will also give you a police contact number for you to use in case you remember something at a later date. In the panic and confusion of the moment you can easily overlook things and you don't think to check on less important or less obvious items.

If your belongings are recovered they will obviously contact you again, as they will if they arrest someone. A lot of people worry about whether they will have to face the burglar in court to give evidence or whether it is up to them to bring a prosecution. Be assured that it is not up to you to prosecute and neither will you have to appear in court unless it goes to the Crown Court and the burglar makes a plea of not guilty. Most burglaries are dealt with at magistrate level and will not involve you at all. However, the police will keep you informed and if someone is prosecuted they will write to you and keep you in the picture, which is reassuring to know.

In fact, reassurance is an important part of the police role and you can take some comfort from seeing that they do address themselves to the wider issues surrounding crimes of this kind.

Support for the victim

To back them up there is also the well-established Victim Support Group scheme. They take over from the police at this point, on the personal side.

The police inform the Support Group about burglaries and other local crimes. Someone from the Support Group will contact you to help you through the sometimes very difficult period after the burglary. On the practical side they can help you fill in insurance and DSS compensation forms as well as helping if you experience any problems liaising with the police.

The Victim Support Group can also play an invaluable role by helping you deal with some very difficult feelings which you may experience as you face the emotional impact of a burglary. Don't be surprised at the anger you feel, or the discomfort at having had your privacy invaded. Sleeplessness is also a common problem afterwards. All these feelings are common, and the Victim Support Group can help you through this difficult time.

If the Support Group does not contact you, but you feel you would like some support or to talk to someone, do give them a ring. Their number is in the telephone book and they are there to help, especially in large cities where vital neighbourly support can be sadly lacking. See the Help section for more details.

Insurance

You should contact your insurance company as soon as possible. Telephone them, explain what has happened and they will send you a claim form to complete. This is where you need that reference number on the letter which the police will have sent you confirming the details of the burglary. If for some reason you do not have the letter, simply phone the police station and they will give you the reference number again.

Prevention

Learning from experience can be painful and whilst the police are sensitive and supportive to burglary victims, it would be better to safeguard your home and minimize the risk of a burglary happening to you, perhaps for the second time. So what preventive measures can you take?

~ SECURITY. Contact your local police station and ask for the Crime Prevention Officer. They will come to your home, assess the risks and advise you on what practical precautions to take. They can put you in touch with reliable builders and specify what sort of locks and doors you need. Helpful leaflets are also available from them.

~ NEIGHBOURHOOD WATCH SCHEME. Find out from your local police station if there is one in your area. Join it. If there isn't one, speak to them about starting one (see chapter 115).

~ INSURANCE. Re-assess your insurance cover. If you are under-insured the company may not settle the claim in full. If in doubt, increase it. Check that your policy keeps your cover in line with inflation and if it doesn't, ask for one which does.

~ BELONGINGS. List all makes and serial numbers now. Security markers are also available from hardware shops, too. If in doubt about jewellery or ornaments which may be valuable, have them valued and if necessary insure them separately. It is also a good idea to photograph them – have you ever tried to describe that garish, but valuable, vase which Aunt Alice left you?

So being burgled can cost you a lot of time, money and emotion. No matter how it strikes you, make sure you learn from your experience and act to prevent it happening again.

CHAPTER 117
THE TWELVE VITAL RULES OF FIRE SAFETY

~

Over 7,700 people died or were seriously injured in domestic fires last year. But you and your family *can* be safe from fire. Read these vital rules of fire safety and be prepared.

Rule 1 Prevention is better than cure

Wherever you are, make it second nature to automatically check for fire exits or escape routes. If you are in a public place of entertainment or leisure, whether pub or art gallery, theatre or shopping centre, look for that vital escape route from fire. If there is none available, or if it is unsuitable because it is locked or blocked then take the following action.

~ Inform the manager that fire regulations are being breached.

~ Leave the building.

~ Let your local fire officer know – ring the number in your directory.

The same goes for your place of work, which should also have formal procedures in case of fire; and at home, where you should ensure you have a quick, easy route out in case of fire.

Rule 2 Get a smoke alarm

There's no fire without smoke – and smoke and fumes from burning material can be more deadly than flames. Smoke alarms are the first line of defence against fire. They cost only £10-15 each: a value-for-money investment in your family's future that will give that vital extra few minutes you need in the event of fire.

Buy those that conform to British Standards Institution (BSI) specification and read the installation instructions carefully. See the Help section for more details.

Rule 3 Protect children

Never leave children on their own in the house – they are twice as likely to be involved in a fire as an adult. Keep them away from matches and cookers. Fix guards around heaters and fires. Keep toys well away from heaters; and remember, some model-making glues are highly flammable.

Rule 4 Don't be a do-it-yourself fire-raiser

DIY enthusiasts should be particularly vigilant about fire. You don't have to drill through hidden power cables to set yourself alight. Straightforward DIY methods and materials involve real fire risks.

~ Use non-flammable materials where possible.

~ Store petrol, paraffin, paint, etc., in safe, labelled, screwtop containers; away from the house if possible.

~ Never use gloss or oil-based paint on polystyrene tiles. They cause fire to spread rapidly.

~ When wiring, never join pieces of flex: use purpose-built connectors. Always replace damaged or worn flex and check fuses and wiring on plugs and sockets. If in doubt, call a professional. Take particular care with heating and lighting in your workshop.

Rule 5 Don't fry tonight

Be extra careful when frying. Kitchens are a real danger area and frying, in particular, is the commonest way fires start in the home – over 15,000 a year.

~ Never overheat oil so that it smokes, and take care it doesn't slop over on to the cooker.

~ Do not overfill the pan with oil or food. Never leave it unattended.
~ Dry wet chips before dropping them into the oil.
~ If the pan bursts into flames: turn off the heat, put a damp cloth or tight lid over it to smother the flames, leave the pan to cool and call the fire brigade if you still feel there's a danger.

Rule 6 **Heat your home without burning it down!**

Get home heating regularly maintained. All fires for heating the home need air, so check that yours are getting their fair share. All fires let off dangerous fumes, so check that waste gases are being removed from the house correctly.

All heaters require expert installation and regular maintenance if they are not to become dangerous, either by allowing the build-up of poisonous fumes or burning inefficiently and dangerously. See the Help section for more details.

Rule 7 **Smoking can seriously damage your house!**

Many fires are caused by cigarettes, matches or lighters setting fire to upholstery or bedding. Smokers should use ashtrays – those that cannot be knocked over or on to something such as a waste-paper basket. Hot ash will easily cause a fire if it falls on to your clothes or furniture. Never leave a cigarette burning unattended, even in an ashtray; and never smoke in bed.

Despite changes in the law, there remains a great deal of upholstered furniture which is not flame resistant let alone flame retardant. Make sure your furniture meets the BSI specifications.

Rule 8 **Blanket warning!**

Never use an electric blanket while you are actually in the bed or if the blanket is damp. Safety experts recommend electric blankets are checked at least every two to three years. You should also check it often yourself for signs of wear.

Rule 9 **For high-rise dwellers**

Take special care if you live in a high-rise flat. If fire breaks out, do the following:
~ Leave the room immediately and close the door.
~ Alert everyone else in the flat.
~ Leave the flat; and when everyone's out, shut the door.
~ Call the fire brigade.
~ Leave the building by the stairs, *not* the lift.

If it's a neighbour's flat, follow the same rules. Remember, the hall of your flat and the stairs of the building are the way out – if you've been obstructing these escape routes with prams, bikes, boxes, clothes-horses, etc., it could cost you your life.

Rule 10 **Help the aged**

Keep an eye on the old and the sick. More than half the deaths from fire are of people over sixty. Keep an eye on the frail and elderly to ensure they are taking precautions against fire.

Smoke alarms are especially important for elderly people. Heaters should be secured, or placed where they cannot be tripped over. Make sure they are aware of electric blanket safeguards and other potential dangers such as the drying of clothes on heaters. See the Help section for useful documentation.

Rule 11 **It *can* happen to you**

Always assume that one day, probably when you least expect it, it will happen to you. And when it does, follow these rules:

~ Do not panic. Keep calm: you know what to do and this will quickly be apparent to others, who will then follow your example.
~ Keep all internal doors closed. They will contain the fire.
~ Ensure everyone leaves the house.
~ Phone 999 for the fire brigade. Double-check the address and wait outside till they arrive.
If you get trapped inside:
~ Go to a room unaffected by fire, at the front of the building if possible.
~ Shut yourself in.
~ Block the airspace under the door. Use cushions, curtains, clothing – anything.
~ Open the window and attract attention.
~ Get down low if the room fills with smoke.
If no help comes and the room gets too hot or smoke-filled to stay, take the following action.
~ Drop cushions and bedding out of the window to break your fall.
~ If you have to break the window, remove any shards from the lower sill and cover it with soft material such as blankets.
~ Lower yourself feet-first from the window and hang by your arms before dropping. This substantially reduces the distance you fall.

Rule 12 **Last priority – fight the fire**

With any home fire, the first priority is to get everyone out and to call the fire brigade. Only then attempt to fight it and only if it's in its first stages. The two main options are:
~ fire extinguishers
~ fire blankets
Buy only BSI endorsed equipment. No extinguisher is suitable for all fires. For general protection, the fire brigade recommend a halon 1211 (BCF), a multi-purpose dry powder, an AFFF or a water-type extinguisher positioned in the hall.

Each kind of extinguisher works best on a specific kind of fire, so consult the supplier or directions to get to know their limitations. You will also need to familiarize yourself with their use and know where best to fix them. An extinguisher should also be placed in your car, garage and shed.

Remember, never use an extinguisher on a blazing chip-pan; and never use a water-based extinguisher on an electrical fire. If in doubt about fire extinguishers, ask the fire brigade for advice.

Keep a fire blanket in the kitchen. Again, buy only a BSI approved type. They are especially useful for smothering chip-pan fires and for wrapping up a person whose clothes are burning. Read all the instructions carefully.

CHAPTER 118
LIVING IN THE AGE OF THE SMART HOME

~

Ten years into the next millennium, you wake up one morning and reflect on your success. It was less than twenty years ago that you were reading about the home of the future in a book called *Superliving!* – now, you own just such a 'smart' home that the book described!

Of course, you're in the minority, so far. The Smart House is still very expensive, and on the leading edge of technology. But in another decade or so, most people will be able to afford the sort of house you live in today.

The morning sun drifts in through the smart shutters, which know exactly how much light you like in the room at this time of day and adjust accordingly. The gently encouraging strains of Vivaldi woke you up, now the aroma of coffee and toast hits your nostrils and you're ready for another day's excitement.

Rather than you doing the housework, wouldn't it be nice if the house worked? One day it will – probably, sooner than you think. In this essay, we tell you what your *next* house will be like. It's not fiction – it's future-fact. Everything which follows is in development now. Have a nice day!

The brains about the house

Wherever you are, SERVANT (that's Sensing, Emitting, Remotely Vigilant And Neural Totality) constantly monitors you and your actions. Servant isn't the old-fashioned idea of a mad scientist's robot. Instead, Servant is the brains and heart of your Smart Home. It uses voice-recognition technology to listen to you, and then executes your direct instructions ('turn on the lights', 'dinner at eight', and so on).

But it does more than just that. It watches you and learns from you, so that it can actually *anticipate* your actions. If the boss calls and you've got a hangover, Servant knows you don't want to speak to her. If you're out and one of your favourite TV programmes is on (Servant knows what you like without asking, because it studies and learns from your viewing habits), it'll videotape it just in case you want to see it later.

Similarly, Servant scans the world's newswires overnight and compiles and prints your individual edition of the morning's newspaper, with just the articles it knows you like to read.

There are still a few minutes available before you have to get up, so you turn to your bed partner with a glint in your eye. 'Notch down', you mutter to Servant, who obediently ceases to monitor you visually. Some people like to be watched by their Servants while they make love, but you're pretty old-fashioned about this sort of thing. Servant will still monitor and control life support systems (in this sense, it can't ever be turned off) and will automatically notch up again to full surveillance level in thirty minutes. Servant knows from past experience that your sexual bouts are usually over in seventeen minutes, in any case. And at your age, it's reassuring to know that full resuscitation procedures are instantly available should the exertion prove a trifle too much for you.

Since you now work in higher management (that brief flirtation with anarcho-syndicalist self-sufficiency on a commune in 2003 didn't work out), you have to leave home every day, as opposed to those who usually stay at home and telecommute.

Your car is linked through radio-telemetry both to Servant at home and to your office network, and data freely flows between the three nodes. Low-level data is transparently exchanged without your involvement, so your car's speed and location is constantly transmitted to your office and home, so that they both know when to expect you.

High-level data transmission, however, requires your participation or consent. Just such a situation occurs on your way to work this morning. The office calls and wants to re-arrange a meeting for later in the evening. Because Servant knows you hate to stay late at the office, it alerts you to a scheduling conflict. What's really happened is that Servant has invented a notional appointment for you to use as an excuse. Basically, your home computer is offering to lie for you. 'Consent', you say. And with no guilty conscience to trouble it, Servant instantly transmits a stream of deceitful data to your office, and the meeting is cancelled.

And so begins another perfect day.

From fiction to fact

All the above is based on existing science and technology – there is no element of science fiction in it. The one assumption it makes – and it is a fair one – is that as computing power becomes cheaper and faster, existing technologies will be centralized and controlled by a neural network resembling a thinking brain – in this case, Servant. It is the next logical step in home design.

Your Smart Home will practically run itself for you. It will be an intelligent creature with a computer-run central nervous system that you will be able to program, very simply, to cater for you and your family's needs and living requirements.

Automatic reception committee

Driving home, you will be able to signal your home to run your bath or water your plants; and you will know when your kids get in from school. When you are at home, adjustments to heat, humidity and ventilation will be made for you; whilst your TV will be a thin, flat screen in the wall that looks like a large picture. So if you're bored with regular channels you can switch to a high-quality, 'living' projection of your favourite mountain scene complete with swaying trees, tinkling brook and sympathetic sound track. Or maybe you'd like to watch a real-time picture of Earth's swirling weather systems from a satellite in orbit? Just give the word . . .

You will even be able to have your room colour and ambience change automatically to suit your mood: your voice tone, speed of movement, and metabolism will all reveal clues about your state of mind, and a suitably corrective colour and decor change will be made automatically.

The Smart Home of the future will be bigger and fancier; it will contain one enormous room, like an artisan's warehouse, where family and friends can gather together, eat, inform and socialize. It will also have a host of specific function rooms 'leaking' off the main room; a room for the jacuzzi (every home will have one), to dress in, and to relax in – and your home office. The emphasis, post-AIDS, will be squarely on the nuclear family.

Inter-communication

Beneath the high-tech exterior, where a voice command turns on your personal CD photo album or starts your dinner cooking, will be a sophisticated, integrated system of wiring where one single conduit carries electrical power and communications links together with gas and water pipes. This will save installation costs and make maintenance access simpler and more effective.

Every service you want will be available at every outlet in the house; no more power 'blind spots' or trailing wires. This integrated scheme, run by microchip, will be safer, provide total entertainment and comfort, and cocoon your Smart Home in a protective web of security so that you and your family can sleep safe from the hostile world outside. And by 2010, it *is* a hostile world.

Even your appliances will have a degree of intelligence. Your cooker, fridge, video, etc., will be able to communicate electronically with each other and with the outside world. So if a component goes wrong, the appliance itself will know and will 'buzz' the relevant repair service into action; and any potential danger, such as your child jabbing a finger into an electric socket, will be by-passed by an automatic switch off.

Your servant's servant

A dream or a nightmare? It depends on you. "Lo! Men have become the tools of their tools," said Henry David Thoreau in the middle of the 19th century, but he might have been talking about the Smart Home of the future.

The downside of hi-tech living is subtle but undeniable. First of all, you lose touch with the outside world. You rely on rigorously processed channels of data to view and shape your opinion of the greater world beyond your own domestic cocoon. You begin relating more to machines than to other people, and in the process, lose touch with that common streak of humanity which ultimately unites us all. Life becomes dull, uniform, predictable. Creativity and inspiration are asphyxiated by technological exactitude. You become the servant of your Servant.

Bio-smart housing

Thus enters the bio-organic housing unit: the other hi-tech approach, which seeks to blend science with a human approach to living. Again, the basics of bio-smart housing are real and here today.

The very essence of the new millennium conjures up an era of peace and harmony. In a world fighting energy crisis, overpopulation, war, famine and declining natural habitats, a more radical, more valid, future construct is one of smaller living units, decreased materialism and a simpler, more collective lifestyle. Illusory? Not a bit. The Kreuzberg district of unified Berlin serves as a glowing beacon for an alternative smart, green-crusading, 21st-century Man. Out of the ashes of derelict, tenement housing has come a model for efficient energy generation, refuse and water re-cycling, and a 'greening' of the detritus of urban neglect.

Will your future home mirror startling developments there? The bio-organic home, along with its cosy nexus of neighbouring living cells, will be virtually self-sufficient in terms of power and water. Electricity will come from solar roofing panels, windmills and a common, on-site, generator powered by gas at 45 per cent greater efficiency than fossil fuels and which, being close to usage, will save a further 15 per cent on costs. Further cost reductions are made by more evenly spread communal usage and off-peak production.

Built-in recycling

Added power-savers like thermal entrance locks (mini-conservatories) to homes and window shutters for winter will be commonplace in the so-called energy 'enveloping' of your home. As the greenhouse effect bites, increasingly precious water is re-cycled by being differentiated into greywater (slightly dirty – from baths, etc.) and blackwater from kitchen and toilet. With water-saving consciousness raised, with rain collection and greywater re-cycled for toilet flushing and plant watering, water consumption will be halved.

Your bio-smart house may have a flat, green roof; a lawned terrace acting as an extra space for growing organic vegetables, an additional recreation area and a kindergarten. The grassed top conserves energy too. For, as with below-ground living, the benefits of earth 'berming', or sheltering with a layer of soil, are more equitable temperatures in winter and summer (see chapter 100). Beneath the green roof will be a green room tailored to the natural habitat of your own choice; a sky-lit, sun-powered tropical room, with exotic butterflies winging between growing peaches, chilis and avocados. Hopefully not a surrogate for long-gone Amazon forests.

The bio-smart house itself will be composed of eco-friendly materials; paints will be mineral-based; insulation, free of suspect rock wool; and, generally, materials will have low environmental-production costs.

No fast-talking, high-tech home designers here. Home building and design will be devolved from planners and specialist architects to *you* and your neighbours. You will participate fully in the building process from start to finish; with concern over environmental impact top of the priority list. The collective genesis of homes will generate greater cooperation at later stages when the houses are completed. Problems of social isolation and vandalism will be reduced. Homes will be less ego-centred with people 'popping' into each other's houses and sharing equipment and experiences. This will engender less emphasis on unique furnishings and keeping-up-with-the-Joneses mentality, while furniture will be simpler and more functional.

So, with the age of the Smart Home but an eye-blink away, you are in for a high-tech heaven or an eco-Eden, according to which school of thought takes your fancy. Either way, your home in the next millennium will be an interesting proposition. Have a nice day.

Book Four

SUPERYOU!

WHEN THINGS GO WRONG: COPING WITH ADVERSITY

CHAPTER 119
SOME THOUGHTS ON DEATH AND DYING

~

"This is my death; and it will profit me to understand it." Anne Sexton

What, you may wonder, is an article on death and dying doing in a book called *Superliving!?* There are three important reasons why you shouldn't skip this section:

~ Death has replaced sex as the last great taboo of our Western society. Today, most of us are still living in the 'dark ages' as far as our knowledge of death and dying is concerned. Even the practical aspects are still clouded in a great deal of mystery for many people. This ignorance is profoundly unhealthy: it creates fear, and it does nothing to help us to prepare for an event which, much as we try to deny it, is an inevitable and natural part of our lives.

~ It is important to die well. From practical matters such as funeral arrangements, to finding personal ways of coping with our own mortality, death is an experience for which it is necessary to prepare. The unprepared do not die well, and there are no second chances.

~ Coming to terms with death allows you to come to terms with life. "Once you accept your own death, all of a sudden you are free to live," says Saul Alinsky. If you can face death happily in life, then you will live to die happily.

Other societies are much better at preparing people for death than we are. In the West, we often sanitize death by using euphemisms or medical jargon. We speak of 'falling asleep', 'meeting one's maker', or being at 'final rest'. Doctors, traditionally taught to regard the death of a patient as a failure, frequently project their sense of defeat on to the patient. "My mother had been diagnosed as having terminal cancer," says David, a 25-year-old advertising executive. "At that stage, the doctors simply didn't want to know any more. She was treated as if she had been a failure: she had failed them and their medicine. She seemed to be an embarrassment for them. They just wanted her to go away and die as quickly as possible, as quietly as possible, without any fuss. They couldn't bear to be reminded that they'd failed."

But dying is not a failure, although some doctors still treat it as such. In fact, it is as much a natural part of life as birth. It is a completion, a closing of the circle. There are, we suggest, four major reasons why our society fears death so much. Let's consider them:

~ THE FEAR OF PAIN. Terminal illnesses can sometimes bring suffering, and it is common for people to be frightened of the pain involved, and to worry about their capacity to bear it.

~ THE FEAR OF LOSS. Being separated from loved ones, and the loss of one's faculties, is a source of anxiety for many.

~ THE FEAR OF MEANINGLESSNESS. "What use has my life been?" is a common reaction, coupled with the fear of having been 'a failure'.

~ THE FEAR OF THE UNKNOWN. What happens after death? Is there a heaven, a hell, or just eternal extinction? The unknown has always been a fundamental cause of great apprehension.

The way to deal with fear

If you can resolve your fear of dying, then you will have indeed conquered death's sting. And where does fear originate from, in any case? The answer is that fear, like worry, comes not from what we know, but from what we *don't* know.

It is a paradox that the less we know about something, the more likely we are to fear it. And the more we fear something, the more we try to avoid it. Death – being unknown to most of us – is an object of deep fear. And because it is feared, we avoid knowing it. And so on, and so on . . .

Clearly, if we are to conquer our fear of death, then we need to break into this vicious circle of ignorance. So consider these four fears again, in the light of the information which follows.

Conquering pain

Books, television dramas and films give us the often-repeated message that dying is an agonizing, excruciating business. Today, this is simply not true. One of the glories of orthodox medicine is its ability – in the right hands – to provide *total* relief from pain and suffering. "Things were going very badly when my mother was finally admitted to a hospice," says David. "Her pain was impossible to describe. She had been in intense distress for days. It was very difficult for me to watch, because there seemed to be nothing that I could do. Her GP was worse than useless. The painkillers he prescribed were simply not working. He either wouldn't, or couldn't, help her any more. Eventually, I bought a crate of whisky and gave her huge glasses of it, to try and stop her suffering. We were both at our wits' end, utterly desperate. On Sunday, I had to call the doctor again, and instead of the usual GP, his locum arrived. He took one look at her, and arranged for her to be admitted to a hospice within the hour. Thank God he did. At the hospice, things couldn't have been more different. They knew how to control her pain, and did it immediately. The effect was miraculous, the pain stopped, and she came home again after a few days. Then we had a wonderful six weeks together, talking, going out for day-trips, sorting things out between us. When she died, it was without pain, without fear, and very peacefully. But I bitterly regret that she had to suffer so much initially – I still feel angry that her doctor was so thoroughly incompetent."

We repeat – there is no *need* for anyone to suffer pain, or the fear of pain. The doctors and medical staff at hospices are *the* experts in relieving pain. They can help *everyone*.

Conquering loss

When life is short, it suddenly becomes precious beyond words. The idea of abandoning life and the living fills us with dread. The finality of extinction seems terrifying.

But when you think about the precise nature of this fear, you will realize that what we really fear most is the incompleteness of our own lives – the opportunities missed, the lost chances never to return. All through our lives, we procrastinate and make excuses to ourselves, using the rationalization that "there will always be another day". Suddenly, our time is up, and there is no 'other day' when we can make amends for our past behaviour, or to keep those postponed promises, to ourselves or others.

There are two useful responses to this feeling. The first is to live life fully – whether it be six more weeks or sixty more years. "The more complete one's life is, the more one's creative capacities are fulfilled, the less one fears death," says Lisl Marburg Goodman. "Death is not the greatest loss in life," believes prize-winning writer Norman Cousins. "The greatest loss is what dies inside us while we live."

Some fortunate people quickly learn this lesson through a close shave with death. "What has changed about me," says black supermodel Iman, after suffering a horrific car crash, "is that I have no fear any more of anything. I believe that we control our destiny so much, so much that what we do in life is the result we get. If we do wrong, we get wrong. If you do good, then good will come to you. I'm finally very peaceful with myself."

"You start looking at life anew," says musician and composer Quincy Jones, who in 1974 survived an aneurysm and two subsequent brain operations, "and loving it second by second, because you finally realize how fragile it is. Life and death – now I know what a real fine line there is between the two."[536]

"For the first time, I think I actually am savoring life," said Senator Richard L. Neuberger, when the cancer that later took his life was first diagnosed. "I have a new appreciation of things I once took for granted – eating lunch with a friend, scratching my cat Muffet's ears and listening for his purrs, the company of my wife, reading a book or magazine in the quiet of my bed lamp at night, raiding the refrigerator for a glass of orange juice or a slice of toast."

The clear lesson is to make the most of the here and now. That is all that really exists – the past doesn't, and neither does the future. Enjoy what is. Don't waste your priceless time anguishing about yesterday, or fretting about tomorrow. Live today, for today, and you will be too busy to bother with silly sorrows.

Now think about the roller-coaster at the fairground. If you've ever taken a ride on one, you will be familiar with the sensations – a long, slow haul up to the top of the steep incline, during which the apprehension and panic mounts. Then at the top, that stomach-churning moment when you flip over the crest, and career down the other side at what seems like a hundred miles an hour! Everyone screams, and everyone has white knuckles – yet we pay for the privilege of being scared out of our wits. Why?

The answer is that fear and joy are human emotions which are actually very closely related. They are strange bedfellows, it is true, but in our minds they are two sides of the same feeling – the one accentuates the other. Curious as it may seem initially, the only real difference between a terrifying roller-coaster ride and dying is that we *believe* that there is life after the roller-coaster. About dying, we are not so sure.

Actually, we should be. Just as there are millions of people who have taken roller-coaster rides and lived to tell the tale, so there are now millions of people who have passed through the shadow of death, and returned to tell us about it.

Millions? Yes, certainly. In 1981, a survey conducted by the Gallup Organization found that 15 per cent of American adults had had a near-death experience. There are more than one hundred support groups that exist in order to help people to better understand these events, as well as a professional journal and a quarterly newsletter (details in the Help section). But what is a near-death experience like?

Let the distinguished philosopher (and fervent atheist) A. J. Ayer tell us. He had just been admitted to hospital, suffering from a severe case of pneumonia. After several anxious days, everyone finally believed that he was on the mend. Then, disaster struck, in a most peculiar way:

"I am particularly fond of smoked salmon," he wrote. "One evening, I carelessly tossed a slice of it into my throat. It went down the wrong way and almost immediately the graph recording my heartbeats plummeted. The ward sister rushed to the rescue, but she was unable to prevent my heart from stopping."

Ayer, who 'died' for four minutes, then underwent a near-death experience which, already familiar to millions of others, served radically to change his established ideas about death being the ultimate extinction.

"I was confronted by a red light," he wrote, "exceedingly bright, and also very painful even when I turned away from it. I was aware that this light was responsible for the government of the universe."

Such experiences of bright lights, both red and white, are very common. In Ayer's case, he also had the strong feeling that "the laws of nature had ceased to function as they should. I felt that it was up to me to put things right".

Ayer returned from the dead, far less certain that death is the end of everything, but still an ardent atheist. "A prevalent fallacy," he wrote, "is the assumption that a proof of an after-life would also be a proof of the existence of a deity. This is far from being the case. If, as I hold, there is no good reason to believe that a god either created or presides over this world, there is equally no good reason to believe that a god created or presides over the next world."[537]

It seems, then, that whether or not you are a religious person, there is strong empirical evidence for life after death. This is confirmed by research undertaken by Kenneth Ring, a University of Connecticut psychologist, who conducted scientifically structured interviews with 102 people who had undergone near-death experiences. His work conclusively showed that belief in religion was *completely unrelated* to whether a person had a near-death experience or not. Furthermore, his evidence clearly demonstrated that near-death experiences are positive, personality-transforming experiences for those who have them.[538]

An analysis of near-death experiences reveals the following common experiences:

- being out of the body (and being able accurately to see and hear doctors while they operate – even blind people have reported this)
- entering darkness
- being in a tunnel
- seeing a brilliant light
- visions of dead relatives
- reaching a heavenly border
- deciding to return to one's body
- peaceful and positive emotions of love and compassion

To put it simply, the evidence is now overwhelming that death is *not* the end. There *is* something beyond the roller-coaster ride we call 'life'. Whether or not you believe in an established religion, you can be certain that there is a very exciting journey ahead of you after your earthly death. As another survivor of a near-death experience puts it:

"Death is just a beginning – it's beautiful. There's light – it's love. If you really love somebody, you've got to be happy for where they're going. It's an adventure and they're not alone. You see, we're afraid of somebody being alone. But they're not alone . . . It's just as though you're being held in a cradle of love, and just being carried to the most beautiful, magical story God could ever create."[539]

To summarize – the fear of loss can be overcome by living your life in the here-and-now, and when the time comes to depart, by realizing that the end of one journey is the beginning of another, far greater one . . .

Conquering meaninglessness

Alienation is a common malaise of our time. Many of us feel that our lives lack essential meaning, and when we approach death, feel that our time has been wasted to no purpose. This is, of course, very sad.

There is one fundamental course of action to conquer this malign feeling which can sap us of life even as we breathe.

It is, simply, to *give* your life meaning and purpose – now, before it's too late. People who have only ever thought about themselves, whose only goal in life has been to amass as much wealth and as many possessions for themselves as possible, are probably in for something of a shock. That there is a higher purpose to life, other than personal cupidity, is a realization which dawns somewhat harshly. A life devoted solely to material gain (society's yardstick of success) is indeed a pathetic waste of human and spiritual potential. Materially rich, and in every other way impoverished.

Right now, write your own obituary. It will help you to assess your own life and values. In giving notice of your own death, you may find you are more aware of its potential reality. If you feel frustrated at reading the contents of this self-written tribute, you can then look at the things you want to change in your life before it really is too late.

So how do you give meaning to your life? The answer lies in one simple word – *service*. By rendering service to our friends, our family and even to our enemies, we give our life meaning. When we stop all our selfishness, when we start thinking about others – our family, our neighbourhood, our city, our country, even our beleaguered planet – then we start to make a difference, and we become significant in ourselves.

Here's another lesson. Spend one hour as if it were your last. Assume all legal and financial matters are already taken care of. You can lie down in the dark and be reflective, or walk around considering what you would do. Write down people you would like to talk to, and things you would like to say. This can bring up important clues as to how you might change the way you behave at present. Think, too, about how you feel and what you want. Then go one step further and imagine your funeral. Who is there? Have some people failed to arrive? How do you feel about this?

"I expect to pass through life but once," wrote William Penn in the seventeenth century. "If therefore, there be any kindness I can show, or any good thing I can do to any fellow being, let me do it now, and not defer or neglect it, as I shall not pass this way again."

When people are serving, life is no longer meaningless.

Conquering the unknown

We have already considered how we may conquer our fear of loss of life by knowing for certain that what we call 'death' is the natural beginning of another journey. Those who have been to the brink and returned have told us this. But what lies beyond that bright light?

It is unknown; uncharted territory, the domain where faith takes over from reason. If you have faith – either inspired by religious belief or by your own innermost convictions – then you must let it be your guide.

Faith is a much misunderstood word. It is often used very loosely, by those who either simply don't understand it, or who are too spiritually poor to manifest any themselves. Faith is not a blind, irrational belief in religious 'fairy tales'. Neither is it unscientific, because it starts where science stops. Nor is it blind devotion to the dogmas of one particular religion (although people often say 'faith' when they actually mean 'religion' – as in 'what faith are you?,' as though faith came in different brands).

Faith is none of these things. So what is it? Sir Arthur Conan Doyle put it very simply, like this: "It is not that I think or believe, but that I *know*."

Faith is what you *know* inside you. For some, it may be called 'intuition'. For others, it is that still, small voice inside which helps us and guides us, if we are quiet enough to listen to it.

In today's world, there is little encouragement to develop personal faith. The reason for this is all too clear. Despite what they may say about the 'importance of the individual', Western consumer societies actually place very little value upon the growth and empowerment of the whole human being.

Our society is based on the concept of dividing people into opposing groups of producers and consumers. For example, one group of people produces food, while another, far larger group consumes it. The same concept applies to other products and services. One group of people specializes in health care, while another group consumes it. One group of people specializes in governing us, while the rest of us more or less do what we're told.

The opportunity for the individual to become a fully-grown, well-rounded person is forbidden almost from birth. Today, we must all be specialists. Unfortunately, an over-specialization in one field results in complete ignorance of others. How many city-dwellers, for example, could manage to feed themselves if all the supermarkets were suddenly removed?

The same concept applies to your personal faith. Just as we allow others to produce food for our bodies, so we allow others to cultivate our faith and our beliefs. However, faith acquired in this way is not real faith at all. It is merely learnt – not truly felt. It comes from the exterior world, not the reality inside you.

For many, the difference between genuine personal faith and society's synthetic substitute only becomes apparent when they are near to death. This is because the counterfeit version cannot survive without constant external help. Since it does not come from within, it has no roots inside you, and will quickly perish when you are, finally, alone with yourself. At that time, people speak in terror of 'losing their faith'. In reality, they never had any real faith to lose.

Take time now to be quiet and listen to the voice inside you. It will guide you through the unknown, if you let it, and never fails.

Proof of other lives

Many of the world's religions incorporate aspects of reincarnation into their belief structures. Knowing for certain that this is not your only life – not your first, nor your last – can also ease the burden of venturing into the unexplored.

Science sneers at the concept of reincarnation, because that is the standard reaction of many humans when they encounter a problem or theory which they cannot readily understand or explain. But that does not mean that the concept is not valid.

Surveys show that about a quarter of the population believe in reincarnation.[540] It is also likely that even more people feel there's 'something in it', but are too shy to reveal it to an interviewer. This, in itself, is not proof of reincarnation, but it certainly supports the idea that many of us instinctively suspect that we may have been here before.

More proof is furnished by the process called past-life regression. In it, you are hypnotized, and guided back to what appear to be memories of previous existences. Here is a dramatic transcript of one such regression:

"I see a fuselage and an airstrip . . . The troop has been destroyed . . . I see buildings destroyed . . . The land is torn up from bombings . . . There are many wounded people."

"Do you have a name?" asks the hypnotist.

"I hear the name Eric . . . Eric . . . There are wings on the jacket. I'm a pilot . . . some type of pilot."

"You fly the airplanes?"

"Yes, I have to . . . I'm in service to fly . . . It is a time of unrest. There's a problem deep in the German government, the political structure. Too many people want to move in too many directions. It will eventually tear us apart . . . But I must fight for my country."

"Go ahead in time to the next flight," instructs the hypnotist.

"There is no next flight . . . I'm running away from the fire. My plane's being torn apart by the fire."

"Do you survive this?"

"Nobody survives . . . Nobody survives a war. I'm dying. Blood! Blood is everywhere! I have pain in my chest. I've been hit in my chest . . . and my leg . . . and my neck. It's so much pain . . . I'm floating . . . away from my body. I have no body. I am in spirit again."[541]

This transcript comes from a series of regressions started in 1980 by psychiatrist Brian Weiss, head of the psychiatry department at Mount Sinai Medical Center in Miami Beach. At the time, he was treating a patient called Catherine, a 27-year-old woman plagued by anxiety, depression and phobias. In an attempt to help her remember repressed childhood traumas (and so resolve them), Weiss turned to hypnosis. What happened from then onwards astonished the previously sceptical scientist.

"For 18 months I used conventional methods of therapy to help her overcome her symptoms," wrote Weiss in his book *Many Lives, Many Masters*.[542] "When nothing seemed to work, I tried hypnosis. In a series of trance states, Catherine recalled 'past-life' memories that proved to be causative factors of her symptoms . . . In a few months, her symptoms disappeared, and she resumed her life, happier and more at peace than ever before."

In the process, Catherine described dozens of previous existences, from Spanish prostitute to German fighter pilot, from Greek student to a young woman who drowned with her baby in a flood in 1863 BC.

"Nothing in my background had prepared me for this," said psychiatrist Weiss. "I do not have any scientific explanation for what happened."

This is by no means the only case of past-life regression. It seems, in fact, that most people can experience memories of previous existences under hypnosis.

What is particularly impressive is the small amount of scientific work which has so far been published in this area. In one study, 230 subjects participated in a hypnotic regression workshop, and were then requested to complete questionnaires. "The possibility that individual consciousnesses existed before birth, reasons for birth in this lifetime, possible past life ties with others in this life now, and the experience of being born were investigated," wrote the researchers. "Almost all the subjects reported experiencing pleasant sensations in the between lives period before birth, and were in no hurry to join another body. Ninety-four per cent of subjects went through a process of decision-making regarding the lifetime to be. Seventy-four per cent of subjects freely chose to be born, though only 30 per cent expressed any great expectations or enjoyment or accomplishment."[543]

Another paper describes how a researcher tried to disprove the past-life experiences of a woman who, under hypnosis, revealed that she had lived in 16th-century Spain. "In an effort to rid the subject of her 'obsession,'" wrote the researcher, "the author attempted to discount the reality of the past life by finding errors in the story. After verifying hundreds of detailed facts in English and Spanish texts, and through trips to Spain, the Caribbean, and North Africa, no errors were found."[544]

Life becomes more logical, not less so, if we accept that our consciousness does not die when our bodies do. This is but one of many lives which you have had, and will have. Accept this, and journey in that knowledge.

There are obvious practical details that have to be attended to, arrangements that need to be made.

The place

The vast majority of deaths occur in hospital. This is often unsatisfactory, for all sorts of reasons. Not only are hospitals alien environments, but they rarely offer the support and practical assistance necessary. Once doctors have nothing more to offer in terms of recovery, they all too often withdraw from direct personal involvement with the patient. Perhaps this is a defence mechanism by which they seek to protect their own feelings. Whatever it is, it is very sad – there is really so much to be done; and when medical care breaks down, the need for something to replace it is all the more important.

This is why so many people are turning to hospice care, which can provide practical help, support, proper pain relief and communication. Hospice patients are encouraged to live until they die, and when they do die, to do it with dignity. In a study of what relatives wanted when someone close to them was dying, some consistent needs were identified. Whether the patient was in hospital, at home or in a hospice, they wanted forewarning of the death; to spend time with the patient without restrictions; to help the patient; to have an opportunity for final communication; to be given information and reassurance about the physical nature of the death; to spend time with the body and to be able to grieve without fear or censure.

Hospitals rarely meet such requirements. Often there is not even a room for grieving relatives to be alone for a while. One woman described her and her family walking the corridors after her son had died because there was nowhere else to go.

Hospices, on the other hand, work in a completely different way. There is a high ratio of nurses to patients; physiotherapists and social workers are present and there is a willingness to take on board other systems of medicine if the patient wishes. Hospices are in fact famous for their relief of symptoms of every kind. They work on the assumption that memory of pain can be damaging in itself, so attempts are made to anticipate pain and administer painkillers before the patient experiences it. The emphasis is very much on choice and the individual. If you want to have breakfast at eleven, for example, that is usually OK. If you are well enough to go to the pub, you can be taken by a non-uniformed nurse. There are, in fact, very few regimented rules.

You can be referred to a hospice by your GP. If you don't like the idea of being a resident, it is often possible to receive home care. Around half of all hospices have home care teams, and 60 per cent of health districts now have access to this sort of specialist care. The more, the better. For more information about hospices, contact the Hospice Information Service (address in the Help section).

Euthanasia

Once you feel comfortable emotionally about death, it can be tremendously valuable to consider the more practical aspects. Perhaps, for example, you would like to consider the idea of voluntary euthanasia – a decision which is best taken before you become very ill. Many people are adamant that if they ever reach a certain state of distress, they want to be able to choose to not live any longer. Here, the Voluntary Euthanasia Society can give you all the advice and information you need (address in the Help section). They can provide you with an Advance Declaration (or Living Will) for you to lodge with your doctor as an indication of your wishes. You should be aware that the law with regards to voluntary euthanasia is still very confused, and urgent reform is needed here.

The will

Seven out of ten people die without making a will. People are often dismissed as morbid for even mentioning the writing of their will, but in taking care of matters like this you can save the people you care about all sorts of unnecessary heartache, and financial uncertainty. The plain truth is, if you die without making a will, the law decides how your estate will be divided up – and the law is hardly likely to arrange things the way you would wish.

It's cheap and easy to have a solicitor draw up a will for you, and taking expert advice can help you and your relatives to minimize the effect of inheritance tax. A good lawyer will also know how to arrange things to benefit other causes or organizations you may wish to support. For example, a 'life interest' in your property could be assigned to your spouse, and upon his or her death, the residue may be willed to a charity of your choice. Take expert advice, and do this now.

The funeral

Have you ever thought about how difficult it could be for the people you leave behind to arrange a funeral with your wishes in mind? If you have specific ideas, write them down. Perhaps you want your funeral to be a celebration with all the guests drinking champagne! This could really put the 'fun' into funerals! Although you obviously can't make all the arrangements, it is possible to pay for your funeral in advance. If you want a secular event you are not alone; the numbers of non-religious funerals have rapidly increased over the last few years. The British Humanist Association can advise you about personal services (address in the Help section).

How much the final bill comes to could be a bit of a shock; the cost of burial is now about £1,000, and rising. Cremation works out a little cheaper at an average of about £800.

Shakespeare wrote: "It seems to me most strange that men should fear; seeing that death, a necessary end, will come when it will come."[545] It is, indeed, a 'necessary end' for those who die, but for those who are left behind, it can be a cruel and bitter time. Let's now turn to consider the survivors.

Working through bereavement

Studies have shown that those people who do not acknowledge, accept or work through their grief after the death of a loved one have a higher mortality rate than those who do. What you experience can sometimes be very distressing, especially in the first few months, but grieving is an important process, and as you find ways of letting out the overwhelming emotions and openly working through them you will eventually see the healing process start.

The emotions you feel will depend on what your relationship was to the person who died, the quality of that relationship, the circumstances in which they died, your own personal circumstances now, and many other considerations. You may experience:

~ Shock – numbness, disbelief or even denial.

~ Anger – towards yourself, the person who died, God, doctors, others, or life in general.

~ Guilt – for saying or not saying things; perhaps because your life has changed for the better with their death; perhaps because you are still living; perhaps because you believe that it was your fault.

~ Fear or anxiety – about how you will cope financially, practically, emotionally, mentally; fear about your own mortality.

~ Sadness – a sense of loss, weeping, longing.

~ Despair – hopelessness, lack of energy, a sense of futility: 'What's the point?'

Some help from others

It is very common for people to feel these emotions. Know that it is all right for you to acknowledge what you are feeling. Here are some suggestions to help you handle them, and to provide a safe framework in which to work through your grief. All these words of advice have worked for others in your situation – let them work for you too.

~ Let the tears and sadness come; don't hold them back. You've got a lot of crying to do.

~ Allow people to help, you will need it. Equally, when you want to be alone, say so – people will understand.

~ It's normal to feel tired because of the tremendous drain on your emotions. Allow yourself the time to sleep as much as you feel you need. Sleep heals.

~ Let your anger out: hit cushions, throw them; lash out at pillows, shout at them the anger you're feeling; do something very physical like running or chopping wood, scouring pans or polishing floors. It's better out than in.

~ If you're having problems accepting the death find a way, comfortable to yourself, of saying your own 'farewell': through writing, praying, visiting a special place, doing something special and meaningful.

~ Loss of appetite is quite common. If you have been staying indoors a lot, when you are ready, try taking some fresh air and some gentle exercise. Eventually you will find your appetite starting to return.

~ Set yourself small challenges or tasks to perform, whatever you feel capable of, even if it's something as small as putting the milk bottle out. Meeting each challenge will help reinforce your sense of moving forward.

Talk

It is important for you to talk through the very confusing feelings and thoughts you find yourself experiencing. Don't try to keep them to yourself. A good friend will patiently listen as you gradually talk out those feelings of guilt, sadness, fear and despair. If you do not feel comfortable expressing yourself with a friend, ask your doctor about finding a counsellor or support group. Your religious community is also there to help, especially during times of bereavement.

As well as talking, some people find comfort in writing – a journal, letters, poems. Other people find painting or drawing helps. The important thing is that you find ways in which you can express your emotions in a way which is comfortable for you.

Helping others

If you are helping someone after a bereavement you can be a valuable resource, especially in terms of:
~ Your patience and quiet understanding.
~ Non-judgmental acceptance of what they say or do as they work through their confusion and grief and find their way again.
~ Awareness – of their feelings; of any possible abuse of drink or drugs; of any indications of decline.
~ Your initiative and practical help: a bereaved person may not necessarily ask for help – but they may still need it desperately. Make cups of tea or offer to take the children to the park, but be careful not to be pushy. Later you can help them make the sometimes difficult transition back into social activities, too.
~ Let them know they are not alone. Sitting with them, even in silence, holding their hand, touching their arm, or whatever you are both easy with, can be useful.

Coping with serious illness

Death does not always come quickly. Many illnesses are slow and degenerative, and improvements in medical care sometimes mean that illnesses whose progress was once rapid now last much longer. This can impose particular strains upon both carer and patient. Here are some words of advice about how to begin facing and coping with the difficult changes serious illness can cause in the lives of those who care.

If someone you love becomes gravely ill, you'll want to help in any way you can. The first step you'll need to take is to find out everything you can about the illness and its implications. Once you've done that, you'll be able to talk it over with your loved one and everyone else concerned to minimize future pain all round. If it's you who winds up being the main carer, the next step should be to get as much support in place as possible – to help you care.

Find out about the illness

If the sufferer is assertive, and has a co-operative doctor, then she or he will know a good deal about what to expect. Otherwise, you can talk to the doctor yourself or to a nurse or health visitor.

You'll want to know how bad it can get, how long it can last, and what further symptoms may develop.

Many illnesses, from Alzheimer's to AIDS, have support groups and societies which will give you detailed and practical information, and put you in touch with fellow sufferers and carers – that's certainly the best way to get a rounded picture. The *Voluntary Agencies Directory* (published by the National Council for Voluntary Organizations, available in libraries) gives a good, comprehensive list of self-help and support agencies.

Talking it over

A young child, or someone suffering from dementia or other mental illness, won't be able to talk it through with you. For anyone else, it's very important for them to take part in all major decisions. Always remember that being seriously ill – and knowing it – makes a person emotionally as well as physically vulnerable.

You're bound to have some doubts and fears you'd rather not load on to the person you care for, and some you can't even share with the family – but don't keep them to yourself! A trusty friend, doctor or social worker can be a good sounding board, or a fellow carer or support group member can help you find out how real or imagined your worries really are.

Caring at home

The more of an invalid your loved one becomes, the more time and work it'll take to care for him or her. It's important to be realistic about this, and consider your own capacities and resources – it can be quite a struggle to get time off from caring, and unless you make it happen (see below), you probably won't get much help either. Caring at home can indeed be rewarding, but it's certain to be exhausting too.

If coping at home doesn't look feasible, it's worth investigating other options thoroughly. Many voluntary organizations are good sources of information – for example, Age Concern have a number of useful free leaflets. Ask questions of those who are in a position similar to yours (establish contact via the *Voluntary Agencies Directory* or your Citizens Advice Bureau), pay attention to what your feelings are telling you, and be as open as possible with the invalid.

Finding out about help

GPs, social workers and hospital specialists are there to let you know what services are available in your area and what you are entitled to.

~ Your GP is a link with all medical services such as health visitors, physiotherapists, continence advisers, etc. They can also be very helpful in supporting your case if you're trying to get home help, housing benefit, speech therapy, day care, and much more. If you don't feel your GP is sympathetic and helpful, you really must change to another one.

~ Social workers have a legal duty to inform you about local authority services, and can help make sure you get them. They often know about local voluntary and support groups, too, and they should be able to advise you about benefits. If you haven't already done so, ring the social services department of your local council and ask to speak to the duty officer. Explain what your problem is and you will be allocated someone who will come to your home and help you sort out practicalities.

~ Hospital specialists are expert in particular diseases. They often have a very good understanding of what you're both suffering, and they have a lot of string-pulling power – so it pays to discuss things in as much detail as your specialist is willing to hear, and ask whether they can organize any help for you.

~ For getting hold of aids and equipment, District Nurses and health visitors – who you contact through your GP – are generally the most useful people.

Financial help

There are a huge number of benefits available. If you have difficulty finding out what they are, the DSS runs a free telephone information service (details in the Help section), as well as producing many leaflets.

~ Charities have millions of pounds to give away, and you or your loved one may well qualify. Your library will have a number of useful handbooks such as the *Voluntary Agencies Directory* or the *Charities Digest.*

!

Support groups

As well as organizations built round a particular illness, there are also groups for carers in general, and there are women's groups too (far more women than men are carers). One way or another, all these groups offer the company of people with experiences like yours – almost everyone finds it a strength and a comfort to be connected with such a group, as well as an invaluable source of useful information. If you think you haven't the time, think again – you owe it to yourself.

Looking after yourself

Many carers find that their whole life is effectively taken up with caring. They may feel it has to be that way – but it doesn't really, and it's not a good thing. It isn't selfish to think of your own welfare too, it's plain good sense.

~ Give up everything else in your life and you'll be left drained and ultimately depressed, while your loved one feels guilty and sad. This is no way to carry on. If you get seriously depressed you won't be able to go on caring anyway – so make sure you keep up some other interests and contacts.

~ Take regular time off – you may get free help with this through family or neighbours. You could help out with babysitting, feed their cat when they're away, etc., in exchange – don't be afraid to ask, people often want to help but don't want you to think they think you're not coping. Voluntary organizations, the NHS, and social services departments may also be able to provide help either free or at low cost. Or if you can afford it, you can pay someone from a private agency.

~ Take holidays too – either you or the invalid should get right away for long enough so that when you come back you're both glad to see each other. Your social services department or district health authority can tell you what's available, and give you guidance about costs and possible help with them.

Caring for a sick person is a hard job, and often severely under-appreciated – but it can be intensely rewarding too. It allows you to show in a very practical way just how deep your love is. If you are the central carer in your loved one's life, remember you're one of a million people doing that job in this country, and remember that every one of you deserves respect and admiration.

Life everlasting?

Cryonics – the freezing of your body for revival at some future date – is no longer the stuff of science fiction. For a comparatively low cost, you can join other corpses currently held in deep-frozen suspended animation in a Los Angeles suburb. And, when medical science one day works out just how to revive you, you will live again – healthy, beautiful and young! At least, that's the theory. Although many people may find the idea grotesque or undignified, it is a real option available here and now – so it needs to be considered.

What happens

The process is simple. When death comes, so will the cryonics technicians. They'll inject you with an anti-clotting agent and your body will be cooled to just above freezing. Your veins are then filled with an anti-freeze mixture, and finally your body will be boxed up and air-freighted off to California, where the world's only 'people deep-freeze' is presently located. There, you'll spend the next few years bathed in liquid nitrogen cooled to 196 degrees below zero.

Will it work?

Of course this is the vital question. At 196 degrees below zero, the freezing temperature for liquid nitrogen, one second's deterioration at normal body temperature takes thirty trillion years. Essentially you'll last forever. But on the way down, at 20 degrees below, the fluids in your cells freeze, causing damaging ice crystals to form. To avoid crystals forming, you have to use an anti-freeze. But anti-freeze is toxic. At the moment, you're in a no-win situation. You can't avoid cell damage with anti-freeze and you can't avoid cell damage without it.

So with present technology, the people being frozen will sustain some damage. How severe is impossible to tell – you'd have to thaw someone to find out.

The challenge, therefore, is either to develop a non-toxic anti-freeze, or a technique which freezes your body so fast that crystals will not have time to form. Both approaches hold much promise.

Can you afford to try?

You probably can. At the moment, it costs $100,000. But you don't have to pay this until you die. The only cost while you are alive is for membership of Alcor, a non-profit 'life extension foundation', at around £60 a year; plus the premiums on a policy paying an inflation-adjusted $100,000 on your death. This would currently cost someone in their mid-twenties about £20 per month. Of this $100,000, the first $20,000 covers the freezing and shipping costs. The other $80,000 goes into a patient care fund, which will keep you frozen for the hundred years they estimate it will take before you're revived, and medical technology sets about repairing the damage to your body, afflicted by disease and the freezing process itself.

Brave new world?

And just what will you be able to look forward to when you awaken? No one can see that far into the future. But adjusting to life in AD 2100 may not be easy. Your great-grandchildren will be old people themselves, or maybe even dead. Hopefully, your savings will have grown in the intervening century, because being destitute in 2100 will probably be even less fun than it is today. And in any case, will the world government even allow you to be re-animated? With the global population at well over 10 billion, the last thing they'll want is more mouths to feed.

Cryonics is a new frontier for the human race to conquer. If you are keen to be a pioneer, then don't be put off. Einstein said that "imagination is more important than knowledge" and that "all great ideas and innovations have always encountered violent opposition from mediocre minds". If you don't believe in an after-life, and you want to live forever, cryonics is currently your best bet. At the very least – it offers us hope.

Chapter 120

What to do if you are the victim of a violent crime

What would you do if someone attacked you? Knowing what to do and how to cope afterwards will help you survive.

Violent crime is not as common as some people make out, but it *does* happen – and anyone can find themselves in the wrong place at the wrong time. Often it's not so much the incident itself – whether it be a rape, mugging, racial or anti-gay attack or anything else – as the long-term psychological effects which are most damaging. The *worst* way to deal with a violent attack is to do nothing.

What to do if you're attacked

So what do you do if somebody attacks you? The two golden rules are:

~ If you get the chance to run away, do!

~ If there are people nearby, scream your head off!

Otherwise, it depends on the kind of attack:

~ If an armed or dangerous-looking assailant goes for your wallet or handbag, give in. Your life is worth more than the contents of your purse. Only consider fighting back if there are people around or you *really* think you can win.

~ If you are attacked violently you can either fight – in which case do so as if your life depended on it – or go limp. A limp body is a less likely target for aggression.
~ If you are threatened by a rapist, try not to look scared or submissive. Look alert and make sure your body language says NO. If he rests a hand on you push it away firmly.
~ You need to assess the situation quickly and act decisively – if action is possible. If it isn't, you'll have to co-operate – at least until you see a chance to act.
~ If you are going to fight, fight dirty! You can defend yourself with:

- A knee to the groin.
- A kick in the kneecaps.
- A jab in the throat.
- A makeshift weapon (hairspray, an umbrella).

Try to stay upright and use the power in your body to maximum effect. If he goes down, run and keep running. Head for people.
~ Don't let him take you anywhere – especially in a car. Passive resistance (like sitting down) will make you harder to move.
~ Talking may help; it's your only chance if attacked by a group. Try to find the weak link – the reluctant participant – and make him see you as a person, not an object.
Whatever kind of attack you suffer, try to remember details of the incident. The police will be looking for:

- Physical description: age, height, build, skin/hair/eye colour, distinguishing features, clothing, accent.
- Vehicle description: make, colour, registration number.
- Other details: exact location, where he came from, where he went to.

What to do about it afterwards

What you do next is up to you. Some people distrust the police; if you don't want to involve them you don't have to. However, you should at least talk about the incident with friends, family or one of the groups below:
~ Victim Support (VS) is a charity supported by the Home Office. It has 350 offices nationwide; ask directory enquiries or check the phone book for your nearest office. The police will put you in touch with VS automatically, but you can call them independently.
~ VS can offer counselling and advice to victims of any violent crime, on:

- Police and hospital procedures
- Court procedures
- Compensation (see below)
- Other organizations you can contact (see below)

They can send a trained worker to visit you at home or elsewhere, and give you support for as long as you need it. They can also accompany you to court.
~ Rape Crisis is a national organization run by women to help rape victims. It has a 24-hour helpline to which you can reverse the charges, on 071-837 1600. The counsellor who answers will offer a sympathetic ear, give you similar advice to that offered by Victim Support and put you in touch with a local counselling group.
~ The Gay Switchboard has a 24-hour helpline on 071-837 7324 for lesbians and gay men. Again, a sympathetic ear is guaranteed, along with advice.
~ The Women's Aid Federation has a 24-hour helpline on 0272-420611, for women who are victims of domestic violence. There are also numerous local Women's Aid offices. They can offer immediate help by placing women and children in secret refuges while they decide what to do next.

~ You can dial 999 for an ambulance without having to involve the police, so if you need medical attention, get to a hospital. If you decide to call the police, dial 999 and a car will be sent out to collect you and take you to the station for an interview. Remember:

- You are free to leave whenever you like.
- You do not have to appear in court.

If you have been raped:

~ Do not wash or change your clothes however disgusting you feel. Doing so removes vital evidence, making a criminal action against the rapist impossible.

~ At the station you will be interviewed by a policewoman and examined by a female doctor (unless you specify otherwise). The interviewing officer will tell you about court procedure and help you make arrangements for pregnancy and sexually transmitted disease tests. She will also put you in touch with Victim Support and any other relevant local organization.

~ If the case does go to court your real name will not be used during the proceedings, or mentioned in the press.

If you are the victim of domestic violence:

~ Most police forces now have domestic violence units (DVU). If an assault is reported a uniformed officer will go to the scene and make an arrest, if possible. The DVU will make contact with the victim(s), get them away from the scene and, if necessary, transport her/them to the nearest Women's Aid refuge. They will offer legal advice about getting an injunction against the aggressor (if you don't want to press criminal charges), put you in touch with a solicitor and help you with Legal Aid. They can also refer you to other organizations like Relate, the marriage guidance group.

Or racial violence:

~ There are also Racial Violence Units at many stations. They will give your case a high priority and set about ensuring that you are protected from further harassment in the event of a trial. Both DVUs and RVUs liaise closely with local councils and social services departments, so they can arrange rehousing, financial support and social worker visits if necessary.

Compensation is an issue of particular importance to mugging victims. Basically:

~ You can only get compensation for loss of property if the perpetrator is found guilty in court. Even then, repayment is made according to the ability to pay.

~ You can, however, get compensation for injuries sustained either as a victim of a violent crime or while trying to prevent one. This is dealt with by the Criminal Injuries Compensation Board (address in the Help section). Applying for compensation is not easy, but Victim Support will be happy to help.

How to stop it happening again

Prevention is obviously better than cure, so take note of the following suggestions to keep you out of trouble:

~ Much violent crime occurs at night, so avoid dark alleys and vacant land. Stick to brightly lit streets.

~ If you're a woman try to arrange a lift or take a taxi. Don't hitch-hike and avoid empty train carriages and buses.

~ Carry a loud and easy-to-use personal alarm.

~ Learn self-defence. Find a practical course that will teach you cunning tricks rather than complicated techniques. Check at your local library or Citizens Advice Bureau for possibilities.

You may never become a victim, but if you do you'll know now where to turn to for help. There are lots of people out there, ready to give you the support you need, so give yourself a chance and call them. And if you are attacked, remember:

~ Money is cheap, but your life is precious – keep it!

~ If you're going to fight, fight hard and dirty.

Chapter 121

What to do when you think your child is taking drugs

~

If you're worried that your child may be taking drugs, don't tackle the problem alone.

It's the sort of situation every parent dreads. You have your suspicions, but you're not sure. And you don't know what to do. You probably feel isolated and frightened, so it is vital you seek support. Fortunately, there are all sorts of groups (often run by people who were once in the same situation as you) who can give advice, help and information.

There's no shortage of information about the symptoms of drug abuse – you can find plenty of leaflets which cover this kind of area. But these lists are not always very helpful. For example, if you are concerned that someone you know may be taking drugs, looking for physical signs like 'poor skin', 'lack of sleep', or 'restlessness' is not the answer. After all, which teenager doesn't suffer from these problems at some time? It's rather like reading a medical textbook – sooner or later you'll convince yourself that you have all the symptoms for every disease in the book.

Responses to drugs are so individual that generalizations are dangerous. The wide-ranging effects of society's favourite drug – alcohol – are known to most people. But imagine if you had never experienced drunkenness; a description of the violence, hysteria and death it can cause would give a wholly inaccurate picture of a substance which usually only leads to relaxation and laughter.

Drugs, like alcohol, can of course be dangerous, but the best way to find information on whether a person is taking drugs and how it is affecting them is to discuss the individual case with an experienced adviser. That way, you have someone to give all-important feedback on your response.

Understand the cause

Our society is based on the concept of instant gratification, and nowhere is this more visible than in the field of pharmaceutical substances. If we have a headache, we take an aspirin. If we want to relax we have a gin and tonic. If we can't sleep, we take sleeping tablets. And if we're tense, the doctor gives us mind-numbing tranquillizers. Drug takers think along exactly the same lines: "If I take this, I'll feel better."

If you find it difficult to understand why your child feels the need to turn to drugs for comfort, first consider whether any long-standing pattern of behaviour has already been set up in your family life. Perhaps, for example, your child has grown up seeing you resorting to all sorts of pills and medications to cure your own unhappiness. It's not a good example to follow.

Cut through the distortions

There is a lot of exaggeration about the drug problem, and it is often very difficult to get hold of the facts. But you *must* inform yourself of the facts of the matter, otherwise you will simply be basing your reactions upon prejudice and ignorance. To put the matter in proportion, bear in mind the following facts:

~ The two legal drugs – alcohol and tobacco – kill thousands of times more people than do illegal drugs.

~ For every one person who dies from the effects of an illegal drug, thirty people die from the effects of alcohol, and 400 die from tobacco.[546]

~ Government publicity and propaganda targeted against illegal drug use is out of all proportion to its efforts to reduce the serious effects of *legal* drug use.

~ For every person who dies from smoking, the government spends £35 on anti-smoking campaigns. For every person who dies from drinking, the government spends £344 on anti-drink campaigns. For every person who dies from illegal drug use, the government spends £1.7 million on anti-drugs campaigns.[547]

~ In 1988, there were 5,212 notified drug addicts in the United Kingdom. In the same year, there were over 25 million prescriptions issued for benzodiazepines (legal tranquillizers). In the words of the government's own publication, *Social Trends*: "If only a tiny fraction of legal prescriptions for benzodiazepines and barbiturates were to people addicted to or misusing these drugs, this would be a far greater problem than notified addicts."[548]

The inescapable conclusion is that legal drugs are much more of a problem for our society than illegal ones.

In some cases, you may just have to accept that drug use for the person you are concerned about is *not* in fact a problem. For example, there is no real evidence to suggest that cannabis use causes any long-term damage. And there have certainly been a great many scientific research papers published on this subject. "The cannabis investigation market has boomed," reports Andrew Tyler, a drugs expert. "There have been something like 15,000 scientific papers as well as cartloads of government-commissioned reports subjecting the drug to the kind of scrutiny that wouldn't pass a broad bean fit. Where a consensus on physical/mental impact does suggest itself, it is that there is no clear and significant damage to be found in adult humans resulting from moderate use of the drug."[549] The most directly harmful effects known to be associated with cannabis use are, firstly, the ingestion of tobacco smoke (cannabis is often smoked combined with tobacco), and secondly, the draconian sentences imposed by the law upon the user.

Often, parents are frightened that use of cannabis is the first step towards using other, more serious drugs. This is, of course, more likely to be a problem as long as cannabis is classified with other, more harmful drugs as illegal, since criminal sources of supply are obviously involved in both operations.

But for many young adults, cannabis use is simply a passing phase. It does not lead on to 'hard' drugs, nor does it produce lasting damage (other than the very real damage done by inhaling tobacco smoke). But what should you do if you believe that your child is taking something more serious?

First, you must be strong

The most important thing to realize – and probably the hardest – is that you *cannot control this situation*. Just as a 'hard' drug controls an addict, if you focus all your attention on the user you will become as helpless as they are. Just as a user is powerless against a drug as long as they continue taking it, so are you powerless against them. You must be there to give the support and love they will need so much, but you cannot take responsibility.

You cannot make the user strong, but you can make yourself strong. You will then be more able to help the person you are concerned about. Anger and hurt are common, understandable reactions when you discover someone you care about is taking drugs. But expressing your feelings through accusations and aggression will not help you or them. Sadly, such action will normally only serve to alienate them further. Think before you lash out.

Before you say or do anything, look at yourself. Before you can be any help to an addict you need to be emotionally healthy yourself. One woman who answers calls from worried parents for a self-help group explained the importance of support. "As a mother of a heroin addict, I had first to solve my problems. One of our problems as a parent may be that we cannot leave our child alone."

Get in touch

If you have any worry about drugs, the first group to contact is SCODA (Standing Conference on Drug Abuse – address in the Help section). As a national co-ordinating service, they can give you information on all the options of help available to you. And they can provide you with details of your nearest source of help.

There are many self-help groups for users, but the decision to join one must be left up to the user themselves. Alcoholics Anonymous for problem drinkers and Narcotics Anonymous for people with drug problems are the two largest. Self-help groups for the family and friends of addicts are often born out of the original user groups. Al-Anon, for example, follows in the footsteps of Alcoholics Anonymous and offers support for close associates of alcoholics. Al-Alteen works in the same way, but is for the teenaged children of problem drinkers, providing them with the opportunity to share their experiences with people of the same age.

In the long run, sometimes the very long run, most addicts kick their habit. Be confident this will eventually happen and see your role as hastening the day, rather than effecting some sort of dramatic cure.

CHAPTER 122

WHY PEOPLE COMMIT SUICIDE AND HOW TO STOP THEM

~

Learn to recognize the signs and you can save a life.

Suicidal feelings are more common than you may think. About half of us consider taking our lives at some point, and in Britain more young men between the ages of fifteen and twenty-four are committing suicide now than at any time in the past century.

What drives people to suicide? A lack of love, unrequited love or unfulfilled love are common causes. Marital and sexual conflict, inadequacy, failure and grief over the death of a loved one also contribute to people taking their lives.

A change in the way people view life may also be responsible. Old inhibitions and deterrents have relaxed so that suicide is often seen as a 'right'. We no longer see ourselves as part of a community. We aim for happiness, and failing that, we choose our own way of escaping misery.

The vulnerable

Young people are very vulnerable because of separation and family break-ups, the greater mobility of society and the reduction of access to working parents. Competition and worries about school and jobs are also extremely stressful. An absence of economic hope and a rejection of the way they dress, the music they like and their friends may also contribute to their feelings of isolation. Drugs and alcohol abuse might also influence them to commit suicide.

AIDS seems to affect the mental outlook of single young men and The Terence Higgins Trust, a charity which deals with AIDS, reports cases of people diagnosed HIV-positive who have committed suicide.

According to psychiatrists at the University of Pittsburgh, the brain chemistry of suicidal teenagers may be important too. Growth hormone, a substance normally produced by the pituitary gland at night, is lower in depressed teenagers who had attempted or planned suicide compared to those who were depressed but not suicidal. In the future, this connection could well help identify teenagers at special risk.

People born during the baby boom are more prone to taking their lives. This might be because they experience a highly competitive job market, increased social stress, and a delayed marriage, which means a delay in establishing intimate relationships. A smaller family and a more limited social network are likely to make them feel very alienated.

Certain professions are associated with suicide. Farmers often take their lives because of long hours, isolation and financial difficulties. For doctors, the constant pressure and the crushing responsibility for people's illnesses combined with access to poisonous substances is too often fatal. But having no occupation is the most stressful of all and the unemployed are the most at risk.

Older people are still the age group with the highest suicide rate, perhaps because they experience great isolation and know that they are a burden to others. They feel a sense of helplessness when they cannot do things which they could before and a general feeling of being unwanted, abandoned and lonely.

Watch for signs

You must be aware of the clues to suicide. A suicidal person may talk about going away, gives away their favourite possessions, conspicuously puts their affairs in order and might diverge from their usual habits of eating, sleeping and working. Traumatic events such as illness, the break-up of a relationship or the death of a loved one are also times of greater risk.

Sadly, our society does not teach us how to cope with crises, emotions and failure. This should be part of our general school education so that we grow up learning the skills of psychological survival. In the absence of such skills, people are left to establish their own life-long coping patterns as best they can, and a person who has tended to run away from difficult situations instead of trying to resolve them may well be prone to take their own life, as the final means of escape.

What you can do

Understand the suicidal mind and you can save lives. A suicidal person is trying to escape unendurable psychological pain. Happiness never makes a person commit suicide.

~ If you are dealing with someone on the verge of suicide, you must try to reduce their suffering in every way possible. If you lessen their pain just a little, the suicidal person will choose to live.

~ A suicidal person has needs such as security and friendship, but these are being frustrated. Find out what these needs are and address them.

~ Suicide is the way out of a crisis, so find out what the problem is and encourage the person to talk. Just knowing that someone is prepared to listen is a therapy in itself. And in talking, problems often become more manageable.
~ A suicidal person believes that no one can help and that the only solution is to take their life. They fail to explore a variety of answers and if you are to help, you must make them see that there are more options available to them than they think.
~ Ambivalence dominates the mind of the suicidal. He or she wants death, but also cries for help. This ambivalence gives you the chance to persuade them to go on living.
~ Most suicidal people give clear indications of their intention to kill themselves. They do not take their lives out of hostility or revenge, but are trying to get others to see their pain and rescue them. A little recognition of this can mean the difference between life and death.
~ Buy time. Although it doesn't seem possible to the person contemplating suicide, most suicidal crises eventually resolve themselves. Help them to put off the fatal decision until they can think about things more calmly: "All I am asking is that you give yourself a little breathing space and a little time to mull things over."
If the worst happens, and a suicide occurs, don't recriminate. "If only I had . . ." is useless, guilt-inducing self-talk. Ultimately, if someone wants to kill themselves determinedly enough, *they will find a way*, and nothing you can do will stop them. You can't be with them twenty-four hours every day. In the final analysis, everyone has the right to bring their own lives to a conclusion, cruel though it may be for us, who survive them, to accept.

Chapter 123
Dealing with depression: not a disease, but a healing process

~

"Snap out of it" is the worst advice to offer anyone suffering from this life-sapping condition. Here, we suggest a radical new way to understand depression. Depression carries within it the seeds of healing: discover how to nurture them.

The Hopi Indians have a word: Koyannisqatsi. It means "crazy life, life in turmoil, life disintegrating, life out of balance, state of life calling for another way of living". As we face the third millennium, it seems a peculiarly appropriate diagnosis of the way most of us live.

Now consider this. The English language has about as many labels for the state of mind known as 'depression' as Eskimos do for different kinds of snow. Low, blue, the pits, dejected, disconsolate, down, gloomy, glum, grave, grim, melancholic, moody, out-of-sorts, pessimistic . . .

Clearly, an analysis of the language we use reveals several telling things. First, it establishes that, as a culture, we are on the most extraordinarily intimate terms with this particular emotion – we know it as well, say, as a connoisseur knows the wine of a certain region. We know the infinite subtleties of depression, we can spot its vintages and its distinctive characters. We are an accomplice to all its thousand faces.

Second, it reveals how preoccupied we are with this unhealthy state of being. Try living for a day without using – or hearing – depression words. It is not possible.

Third, it sadly demonstrates how hard it is for us to resolve the depressive condition, and conquer it. Depression is our constant companion, and our bedfellow – we sorely lack the language, and the tools, to triumph over it.

Our doctors – themselves often depressive people – remain by and large convinced that depression is a chemical problem, with a chemical answer. "Since its launch in America in 1987, an anti-depressant drug called Prozac has been a phenomenal success," reports *The Economist.* "This year it could bring Eli Lilly, Prozac's American manufacturer, $675m from sales throughout the world."[550]

But what if depression is not a chemical error, but actually an entirely valid and appropriate response to the crazy, Koyannisqatsi-style lives we lead today?

Consider the state of the world – the state of our own lives – with an open mind, and you will come to the inescapable conclusion that it is indeed a "state of life calling for another way of living". Viewed this way, depression has a positive side to it. Perhaps depression is actually a manifestation of the beginnings of positive change.

Instead of trying to cure our depression, perhaps we should allow our depression to cure us.

The symptoms of change

At least three million people in the United Kingdom suffer from depression. The symptoms often include self-doubt, recrimination, loss of appetite, and bodily aches. Much depression is overtly caused by a sudden change – such as the loss of a loved one, redundancy, or the break-up of a relationship. Even very successful people are prone to it. They are often ambitious to the extent that any minor failure is intolerable. This is particularly true of the business world, which is dominated by mergers, acquisitions, and rising competition.

Those at the very top of the company often feel intensely isolated, a dehumanizing feeling which is a breeding-ground for depression. Says Philip Caldwell, retired chairman of Ford Motor Company: "You just don't have the freedom to share your innermost thoughts with anyone, and yet the feeling of confidence and success must be imparted throughout the organization."[551]

What you can do

Orthodox medicine is very adept at suppressing symptoms without removing the underlying cause. Consequently, depression is usually treated with chemicals. However, if your depression is actually a reaction to environmental factors, then clearly, you must change your surroundings. A holiday, or at least a change of scenery, may help. Consider changing your job. Find a way of spending some days away from your family. Break the routine in your life. Take up a really challenging task – something that will stretch you maybe beyond your limits – the sort of thing that would cause most people to say: "What? But you can't do that!" Try any or all of these measures and see what effect they have on your mental state. If it improves, you've found the problem, and the solution.

Whether your depression is fundamentally caused by your environment or by body chemistry, here are further simple practical steps you can take to prevent and alleviate it:

~ Make sure you eat and sleep well, working off stress with physical exercise.

~ Develop an interest outside work or the family, avoid nicotine, alcohol, tranquillizers and coffee.

~ Seek reconciliation in family relationships, explore ways of building your self-esteem, and casting away regrets and bitterness.

~ About 12 per cent of all women who give birth are likely to suffer a clinical depression. Post-partum depression, as it's called, can be very serious, and if left untreated will damage the woman and her family. What causes post-partum depression? Many think that environmental factors bring it on. Dr. Sandra Elliot, a

British clinical psychologist, believes that the majority of women are only depressed because of what is happening in their lives. She maintains that if there are marital or financial problems, the mother could easily become depressed. Her research shows that women who receive counselling before and after giving birth are less susceptible. However, Dr. Katherine Dalton, another researcher, is convinced that hormonal surges are responsible and has found that mothers treated with progesterone supplements after birth are less likely to become depressed. Treatment for this may therefore involve counselling or drug therapy, and it is effective. But in order to work, first it must be recognized and diagnosed.

~ The way we explain bad things happening to ourselves can affect our future behaviour, and can have serious implications for our mental and physical health. Bad things happen to everyone. But people vulnerable to depression feel that *they* are somehow responsible for every bad event in their lives – whether or not they had any control over the matter. This is a behaviour pattern we learn when young, and it may require professional help to finally eliminate.

~ The American tycoon Lee Iacocca says that he was "coming apart at the seams" after being fired by Henry Ford II in 1978.[552] He took to drink and became depressed. Finally, he says, he decided to deal with his problem: "I had a simple choice: I could turn that anger against myself, with disastrous results. Or I could take some of that energy and try to do something productive." So-called 'winner depression' can afflict anyone with drive and ambition. Things get to the point where even the smallest setback is unbearable. Professional help is the last thing somebody in this position thinks about – but in fact, that's the first thing they need. The alternative is to be consumed in a depression fed by frustrated ambition.

~ Many people use their depressive bouts creatively. Woody Allen is open about his depressive moods, and he uses pain and sadness to make the world laugh. Almost like a phoenix, he is reborn through every experience, however difficult – and it becomes a film. Try following his example.

~ Seasonal affective disorder (SAD) can affect a significant number of people, and most sufferers can be cured by supplemental lighting (see chapter 45).

Above all, our attitude to depression must change. For too long we have seen it as a negative, self-indulgent state. 'Pull yourself together' is the futile message many depressed people receive. But depression is our natural response to pain and change – whether it is the woman whose life is irrevocably altered by the birth of her child, whether it is the executive who has seen all his colleagues dismissed, or whether it is the child who has lost its mother. Depression is our body's way of getting us to slow down and reconsider our life, and hopefully change things. It is an opportunity to change direction and find new values. It is a time when the healing powers of the brain take over and the hurly-burly of the outside world becomes irrelevant. Depression carries within it the power to heal us.

CHAPTER 124
ENJOYING YOUR PRIME TIME: HOW TO BE YOUR OWN MIDLIFE MIDWIFE

~

"Don't worry about middle age: you'll outgrow it."
Laurence J. Peter

Are you worried about the 'mid-life crisis'? The phrase itself is enough to send shivers down your spine, but your middle years don't have to be miserable. If you approach the forty-year mark fully prepared and in the right spirit, the next thirty years will be a time of growth and happiness.

This period is a time of change, much the same as adolescence. Just as your teenage years are supposed to be traumatic but often aren't, you can get through mid-life without encountering a crisis. The problem is that most people don't realize that what they're experiencing is a natural part of their development, so they fight it. You need to approach change positively and guide yourself forward into your second forty years.

Mid-life begins at around forty and it's usually brought on by some kind of realization that you are ageing. Perhaps:
~ A parent dies.
~ You notice grey hairs or wrinkles in the mirror.
~ Your son beats you at tennis for the first time.
Some people experience a foreboding of death; for others a sense of tiredness or decline which brings on the mid-life blues. Women have to deal with the physical and mental effects of the menopause.

Questions, questions

The mid-life blues are the first stage of the transition from early to mature adulthood. They manifest themselves in questions and doubts about yourself and your life:
~ Where's my career going?
~ Why am I in this relationship?
~ I'm wasting my life.
~ I'm no longer attractive.
The list could be endless, and for many people this can be a painful and trying period. The mid-life blues are made much worse by our society's low opinion of middle age.
~ We love the young and beautiful and the old and venerable. Middle-aged people are in between, forgotten.
~ The middle-aged man is overweight, balding, unsexy.
~ His female counterpart is simply menopausal.
~ On a personal level you may contrast the dreams of youth with the reality of the present. The time left for success appears limited.
~ Most people suffer doubts about their career at this time. You suddenly seem to be surrounded by bright youngsters whose presence makes you feel old and useless. This feeling is reinforced by many companies' poor attitude towards mature employees.
No wonder people suffer greatly at the thought of becoming 'middle-aged'!

It ain't over yet!

The secret of survival and growth lies in facing up to the fact of ageing, refusing to be put off by myths and responding to doubts, questions and physical changes in a positive way. For example:

~ At work, you may be tempted to work harder, for longer hours. This approach is only likely to make the situation worse. Instead, take a step back and think about what you *really want* from life.
~ It is never too late to change. If you're not fulfilling your dreams think about a different career. You've got plenty of time ahead to make it work. But act now!
~ Put your happiness first. Don't keep doing the same old thing because you feel your responsibility to others makes change impossible. *You* are the most important person in your life.
~ Escape from the tyranny of success. If you can't compete with the high-flying youngsters (and they'll be entering mid-life soon enough) take a step sideways or even down in the success pyramid. Money and position aren't everything, so move to wherever you feel happiest.
~ As an experienced person you can fill roles in which good sense and knowledge matter more than sheer energy.
~ As men get older their bodies produce more female hormones, a physical change that can result in a shift of interest away from go-getting and towards a more caring role. Don't fight it! Follow your inclinations wherever they may lead.
~ Women, on the other hand, are likely to find themselves free of children and anxious to make something of their lives. Don't let anyone stop you, if that's what you want to do. And don't let your age hold you back; you've got plenty of years ahead of you.

The menopause

For women, the most obvious aspect of mid-life is the menopause, often viewed as a kind of living hell. Yet many women suffer very little and that suffering can be reduced still further by knowing what to expect, and what to do about it.
~ You know you have reached the menopause when you haven't had a period for a year. At this stage your body stops ovulating, and stops producing female hormones.
~ This doesn't mean that your sex life ends. Women often enjoy sex *more* in their fifties than in their twenties. And you are no longer hampered by periods or the threat of pregnancy!
~ Most women suffer hot flushes for a time, but you can minimize your discomfort by keeping a log of the circumstances preceding an attack, noting factors that seem to bring them on – like drinking alcohol – and avoiding them.
~ Before bed, have a bath in tepid water to cool your body down and relax you for sleep.
~ Don't worry about losing your looks – worry will age you faster than anything else. Forget the past and accept yourself as you are. You'll stay younger-looking longer if you:
~ Keep to a moderate diet, with a good supplemental source of minerals and vitamins (see chapter 85 for one suggested regime).
~ Take regular exercise. Walking and cycling are fine.
~ Keep busy, but avoid stress.
~ Hormone replacement therapy, to replace the oestrogen no longer produced by your body, is available if you suffer from severe psychological or physical problems as a result of the menopause (see chapter 40 for more information). Ask your doctor about it.
Depression and self-doubt are more likely to be caused by the mid-life blues than the menopause. In other words, feeling bad is not something you just have to put up with; by acting positively you can be menopausal and happy at the same time.

Myth of the male menopause

Contrary to popular belief, men *don't* go through an equivalent menopausal period. Most are quite capable of having sex and fathering children until at least their sixties, often well into their nineties!

~ Men's sexual performance reduces in terms of frequency – but *not* in terms of skill or enjoyment. It actually gets better!

~ Impotency is most often related to stress, ill health brought on by smoking, drinking and overeating, or simply worry. The first three are obviously lifestyle-related. Adopt more moderate habits, start taking regular exercise and think about a less pressurized job.

~ Worry is the major cause of impotence; one failed erection can produce many more. Don't worry about it and you'll perform successfully for years.

~ For men and women the best way to ensure a long and happy sex life is to keep having sex!

This shouldn't mean that you jump into bed with everyone you meet at the drop of a hat. Many people make the mistake of thinking divorce and infidelity are the best cures for the mid-life blues – only to discover they've simply destroyed the best relationship of their lives and gained nothing.

Sleeping with more, younger partners is a symptom of your refusal to face up to the ageing process. Instead, accept the older you and look at positive ways of making your life happier:

~ Changing your job.

~ Getting involved in the local community.

~ Taking up a worthwhile and personally rewarding interest.

Become the person you really want to be and you won't need to prove your sexual prowess at every occasion.

~ If you feel your relationship is stale, don't give up on it. Talk about it with your partner. Spice it up with a holiday, some romance, or sex games (see chapter 125).

~ You will find both of you are changing and conflict is assured unless you communicate. Remember, you're both going through a difficult transition, so try to be tolerant and supportive. Be a help, not a hindrance.

Mid-life can be a difficult time. But it's also the time when you can at last begin to feel that you understand what life is all about. It's a game you've played for some time now, and let's face it – you haven't done too badly just to make it this far! You must also learn to value yourself for the experienced person you have become. Experience is priceless, and it brings the knowledge you need to look at your life and decide how you really want it to be. Forget myths and conventions and, for the first time, really become yourself. Let go of the past, embrace the present – and enjoy the future!

MAKING THINGS GO BETTER: TOOLS FOR SUCCESS!

CHAPTER 125
SEX PROBLEMS AND SEX THERAPY

~

Everyone has sexual problems sometime during their life. It's what you do about them that makes the difference between happiness or misery.

If you have a problem with sex you are not alone. According to sex researchers Masters and Johnson, half of all married couples suffer from sexual difficulties that cause a conflict in the relationship. An activity which takes up so much of our attention, physically and emotionally, is bound to cause problems once in a while. The difficulty may, in fact, have nothing to do with the act of sex itself; if you are stressed or unhappy, your sexual relationships are almost always the first part of your life to suffer.

Acknowledge the problem

The biggest problem you face may lie in admitting that anything's wrong in the first place. Sadly, many people carry on for years with an unhappy sex life, never coming to terms with the fact that things are not as they should be. Despite an increased openness in this area in all sections of society, sex is still a very fragile and personal thing, so it is not surprising if you're reluctant to discuss the subject, or even to admit to yourself that things could be better.

But it would indeed be tragic if this reluctance prevented you from seeking help. You cannot shock or embarrass a sex therapist; they have heard it all before. And once you have figured out the puzzles in this most perplexing area of your life, you'll find that your general well-being will improve, too. It isn't called intercourse for nothing; sex is the ultimate communication. If you are sexually frustrated in whatever way, it is important that you come to terms with it, as it may be part of a much wider problem. Anger and resentment often lie at the root of sexual problems – when people find it hard to express themselves verbally, the feeling gets enacted in the sexual relationship, often with one partner withdrawing altogether. On the other hand, the root cause may be a physical one which can be treated medically, sometimes by your doctor. To many people it is a great relief just to discover that the problem is not in their mind and easily curable.

Pin down the problem

Sexual difficulties can be divided into two sorts. If there has always been a problem then it can be described as primary, while in the case of more short-lived disorders, the term secondary is used.

One of the most common reasons that both men and women consult a therapist is simply lack of interest in sex. Men may experience potency or erectile problems, difficulty with ejaculation or painful intercourse. For women, the most common problems are non-consummation, orgasmic dysfunction and painful intercourse. All of these problems can often be resolved after a number of sessions with a well-trained sex therapist.

A good therapist will try to find the root of the problem. For example, if you can't enjoy sex with your partner, it may be due to all sorts of reasons. Perhaps you are stressed at work, or you feel your lover has not made enough commitment to the relationship. Or, the problem may be completely unrelated to present circumstances and linked to past family situations. If the problem has been around for a long time, a therapist may ask you why it is being presented now. You may also be approached about your motivation – what do you want to achieve from therapy?

A therapist will be aware that the person complaining of a problem may not be the one with the problem at all. If sex is not satisfying for you it may be because of a difficulty your partner has, or a problem with the relationship. If this is the case, some therapists may ask to see your partner as well. This, of course, can bring all sorts of difficulties; the partner may feel accused, resentful, or even just refuse to come to a session. A therapist should respect your wishes in this area; if you do not want your partner to join therapy with you, that is your right. You should be aware, though, that counselling on your own may take a lot longer to resolve the issue.

Many reasons to be unhappy

All sorts of external factors threaten a happy and healthy sex life. Maybe some of the common causes that follow will ring true with you . . .

~ Some people have been left with an intense guilt and shame about enjoying sex, from parents, religion or school education. If your parents had negative sexual attitudes, you are likely to feel sex is dirty and disgusting, too.

~ Others may have actually been abused by their parents or other relatives, which can understandably result in the avoidance of sex altogether.

~ Some people may have difficulty relating to the opposite sex because they have not yet resolved issues from the past. Perhaps they are still desperate for the love of a parent, or unhappy about a past relationship.

~ Job loss, and even promotion, can put a strain on a couple's sex life as expectations outside the relationship change.

~ The arrival of children is a common reason for a less-active sex life. Women are often fatigued and men may feel jealous or even inadequate.

~ Certain methods of contraception may have a part to play in sexual activity. Some men, for example, find themselves becoming impotent when their partner uses the cap because they feel they are then expected to 'perform'.

~ Similarly, sterilization, by taking away fertility, can cause some people to feel less virile and sexual.

~ Rape can cause significant problems for both partners. While the woman obviously feels distrustful of sex after a rape, a man may find the sexual act difficult because he feels impotent for not protecting his partner.

~ Physical illness as well as depression and anxiety can cause all sorts of problems with potency and sexuality generally. Cultural and religious factors may also be worked through with you by a therapist.

A problem shared . . .

Many people find that just letting their problem out into the open is a great relief in itself. Talking to someone who is attentive and understanding can make all the difference. Too often local GPs do not have the time necessary to deal with a problem of this sort. But even if you feel that your doctor is not the right person to discuss the matter with, you may have to ask them for a referral to a sex therapist. If, however, you feel particularly comfortable with your doctor, you may like to ask for a longer appointment to discuss your worries.

The point is, don't let yourself be cornered into something you are unhappy with; it is up to you to express your wishes. Certain drugs can cause sexual dysfunction, so if you are taking any medication, it is definitely worth asking your doctor. They should also rule out any illnesses which might be causing the problem, such as diabetes, spinal cord injuries, alcoholism, multiple sclerosis and endocrine disorders. Also, don't forget that excessive drinking can have an effect on sexual performance.

What happens in therapy

Some therapists use a method called sensate focusing. This involves an initial 'ban' on any sexual activity, even including touching. This ban can help in itself as it removes any pressure couples may feel about performing. The couple then gradually learn to touch and feel each other pleasurably without intercourse or stimulation of the genital organs. The emphasis is on communication and couples are encouraged to say what makes them feel good.

Specific techniques can be taught for different problems, with emphasis again on communication about what each partner enjoys. For example, in the case of premature ejaculation, a woman may learn from her partner how to touch his penis so that he feels near to ejaculation. Then, she can either stop the action or use the 'squeeze technique', involving squeezing the penis in a certain way between the fingers and thumb. By learning to prolong sexual pleasure in this way, it is possible to exercise more control over the moment of ejaculation, and as confidence grows, the 'squeeze technique' can be used less.

One of the most common female problems is failure to reach orgasm. This is sometimes, and quite incorrectly, called 'frigidity'. But sex therapists don't use this word, except to describe a very rare phenomenon: a person who can't be sexually stimulated in any way at all. Most cases of so-called 'frigidity' are, in fact, women who simply find difficulty in reaching orgasm. And in many cases, the cure is simple:

~ Some women don't have orgasms just because they're trying too hard. In this case, you'll find that the more you work towards it, the further off it seems! The remedy lies in learning how to relax and let your body take over.

~ Men and women reach their climax at different times. Research conducted by psychiatrist Domeena C. Renshaw of the Loyola University of Chicago's Stritch School of Medicine shows that women take on average 13 minutes from sexual arousal to reach orgasm. Men, on the other hand, only take an average of 2.8 minutes before they ejaculate! No wonder that many women are left disappointed!

~ Too much too soon. Apart from their shorter performance times, men tend to want to rush ahead and insert the penis in the vagina as quickly as possible, with minimal attempt at foreplay. But you can't do this and expect your partner to be satisfied. Scientific research shows that there are several distinct stages in sexual arousal, which must be experienced before orgasm can usually happen. The first stage – *excitement* – arouses the thrill and anticipation of sex, the nipples harden and the vagina moistens. Then the *plateau* stage follows, during which the clitoris becomes erect and the inner labia lips change colour from pink to deep red as blood flow is increased. The third stage is *orgasm* itself – the muscles of the vagina respond to sustained arousal with strong contractions and a feeling of well-being spreads throughout the body. Miss out the early stages, and you don't get to the Big O!

~ Sometimes a woman will feel inadequate because she is unable to have an orgasm without direct stimulation of the clitoris. But the fact is, the rubbing and thrusting motion of the penis during intercourse just isn't enough to produce an orgasm in most women. More direct stimulation, usually with the fingers, is needed for most people. But some women may feel that this is similar to masturbation, and therefore 'dirty', or they may still believe that so-called clitoral orgasms are inferior to vaginal orgasms (in fact, the distinction is false – there's no difference between them). It was Freud who originally proposed the idea that a clitoral orgasm was 'infantile', and he was, quite simply, wrong. In fact, it is entirely a male fantasy to believe that a woman should experience orgasm solely through penile thrusting. The penis usually provides only indirect stimulation of the clitoris, and is rarely enough to produce orgasm by itself. There are several ways of arousing the clitoris, and it's fun to experiment! Try rubbing your partner's penis against, it, or your partner's lips or tongue. Or you may find other methods to investigate . . .

~ The position you adopt during love-making can determine whether you reach orgasm or not. The man on top 'missionary position' is probably the least likely to succeed, particularly if you don't vary it during intercourse. If the woman goes on top instead, she'll be able to find the right speed and angle of the penis which will stimulate her clitoris most successfully. Alternatively, rear entry (where the man inserts his penis into the vagina from between the buttocks) leaves both partners with their hands free and well positioned to stimulate the clitoris.

~ Some women feel inadequate because they only achieve one orgasm, and they feel pressure to achieve the much-publicized 'multiple orgasm'. In fact, and bar-room boasts to the contrary, almost no men can achieve more than one orgasm either. If you want multiple orgasms (and why not try for fun?), you'll have to use some form of masturbation for most of your orgasms.

More help

If your therapist feels that he/she cannot deal with your particular problem directly, he/she may refer you to a specialized psychosexual clinic. These are found either in community clinics or out-patient departments of hospitals. If there is an organic, or physical cause of impotency in a patient, a patient may be referred to a specialized unit, usually in a urology department. Sometimes the drug papaverine may be administered, which normally produces an erection. The patient will be taught how to use it himself, but overdosage can be dangerous. Surgery is very rarely necessary.

Finding a therapist

There is a lack of legislation and registration for therapists generally, but the problem is even greater with sex therapy. Because the approach is relatively new, it can take some time to find a properly trained therapist. Some untrained people set themselves up as sex therapists because it is seen as an easy area to break into. The answer is to find properly qualified people through universities and hospitals with sex clinics. Your doctor may be able to advise you on possible sources, or ask any health professional you trust for advice.

If you do not want to be seen in a sex clinic or hospital you can ask for a referral for a consultation to take place in a private setting. It is vital that you feel comfortable, so do not be afraid of asking for background, training and any particular area of specialization. Ideally, this should be done over the telephone before you have committed yourself to treatment. Also, ask the therapist if she/he deals with your particular problem and check their method of working – some therapists only work with couples.

If the therapist does agree to deal with your problem, ask how it will be treated and for an estimate of how long it will take. Unlike traditional psychotherapy, sex counselling is usually short-term, lasting between two and six months.

Relate, the recently re-named Marriage Guidance Council, were at the forefront of the development of sex therapy in this country. They do not ask for a specific fee but request a donation according to means. And you don't have to be married to use the service; Relate is for anyone in a relationship. The British Counselling Association can also provide information about therapy.

Sex over sixty

The urgent thrill of youthful sex is great – but the ignorance! The vanity! The haste! There's lots to be said for slower sex with less emphasis on penetration, between experienced people who know what they're doing and don't need to show off. That's right – *older* people!

If you think that by the time you're in your sixties your sex life will be in decline, you're almost certainly wrong. A recent survey found that 91 per cent of sixty to eighty-five-year-olds are still sexually active to around the same degree they were in their forties.

Those hormones

It is true that the sex hormones are at much higher levels in youth than in age. But that does not affect your potential for full sexual arousal or satisfaction – just the speed at which you reach them. That promotes more imaginative and considerate sexual exchanges.

There are other physical changes too, of course, in both men and women. In a woman, the fact that conception is now impossible can be liberating in itself, and the fact that contraception is no longer needed should be a blessing for both parties. For both sexes there are some changes in how their sexual organs feel.

Changes in women

~ Vaginal dryness is widespread after menopause – it is not evidence of lack of arousal, just lack of oestrogen. It can be overcome by hormone replacement therapy or, less drastically, by the use of fairly low dose hormone creams. Both those methods require a medical prescription. A less medicinal approach is to apply lubrication, either in the form of a jelly like KY, or by oral sex (which has its own built-in lubrication) or by using body massage oils.

~ Vaginal slackness can be the result of child-bearing, but it's often compounded by a thinning of the vaginal walls caused by lack of oestrogen. Once again, some form of hormone therapy can be used – but it does nothing for muscle tone, which is the real issue. There are two easy exercises for this you can do anywhere, anytime – though you may need to control your facial expression! Both involve your imagination:

~ First, pretend you're trying not to pass water and hold tension in those muscles for five seconds; then pretend you're trying not to have a bowel movement and hold those muscles tense for five seconds. Alternate in this way for one minute and repeat several times each day. It may help you to imagine that the muscles of the perineum are shaped in a figure of eight and that each time you tense them you are reducing the size of the eight – as would happen if you pulled a drawstring.

~ Second, imagine the opening to your vagina as tight but elastic and try to feel a sensation in this area while you do so. Now imagine the feeling of tightness slowly travelling up your vagina, as a lift travels up a tall building. You should feel some muscular tension in your abdomen as you practise this exercise. When you have lifted upward for at least five seconds, stop and hold the lifted sensation for a further five seconds before you slowly and deliberately reverse the exercise and allow relaxation to travel down your vagina. Repeat this exercise several times each day. The best time to start these exercises is right after child-bearing, but it's never too late.

Changes in men

~ It's normal for the testicles to shrink a bit, but that does nobody any harm so don't let it worry you. The sperm count gets lower too, but that only matters if conception is the aim.
~ The penis tends to become less erect when hard, in other words, the angle between it and the abdomen becomes greater. That's because of shrinkage of blood vessels, not lack of drive, and, for the same reason, it may also be less hard. If the base of the penis is gently squeezed and stroked it stimulates the blood supply – but *not* at a sharp angle to the body, or it can actually squash the blood vessels so that less gets through. It can also be fun, and effective, to stuff it into the vagina while it's still quite soft and give it a few nice wet squeezes inside.

Getting aroused

This will tend to involve longer and more widespread physical contact than it used to – you may finally discover how erotic toes can be, for example! (for your information, it's called 'shrimping' among those who go in for it!).
~ Gentle, physical contact which need not necessarily build into full-blown intercourse can be an enduring pleasure. Massage, for example, can be highly erotic. Do it knowing that it may, or may not, lead to intercourse, depending on the moment. This has the effect of relieving the pressure to perform, and so liberating you to a new world of continual pleasure.
~ Try sharing fantasies. Many people are embarrassed, even after years of marriage, to reveal their innermost fantasies to their partners. Well, now is the time! Do it on an equal basis – exchange one fantasy for another – one of mine for one of yours. "I lived for twenty years with my husband," says Mary, 57, "without telling him what I really found sexually exciting. Then, one day, I happened to make a joke about wearing a kinky plastic raincoat. He responded by challenging me to wear one – so I did, although I felt a bit foolish, just that and nothing else. Well it really got us both going; it surprised and thrilled me. We made love in broad daylight, we were laughing but it was very arousing, too. I don't know why I waited so long to do it."
~ Use the video. Many people have home video cameras, which can be used as tremendously exciting sexual tools. Initially, set it up so that you can see what you're up to on your television set, live, as it happens. It will be great fun, and not a little arousing, too (a modern equivalent of the mirror over the bed). "I found it very funny," says Colin, a retired charity worker, "then I saw that we were both getting quite a kick out of it. We were just touching and kissing each other to begin with, then as I began to slowly peel away her clothes, we both became quite sexually charged. The presence of the camera turned us both on, and how! Perhaps we're a bit exhibitionistic – it was like being watched, and we really enjoyed showing off." Note – if you press the 'record' button, hide the tape when the children come round!
Could all this get too stimulating? If you have a heart condition, you're probably a bit worried about getting too excited. Well, if you can climb two flights of stairs and feel basically sound, then sex should pose no health threat. To be on the safe side, wait two or three hours after a meal, because digestion and sex both make demands on the blood supply.

Intimate physical contact is a fundamental human want, and sexual arousal is a sublime pleasure which makes life worth living. If you believe you're desirable, if you want to be desired, then you are. There's an upward spiral here – and you can use your intelligence to begin going up it. Think sexy and you'll *be* sexy.

When you're young and headstrong, sex is a deadly serious business. When you reach maturity, you begin to understand the difference between 'copulation' and 'eroticism'. The one is not always pleasurable, the other *always* is!

How counselling can help your relationship

Counsellors come in many guises: family, friends, clergy, doctors, psychiatrists, social workers, Samaritans or Relate. Most people automatically resort to friends or family first, but if relationship problems persist, a trained counsellor can be a great help.

Every year in Britain about 100,000 people with marital difficulties seek help from trained counsellors. You don't have to be married or heterosexual to see a marriage guidance counsellor, and neither do you have to go along with your partner. People of all ages seek help and you can refer yourself directly (see the addresses in the Help section), although 50 per cent are also referred by other agencies like the Citizens Advice Bureau or doctors. Some go to see a counsellor after a relationship has already broken up.

What it can do

Counselling is of positive help to about 65 per cent of people. On average, you have between eight and ten hourly sessions, although it can range between one session and weekly sessions over eighteen months. Marriage guidance is free unless you choose to refer yourself to a private psychiatrist or counsellor. Relate does ask you to make a voluntary contribution, but there is no obligation to do so.

Relate sees people either at their centre, your local health centre, surgery or Citizens Advice Bureau and they make home visits to disabled people. Other agencies tend to see people in their offices. The aim of counselling is to help you to:

~ Communicate with your partner what you feel, what is satisfactory and what is not, what your needs are, how you see your future and so on, by creating an atmosphere which is devoid of criticism, aggression or judgement.

~ Understand each other better.

~ Find out what is missing and help you face up to what the real issues are.

~ Decide what needs changing and how.

~ Motivate yourself to change your behaviour patterns as a couple within the relationship.

The counsellor will do a lot of listening. If you are attending on your own, the counsellor will discuss with you the possibility of inviting your partner along. Any problem in a relationship is the result of both people and it is important for both sides to be heard. Assuming you are attending with your partner, the sessions will go something like this:

The first session

You will sit next to each other, facing the counsellor. The session will last approximately an hour. After the counsellor has introduced him/herself, he/she will tell you if they are going to take any notes during the session.

Initially, you will be asked to tell them a few basic details: your ages, how long you have been together, how many children you have, and so on. The counsellor will then ask you about what the relationship difficulties are. They will interrupt as little as possible as you both talk, except to clarify points. The counsellor will listen to the whole story and then ask questions about any of these areas which haven't been mentioned: emotional, spiritual, sexual, social and intellectual.

The counsellor will ask about each of your backgrounds: how many sisters or brothers, your relationship with parents, type of home life, and so on.

After listening to your replies, the counsellor will then make a preliminary assessment or summary to make sure that they have heard and understood correctly what has been said, and to try to establish agreement on what the mutual complaints are. Denials are listened to and discussed. The counsellor then reformulates a summary of the situation again, listens to objections and carries on in this way until there is all-round agreement on what the issues are.

Once this formulation of the problem is agreed upon, the counsellor will then move on to diagnosing the root causes – the reasons why the difficulties have arisen. In general, it will be either because one or both partners are not having specific needs met, or because unacceptable behaviour patterns are causing problems. There may be just one reason underlying your relationship problems, but it is more likely to be a combination of many. It is unlikely you will have time to establish all of them within this first session, but the counsellor will help you start to discover what those reasons are, which of them have the highest priority and which can be changed most quickly.

At the end of this first session you will at least have a formulation of the problem. The counsellor will agree with you on a plan of action for you to follow until the next session, which may be the following week or two weeks or more later. The plan of action will be either to continue discussion on specific points or to act in an agreed way which is relevant to your particular situation and problems. For example, you might agree to take the children out on Saturday afternoon whilst your partner agrees to do breakfast every other day.

It should be mentioned that after listening to the nature of your specific problems, the counsellor may suggest therapy with another counsellor, for example a sex therapist if your difficulties are in this area. Don't feel brushed aside if such a suggestion is made; they will only make the suggestion if they really feel that you will benefit from someone with specialized knowledge and counselling skills. If you are in doubt, ask the counsellor about their suggestion and discuss it openly with them.

Subsequent sessions

You will be asked to recap on what has happened since the last meeting. The counsellor will again reformulate the situation, continue with helping you establish the diagnosis – the underlying reasons for the difficulties, and to set new targets. Throughout, the counsellor will be helping you both to understand the nature of the problems and what you can both do about them.

The sessions will continue in this way with each one concluding with agreed interim action until the next session.

In the hands of a trained counsellor, partners can make great strides forward in remedying problems, but, of course, counselling doesn't guarantee reconciliation. It may be that a viable relationship no longer exists between you and your partner. If this is the case, the counsellor will help you to realize this, and help you both agree to parting on more amicable terms instead of amidst possible recriminations, confusion or hurt. One partner can be reluctant for this to happen, in which case the counsellor will help them find the strength and courage to face the reality of the situation and give encouragement for them to become independent.

Whilst counselling cannot guarantee to bring back the lost magic into every ailing relationship, it can help you reach a greater understanding of the way to resolve your difficulties. If your relationship is undergoing problems, with the help of counselling you could succeed in steering it clear of those rocks and discover the best way forward for both of you.

Chapter 126
Becoming a person of power

~

Becoming assertive

If you think self-assertion is simply being aggressive, you're missing out. Being assertive is about ensuring you are treated as you ought to be – with respect – but this is achieved through negotiation not intimidation.

There are three fundamental types of human behaviour – aggressive, passive and assertive. To illustrate them, let us imagine that you have a problem with a partner or flat-mate who refuses to wash up:

~ The *aggressive* approach would be to confront the culprit, accuse him of laziness and threaten dire consequences if he refuses to cooperate.

~ The *passive* approach would be to bring the subject up, but accept his excuses or back down in the face of his aggressive or incredulous reaction.

~ The *assertive* approach would be to express your concern about the problem, refuse to be fobbed off with excuses or disinterest and suggest a plan for more equal sharing of the household chores. You would reward cooperation with thanks and leave out the threats.

You can see now that assertive behaviour is the type best designed to achieve mutually beneficial results in any conflict of interest. It is the most socially useful form of behaviour – as well as your key to becoming a person of manifest power.

What do we mean by 'a powerful person'? Today, our idea of personal power has become so corrupted that we inevitably think of a person who has vast control over others – the President of the United States, for example, or the head of a large corporation. Strangely, we don't consider that personal power might just mean 'power over that which lies inside us'. Perhaps this is why there are so many essentially powerless people around today. In this chapter, we present you with some tools to become a more powerful, more effective person.

The elements of assertiveness

Behaving more assertively will enable you to:

~ Express your feelings – whether of approval or disagreement.

~ Speak up for your rights. You can say 'no' and ask to be treated fairly. You can complain without feeling guilty.

~ Be persistent in the face of resistance.

~ Question orders and ask for clarification if unhappy or confused.

~ Use these qualities to negotiate with other people so neither party feels they're getting a raw deal.

And the benefits of living in this way are enormous:

~ You will be able to relate more openly with other people.

~ No more subservience.

~ Far less worry, guilt and frustration.

~ More friends!

The secret of assertiveness

The secret of assertive behaviour is effective negotiation. Whatever the scenario, you need to establish a win-win situation, whereby both parties stand to gain by your discussion. There is a simple, three-step way to resolving any possible conflict in this way:

~ *First,* describe the problem or unsatisfactory situation accurately and objectively.

~ *Next,* describe your feelings about it without passing judgement or making the other party feel guilty.

~ *Finally,* propose a change in the situation or in the other party's behaviour that is reasonable and specific, and outline the favourable consequences of cooperation, something the other party stands to gain.

Now let's consider a case history. As it unfolds, see if you can spot the tactics and techniques being used.

Anthony, a 20-year-old graphic designer from the south of England, has always experienced a rather fraught relationship with his domineering mother. Anthony's father died three years ago, and Anthony was forced, by his mother, to fill the gap in her life. He still lives at home, and to some extent is still treated as if he were a young boy – his mother makes his bed, does the washing, prepares the meals, and generally looks after him. There is an emotional price to pay for all this lavish attention, however, and it is this: Anthony has no private life, no friends of his own, and no prospect of escaping. There was an argument some months previously, when Anthony threatened to leave home. His mother reacted by tearfully begging him not to, with a little emotional blackmail thrown in and, since then, the subject hasn't been raised again.

Clearly, it is not a good relationship for either person. Anthony's mother is trying to compensate for the loss of her partner by clinging protectively to her son; in this, she fails, because nothing can actually bring her husband back. Anthony himself is imprisoned in a situation which, although satisfying his basic needs for food and shelter, denies him any outside social life. The longer it goes on, the more of a casualty he will become.

Previous attempts to sort out the situation have failed dismally. Now, Anthony, who is naturally shy, has made up his mind to become more assertive.

This time, he has prepared himself beforehand. He has made some notes on what he wants to say and how he wants to say it. He opens the discussion on a Saturday afternoon, when his mother isn't occupied about the house.

"Can we talk for a few minutes?" he asks. His mother agrees, and sits down.

"We need to sort out a few things," he says. Before he can go any further, his mother swiftly interrupts.

"Please, darling," she cuts in, "I've got so much to do at the moment, it can wait, can't it?"

He was prepared for this.

"Not really. It's important for you, as well as for me. And there's nothing you've got to do which can't be put off for a few minutes."

"Please, Tony," she replies "Don't argue with me. I don't think I could bear it. You know what my doctor said. Please don't."

Another distraction. But Anthony isn't put off.

"I want to talk about your health, as well as mine. And an argument is the last thing I want, too."

"Then be a good boy, please don't upset me. You know how angry it would make your father, if he were here. Now let's have some tea. What would you like for tea?"

Again, a further attempted diversion. However, Anthony is quietly determined to make himself heard.

"Look mother, we have to talk. You know we do. If you don't want to talk now, then it'll have to be tomorrow. If not tomorrow, then the next day. But for both our sakes, it would be better now, rather than later."

Anthony's mother is silent, for a moment. She now realizes that he's serious, and won't be put off.

"Darling," she says after a pause, "I'm so sorry. I try so hard to make you happy. Ever since your father died you've been a wonderful friend to me. But I'm not making you happy, I can see it. Oh, darling, what else can I do? Just tell me, and I'll try so hard to make you happy." The tears are welling up in her eyes.

"Please listen to me."

His mother sniffs. "Go on."

Anthony takes a deep breath, and begins. "I love you, and I know that you love me, too. And I want you to know that we will always love each other. Now, I want to try to describe what I think is making us both unhappy, and see if we can sort it out. There are three things.

"Number one. You are wearing yourself out round the house, looking after me. I know that you're only doing it because you love me. And I know that I've been selfish, and allowed you to do things for me which I should have done for myself . . ."

"But I'm just being a good mother!" she interrupts.

"Please," replies Anthony. "Let me finish. Number two. Neither of us has any social life. You don't get out as much as you would like to, because you're busy doing things for me. And I'm not getting out either.

"Number three. I'm 20 years old, and many people younger than me already have their own place to live. It's time I did, too."

"You're going to leave me!" his mother exclaims. "I can't stand it, it will break my heart . . ." and she cries.

Anthony now has to decide what to do. He has described the problem and, at this point, it would be all too easy to cave in and to allow the status quo to continue indefinitely.

"Mother," he says, "I'm sorry you're upset. But please believe me, it's not my intention to hurt you. I want to sort this situation out, so that we're both happy again. At the moment, I feel as awful as you do. But I know that we can sort things out. Let me explain how."

"What do you mean?" she replies.

"What I propose we should do is this. We've had some good times in this house, but nothing lasts for ever, and now it is time for us to move on. This house is too much for us now, so I suggest we sell it. With the money, I propose we buy a smaller place which is easier for you to look after, in a nice area where you'll have lots of friends and a good social life. And, if you are willing, you could help me to put down a deposit on a flat of my own. Would you be willing to help me like that?"

"Oh Tony," his mother replies, "I couldn't sell this house. Your father and I were so happy here."

"Yes, I know you were happy here," says Anthony. "But in the last three years, things have changed. You know that. What I want to do is make us happy again. Now, would you be willing to help me in the way I've just asked?"

Let's analyse what happened in this small drama. Anthony's mother, of course, had a shrewd idea of the nature of the likely course of the conversation right from the start. Instinctively, she deployed a number of tactics to forestall it:

~ The 'I'm busy' line. "I've got so much to do at the moment, it can wait, can't it?"
~ Intimidation. "Don't argue with me. I don't think I could bear it. You know what my doctor said . . ."
~ Refusal to take you seriously. "Be a good boy, please don't upset me . . ."
~ The instant apology. "Just tell me, and I'll try so hard to make you happy . . ."

All of these tactics can be defeated, as Anthony did, by not being side-tracked or cowed by them, and by pressing ahead with your main point.

After overcoming these hurdles, Anthony could at last proceed to the first step of his pre-planned delivery by describing the problem accurately and objectively. In this case, Anthony chose to break the problem down into three parts – numbers one, two and three.

Then we got to the moment of truth. At this point, his mother broke down, and cried. This was a very difficult stage, because the strong temptation is to withdraw, apologize, and never bring the subject up again. Of course, this is entirely the wrong course of action, but it nevertheless requires nerve and pre-planning to get through this part. Anthony acknowledged her distress ("I'm sorry you're upset . . . it's not my intention to hurt you") but was not deflected from the second stage, which was to describe his own feelings about the situation, without passing judgement or making his mother feel guilty.

The third stage consisted of his proposed solution to the problem. In it, he demonstrated that his preferred course of action would be advantageous for her as well as for him ("a smaller place will be easier for you to look after . . . you'll have lots of friends").

Of course, a situation like this is not going to be resolved completely with one short conversation. However, something significant *has* been achieved. Anthony has, calmly and clearly, asserted himself. He has crystallized the problem, and put forward an acceptable solution. Whatever happens in the future, he has taken the discussion further than it has ever gone before, beyond a certain, critical watershed, and it will never be possible to pretend that it hasn't taken place. His closing question, asking his mother whether she would be willing to help him put down a deposit for a flat, was cleverly chosen, because it allows her to fulfil her very real desire to do the best she can for her son, while at the same time establishing a degree of independence between them.

Now, what prevents you from dealing like this? There are two major barriers between the mild-mannered or aggressive you and the Assertive You:

~ Low self-esteem

~ Fear

Let's examine them both, and see what can be done to correct them.

Raising your self-esteem

Self-esteem is about your opinion of yourself. This is very important because if you don't think you're up to much it's unlikely that anyone else will. So your first step is to convince yourself you're worth taking seriously:

~ Write down on a piece of paper all the adjectives you would use to describe yourself, positive and negative. Add to the list any points you think are important, such as:

- I am a good tennis player.
- I never speak up at meetings.

Put the date on your list, so that you can refer back to it in the weeks and months ahead, and register your progress. Now you know what you think of yourself, you can set about reinforcing the positive and discarding the negative, by following these ten dynamic techniques (dynamic means 'active' – you must *act* upon them if they are to work for you):

1 Communicate more

Think how our society tries to strangle communication. We sit in silence on the bus or train, we communicate at work only when it is neccessary ("I don't want to catch you gossiping in the company's time"), and we sit in silence at home again while professional 'communicators' talk to us from the television.

Be aware that you have to reverse this trend towards a mute society. Strike up conversations with people at the bus-stop, in the launderette, on the train, at the supermarket. Find organizations to join which encourage formal or informal conversation – your local Further Education College, library or Citizens Advice Bureau can supply details of what's available in your area. You may well find that there are assertiveness courses to join, too. Basically, you must seize every opportunity to communicate – and when there doesn't seem to be one, create it. Quite simply, the more you do it, the easier it gets.

2 Listen more

This is a very, very important skill which – perhaps more than any other – can do wonders for your social and personal success. If you doubt the importance of learning how to listen, just think about the way professional sales people go about their jobs. Unlike the traditional stereotype, a good salesperson is not a slick, foot-in-the-door, silver-tongued rogue who boasts about selling coals to Newcastle or refrigerators to Eskimos. In reality, the most successful sales people – often earning truly staggering salaries – are quiet, pleasant types who are, first and foremost, good listeners. The best sales people may be selling insurance, or power stations, or television programmes, or complex computer systems – but whatever they're selling, they know they'll get nowhere – and earn no commission – if they don't listen very hard indeed to what their customers really want.

For a sales person, therefore, the choice is easy – you either become a good listener, or you don't make sales, and consequently don't earn money. This provides a powerful incentive to learn the art of listening. But the rest of us don't have nearly such a powerful, and obvious, incentive to cultivate this art. Which probably explains why most of us are so poor at it.

The trouble is, everyone and everything seems to want our attention nowadays. Television, radio, advertisements, politicians, religions, junk mail, family and friends . . . the list goes on and on. With less and less time to divide our attention between all these things, it's not surprising if we slowly start to shut off, block off outside voices, and forget how to listen.

When we watch television, we rarely devote our full attention to it – our mind may be thinking about dozens of other things, or we may be eating, or reading the paper, or cooking a meal. And when someone starts talking to us, our mind rarely concentrates on what they're really saying, but drifts off to any number of different subjects. This also means, of course, that when it's our turn to talk, our mind becomes so used to dividing its attention between many tasks that we often don't think about what we're actually saying.

A world full of talkers but empty of listeners is a very lonely world indeed. This is why it is essential for all of us to become good listeners, as well as good expressers of our thoughts and feelings.

So how do you start to become a good listener? First, realize that listening is *not* a passive experience – unlike having your hair cut, or your nails manicured, listening is a vital, active experience that demands all the attention you have. Like any skill, it must be practised if you are to become any good at it. So here's an exercise which will help you to become that rarest of all human beings – a good listener.

~ This exercise is both enjoyable and effective. What you're going to do is practise *intelligent listening.* You're going to need a pen and note pad to help you do this. First, you must find someone to listen to. To begin with, don't try this with just one partner – instead, find a talk or lecture that you can easily get along to. It can be about absolutely any subject – in fact, for reasons which will become clear later, it's *better* if the subject is one which initially doesn't seem very attractive or interesting to you. Most towns and cities have meeting rooms where local groups or societies regularly arrange lectures, so make a note of the next one, and arrange to be present. If you can't get out in the evening to do this, listening to a broadcast talk (Radio Three has a talk almost every day of the week) is just as good.

Now settle yourself down and write the title of the talk and the speaker's name at the top of the page. Listen carefully as the speaker gets into the talk, and jot down the main points and conclusions he or she makes as they come along. Don't try and transcribe the entire talk word for word – the whole point of the exercise is to listen carefully, and identify only the important pieces. This is the sort of thing journalists do when they interview someone about a story. Here's a sample:

Title: So You Want To Be A Vegetarian!
Speaker: Peter Cox

People Are Eating Less Meat
- Survey shows 7 million people in UK have cut out meat
- 33 per cent of population claim to be 'eating less meat'
- 11 per cent of children under 16 don't eat meat

Why Is This Happening?
- Health: vegetarians have less cancer, heart disease, high blood pressure, etc.
- Morality: children especially aware of cruelty to animals
  George Bernard Shaw: "Animals are my friends, and I don't eat my friends"
- Food Resources
  - People more conscious of world hunger
  - Animals very inefficient use of protein
    - Only 5 per cent of grain fed to a cow is turned into meat
  - Meat animals now eat more of world's food than humans do

What Are The Drawbacks?
- People worry about protein
  - Protein is present in most food, not just meat
  - Too much protein in diet is bad
  - Evidence shows vegetarians get enough protein
- Eating In Restaurants Sometimes Difficult
  - Most restaurants now cater for vegetarians

How To Eat Well
- Importance of fresh food
- Food preparation should be a shared pleasure
- Humans are primates who experiment with new food
- Variety important, lots of vegetarian cookery books on sale

- and so on.

You can see that this exercise will, very quickly, help you to find and concentrate upon the important points in what you're listening to. And what's more, you'll discover a very important truth – that irrespective of the subject matter of a talk or conversation, if you are prepared to *make some effort* to actively listen, then you will find that the subject automatically begins to interest you!

To be a good listener, you must first of all accurately hear what your partner is saying. But that's not all – nor is it enough in itself to make you a good listener. The next stage is to develop empathy – to understand *why* the speaker is talking to you, and *what* his or her words really mean in human and emotional terms, deep down under the surface. This is a subtle skill, but one which will mark you out as a very special human being if you develop it.

Let's consider an example. A woman who has been raped is talking to her friend. Apart from the physical and mental trauma of her ordeal, it now appears that she is pregnant. She is deeply distressed by this news, and is considering an abortion. Her friend, who opposes abortion on moral grounds, is encouraging her to have the child and have it adopted.

The conversation isn't going well, and both participants are emotionally upset. When it ends, the woman and her friend have fallen out, and most importantly, the woman's own feelings are now more disturbed and distressed than before. What's gone wrong?

In this example, you don't have to be a psychoanalyst to see the problem. Obviously, the woman in question needed, more than anything else, a sympathetic ear to listen – non-judgementally – to the emotional turmoil she was experiencing. And just as obviously, she didn't get it.

From this, we can characterize a bad listener as someone who is judgemental, and rapidly forms hard opinions – often based on incomplete facts – which they are only too quick to voice. When they speak, it is usually from ingrained attitudes, rather than in response to the human being they're supposed to be listening to.

On the other hand, a good listener will suspend judgement – no matter how strongly or deeply they feel about the issues being discussed – until they have heard all the facts, and, most importantly, until they have had a chance to understand not just what's being said, but the *underlying reason* for their partner's thoughts and feelings.

Another special quality found in good listeners is the ability to ask exploratory questions. This is probably the most important way you can help anyone in real emotional difficulty. By acting as an outside observer, and asking neutral questions that clarify the issues raised, you can often help your partner to confront and solve their own problems. Questions such as the following are always valuable to ask:

~ How did that make you feel?
~ What thoughts were in your mind then?
~ What effect did that have?

How do you practise these skills? Simply by doing them whenever possible. Use the following mnemonic to frequently remind yourself of the attributes of a good listener. As you listen, you should frequently ask yourself whether you're using all the skills at your disposal. It will soon become second nature.

~ Q is for Questions: ask neutral, helpful questions that clarify thoughts and feelings for both of you.
~ U is for Understanding: check yourself to make sure you do.
~ A is for Advice: Don't offer it!
~ D is for Disagreement: don't be judgemental or you'll provoke a disagreement which will hurt both of you.

3 Steer clear of underminers

This is a simple rule. Things are tough enough without 'friends' who habitually put you down. If someone does this continually, don't be afraid to 'fire' them from your lives – they are only damaging your self-esteem. Negativity is an infectious disease. One person can, and will, pass it on to another. If you have to place an acquaintance in 'quarantine', then so be it. Replace them with friends who boost your self-esteem – who compliment you, who listen to you, who make you feel special. Try to avoid situations that undermine your confidence. When you do have to deal with someone who puts you down, stand up to them. Let them know you feel different. It will preserve your confidence and give them something to think about.

4 Be willing to forgive yourself

Everyone makes mistakes, but playing and re-playing recorded memories of the *mistakes* you've made in the past can only send your self-esteem on a downward spiral. Learn to laugh at your mistakes and concentrate on the really positive things you've done.

5 Be generous with compliments

Compliments show that you have enough self-confidence to sing someone else's praises. Compliments operate on a boomerang principle – they always find their way back to whoever gave them in the first place. So they build your self-esteem in two ways – by giving and by receiving.

6 Conquer your shyness

You're shy – so what? Lots of people are: 40 per cent of all adults according to a Stanford University study. The trick is not to let it dominate your actions – you can either be paralysed by fear, or you can do something about it. Shyness is often an excuse for inaction. Make the effort and it will be rewarded. Fear and anxiety are often manifest as shyness, so read the section on handling fear which follows.

7 Be well informed

Crawl out from your shell and take in a little of what's going on around you. Keep up to date with current affairs, start going to the theatre and reading book reviews and learn a new poem every week. Easier still, read books of quotations and equip yourself with borrowed wit. Knowing what's happening makes you feel smart and well informed.

8 Develop a passion

Everyone loves to hear people talk about the things that inspire them, be it collecting beer cans or making hand-made chocolates. When you talk about your passion, you radiate a highly contagious and attractive enthusiasm. Pursuing a hobby is also an excellent way to make new friends.

9 Take a few risks

Approach people. Smile, talk to strangers. Others will find your confidence attractive, and, besides, just reaching out will make you feel good about yourself. And learn not to stake your self-esteem on every encounter – what does it matter if Mr. Gold Medallion ignores you – when the party finishes, you'll have a lot more new friends than he will.

10 Take time to look good

The more attractive you feel, the more highly you think of yourself. You don't need a glossy magazine look, only the shine you get from regular exercise and a healthy diet.

Handling fear

Fear can turn an assertive confrontation into a fiasco, but you can deal with it in two ways:

- By preparing yourself mentally beforehand.
- By learning to curb your anxiety.

Desensitization is an effective form of mental preparation. Picture the confrontation, test or problem then write down ten steps leading up to it. For example, imagine you are due to discuss a pay rise with your intimidating boss. The first step may be a picture of you having breakfast; the second, sitting on the bus, the third and fourth doing morning tasks and so on until you are actually sitting in the office with your boss ready to begin. Focus on each step in turn until you can picture it in your mind without becoming nervous; start with the easiest and work through them until you can imagine your boss's unfriendly face without fear. When the day comes, concentrate on each step as you carry it out, and you will find your nervousness much reduced.

Also, try using your friends and family to discuss your course of action before the event. Frankly admit what your feelings of anxiety and nervousness are. One of the authors of this book was sitting in the departure lounge of Los Angeles airport waiting for the flight back to London recently when a businessman came in, accompanied by his wife. "She made a beeline for me," said Peter. "And without beating about the bush she told me that her husband was terrified of flying, because whenever he flew, he believed that the plane was in danger of breaking apart. From his nervous state, it was obvious that he was going to go through eleven hours of pure hell before he got to London. But because his wife had asked me to look after him, and had brought his problem right out into the open, we could talk freely about his anxiety. If she hadn't approached me, he would have been too scared and embarrassed to speak to anyone. We chatted away, and by the time we reached London, his fear of flying had gone." So expose your deepest feelings of fear and anxiety to the healing light of day – they may just disappear!

Curbing anxiety

It's night and you are in a deep sleep. You wake abruptly to the sound of bangs and tappings. Heart pounding. Is it a burglar? Is it a rat? You are overcome by anxiety.

Anxiety is one of our most common modern feelings. Fear evolved to help us survive so that we could respond quickly if in danger. The 'fight or flight' response was intended to prepare an individual in a dangerous situation to fight or run away from an enemy. When we're threatened, our blood pressure increases, as does our heart rate, the rate of breathing, blood flow to the muscles and general metabolism. Epinephrine, a hormone that stimulates the heart, and norepinephrine, a hormone that constricts blood vessels (this limits bleeding in case of injury) flood into our system. Breathing becomes very rapid and shallow. All very useful, life-saving measures for the kind of life-threatening stress our ancestors had to cope with. But not very useful for today's high-stress lifestyle.

Modern life has unprecedented dangers, but they're usually not the sort you can hit on the nose or run away from. So our anxiety accumulates, and our bodies are powerless to resist the pernicious effects of anxiety.

Anxiety knocks your confidence and damages your health. During stressful periods, your body produces large amounts of a steroid called cortisol. This inhibits the work of your immune system so that your body no longer responds so effectively to infection. Here are simple practical steps you can take to lessen anxiety or prevent it:

~ If you're giving a speech, taking an exam, attending an interview, or in some other way thinking forward to an anxiety-provoking occasion, the rule to remember is: *anxiety flees when confidence comes*. And you can gain confidence by making sure you know your subject backwards. Find out what you'll be covering well in advance and take time to read and think about it. Test yourself with searching questions. Then have faith in your preparations. If you've done the work you *will* succeed.

~ If you think the situation will be hostile, think about your weak points and ask yourself questions posed in a difficult or belligerent way.

~ You can prepare for the most unlikely situations – not just interviews or examinations. Before a dinner party, find out who is on the guest list and their occupations – then think about possible topics of conversation. This way, you are no longer entering the unknown!

~ Rehearse. A well-known author says: "Each time I have to go on television to talk about my new book, in front of millions of people, I'm nervous. But I can conquer it by rehearsing beforehand. So I ask the publishers to send me to the smallest out-of-the-way radio station they can find before I venture on to TV. This way, I can find my feet and prepare myself so that when the big one comes, I'm well prepared and ready."

Everyone who has to stand up in front of an audience and perform – entertainer, politician, TV presenter – is nervous. But you can minimize the symptoms of nervousness just before you take the plunge by following these clever tricks that the professionals use:

~ Whenever you get an attack of butterflies, take a deep breath, and let it out as slowly as possible. Repeat several times. This will slow down your body's production of the fear-inducing hormones, noradrenaline and epinephrine.

~ Concentrate on developing a positive attitude. In other words, get psyched up! A good technique is to repeat some phrase to yourself, like 'I can do it!' This is your Positive Mantra; it will keep negative thoughts at bay and allow you to enter the situation feeling calm.

~ Behave as if you *were* confident! The way that you act influences the way you feel, so if you smile you'll *feel* more like smiling! Think of the professional dancers you see in variety shows on television and in cabaret. A professional dancer's life is hard, very competitive, lots of physical work and an uncertain future. Not much to smile about, really. But when they come on and strut their stuff, they're smiling as if they haven't a care in the world! That's professionalism; you can do it too!

~ Your manner and expression tell people what sort of person you are, so give them a good impression. Smile when you meet somebody and look them in the eye when you talk to them. Keep your expression bright and alert so you come across as a friendly, open individual – people will respond to you in the same way.

~ Your bearing also describes you to people, so look purposeful. Walk with your head up wherever you are – people will mark you down as a person who knows what they're about. To have someone respond to you like that makes for great self-esteem.

~ Try to give off an aura of calm by keeping your hands and body still. Don't fidget! If you're addressing an audience, and you really don't know what to do with your hands, put them in your pockets; it'll make you appear relaxed. If you've no pockets, hold them behind your back.

~ A firm, dry handshake is a sign of confidence. If your palms sweat wipe them surreptitiously before you shake.

Above all, be yourself. Don't give in to the urge to hide your personality under a rock. If you feel 'different' it's because you are, just like everyone else! That's what makes you interesting, so let your individuality sparkle.

More generally, you should also consider the following:

~ Give up caffeine. Caffeine in even small amounts can provoke panic attacks in susceptible people and large amounts can cause nervousness and anxiety in almost anyone (see chapter 8). Bear in mind some caffeine counts: Ground coffee: 80mg per cup. Instant coffee: 60mg per cup. Decaf: 3mg per cup. Tea 30mg per cup. Cola 48mg per 12 oz. Chocolate bar: 20mg.

~ Learn to laugh at stressful situations. Laughter is a tremendously powerful healing force. Make fun of an infuriating situation by imagining the most ludicrous and exaggerated outcome! And start to make time in your life for humour. Go to comedy films, hire videos, read humorous books, catch comedy shows and cabaret.

~ Tell someone what is bothering you, because bottled up feelings cause anxiety. Remember to confide in a friend or relative who really cares about you. And if this doesn't work, write down your feelings and later on throw the piece of paper away. If you are suddenly gripped by 3am anxiety, get out of bed, write down the problem. Tell yourself that you will deal with it tomorrow morning at 9.30. By making this appointment you solve the fundamental problem: deciding to face the cause of your worry.

~ Take a bath and imagine feelings of relaxation spreading all over your body. The most soothing baths are warm, about 100 degrees. Hot water is a shock to your system, but warm water calms by increasing circulation and relaxing muscles. Heating the body can induce deeper sleep.

~ Breathe deeply. This makes your body release endorphins, hormones which have a calming effect within thirty seconds. Most of us breathe in the top part of our chest only. This doesn't help to relax us, because most of our lower chest muscles still stay rigidly tense. Instead, breathe in slowly through your nose, expanding your lower abdomen (stick your tummy out!) and then your rib cage. Then release the breath through your mouth very slowly and silently say 'Relax'. After a few months you will automatically breathe slowly in tense situations.

What you can do about extreme anxiety

"One night I was coming home from work on the bus, and suddenly I felt a feeling of unreality and impending doom. I felt flushed, nauseated, dizzy. My heart started pounding. I remember just sitting on the bus and thinking I was going to die."

That's how the panic attack started for Martine, a 32-year-old teacher with no previous concerns about anxiety or nerves. Panic attacks (or panic disorder, or anxiety attack, or agoraphobia – the terminology varies, the symptoms are much the same) are getter more and more common, and they happen to all sorts of people. Once you've had one, you'll go on having them until you're cured, or to be more precise, until you cure yourself. Every panic attack is an extremely unpleasant occurrence. To begin with, you may feel as if you're having a heart attack. So any treatment should begin with a thorough physical examination, simply to rule out any medical causes of the symptoms. Then it's up to you and your medical advisers to sort out a cure. And they *are* curable . . .

First of all, there is immediate first aid. When you're in the throes of a panic attack, there are several things you can do to regain control:

~ Do your utmost to stay with the situation. If you run away this time, you're initiating a self-defeating pattern of behaviour.

~ Make a big effort to slow down your breathing. Take a deep breath – expand your diaphragm so your stomach pushes out – and hold it while you count to four. Then exhale slowly. Aim for between eight and twelve breaths per minute.

~ Distraction can be a powerful weapon. Instead of focusing on your physical symptoms, start talking to somebody – or even to yourself – or pay extra attention to your breathing. You'll notice that the panic starts to subside almost immediately.

~ Try splashing cold water on your face.

~ Carry a cassette of relaxing music and put it on. This is a very simple, yet powerful, technique to shut the world out. In particular, you will find a tape of relaxing music combined with subliminal relaxation commands to be very useful (see chapter 102 for more details of subliminal cassettes).
~ Use the Bach Rescue Remedy (see chapter 68). This is another extremely effective way to rapidly bring the situation under control. Place five or six drops of the undiluted solution under the tongue, and repeat whenever necessary.

Next, you must find someone to talk to who can help you understand what's going on. Your GP is the obvious place to start, and if he/she has an interest in this problem, it could be all the help you'll need. Too often, however, you won't get satisfactory or sympathetic treatment. Some doctors still think that sufferers are merely hypochondriacs. So it's important that you keep on looking until you find someone who *can* help you make sense of this crippling condition. Don't be discouraged. Sometimes teaching hospitals or universities will have a lecturer with a special interest, or maybe even someone who runs group classes.

Whether you should take medication or not to control the problem is up to you. But tranquillizers have side effects, and coming off them can be more difficult than tackling the real cause of your attacks. So don't be pushed into pill-popping. Here are some useful pieces of advice designed to help you get on top again:
~ Certain activities will provoke an attack. While you may have to avoid them to begin with, when you feel able, you should slowly expose yourself to them again. For example, someone afraid of driving on the open road may begin to face her fear simply by sitting in a car, then driving around the block.

Slowly does it. Step by step, you can desensitize yourself to the situation. If you can't leave the house without an attack coming on, start by opening the door and looking out for a few minutes. Then down to the end of the garden. Then onto the path and back again. And so on. Have a friend within sight to give yourself confidence.
~ Some therapists advocate the 'implosion' technique. This involves total immersion in the situation which brings on an attack until you are no longer affected by it. For example, if you get a panic attack riding on crowded buses, buy a day ticket and spend twelve hours riding them. Take a friend (or your therapist) for support. You *will* have an attack, of course, to begin with. But you'll live through it. And having conquered it, you will have the confidence to do it again. Obviously you need to discuss this technique with your therapist before you do it.
~ Avoid all caffeine-containing foods and fluorescent lights. You may be highly sensitive to both.
~ Realize that *you're* in control. To the victim of a panic attack, it seems as if the world suddenly goes out of control. This is terrifying, and fear of having another panic attack builds up a vicious circle of fear-panic-fear. You can break this by taking control again. In fact, you must!

Fighting phobias

Spiders . . . blood . . . flying . . . heights . . . snakes . . . dentists – do any of these words make you flinch? Maybe you have only to hear a barking dog to be seized by panic. Or perhaps the very thought of getting into a car makes you feel faint. And what happens if you confide your anxiety to a friend? Sadly, a common reaction is: 'You're kidding!' or 'Don't be so silly!' Not that your friend is being deliberately unkind. It's just that other people find it extremely difficult to understand – or empathize with – the real terror you experience if you suffer from a phobia.

The good news is that phobias *can* be overcome. And you can take the first step right now, by understanding exactly what a phobia is, and what might have caused it.

Quite simply, a phobia is an irrational and inappropriate fear of a particular object or situation. Most phobics manage to cope by avoiding whatever it is that frightens them. So in an extreme case, someone suffering from agoraphobia becomes completely housebound. After all, one of the easiest ways to 'cope' with a phobia is avoidance. People have been known to turn down promotions, because the new job involved a lot of air travel. Or ended up with a set of false teeth rather than attend regular dental check-ups. One American researcher discovered that in fact most phobics wait for between eight and ten years before seeking the help they need – for fear of the treatment itself!

Phobics are more likely to be women, particularly those between twenty-five and forty-five. Having said that, now even male victims will more often follow the avoidance strategy of 'coping', since they themselves are conditioned to regard a display of fear or anxiety as particularly weak.

Phobics are not, as you might imagine, innately timid people. On the contrary, they are much more likely to be 'take charge' individuals who feel they need to be in control. Phobics also tend to be more than averagely sensitive and highly strung. They may well find it difficult to deal effectively with stress. And their resting heart and breathing rates are often higher than normal.

Have you ever stopped to try to work out exactly what it was that triggered your phobia in the first place? There's no single cause, but there's often what amounts to a logical explanation for behaving irrationally.

To give just two examples: Some people have no problems flying until they have their first child, at which point they begin to worry about what would happen to the family if they were to die. For others, the roots of a phobia may lie in a barely-remembered childhood incident; is it possible that your claustrophobia can be traced to the moment when an adult threatened to lock you in a cupboard next time you misbehaved?

An unconquered phobia feeds on itself. It becomes a habit. And ultimately, you come to be afraid of feeling afraid.

The encouraging news is there's an extremely high chance of conquering your phobia – for good – within a relatively short period of time, if you take the first step towards treatment. If you have a sympathetic doctor you should pluck up your courage and ask to be referred to an experienced practitioner. It's possible to be treated on the National Health Service, but you may be in for a long wait. So consider going privately.

The whole idea of therapy is for you to learn how to change your behaviour. And to do that, you need to change your habitual way of thinking about and dealing with the sensations of anxiety. Naturally, the precise treatment is tailored to your individual needs. But here's an idea of what to expect:

~ Your therapist will encourage and help you to confront the situations that you've been avoiding. For example, if you're afraid of snakes, you might begin to face your fear simply by reading about them, or by looking at a photograph. If the result is a panic attack, you're shown specific relaxation techniques to help you calm down. Then, with the support of your therapist, you gradually move closer to the feared situation once more.

~ As a result of therapy, your confidence grows. You realize that by remaining in the situation, you can allow your anxiety to pass.

~ You may be invited to attend group therapy sessions; there's added strength in numbers – and mutual support is always helpful.
~ Your therapist may also recommend the use of anti-anxiety drugs or beta blockers, which wipe out the physical symptoms of the panic attack. But these are usually used as a short-term solution, to help give you courage to confront your phobia. Don't depend on them.

Provided you're highly motivated – you've come to the conclusion that you no longer want to live life *around* your phobia – you can almost certainly conquer it. But it's never going to happen unless you take that difficult first step. Half the battle is admitting the phobia and seeking help. Don't delay!

Chapter 127
Managing your relationships

~

For most of us, a relationship is something which controls us. We are, in a sense, its victim – going wherever it leads us, suffering whatever it imposes on us. Well, here we propose a new model for dealing with relationships – management. When you learn how to manage your relationships, you will find they reward, not rob you.

How much thought do you give to your relationships? We all spend time thinking about our friends and partners, but often fail to consider exactly what we are getting from them (and indeed what we are giving). Everyone is guilty of continuing to give time to people who they would rather not see at all. Whether it is a failing marriage or a flagging friendship, it can be very difficult to make the break. By the same token, we may take the people we *really* care about for granted (especially if a large part of our energy is going into sustaining unsatisfactory relationships). So, how do you make sure your emotional energy is being properly directed?

A friendship audit

The first step is to take stock. Look back on past relationships – can you identify specific patterns? This may be difficult to do immediately; often our behaviour and attitudes are so deeply rooted in habit that it is almost impossible to be analytical about them ourselves. If you feel there may be some deeper patterns to work on, don't try to do it alone – get the help of a counsellor or therapist.

Consider what you need from others: are you very demanding of their time and commitment, for example. Think too about what you have to offer in a relationship, because the basis of any good partnership is give-and-take. Look then at the relationships you do have and ask yourself what is good and bad about them. Don't avoid this, although it may be painful; write down a list of points, so you are forced to consider them. You can then congratulate yourself: you will have done what most people rarely have the guts to do. You will (at least in part) have faced up to the reality of your relationships in a very measured way. It can be difficult looking our emotional life straight in the eye, but thinking logically in this way isn't a case of being calculating, it is giving your relationships the measured consideration they surely deserve.

When things change

Relationships, like everything else, change and it may not be the fault of either party. Increased wealth or status can cause a strain on even the best of friendships. If you begin to earn a lot more money than your best friend from college, be tactful. You may think you are being generous by taking her out for expensive meals, but she might just end up feeling intimidated. Men, particularly, have very fragile egos in this area and it can be difficult for them to cope with a partner with high earning power. Of course, the problem here isn't just a question of money; when a man feels uncomfortable with a successful woman it is usually about power and independence rather the financial jealousy.

That green-eyed monster does, however, break up a lot of people. Envy can rear its ugly head in the most unlikely situations. You may, for example, be astonished to discover that your independent fast-living friend is deeply jealous of your two-year-old toddler. But envy needn't be destructive; if you feel twinges of green at someone else's luck, use it and tell the person how you feel. This will not only make them feel good, but it may even prompt them to exclaim that they had always been jealous of your lifestyle. This will then make you feel good and you will both be closer for sharing this supposedly terrible secret. But the most important thing about admitting negative thoughts is that just talking about them somehow, miraculously, is a purging. Try the same approach with anger, guilt and any other bad feelings.

Honesty and anger

Don't be afraid to argue – confrontation is healthy. This is often very difficult for women who traditionally shy away from conflict. The key to working out difficulties is not to accuse. Be careful about your choice of words; talk in terms of how you feel: "I am upset and hurt that you did this," rather than condemnation – "you are thoughtless and spiteful for treating me in this way." It is a real art and one that is well worth learning for the emotional dividends it brings. You will find that after a resolved difficulty the relationship will actually be stronger.

That song about perfect friendship is a musical fairy tale. Sadly, there are no ideal relationships. There are, however, lots of very good ones and these rely on communication, change, openness and trust. Relationships, even successful ones, have to be cultivated and then maintained, otherwise they will just go to seed. Just as with anything else dividends are only brought about by investment.

If you are busy with your job, relationships can be the first to suffer simply because there doesn't seem to be enough hours in the day. But remember, it only takes a couple of minutes to give someone a call to tell them you are thinking about them. Try inviting a few friends around at the same time if you really can't see them on their own. It is a matter of priorities; you *can* have a career and a good social life, you just have to work at it.

Making friends

What if your problem is not keeping friends, but making them? Some people are simply not very good at forming new relationships, but everyone has it in them to 'win friends and influence people'. Part of the problem probably lies in your own self-image. If you secretly think that you are pretty worthless, people very quickly pick up on that fear and believe it themselves. But, amazingly, as soon as you take a more positive approach you will find the balance will soon tip in your favour. Others will begin, however gently, to respond to your good attitude and the cycle will be broken. As you begin to get positive feedback, your own self-image will be reinforced, and you will feel even more attractive. Perhaps this sounds too easy, but the hard part really is just getting the ball rolling.

Cutting cords

But what about saying goodbye? Anyone who has ever gone away to college knows the truth of that old joke that you can spend your whole time there trying to avoid fellow students you met in the telephone queue in the first week. It is not always such a joke, either. Life is too short to spend reluctant time with social limpets. You may tell yourself that you are acting out of loyalty, but who are you kidding? That sort of favour doesn't do much for anyone's self-esteem. How would you feel if you knew someone you were with was just acting out of pity? It is all part of a cycle as well; if you show respect for other people (whether you decide to be friends with them or not), you will find respect will quickly come your way.

Very often this much cited 'concern' is not the real reason at all. When people talk of wanting to finish with a partner but being afraid of hurting them, they may be hiding a much greater fear – the fear of solitude. Many of us are scared of being alone, but clinging to an unsatisfactory relationship is by no means the answer.

If you have a problem cutting emotional cords try taking a practical approach. Look at how others, especially your family, have treated you. Perhaps, because of past relationships, you have a nagging doubt that you are not really worthy of anything better. You may feel that you are lucky to have anyone at all and should not let them go because you will never find someone to replace them. This is dangerous, dependent thinking and the only solution is to break down those old attitudes so that you can begin to value yourself. This, again, will not happen overnight, so be patient and try to get support of some kind.

There are in fact very few of us who haven't stayed with a partner after we knew it was already well and truly over. There may be all sorts of sensible reasons for this. Often a period of adjustment is needed to come to terms with this dramatic shift in circumstance. Some people hold on to the idea that there is still a slight chance that things will be all right again, and many are just struggling with that old fear of being alone and unloved. It is important to give appropriate time to these natural concerns, but don't drag it out. It may be hard saying goodbye, but until you have managed to shut old doors, new ones rarely open.

You sometimes have to make frightening decisions and take risks, even if that means committing yourself to being on your own for a while. And that may not be the terrible state you imagine; living without a partner in a healthy relationship with yourself has to be better than being one of an unhappy couple. The old saying that "until you have learned to be happy with yourself, you cannot really be happy with someone else" really is true.

Attitudes of others can be just as much of a problem. If you are considering splitting up, you may feel pressured from parents and in-laws to stay together when children are involved. Not only is fear of disapproval no way to live your life, but acting in the best interest of others doesn't work. Children are a lot more aware than we give them credit for, and they are especially quick to pick up on any negative feelings. If you remain in a unhappy relationship for your children's sake not only will you end up feeling emotionally deprived, but you may also wind up resentful of the sacrifice you have made. And however much you try to contain those feelings, your children will know. Anyway, a household in which the parents do not love each other is hardly the best environment for a child to grow up in.

If you are still unsure of what path to take, ask yourself some questions. Is the person you are with special to you in their own right, or are they just filling a role – as husband, girlfriend, etc? Do you have an identity of your own, or do you depend on your partner for your sense of value in the world? What were the reasons for the relationship in the first place: were you lonely or on the rebound? On the other hand, are you just bored with life generally and see a relationship break as the fastest path to change?

Relationships are central to the way we live; they affect every other single area of our lives. Our job performance, health and mental state can all deteriorate as the result of unhappy relationships, while good ones are the foundations of positive living. It is worth giving some thought to cutting the dead wood out of your social life and committing yourself to making sure the rest is blooming healthily.

The problem with men

Does your man have friends, or just workmates? Does he even know the difference? If not, it's time for you to act.

"I was thirty-five years old," says Andrew, a company director, "and suddenly I realized that I knew lots of people, but didn't have one single person who I could call a friend. All my relationships were either business or sexual. Friendship just didn't enter my life, and hadn't done since I left school."

It's one of the most tragically neglected areas of men's lives. All too often, says psychologist Abraham Maslow, men don't have a friend in the world. They have acquaintances, of course, men they meet for a chat, a drink, a game of tennis. But how many of those could they call on in a tight spot, or talk to about their inner fears and failings? The camaraderie of 'drinks with the boys' is renowned, as is the bonding of male groups in combat. But how much of this persists on a one-to-one basis when the danger is over and lives move on?

Men need friends

The intimacy that women often achieve in their friendships seems to elude their mates. Yet men need friendships, and marriages can benefit from the nourishment they offer. Nearly all men will confess they want deeper, more profound friendships than they have. Many men look back fondly on the friendships they formed in childhood. If boys can be buddies, what goes wrong as men grow up?

Taught to be separate

The answer lies in the way men are brought up. Taught to repress tenderness, to fight fear, to avoid talk about feelings, boys identify with fathers for whom rough-housing is often a readier expression of physical affection than kissing or touching. When you're taught to be strong, how much harder to open yourself to attachments that involve risking rejection and revealing vulnerability.

What is more, for little boys to identify with their fathers they must disconnect from the mother, with whom they've been bonded since birth, and that means working on separateness rather than attachment. This sets the pattern for the way they maintain friendships and relationships later on. As they grow up, boys are encouraged to be team players, grouping together to challenge the outside world, and they shy away from the one-to-one heartsearching that comes naturally to girls.

Bred in a spirit of rivalry with other males, men find it hard to shed their armour. The friendships they have tend to go on being based around an activity and do not promote the baring of souls. Group friendships, while holding out the comfort of shared male assumptions about sex, money and sport, can keep up the traditional pressures on a man to go on proving his masculinity. The clap on the back, mock assaults and ironic joking that men use when they meet symbolize the combative nature of men's relationships while paradoxically expressing affection in one of the few ways available among men in our society.

Homophobia

A fear of homosexuality is a very real bar to close male friendship. Victorian repression and popular interpretations of Freudian theories have fostered the notion that there must be a sexual motivation for virtually all human impulses, particularly in the realm of interpersonal relations. Touching, embracing, holding hands – an everyday part of male contact in some societies – are seen as taboo, and even the term 'men friends' can raise eyebrows.

At the same time the changing role of women is forcing men into a reappraisal of what it means to be a man. With the old concepts of 'manliness' still sounding in their ears and a persisting confusion of gender identity with sexual preference, most heterosexual men will run from any whisper of doubt over their sexual orientation. The liberation of women has also heightened expectations of finding sex and friendship together in one male-female relationship. Indeed, most people declare that their spouse is their best friend, although interestingly many more men say so than women.

Being all things to your spouse can put an intolerable strain on the best of marriages, however. Studies show that, far from being a threat or a distraction, a couple's separate friends make partners more interesting to each other and can help a marriage to thrive.

How to help

So how can men be helped towards the kind of sustaining friendships that women often take for granted?

Friendships don't just happen, nor of course do all female friendships go beyond the superficial. However, where men are wary of sharing concerns with their working colleagues, women at work will usually have the option of sharing details about other everyday matters. They can share child-care, exchange favours, admire each other's appearance, laugh together without the pretext of a ribald joke. Men may need to foster interests and contacts that are outside or peripheral to their work or to draw on friendships maintained from childhood that still hold a valuable playful element. But a shared interest, activity or experience shouldn't be the *raison d'être* of the relationship.

~ Men need to be encouraged to get beyond talk about women or sport into talk about themselves and each other, about friendship itself. They have to see it as a strength to risk showing their shadowy or vulnerable side, to acknowledge their need for others. Developing a willingness to ask for favours can help, sacrificing a degree of independence, and learning to make the first and even the second move.

~ Studies show that both sexes look for the same qualities in a friend: loyalty, mutual support, sympathy and understanding, a willingness to help out when the going gets rough. Both see a friend as someone you can be yourself with as well as to confide in. Many men just don't realize what they are missing. Encouraging them to see how much friendship could add to their lives can lead them to seek it more actively.

~ A change of work is often a cathartic event for a man. Losing a job, moving, or being promoted can suddenly make a man understand how shallow his previous relationships really were. So can a spell of illness or hospitalization – it's depressing to see how few colleagues bother to stay in touch for more than a week or two. Use this life event positively. While work-based relationships are often shallow and crack under pressure, friendships built up outside of work are deeper and more likely to endure. It's not surprising: at work, we're stuck with our fellow employees, and we aren't able to choose them as we would our friends outside. When a man begins to place a value on friendship for its own sake – and not because it's desirable for work – then he will automatically attract more friends. Show people you like them, and they will like you. People have a value beyond their immediate usefulness at work – and when a man understands this, and values people for their own sake, then he will begin to grow.

~ The growing informality of manners, greater casualness in the workplace, the nostalgia for naturalness, and the wider acceptance of emotional expressiveness fostered by psychotherapy, encounter groups, radio and TV discussions, magazines for men that treat their deeper concerns, are signs of change. It's a change from which both sexes have everything to gain. For studies show that men with good friendships have a clearer sense of their own identity and better sex lives, as well as enjoying happier relationships all round.

How transactional analysis can improve your relationships

Transactional Analysis (TA) gives you the tools to become your own psychotherapist. Its basic premise is that you can change yourself, by understanding and analysing the ways in which you deal with other people. TA calls these interpersonal dealings 'transactions', and all of them are fundamentally based on recordings held in your brain of internal and external events which happened during the first five years of life. These permanent recordings are classified into three behaviour modes – 'Parent', 'Child' and 'Adult'. All three always exist in everyone, and the first step towards changing is learning to recognize those different states.

Parent

In your Parent are recorded all the external events, straight and unedited, especially everything that parents say and do. The uncritical child takes in all the do's and don'ts, the cuddles and disapprovals, the praise and blame, and has it for the rest of his or her life. Try recognizing Parent behaviour in yourself:

~ Head wagging in a parental way
~ Horrified looks
~ Raised eyebrows
~ Folded arms
~ The mannerisms of your own parents
~ Saying things like 'how many times have I told you?', 'If I were you . . .', 'Always remember . . .'
~ Unreflective reactions like 'disgusting!', 'cute!', 'typical!', 'now what!' or 'not again!'

In other words, the Parent tends to be trite and dispiriting.

Child

In your Child are recorded all the internal events and responses to what the child saw and heard, together with most feelings. Many of those feelings are happy and delightful, but – being clumsy and helpless – the child also learns 'I'm not OK', however loving the parents are. This sad feeling tends to dominate all others, and can be most easily reawakened. When the Child later appears in transactions, the clues are:

~ physical tears
~ quivering lips
~ whining voice
~ pouting
~ teasing
~ laughter
~ nail-biting
~ squirming
~ Saying things like: 'I wish', 'I want', 'I don't care', 'bigger', 'highest', 'better', 'best'

Whilst tending to be boastful and demanding, the Child can also be charming, delightful, and creative.

Adult

In your Adult are recorded whatever you learn out of your own awareness and original thought. Calm assessment, decision-making, and estimation of likelihood are all Adult functions.

The Adult is frail and tentative in the early years, easily knocked out by Parent's commands and Child's fears, but through training and use, the Adult grows. Clues to recognizing the Adult are:

~ A mobile, straightforward face
~ Using all the question words
~ Saying things like: 'true', 'false', 'possible', 'I think', 'it is my opinion', and 'I see'.

The Adult is reasonable and considerate.

Your life position

All transactions between people come from, and address, one or other of these states (P-A-C). Deep problems, which may need expert help, come from blocking out one of them. More common, and less severe, the Adult may be contaminated either by the rigid out-of-touch beliefs of the Parent (which lead to prejudice), or by the fears of the Child (which lead to delusion).

There are four possible life positions:

1 I'm not OK – You're OK
2 I'm not OK – You're not OK
3 I'm OK – You're not OK
4 I'm OK – You're OK

The central tenet of TA is that we all start in position 1, and that we can all choose as Adults to take position 4. Position 1 describes the Child's understanding of his or her relationship to the Parent – lack of power or control, striving for approval, but often mysteriously denied it. The self-image created at this confusing period in our growth is that, while our parents are 'OK', we are 'Not OK'.

Games people play

The most common way of dealing with the almost universal 'I'm not OK – You're OK' position is by playing games: they are a 'solution' which compounds the original misery and confirms the Not OK. A 'game' is a series of complementary transactions with a concealed motivation and predictable outcome: all games are probably versions of the three-year-old's 'Mine is Better than Yours' game. The Not OK Child longs to be stroked, but without the risks of genuine intimacy; games are defences against the pain of being Not OK. Although games get attention from others, they end up precisely where you started, by confirming the initial Not OK position. Miserable, but secure.

Many games are easily recognizable: 'If It Weren't For You I Could . . .', 'Why Don't You . . .', 'Yes. But . . .', 'Now I've Got You, You So And So . . .' and many more. As you watch people around you, it's informative to analyse their behaviour in this way, and watch them repeat the same games again and again.

What you can do

Consciously choose the number 4 life position: 'I'm OK – You're OK'. Emancipate your Adult! Evaluate your Parent! Let your OK Child through! Expose your Child to genuine Adult-Adult intimacy! If you notice that you and your partner are playing a game, stop! Always ask yourself what is the most loving thing to do. When in doubt, stroke!

What you can do together

Use P-A-C as a tool to unlock your struggles by:
~ Learning the vocabulary of TA
~ Identifying the clues to each other's P-A-Cs (you could write them down, and check lists)
~ Identifying the games you're playing (but don't let a Parent in!)
~ Pointing out whenever Parent or Child appears (and learning to laugh at yourself)
~ Stroking a lot, and affirming I'm OK – You're OK.

Other relationship therapies

Too often embarrassment or fear prevents us seeking help. The need for professionals in all other areas of our lives is generally accepted, but somehow there is a feeling we should be able to deal with any emotional problems ourselves.

One British review found that 250 people out of every 1,000 in the general population have psychological difficulties in any one year. Of these, 230 go to their GP for help. The problem will be recognized in 140 of these patients, resulting in 23 going on to receive psychiatric care.

Unfortunately, most GPs have neither the time nor the training to provide the necessary assistance. They may be able to refer you to a professional better suited to your needs, but too often both doctors and psychiatrists simply prescribe antidepressants or other drugs. Although these may help in the short term, they fail to deal with the cause of the problem and so do not offer any real solution.

If only there was a therapist available to everyone on the NHS in the same way as a GP. This would perhaps end the stigma currently surrounding therapy and put an end to the baffling process of choosing a therapist from the private sector. Psychotherapy encompasses a range of approaches – some of which will not be suited to your individual needs. So, if you do decide to seek help, be prepared to take some time to find an appropriate therapist.

Psychotherapy is a form of psychoanalysis requiring self-analysis and active participation. It is an attempt to examine the pain rather than just 'cure' it, and is very much a two-way process. So before you go about finding a therapist, it is often a good idea to think in depth about your 'problem', possibly keeping a record of how you feel. Consider what you actually want to get out of the treatment, and what you want to change.

There is often a fear of lack of control when considering therapy, as if the letting-out of emotions means handing over responsibility. Usually this is overcome with a good therapist. However, there can be a much more real danger of over-dependency with some individuals; again, a good therapist should be able to deal with this.

How to find one

An individual therapist and how you personally relate to them is probably more important than any theories they follow. If you cannot get a personal recommendation from someone, then look for qualifications. It is always a good sign if a therapist is actually having therapy themselves, so ask. When you do decide on somebody, talk on the phone first to try to find if some sort of helpful relationship could be possible. Then ask for an introductory session and do not feel obliged to continue if you are not satisfied.

The cost of treatment varies, but higher charges do not ensure a better standard of therapy. Some innovations, such as group and family therapy, may seem attractive because of their lower cost, but the form of therapy should ideally be chosen for its relevance to the client, and not for any consideration of cost.

Although most therapists are eclectic, they will usually follow a specific approach. 'Psychotherapy' is a broad term encompassing many schools of thought which are not easily compared, partly because they interrelate so much. The following are the four major approaches:

Psychodynamic therapy

This approach is very broad, including ideas put forward by Freud, Klein and Jung. The emphasis is very much on the unconscious and the past, focusing on the past root of the problem rather than the present one. It may include dream therapy.

Person-centred (or humanistic) therapy

This form was established by Carl Rogers, who broke the hold that medicine and psychiatry once had in therapy. Using the minimum of techniques, it is a highly pragmatic form, aimed at penetrating the individual at a very deep level. Rather than trying to restore supposed normality, the emphasis is on affirming personal uniqueness.

Behavioural therapy therapy

Based on the idea that problems are due to incorrect learning, this approach takes into account environmental influences. The therapist attempts to narrow the problem to a specific manageable piece of behaviour which can then be brought under control. This approach is often used to overcome phobias.

Cognitive therapy

A cognitive therapist holds that thoughts influence our feelings, which then in turn affect our thoughts. He aims to help the individual identify his negative thoughts (which are often created unintentionally), to establish more positive feelings and behaviour.

Other approaches falling under the umbrella of psychotherapy include:

~ BIOENERGETICS. Followers of this form believe that through tensing our muscles we stop the movement of vital energy in our body, but with the help of certain exercises, this can be released.

~ BIODYNAMICS. Using massage to release blocks.

~ ENCOUNTER. In a group, attempts are made to relate to others in a more honest way than we normally manage in social situations.

~ FEMINIST THERAPY. This rejects the sexist assumptions felt to exist in some therapies and also helps those with problems specifically related to being female – such as eating disorders.

~ GESTALT THERAPY. Individuals are encouraged to see themselves as responsible for all aspects of their lives, so that if you express a feeling of unhappiness, for example, a gestalt therapist may ask you: "How do you make yourself unhappy?"

~ HYPNOTHERAPY. Clients are hypnotized so they feel deeply relaxed and can let go of their conscious feelings to explore themselves at a deeper level.

~ NEURO-LINGUISTIC PROGRAMMING. Using a technique to reorganize our behaviour and emotions, NLP therapists try to reverse any unhelpful established systems of thought or action.

~ PSYCHODRAMA. A group acts out one of the member's problems, with the therapist as 'director'. Roles are reversed, with discussions following.

For further information on relationship management and other topics discussed in this chapter, contact one of the organizations listed in the Help section.

CHAPTER 128
THE FRONTIERS OF THE NEW FAMILY

~

Your relationship with your parents is the most important relationship you will ever have. It's part of your history – of the process that created the person you are now. So it follows that if you're unhappy with your past, you cannot be truly happy with yourself now. On the other hand, if you come to terms with the past and forgive your parents, then you can accept yourself and look forward to a happy future.

When you think about your parents what do you feel? If there's guilt, anger, resentment or fear there, then something is wrong. Perhaps they mistreated you as a child. Perhaps there has been conflict over your sexuality or your marriage. The scenarios are endless; one thing is certain – these negative emotions poison your life.

To rid yourself of them, you need to approach your parents, discuss your conflicts, and forgive. Think what you have to gain:

~ With the barriers down, you can be happy with your parents. Imagine family gatherings in the future, free of tension and bitterness.

~ When they die, you will have happy memories, not sad ones tinged with guilt.

~ Acceptance of your self. Whatever our conflict with our parents, there is always a feeling that *we* are somehow at fault. Parents are experts at making their children feel guilty – the exorcism of this guilt allows you to be happy with yourself, perhaps for the first time. It may not be easy, but it will be worth it. You need to do the following:

Understand the conflict

You need to understand the conflict yourself before you attempt to discuss it.

~ Think over past events. What went wrong? Was there a particular incident? How did you feel? Where has this anger, guilt or fear come from?

~ Humanize your parents. Try to find out what their lives were and are like. Consider their problems and ambitions. Think of them as characters in a book, with you as a sub-plot, not the main story.

~ Look beyond the stereotypes. They do not behave 'as parents' but as people. To say, "My parents want to run my life" is simply applying a parent stereotype. You must look beyond it. Ask why.

Understanding the problem means seeing both sides. When you have done this you will feel less resentment and will want to get things sorted out. Now you can . . .

Approach your parents

~ Start gently. Don't descend on them out of the blue with your ideas. They will come as a shock. Try communicating generally, then work towards the big discussion.

~ Make it clear that you're doing this for everyone concerned. If they think you just want to criticize them they will run a mile. Explain that you feel there's something wrong between you and want to put it right.

~ Act like you want to be close to them. Take an interest in their lives. How often have you asked them how their careers are going, what's troubling them or what their interests are?

~ Give them time to prepare for your discussions. They will be terrified by the thought of this emotional surgery. Remember the stereotypes – parents aren't supposed to admit their faults!

It is a little-known fact that the population of many Western countries is actually declining. For a population to remain the same size, every woman has to bear an average of 2.1 children. But in Europe, the average is 1.7, and in the United States 1.8.[553] Governments are already taking steps to ensure their populations don't fall further – in France, there are generous family allowances, special provision for the housing of large families, more facilities for working mothers, and even an advertising campaign bearing the slogan "Sex Isn't Just For Pleasure!" All this means that the death of the traditional family – long predicted – just won't happen. The new millennium will be the era of the family – the same old structure, but new and different problems.

Don't rush, but when the time is right sit down and talk. This could be the most important conversation of your life.

Work through the problems

~ Take a specific problem or event for discussion. If you try to cover everything at once your parents will feel overwhelmed and react defensively.
~ Don't accuse! Remember, you are trying to resolve a conflict together, for all your sakes. If you say they've ruined your life they'll be hurt and go on the defensive. Instead, tell them you're upset that there's a conflict and ask for their help in resolving it. Make it into an objective issue with no blame attached.
~ Express your feelings then ask them for their side of the story. It is vital that you give them the same freedom of expression you give yourself. Keep yourself under control even if you think they've got it all wrong. Sometimes what they say will hurt, so keep telling yourself how good you will feel in the end.
~ Try to work together against a common enemy. Bring up the myths and stereotypes influencing your perceptions of each other. Point out that both parties have been deceived by society's ideals. No one likes to feel a fool.
~ Nine times out of ten your discussions will reveal mistakes and misunderstandings on both sides. But they will also reveal something very important – your parents act as they do out of love, not malice. Once you understand and accept that, you can forgive them.
~ You will have won even if your attempted reconciliation fails. Even if your parents turn out to be thoroughly unpleasant you will have discovered that you and they are people with ordinary good points and failings. You need feel no guilt about the failure of your relationship; you are not to blame. You have exorcised the ghosts of your past. At last you know what really happened and why. The uncertainty is gone.
You will also have achieved a remarkable feat of courage. This will give you the confidence to challenge yourself again.

Imagine a life free of guilt and hate. If you make up with your parents, that is the kind of life you can look forward to. So be brave, do it.

Ten golden rules for happy families

Having children is one thing; living with them – and your partner – for years is another! Here are ten basic principles that form the foundation of family life. Pin them up; read them out; and act on them!

1 *Everyone has rights*

~ Share responsibility for the children's upbringing and domestic chores. In the modern world men are no longer the boss. Women can live wholly independently of men; giving up a good career to have children is a sacrifice made voluntarily, so men are expected to do something in return.
~ It also works the other way round. If the father is expected to make sacrifices he has the right to share the children. Father should be included in the intimate details of child-rearing: dressing, feeding, comforting.
~ Acknowledge the rights of your children. They are small humans – not alien beings. And as such, they are worth respecting.

2 *Learn to communicate*

It's not just your children who need to learn how to talk. Communication is something few of us are good at, yet how you talk and listen can make or break a family.

~ Express yourself clearly and gently, whoever you're talking to. Use positive body language to indicate affection and support.

~ Listen patiently but actively; show you're interested. Let children – especially teenagers – express their feelings without you contradicting or judging them.

~ Encourage the development of speech and self-expression through regular conversation.

~ Never say "I don't want to talk about it". Problems rarely disappear by themselves.

3 *Be a family unit*

The pressures of work and outside activities can make you neglect your family – and make older children neglect you. So make active efforts to keep the family unit strong.

~ Both partners should give each child their full attention for a period every day. This time is for talking, telling stories and creating bonds between parent and child. It makes children feel wanted.

~ They should also do the same for each other – since the strength of their bond is a vital element in the family's cohesion.

~ As children grow older make special occasions for the family to be together – Christmas, birthdays, Sunday lunch. And make them fun!

4 *Get into the habit of consultation*

In the traditional family model the parents make all the decisions and the children obey. However, if you want your family to really function as a unit, everyone must be allowed a say.

~ Have informal family meetings to discuss different issues. Let even young children have their say and listen to them sincerely. This will not only boost their self-esteem; young children are just as clever as adults and can provide interesting ideas.

~ Children are far more likely to understand and accept a decision which they have been allowed to discuss.

5 *Allow everyone their own space*

This applies to everyone in the family. Each parent should have a room or a time for their own thoughts and relaxation. Children – especially teenagers – should be able to feel that their bedroom is private and sacrosanct.

~ Private space should be respected at all times, otherwise trust is lost.

6 *Let everyone be themselves*

Unless there is something anti-social about their behaviour, everyone in the family should be allowed to be themselves.

~ You shouldn't criticize your children's likes and loves, and neither should they be allowed to criticize yours. Neither partner should expose the other's idiosyncrasies in front of the children.

~ Encourage your children (and partner) to be what they want and grow in their preferred direction. Don't try to force them into particular roles.

~ As time goes by, allow your children greater independence. Let them run their own lives, but be ready with help and advice. Don't criticize mistakes – help repair the damage.

7 *Stand by your children and partner*

Everyone, no matter how old, needs support and reassurance. A harsh word at the wrong moment from someone you think is on your side can be devastating to your self-esteem.
~ Encourage family members to bring you their problems: listen patiently and react supportively. Even children know when they've done wrong; what they need is a sympathetic ear and sound advice.
~ Never break that trust – especially in front of other people. One lapse in your supportive role could destroy it forever.

8 *Use positive, not negative, discipline*

If you reward good behaviour, the absence of the reward is a punishment in itself – but you must explain what the child's done wrong.
~ Hugs, kisses, compliments – these are all rewards you can use to encourage good behaviour. A child will make more effort to get these than he will to avoid a beating.
~ Angry abuse, whether verbal or physical, results in fear and alienation. And it doesn't work.
~ Guilt is a horrible emotion, especially when you're a child. Make sure he understands he's broken a standard of behaviour, not offended you personally.
~ Withdrawal of a privilege, like an allowance, is the best punishment for a serious 'offence'.

9 *Treat all your children equally*

It's very easy to have favourites, especially when there's a sweet new-born baby in the house. But the effects can be terrible. Being the least-favourite can affect a person their whole lives.
~ When a new baby is due, make sure your other children know what's going to happen. If you've only one child already, try to soften the blow by involving him in the excitement, reassuring him of your love and giving him as much attention as you can.
~ Treat all sibling rivalry as objectively as you can. Discourage tale-telling and don't always side with the most innocent-looking!
~ If one child is more successful than another give extra support to the second. There's nothing more demoralizing than a big brother or sister who's always better than you.

10 *Encourage a positive outlook and make life fun!*

Children's development is enormously influenced by their home environment. So make home a happy place!
~ Turn chores into play wherever possible. Better haphazard than dreary cleaning.
~ Encourage laughter and joke-telling (though not teasing). Turn meals into parties.
~ Show your children being grown up isn't all work and no play. Let your hair down at weekends.
Family life can be fun – if you know what you're doing. It's impossible to plan beforehand for all contingencies, but if you follow the Ten Golden Rules, you'll be giving yourself and your family the best chance of having a happy, loving and memorable life together.

Telling children about sex

At some stage your child will start to ask you questions about sex, so you need to think carefully about how you are going to handle them before they arise.

Educating children about sex is a continuing process, and different questions will continue to arise throughout their childhood and well into their teenage years. Besides the facts, you and your partner must decide together what else you want to convey:

~ Healthy, positive attitudes.

~ Sex in the context of loving and caring relationships.

~ That they should feel confident in asking you questions, develop confidence in their bodies and develop confidence in themselves and in your relationship with them.

~ That their bodies belong to them and no one has a right to touch them anywhere they don't want them to, especially in their 'special places'.

Be open

In order for this to come across you need to have developed an open atmosphere within your family which encourages questions, discussions and honesty with lots of affection and love.

Don't worry about feeling embarrassed when they first ask – it will pass, but do:

~ Answer directly, openly and honestly.

~ Use the correct words – penis, vagina – even with small children.

~ Keep it simple – a five-year-old can be told babies grow in mummy's tummy from seeds which daddy gives to mummy.

~ Tell them as much as they want to know; the older the child the more detail you can go into. If your daughter hasn't asked already, tell her about menstruation before her periods start so that she is well prepared, both emotionally and practically.

~ If you are unsure of the facts, bone up on them, or admit you don't know and go with them to the library to find out together, or wait until your partner is present and then you can ask them, with your child, if they know. Make it family orientated!

Be honest

The difficulty in talking about sex is in trying *not* to convey your own prejudices. You may not like having periods, for example, but it would be unwise to pass on that same attitude ('the curse') to your daughter. Concentrate instead on conveying warmth and directness and being honest about the facts.

The same goes for questions about abortion, contraception, homosexuality, love, venereal diseases, and, of course, AIDS. Your aim should be to give them the facts which they need to know, and when they are older encourage them to make their own wise decisions.

Whatever question arises, answer them in the context of loving, caring relationships. Sex is not only a biological function, it is also beautiful. Explaining it in this context will also make it easier for children to understand about people who could harm them.

Child molesters and perverts are therefore explained in terms of them being sick strangers who *hurt* children: "The best thing is to keep away from them just like we'd keep away from someone who had chicken pox." This way of warning children does so without actually frightening them, but do back it up as well with some simple rules about never getting in cars with strangers nor accepting sweets or gifts.

When your child asks questions about sex, it provides a welcome opportunity to give him or her the knowledge and understanding to help them grow up without hang-ups, guilt or misunderstanding. Answer questions about sex directly and openly, with warmth and love, and as you give them the confidence to talk to you about it, so your own confidence will increase.

The adoption option

There are lots of good reasons to consider opening up your family to another child. Offering a loving family relationship in which to grow up is, perhaps, the most wonderful thing you can ever do for someone else. If you've ever wondered how you'd go about adopting a child, here's the answer:

First, write to Families Forever (the new name of the British Agencies for Adoption and Fostering – address in the Help section) for their booklet *Adopting a Child.* It tells you:

- How to go about it
- What's involved
- A list of recognized adoption agencies. Since 1982 all adoptions must be via an agency recognized by the Secretary of State. Whilst all local authorities have a duty to provide an adoption service there are also other independent adoption organizations, such as Barnardo's.
- Specific agency rules – the minimum age to adopt a child is 21; the maximum age varies from agency to agency as does your eligibility if you are single or divorced.

Families Forever, besides being an adoption agency in its own right specializing in children with special needs, also provides a wide range of support services to professionals associated with adoption and fostering work, and acts as an information service for the public. It is a registered charity and limited company.

Assessment

~ Next, decide which agency you wish to apply to and contact them. They will take a few basic details and may send you brochures and an application form. Once they have your details they will either invite you to attend an information meeting along with other prospective parents, or arrange for a social worker from either the local authority or from the agency (if it is an independent one to which you are applying), to visit you for an informal chat.

~ If you then decide to proceed further, you should make out a formal application. You will be asked for the names of two referees: people who know you well, and who are able to talk to the social worker about your interest in adoption.

~ The social worker will then make at least one more visit to talk in greater depth about you and your family situation in order to make an assessment of your suitability as adoptive parents. The interviews are pleasant but lengthy, detailed and searching. You will at this stage also be asked to have a medical. If you do have a medical condition your doctor will be asked to report on its control and prognosis and will be asked for his/her opinion as to your suitability to adopt in terms of health. You will also be asked to give your consent to your background being checked with: the police, probation service, NSPCC and social services department. You will be questioned very carefully by the social worker if records show, for example, aggressive behaviour, thefts, drug addiction, alcohol-related problems. These will not necessarily preclude you from adopting, but the social worker will need to know quite clearly the circumstances you were in then and where you now are as a person.

~ After these assessment interviews have been completed a second social worker may visit in order to give a second opinion about your suitability. This visit also provides you with another opportunity to ask any remaining questions or to reaffirm your understanding about what happens next.

Acceptance

~ All the information which has been collated about you and your application will be presented to the agency's assessment panel by the social worker on your behalf. The panel may consist of the following: medical advisor, child psychologist, social workers, health visitor, councillor or social services representative and any other professionals whose input will help the panel reach a decision. If your application is approved you are then accepted on to the agency's list. The panel may go on to discuss a particular child to match your application or you are placed on their waiting list.

~ You will be notified of the panel's decision in writing, although the social worker may also phone you after the meeting. It will take at least six months up to this point.

If you are not accepted by the agency you may wish to talk to the social worker about the panel's decision, although it must be pointed out that they are under no legal obligation to do so. However, most will talk you through and help you to think carefully again about adoption and whether you should apply to another adoption agency.

~ If you are accepted you may have to wait for a child to become available. If you want to adopt children with special needs or 'difficult to place' older children your wait will be much shorter.

Meeting the child

~ You will already have specified what sort of child you wish to adopt – ethnic background, sex, age, special needs and so on. When news of a suitable child is received, you will be invited to discuss them further with the agency staff. Afterwards you can decide whether or not to meet the child.

If you decide to go ahead, a first meeting will be arranged quite quickly and followed up with several others, depending on the child's age.

~ Adoption 'parties' are also held by some agencies where groups of children and prospective parents meet. The benefit of these parties is that it helps avoid the pressure of sometimes difficult one-to-one meetings.

~ If things go well after the initial meetings the child will visit your home for a day or perhaps a weekend. There is still no commitment on your part (or the child's, if they are old enough to say so) at this stage.

~ A probation period where they come to live with you is next. This lasts at least thirteen weeks (not including the first six weeks for newborn babies) during which time both you and the child have a better opportunity to get to know each other. The social worker who will have been working with you from the beginning will continue to visit you during this period. If you are adopting an older child you will probably meet the child's own social worker as well. When you feel sure that this is the child you wish to adopt you must give the local authority three months' notice that you wish to proceed with adoption.

~ When the local authority receives this notice, a reporting officer (who is independent of either the agency or local authority – perhaps a social worker from another authority) will come to interview you and look into your application.

Legal adoption

~ Adoption orders which make the adoption legal are granted by courts. You will be asked to attend the hearing and so will the child if old enough. The reporting officer will be present at the hearing and will make their report to the court. Once the adoption order is granted by the court the adoption is complete. From the start of the probationary period to this point will take at least three months, assuming you notify the court at the very start of the probation period; however, it is more likely to take up to six months, possibly more, depending on how busy the courts are in your area.

There are, of course, variations within this procedure depending upon the individual nature of each case. In general, holdups only occur if there are problems with the natural parents, for example if they start to change their minds, but the social worker will guide you through and explain everything to you as it happens.

The adoption process can seem painstakingly slow at times. But persevere! The rewards of giving a child a much-needed family life are well worth waiting for!

The cruelty-free child

There is a cruelty-free way to bring up your children – and a good reason to do so, too. New research clearly points to the fact that smacked or beaten children are more likely to become difficult teenagers, often with criminal records.[554] And studies of mothers who hit their children show that, far from 'disciplining' them, the children actually have more tantrums than children who aren't beaten.[555] This sort of evidence calls into question the whole concept of physical punishment.

Depression

Shockingly, 63 per cent of all babies have been hit by the time they are one year old.[556] As parents, surely what we really want is for our children to grow up to be happy, emotionally healthy adults? But studies by psychologists show that those experiencing corporal punishment at home or school were more likely to suffer from depression and low self-esteem when grown up.[557] So physical punishment not only doesn't work as a form of discipline, but it may cause mental illness in adulthood. Quite a legacy!

But apart from the physical and emotional harm you could be inflicting on your children, there's another important factor to be considered. Each time you resort to physical punishment, whether it's just a slap in the supermarket or a beating behind closed doors, you're setting an example for your child. You're telling him or her that the only way you know of sorting out problems is to resort to physical force. No wonder our society is becoming more violent.

Mental cruelty

If you stop expressing yourself physically and fail to find another outlet, you may then end up hurting your child through mental abuse. As you stop yourself from smacking it is easy to fall into the trap of using verbal abuse. Maybe you manage to restrain your blow, but then cannot help but tell your child how stupid they are, or even that you wish you never had children. Although you will quickly forget such comments, a child rarely will. A few cutting words can destroy any sense of self worth and even the important belief that they are loved. The scars of mental cruelty may not be so obvious as the marks of physical abuse, but they often last for life.

What to do instead

Children, when old enough, need to be told *why* something is wrong. Often when a child misbehaves they are just testing the water; they want to know where the boundaries lie so they can create some sort of certainty in the chaos of social rules. So-called 'naughty' children are usually just hungry – for love, time and emotional support. You will not always be able to give this on demand, but you can try to reassure them.

~ When your child persistently disturbs you when you are busy with an important project, be firm. Don't give in, tell them you do love them; you are busy now, but you will give them a cuddle/read them a story/get something to eat just as soon as you are finished. Children are more intelligent than we give them credit for and will appreciate straight talking.

~ Don't forget to tell your children you love them, however obvious it may seem to you. This should be appropriate to their age; while a five-year-old will love a hug and an 'I love you', a ten-year-old may appreciate a game of cards or a walk together.

~ A very useful principle can be applied when dealing with children: just think about how you would treat an adult in the same situation. You must have been in arguments when the other person has apparently so completely disregarded your point of view that the only thing you really felt like doing was resorting to physical attack. Of course, some people do resort to this, but the man who hits another in the pub saying 'that'll teach him' knows it really won't. The victim is no nearer appreciating the other's point of view. We all know this, so why do we so blatantly choose to disregard it in the case of children?

~ Just as adults need common ground and communication for a healthy relationship, so do children. You cannot expect your child to listen to you if you only talk at him. Try to foster a good rapport where you can do things you both enjoy. Children will love to do things that you as an adult enjoy. When you read that story about the whale for the seventh time it will probably be impossible to hide your severe boredom. Your child isn't unaware of your tedium, but he would rather have this sort of attention than none at all. So, next time your child pesters you to play with him, try suggesting you go for a walk together, or look through a book of your favourite paintings – it will make all the difference.

~ When your children do misbehave, tell them so, without making them feel worthless. Make sure they understand the issue is not whether they are a good person or not, but that certain actions are unacceptable. Don't leave it at that; reinforce good behaviour as much as possible.

~ When making an explanation, be careful not to nag or mock and never make empty threats as your child will spend a lot of time trying to test if you meant it. Again, look at how you would behave with an adult. If your partner threatened that unless you came out with him that night he would leave you, you would either lose respect for him for resorting to such tactics or laugh at him for making such ridiculous comments. Children will frequently respond in a similar way, although not overtly; they know when you are talking like a desperate parent and that only strengthens their resolve!

~ If your child disagrees with you, you can only respect the fact that he is his own person and has the right to differ from you. You can lead your offspring to what you consider to be the fountain of your knowledge, but you must secretly know you can't make them lap it up! On the other hand, they have to accept that there are certain decisions that you as an adult have to make. This is where the battle begins. Along the way, try to keep any arguments as impersonal as possible. It can be harmful (and almost always counterproductive) to make comparisons with other children. Comments like "why can't you be more like your sister" lead only to feelings of inferiority and rivalry rather than any constructive changes of behaviour. The implication of such a remark is that you want him to be a different person, while all you are trying to do is make him modify the way he does certain things. Instead, try to focus criticisms as much as possible and offer workable improvements.

~ Consequences should be as detailed as possible too. Rather than saying "don't do this or there will be trouble", make it clear that if your request is not acted on, your child will miss swimming the next day. By the way, the punishment should fit the crime as much as possible.

~ You don't need to use a belt if you have example – one of the most powerful tools you have. The word discipline comes from the same Latin root as disciple, which means follower. And it's true: children do need you as their role model. Children pick up all sorts of things from adults, and the way you behave certainly won't go unnoticed. You will only bring up a good human by being one yourself!

Setting limits, being firm and fair, giving lots of love and attention may take a little longer than a hard smack, but the long-term rewards are certainly worth it.

Coming next: the home school

Most of us had a hard time at school – so why do we make our children go through it? When you think about it, school is a symptom of the industrial society – it is mass-production applied to human beings. But now that the post-industrial society is dawning, shouldn't we bring our children home from the learning factories?

It is a common fallacy to suppose that the law requires you to send your children to school. It does not. Home education is not only perfectly legal, it is effective, practical and in many ways massively superior to 'the system'. Before you pack your children off to years of institutional learning, give some serious thought to your only real alternative.

In Britain, parents are legally required to provide for their child 'efficient, full-time education suited to his age, ability and aptitude . . . either by regular attendance at school, or otherwise'. In other words you, as a parent, have a *choice*.

Down with school!

There are lots of good reasons for considering a veto of the school system:

~ It doesn't work. Why else do children fail exams?

~ It gives children little choice in their activities and uses forced teaching techniques incompatible with genuine learning.

~ It inhibits self-motivation, self-expression and creativity.

~ It puts children under massive psychological and emotional pressure to succeed during adolescence – a time of complex personal adjustments.

~ It exposes children to bullying and negative peer group pressure, which can leave them scarred for life.

Up with home education!

On the other hand, there are several good reasons for actively choosing home education:

~ Education means learning and growing. Any life experience – not just school – is a valuable learning experience.

~ Children are, like adults, able to determine what they want to do and do it without coercion.

~ Educating your children is fun! It's natural for a family to be together, and learn together.

Join the club

If you've never really thought about your child's education, now is the time to start. Initially, the idea of home education may seem cranky and bewildering, so talk to the people who've done it.

Education Otherwise is a 2,000-strong national organization made up of parents who have rejected the mainstream school system. They have a strong sense of solidarity and commitment. Local groups hold regular weekly and monthly meetings and a newsletter is published bi-monthly. Education Otherwise always welcomes newcomers with moral support and practical help (see the Help section for addresses). A good first move is to join this group and learn about other people's experiences of home education. Once you are part of a group you will gain considerable reassurance from those who've already done it.

Yes, you can do it!

There is no one system of home education; how you do it depends on your circumstances, abilities and beliefs. The important point is that almost *anyone* can do it – you don't have to be highly qualified or an expert in dozens of subjects.

~ Children are natural learners. They manage to walk and talk without formal education – why shouldn't they be able to read and write?

~ And *you* are a natural teacher! You can provide greater security and encouragement than any trained teacher and, as an adult, you have access to vast amounts of information with which to answer questions.

~ Your job is to guide your children's natural curiosity in directions you think are important. There are many books and study aids available to help you teach the three Rs (Reading, Writing and Arithmetic), but your support and encouragement are what really count.

~ Forget the difference between work and play: every experience is a learning experience. A simple shopping trip will provoke innumerable questions. Much can also be taught through 'hands on' projects: thus the building of a new extension becomes a lesson in planning, drawing, maths, and so on.

~ As your child gets older you may want to adopt more formal teaching patterns. Open School is a charitable organization which aims to help small schools and parents. It can provide curriculum suggestions and teaching materials too (see the Help section for the address).

Equipment

Numerous study aids to help you are available. BBC Radio and Television offer educational programmes and videos, as does Independent Television. There are thousands of books, computer programs and educational games on the market, and instead of being forced to use the ones which a school has decided on, you can choose the best for your own needs (fellow home educators will help you here with lots of advice and encouragement).

Results

Your child does not have to follow the National Curriculum or sit GCSEs, but qualifications may be essential in later life. The records show that home-educated children do just as well in exams as those in school.

GCSEs can be taken externally (i.e. privately) or internally (within a school). The latter is cheaper and many schools will allow you to register your child so he can sit the exam. Otherwise your local Education Authority will tell you how to go about arranging the exam externally.

You can get help with special coaching from a variety of sources, including local teachers, tutors (for hire by the hour), and further education colleges – who will allow children under sixteen to join in part-time courses, especially useful in Maths and Science. Or, if you prefer, your child could go to school or sixth form college at this stage. That option is always open.

Some common questions

So, you see, you *can* do it – and thousands do. But there are probably still doubts and queries running through your mind. Won't my child lack social skills if he's educated at home? How will he cope with Real Life?

~ Children educated at home acquire advanced communication and negotiation skills, because they are encouraged to ask questions and try to get what they want. School children are simply told what to do. Which is a better training for life?

~ People often worry that their children won't have any friends if they're educated at home. Experience shows that this isn't so. There is plenty of scope for contacts and friendship in the Education Otherwise network, as well as local clubs and societies, to say nothing of your child's friends in the neighbourhood. Home educated children tend to have deeper friendships – because they're made out of choice. Remember, loneliness is common at school, where the playground is often a system of cliques and outsiders; most people generally learn to create positive relationships *after* they've left school.

~ Business and industry do not want people who can simply learn and regurgitate facts. The fast pace of modern technology means the ability to think flexibly is invaluable.

~ How do you find the time and the money? Home education will require you to re-prioritize your life, but which is more important – a new car or your child's education? Parents should try to share the workload of teaching – or at least of family life in general. To ease the pressure, enlist the help of family, friends and fellow home educators; 'child-swapping' with someone who has a different schedule to you is an ideal relief method.

~ If you can make everyday life an educational experience you can minimize the time spent sitting down and actually teaching. This will also cut down expenditure on books and other materials.

~ You can cut domestic chores by planning meals ahead, shopping in bulk and keeping housework to the bare minimum needed to preserve a state of hygiene.

~ What about the legal requirements? Your local Education Authority has the job of ensuring that you are educating your children, and their inspectors will call at odd intervals (anything from a month to five years). They have no right to test your child, enforce a curriculum or enter your house without permission. However, it's best to keep them happy, so show them you're serious and organized. Before a visit, prepare:

- To explain what you're doing and why.
- To show 'evidence' of educational activity, anything your child has written or made.
- A list of all the activities your child has been involved in that you consider educational.

~ What if your child wants to go to school? Let them try it! An interest in school is natural, but try explaining that he or she will have to spend eight hours every day there and see how long the enthusiasm lasts! However, if it becomes an issue, let them try school for themselves, and choose which they prefer.

~ What if your child is slow, or won't work? All children are different; there is no 'normal' age at which a child should, for example, be able to read. One of the main ideas of home education is that a child is free to grow in the direction most suited to his abilities and inclinations, so try not to worry or push. If you are worried, contact fellow home educators for advice.

~ How do you know if you're doing it right? You don't! But then, who does? What you do know is that you are giving your child the best possible chance to learn and grow in a positive way.

Chapter 129

Are you ready for the future? Your fate revealed

~

You can learn something about *your* own approach to the future by reading the following statements and deciding whether you agree or disagree with them. Check your answers against the scores below to find out how well *you're* going to cope with everything the future may have in store for you . . .

Don't think too much over each statement – it's your first reaction that counts. Then, get a friend to fill it in while *pretending* to be you – this will give you an intriguing insight into how others see you.

AGREE / DISAGREE

1. Once I make my mind up I rarely change it.
2. I undertake at least one activity outside of work which is creative.
3. Like most people, I'm confused about healthy eating.
4. People who break the law should expect everything they get.
5. I like to be popular with friends and colleagues.
6. Work is a means to an end.
7. Persistence is the key to success.
8. I never forgive an enemy.
9. There's no such thing as a fair fight.
10. When I'm financially secure I'll do more travelling.
11. I expect to change my career several times.
12. Two plus two is twenty-two.
13. Young people should fight for their country.
14. I hate extremists.
15. Some of my best ideas come in dreams.
16. Money is your best friend.
17. I like to work alone.
18. I don't like to appear foolish.
19. Tomorrow will be much the same as today.
20. Sex should be exciting and impulsive.
21. Sometimes I catch myself getting bored for no reason.

To Score Your Answers:

Start off with 10 points to begin with. Then add or subtract points as shown below to arrive at your final score:

1. Agree–2 Disagree+1
2. Agree+2 Disagree–2
3. Agree+1 Disagree–1
4. Agree–2 Disagree+1
5. Agree–1 Disagree+0
6. Agree–2 Disagree+2
7. Agree–2 Disagree+2
8. Agree+1 Disagree–1
9. Agree–2 Disagree+1
10. Agree+2 Disagree−2
11. Agree+1 Disagree−2
12. Agree–1 Disagree+1
13. Agree–2 Disagree+2
14. Agree+2 Disagree–2
15. Agree–1 Disagree+1
16. Agree+1 Disagree–1
17. Agree–1 Disagree+2
18. Agree–2 Disagree+2
19. Agree+2 Disagree+0
20. Agree–2 Disagree+1

How To Interpret Your Score:

Less than 20 points

A score in this region indicates excessive caution, and a marked reluctance to face the future and seize the opportunities which it will present. Less than 10 points indicates a very rigid and hidebound attitude which may prevent you from achieving either significant personal or career success. Remember that knowing *how* and *when* to break the rules is just as important as knowing what the rules are in the first place. Conformity brings no spectacular rewards, just dullness of spirit and ultimate dissatisfaction. Your pursuit of security is illusory – the only real security that exists for any of us is that which we make for ourselves. Come out of your shell and learn how to be adventurous.

20 to 30 points

This is a survivor's score. A successful blend of caution and creativity, your personal characteristics will tend to keep your sunny side up, no matter what the adversity. And when fortune smiles, you more than most others will be ideally placed to take full advantage of the opportunities which come your way. You know how to take risks, and when not to. The future is yours for the taking.

Over 30 points

You see life as a casino, and you just can't resist backing the long shots, can you? You have a reckless, impulsive character which could either make your fortune or ruin you – and probably the latter. Sure, if you want to get ahead, you've got to be brave and take risks – sometimes. But the essence of a successful life-strategy is knowing how to balance the risks with the certainties. You've got to understand that the best time to take a gamble is when your downside exposure is minimal, not when you most need to win. Learn a little prudence and stop tempting fate!

THE HELP SECTION

Companies or organizations mentioned in this section are included because we genuinely believe they may be able to provide you with useful products or further information about the topics discussed in *Superliving!*

CHAPTER 1: WHAT CONTAMINATES YOUR DRINKING WATER – AND WHAT TO DO ABOUT IT

Cheap do-it-yourself test kits for aluminium and nitrates can be obtained from: Verify Aquatest, Verify Ltd, 150 Brompton Rd, London SW3 1HX. They also offer a lead testing service by post

National Pure Water Association, Bank Farm, Aston Pigot, Westbury, Shrewsbury, Shrops SY5 9HH. Tel: 074 383445. A voluntary group established to prevent tap water pollution and fluoridation.

National Anti-Fluoridation Campaign, 36 Station Road, Thames Ditton, Surrey KT7 0NS. Tel: 081 398 2117

CHAPTER 3: WHAT YOU SHOULD KNOW ABOUT FOOD IRRADIATION

Advisory Committee on Irradiated and Novel Foods (ACINF), Ministry of Agriculture, Fisheries and Food, Whitehall Place, London SW1

The Food Commission, 88 Old Street, London EC1. Tel: 071 253 9513

CHAPTER 4: WHAT TO LOOK FOR WHEN YOU READ A FOOD LABEL

Food Advisory Committee, Ministry of Agriculture, Fisheries and Food, Whitehall Place, London SW1

Food and Drink Industries Council (FDIC), 25 Victoria Street, London SW1H 0EX. Tel: 071 222 1533

The Food Commission, 88 Old Street, London EC1. Tel: 071 253 9513

CHAPTER 5: FOOD POISONING: PROTECT AND SURVIVE!

Food Safety Advisory Centre, Foodline, PO Box 391, London WC1A 2PX. Tel: Foodline 0800 282407

The Consumers Association, 2 Marylebone Road, London NW1. Tel: 071 486 5544

Contact your local Environmental Health Officer if you need to report a likely source of food poisoning

CHAPTER 7: HOW TO AVOID CHEMICAL RESIDUE IN YOUR FOOD

Friends of the Earth, 26-28 Underwood Street, London N1. Tel: 071 490 1555

The Food Commission, 88 Old Street, London EC1. Tel: 071 253 9513

Advisory Committee on Pesticides, Ministry of Agriculture, Fisheries and Food, Whitehall Place, London SW1

The Pesticides Trust, 23 Beehive Place, London SW9 7QR. Tel: 071 274 8895

The Soil Association, 86 Colston Street Bristol BSl 5BB. Tel: 0272 290661 Campaigns for the promotion of organically grown food

Farm and Food Society, 4 Willifield Way, London NW11. Tel: 081 455 0634. Researches farming techniques and campaigns for less use of toxic chemicals and safer food

CHAPTER 11: EATING GREEN – HOW AND WHY YOU SHOULD GO VEGETARIAN

Most supermarkets and health food shops sell vegetable burgers, sausages, meatless pies, pasties, steaklets and a wide range of other new-age foods. Here's a selection of some of the products you can find in major supermarkets, but do remember that the range is constantly improving.

ARGYLL STORES
Realeat VegeBurgers
Dalepak Vegetarian Grills
Nature Store Vegetable Burger
Realeat VegeBangers
Nature Store Vegetable Bangers
Good Life Bean Burgers
Good Life Vegetarian Cutlets
BEJAM
Bejam Vegetable Burgers
Bejam Vegetable Grills
CO-OP
Birds Eye Vegetable Burgers
SAINSBURY
Realeat VegeBurgers
Birds Eye Vegetable Burgers
Dalepak Vegetable Grills
Sainsbury's Vegetable Burgers
TESCO
Tesco Vegetarian Burgers
Dalepak Vegetable Grills
WAITROSE
Dalepak Vegetable Grills
Realeat VegeBurgers

For more information about Quorn, contact: The Quorn Information Service, Freepost, Ashford, Kent TN23 2WY
Stockists: Harrods, Sainsbury's, Asda, Waitrose, Holland and Barratt

CHAPTER 13: 'GREEN BLOOD' – THE SECRET OF WHEATGRASS JUICE

Hippocrates Health Institute, 25 Exeter Street, Boston Massachusetts, USA 02116. Tel: 010 1 617 267 9525

CHAPTER 15: THE SEEDS OF THE FUTURE

Enco Products Ltd, 71/75 Fortess Road, London NW5 1AG. Tel: 071 267 2617

Infinity Foods Co-Operative Ltd, 67B Norway Street, Portslade, Brighton, East Sussex BN4. Tel: 0273 424060

Real Foods Ltd, 14 Ashley Place, Edinburgh EH6. Tel: 031 5544321

Suma Foods Ltd, Unit AXl, Deanclough Industrial Park, Halifax, West Yorkshire HXV. Tel: 0422 45513/66438

CHAPTER 19: ZEN MACROBIOTICS – THE HEALING DIET

Macrobiotic Information Service (Nutritional Advice), East West Centre, 188 Old Street, London EC1. Tel: 071 251 4076

CHAPTER 21: WHY DIETS FAIL YOU – AND WHAT TO DO ABOUT IT!

Overeaters Anonymous, 27 Verdant Court, Verdant Lane, London SE6 1LE. Tel: 081 981 9363. Phone for details of regular meetings held in central London (a recorded message). For a more detailed list of meetings, send a SAE to the above address

CHAPTER 24: HOW TO BE A CARING CONSUMER

World Development Movement, Bedford Chambers, Covent Garden, London WC2E 8HA. Tel: 071 836 3672

CHAPTER 26: FOODS TO FIGHT ARTHRITIS AND RHEUMATISM

Arthritis and Rheumatism Council for Research, 41 Eagle Street, London WC1R 4AR. Tel: 071 405 8572

Arthritis Care, 6 Grosvenor Crescent, London SW1X 7ER. Tel: 071 261 0110

National Ankylosing Spondylitis Society, 6 Grosvenor Crescent, London SW1X 7ER. Tel: 071 261 0110

CHAPTER 27: FOODS TO FIGHT CANCER

The Gerson Institute, PO Box 430, Bonita, California, USA 92002. Tel: USA (619) 267 1150. The Gerson therapy is an intense combination of diet and supplements to treat cancer

CHAPTER 31: FOODS TO FIGHT DIABETES

British Diabetic Association, 10 Queen Anne Street, London W1M 0BD. Tel: 071 323 1531

CHAPTER 32: FOODS TO FIGHT ECZEMA AND PSORIASIS

National Eczema Society, Tavistock House, Tavistock Square, London WC1 9SR. Tel: 071 388 4097

Psoriasis Association, 7 Milton Street, Northampton, Northants NN2 7JG. Tel: 0604 711129

Alternative Centre for Psoriasis and Eczema, College House, Wrights Lane, Kensington, London W8 5SH. Tel: 071 351 2726; 071 938 2645

CHAPTER 38: FOODS TO FIGHT MIGRAINE

The British Migraine Association, 178A High Road, Byfleet, Surrey KT14 7ED. Details on support groups for migraine sufferers

The Migraine Trust, 45 Great Ormond Street, London WC1N 3HZ. Tel: 071 278 2676

CHAPTER 39: FOODS TO FIGHT MULTIPLE SCLEROSIS

The Multiple Sclerosis Society of Great Britain and Northern Ireland, 25 Effie Road, Fulham, London SW6 1EE. Tel: 071 736 6267

Action For Research Into Multiple Sclerosis, 11 Dartmouth Street, London SW1H 9BL. Tel: 071 222 3224; Counselling Service: England and Wales Tel: 081 568 2255; Scotland Tel: 041 637 2262

CHAPTER 40: FOODS TO FIGHT OSTEOPOROSIS

National Osteoporosis Society, Barton Mead House, PO Box 10, Radstock, Bath, Avon BA3 3YB. Tel: 0761 432472

CHAPTER 41: FOODS TO PROMOTE LONGEVITY AND FIGHT SENILITY

Age Concern, Bernard Sunley House, 60 Pitcairn Road, Mitcham, Surrey CR4 3LL. Tel: 071 274 6723

Age Concern Scotland, 33 Castle Street, Edinburgh, Scotland EH2 3DN. Tel: 031 225 5000

Alzheimer's Disease Society, 158/160 Balham High Road, London SW12 9BN. Tel: 081 675 6557

CHAPTER 43: WHAT YOU CAN DO ABOUT WORLD HUNGER

Oxfam, 274 Banbury Road, Oxford OX2 7DZ. Tel: 0865 56777

Christian Aid, 35 Lower Marsh, London SE1 7RL. Tel: 071 620 4444

Save the Children, Mary Datchelor House, 17 Grove Lane, London SE5 8RD. Tel: 071 703 5400

CHAPTER 45: FEELING S.A.D.? WHAT TO DO ABOUT SEASONAL AFFECTIVE DISORDER

Seasonal Affective Disorder Association, The Secretary, 51 Bracewell Road, London W10 6AF. Tel: 081 969 7028. Please enclose a SAE

CHAPTER 46: FOODS THAT BITE BACK – ARE YOU ALLERGIC?

Action Against Allergy, 43 The Downs, London SW20 8HG. Tel: 081 947 5082

Environmental Medicine Foundation, Furnival House, 14/18 High Holborn, London WC1 8BX. Tel: 0442 58112/45848

Food and Chemical Allergy Association, 27 Ferringham Lane, Ferring by Sea, Sussex. Tel: 0903 41178

CHAPTER 48: WORN OUT? HOW TO COMBAT THE HIDDEN EPIDEMIC OF CHRONIC FATIGUE

ME Association, PO Box 8, Stanford-le-Hope. Tel: Stanford-le-Hope 642466

National CFS Association, 3521 Broadway, Suite 222, Kansas City, Mo. 64111. Tel: USA (816) 931-4777

CF and Immune Dysfunction Syndrome Association, PO Box 220398, Charlotte, N.C. 28222-0398. Tel: USA (704) 362-2343.

CF Immune Dysfunction Syndrome Society, PO Box 230108, Portland, Ore. 97223. Tel: USA (503) 684-5261.

CHAPTER 49: WHAT YOUR MOTHER NEVER TOLD YOU . . . ABOUT THE PILL

Marie Stopes House, 108 Whitfield Street, London W1P 6BE. Tel: 071 388 2585

Fertility Awareness Methods, 11 Astra House, 53 Mount Pleasant Villas, London N4 4HB. Tel: 071 482 1247

. . . ABOUT PREGNANCY

Foresight, The Old Vicarage, Church Lane, Godalming, Surrey GU8 5PN. Tel: 0428 684500. Information on preconceptual nutrition and care to ensure a good start for your baby

Active Birth Movement, 32 Cholmeley Crescent, Highgate, London N6 5JR. Tel: 081 348 1284

International Centre for Active Birth, 55 Dartmouth Park Road, London NW5 1SL. Tel: 071 267 3006

Association for Improvements in Maternity Services (AIMS), 163 Liverpool Road, London N1 0RF

Independent Midwives Association, 65 Mount Nod Road, Streatham, London SW16 2LP

Maternity Alliance, 15 Britannia Street, London WC1X 9JP. Tel: 071 837 1265

National Childbirth Trust, 9 Queensborough Terrace, London W2 3TB. Tel: 071 221 3833

. . . ABOUT CHILDBIRTH

Birthrights, 2 Forth Street, Edinburgh, Scotland, EH1 3LD. Tel: 031 557 0960 or 031 667 5701. Support and preparation for home birth

Women's Health and Reproductive Rights Information Centre, 52 Featherstone St., London EC1Y 8RT. Tel: 071 251 6580/6332

Association of Radical Midwives, 62 Greetby Hill, Ormskirk, Lancs L39 2DT. Tel: 0695 72776

Association for Post Natal Depression, 7 Gowan Avenue, Fulham, London SW6

Association for Post Natal Illness, 25 Jerdan Place, London SW6 1BE. Tel: 071 386 0868

National Childbirth Trust, 9 Queensborough Terrace, London W2 3TB. Tel: 071 221 3833

. . . ABOUT BREASTFEEDING

Association of Breastfeeding Mothers, 7 Maybourne Close, London SE26 6HQ. Tel: 081 778 4769 (24 hours)

La Leche League (Great Britain), 27 Old Gloucester St., London WC1N 3AF. Tel: 071 242 1278 and 071 404 5011

. . . ABOUT PREMENSTRUAL SYNDROME

National Association of Premenstrual Syndrome, 2nd Floor, 25 Market Street, Guildford, Surrey GU4 1LB. Tel: 0483 572715

CHAPTER 51: HOW TO AVOID BEING CURED TO DEATH

Dorland's Illustrated Medical Dictionary, WB Saunders Company
Materia Medica for Nurses, W. Gordon Sears and R. S. Winwood, Edward Arnold (Publishers) Ltd
British National Formulary, BMA and RPSGB

CHAPTER 54: A CONSUMER'S GUIDE TO EVALUATING EXERCISE PROGRAMMES

The National Association for Health and Exercise Teachers (ASSET), 202 The Avenue, Kennington, Oxford OX1 5RN. Tel: 0865 736066

AFTA (Aerobic Fitness Teachers Association), 29 Hursley Road, Chandler's Ford, Hants. Tel: 04215 3084

CHAPTER 55: WHAT YOU NEED TO KNOW ABOUT EXERCISE DURING PREGNANCY

Active Birth Movement, 32 Cholmeley Crescent, Highgate, London N6 5JR. Tel: 081 348 1284

International Centre for Active Birth, 55 Dartmouth Park Road, London NW5 1SL. Tel: 071 267 3006

CHAPTER 56: EXERCISING INTO YOUR EIGHTIES

Keep Fit Association, 16 Upper Woburn Place, London WC1H 0QW. Tel: 071 387 4349

Association of Swimming Therapy, Treetops, Swan Hill, Ellesmere, Shrops SY12 0LZ

CHAPTER 57: RELAX AND HEAL YOURSELF!

International Stress and Tension Control Society (UK), c/o Priory Hospital, Priory Lane, Roehampton, London SW15 5JJ. Tel: 0532 664260

Flotation centres in the UK include:

The Floatarium, 3 Dukes Court, Dukes Street, Brighton BN1 1AR. Tel: 0273 26965

The Raphael Clinic, 211 Sumatra Road, London NW6 1PF. Tel: 071 794 0321

International Stress Management Association, c/o Priory Hospital, Priory Lane, Roehampton, London SW15 5JJ. Tel: 0532 664260 and 25 Sutherland Avenue, Leeds LS8 1BY. Please send SAE

Relaxation for Living, 29 Burwood Park Road, Walton on Thames, Surrey KT12 5LH. Tel: 0932 227826

Relaxation Therapy Association, Main Street, Northiam, Sussex TN31 6LP

Stress Control Institute, 3 Ryde Mews, Binstead Road, Ryde, Isle of Wight PO33. Tel: 0083 63893

Transcendental Meditation, freephone 0800 269303

CHAPTER 59: WHAT TO DO ABOUT A SICK HOUSE

National Radiological Protection Board, Chilton, Didcot, Oxon OX11 0RQ. Tel: 0235 831600

Friends of the Earth, 26-28 Underwood Street, London N1 7JQ. Tel: 071 490 1555

The Association of Facilities Managers, 30 Abbotts Road, New Barnet, Herts

London Hazard Centre, Headland House, 308 Grays Inn Road, London WC1X 8DS. Tel: 071 837 5605

Building Research Establishment, Garston, Watford WD2 7JR. Tel: 0923 664800

The following American organizations also produce relevant information:

Indoor Air Quality Research Laboratory
Department of Natural Resources
Ball State University
Muncie, IN 47306
Tel: USA 317-285-5782

Environmental Health Watch
4115 Bridge Ave
Cleveland, OH 44113
Tel: USA 216-961-4646

Consumer Federation of America
1424 16th Street, NW
Suite 604
Washington, DC 20036
Tel: USA 202-387-6121

For medical information, contact:

American Academy of Allergy and Immunology
611 E Wells Street
Milwaukee, WI 53202

American Academy of Environmental Medicine
PO Box 16106
Denver, CO 80216

American Lung Association
1740 Broadway
New York, NY 10019
Tel: USA 212-315-8700

National Environmental Health Association
Battery March Park
Quincy, MA 02269
Tel: USA 617-770-3000

For the No-Rad, contact: Ion Systems Inc, 2546 10th St., Berkeley, California 94710

CHAPTER 61: WHAT YOU CAN DO ABOUT ELECTROMAGNETIC POLLUTION

Sigma Designs Inc, 46501 Landing Parkway, Fremont CA, USA. Tel: 0101 415-770-0100

CHAPTER 62: WHEN NIGHTMARES COME TRUE – HOW TO SURVIVE A NUCLEAR DISASTER

Larkhall Laboratories, Cantassium, 225 Putney Bridge Road, London SW15 2PY. Suppliers of Selenium Alginate Formula which counters radio-strontium; 20 tablets a day for an adult should prevent its absorption.

For radiation detectors (geiger counters):

Appleford Instruments Ltd, PO Box 78, Abingdon, Oxon OX14 4HE. Tel: 0235 510370

Canberra Packard Ltd, Brook House, Station Road, Pangbourne, Reading RG8 7DT. Tel: 0734 844981

The Nukebuster, which meters Alpha, Beta, Gamma and X-ray radiation, is available from Solar Electronics, PO Box 39, Summertown, TN 38483 USA

For nuclear decontamination services and waste disposal:

NEI Thompson Nuclear Engineering, PO Box 100, Spring Road, Ettingshall, Wolverhampton WV4 6JY. Tel: 0902 353 3353

For safety equipment:

Lewis's Medical Systems, Compstall Mill, Compstall, Stockport SK6 5HN. Tel: 061 949 8156

For radiation shielding:

Chemring Ltd, Alchem Works, Fratton Trading Estate, Portsmouth PO4 8SX. Tel: 0705 735457

Leadatom Europe Ltd, Unit 1, Shamrock Enterprise Centre, Brockhurst Industrial Estate, Wingate Road, Gosport, Hants PO12 4DP. Tel: 0705 523973

For more information generally on nuclear contamination risks:

ALARM: Alert Londoners Against Radioactive Waste, 47 Roderick Road, London NW3

Radiation and Health Information Service, PO Box 805, London SE15 4LP

British Medical Association, BMA House, Tavistock Square, London WC1H 9JP. Tel: 071 387 4499

National Radiological Protection Board, Chilton, Didcot, Oxon OX11 0RQ. Tel: 0235 831600

CHAPTER 63: PLAIN TALK ABOUT COMPLEMENTARY THERAPIES

Institute for Complementary Medicine, 21 Portland Place, London W1N 3AF. Tel: 071 636 9543

British Holistic Medical Association, 179 Gloucester Place, London NW1 6DX. Tel: 071 262 5299

CHAPTER 64: WHAT TO EXPECT FROM ACUPUNCTURE

The British Acupuncture Association, 34 Alderney Street, London SW1. Tel: 071 834 1012.

British Medical Acupuncture Society, 68-69 Chancery Lane, London WC2 1AF

International Acupuncture Society (UK), Morley Acupuncture Clinic, 1 Queen Street, Morley, Leeds, Yorks LS2 8EG. Tel: 0532 380208

Medical Acupuncture Society, 15 Devonshire Place, London W1N 1PB. Tel: 071 935 7575

Register of Traditional Chinese Medicine, 7a Thorndean Street, London SW18 4HE. Tel: 081 947 1879

Traditional Acupuncture Society, 11 Grange Park, Stratford-upon-Avon, Warwickshire. Tel: 0789 298798

CHAPTER 65: WHAT TO EXPECT FROM THE ALEXANDER TECHNIQUE

A list of recognized practitioners can be obtained by sending a SAE to:

Society of Teachers of the Alexander Technique (STAT), 10 London House, 226 Fulham Road, London SW10 9EL. Tel: 071 351 0828

CHAPTER 66: WHAT TO EXPECT FROM AROMATHERAPY

To find an aromatherapist, contact one of the groups below:

College of Natural Therapies and Aesthetic Treatment, 22 Bromley Road, London SE6 2TP. Tel: 071 690 2149. Write for a list of its full members

The Association of Tisserand Aromatherapists, The Secretary, 31 Craven Street, London WC2. Tel: 071 930 3340

The London School of Aromatherapy, PO Box 780, London NW6 SEQ. Tel: 071 328 9504. Send a SAE for a list of registered practitioners

CHAPTER 67: WHAT TO EXPECT FROM AYURVEDIC MEDICINE

Association of Ayurvedic Physicians in the UK, 12 Agar Street, Leicester. Tel: 0533 666746

The Association of Ayurvedic Practitioners, 7 Ravenscroft Avenue, Golders Green, London N11 0SA. Tel: 081 455 3909. For details of practitioners and further information enclose SAE

Ayurvedic and Unani Register, 141 Plashet Grove, London E6 1AA. Tel: 081 471 4627

Ayurvedic Self Help Group, 121 Coral Street, Leicester LE4 5BG. Tel: 0533 662475

Society for Ayurveda, 18 Commondale, West Putney, London SW15. Tel: 081 788 1063

CHAPTER 68: WHAT TO EXPECT FROM BACH FLOWER REMEDIES

Dr. Edward Bach Centre, Mount Vernon, Sotwell, Wallingford, Oxon OX10. Tel: 0491 39489

CHAPTER 69: WHAT TO EXPECT FROM CHIROPRACTIC

The British Chiropractic Association, Premier House, 10 Greycoat Place, London SW1P 1SB. Tel: 071 222 8866. For a register of qualified practitioners, send a 9 × 6 in SAE

Chiropractic Advancement Association, 38a Upper Richmond Road West, East Sheen, London SW14 8DD. Tel: 081 878 3989

CHAPTER 70: WHAT TO EXPECT FROM COLONIC IRRIGATION

The Colonic Irrigation Association, 26 Sea Road, Boscombe, Bournemouth, Dorset BH5 1DF. Tel: 0202 36354

CHAPTER 71: WHAT TO EXPECT FROM COLOUR THERAPY

International Association of Colour Healers, 33 St. Leonard's Court, East Sheen, London SW14 7NG

CHAPTER 72: WHAT TO EXPECT FROM CRYSTAL, GEM AND ELECTRO-CRYSTAL THERAPY

For further information about crystal therapy or a list of qualified practitioners, send a SAE to:

Association of Crystal Healing Therapists, 5 Sunnymead Vale, Holcombe Brook, Bury, Lancs BL0 9RR. Tel: 020488 3482

Flower and Gem Remedy Association, Anubis House, Creswell Drive, Ravenstone, Leicester LE6 2AG. Tel: 0530 510864

Institute of Crystal and Gem Therapies, 9 Creswell Drive, Ravenstone, Leicester LE6 2AG. Tel: 0530 510864

The School of Electro-crystal Therapy, 117 Long Drive, South Ruislip, Middlesex HA4 0HL. Tel: 081 841 1716

CHAPTER 73: WHAT TO EXPECT FROM THE GERSON THERAPY

The book *A Cancer Therapy – Results of Fifty Cases* by Max Gerson MD is available from: The Gerson Institute, PO Box 430, Bonita, California, USA 92002. Tel: USA (619) 267 1150

Also worth seeking advice from (but not in any way connected with Gerson therapy):

Cancerlink, 17 Britannia St, London WC1 9JP. Tel: 071 833 2451

There is an interesting chapter on the work of Max Gerson in the book *Improving on Pritikin* by Ross Horne, Happy Landings Pty Ltd (PO Box 277, Avalon Beach, NSW Australia), 1988

CHAPTER 74: WHAT TO EXPECT FROM GESTALT THERAPY

Gestalt Association, 11 Weech Road, London NW6. Tel: 071 435 0581

CHAPTER 75: WHAT TO EXPECT FROM HAND HEALING

The Confederation of Healing Organizations, 113 Hampstead Way, London NW11. Tel: 081 455 2638. An umbrella group holding a central register of all healers in the country

National Federation of Spiritual Healers, Old Manor Farm Studio, Church Street, Sunbury on Thames, Middlesex. Tel: 0932 783164. A national group with a traditional hands-on approach; contact them for a register of their members

The Association for Therapeutic Healers, 67-69 Chancery Lane, London, WC2A 1AF. Tel: 071 240 0716. Maintains a register of members, all of whom are also therapists such as acupuncturists and counsellors. Depending on the individual healer, colour, sound and visualization may all be used in addition to touch

CHAPTER 76: WHAT TO EXPECT FROM HERBALISM

National Institute of Medical Herbalists, 9 Palace Gate, Exeter, Devon. Tel: 0962 68776

CHAPTER 77: WHAT TO EXPECT FROM HOMOEOPATHIC THERAPY

British Homoeopathic Association, 27a Devonshire Street, London W1N 1KJ. Tel: 071 935 2163

Weleda (UK) Ltd., Heanor Road, Ilkeston, Derbyshire DE7 8DR. Tel: 0602 303151. Manufacture homoeopathic medicines; they will send you free information leaflets and a booklist.

CHAPTER 78: WHAT TO EXPECT FROM HYDROTHERAPY

Association of Swimming Therapy, Treetops, Swan Hill, Ellesmere, Shrops SY12 0LZ

CHAPTER 79: WHAT TO EXPECT FROM HYPNOTHERAPY

Association of Qualified Curative Hypnotherapists, 10 Balaclava Road, Kings Heath, Birmingham, West Midlands B14 7SG. Tel: 021 444 5435 (24 hours)

British Association of Therapeutic Hypnotherapists, The Secretary, 4 Buttermere Grove, Bishop Auckland, Durham

British Hypnotherapy Association, 1 Wythburn Place, London W1H 5WL. Tel: 071 723 4443

British Society of Hypnotherapists, 51 Queen Anne Street, London W1M 9FA. Tel: 071 935 7075

CHAPTER 80: WHAT TO EXPECT FROM IRIDOLOGY

National Council and Register of Iridologists, 80 Portland Road, Bournemouth, Dorset BH9 1NQ. Tel: 0202 529793

CHAPTER 81: WHAT TO EXPECT FROM KINESIOLOGY

British Touch for Health Association, 78 Castlewood Drive, Eltham, London SE9. Tel: 081 856 7717

Association for Systematic Kinesiology, 39 Browns Road, Surbiton, Surrey. Tel: 081 399 3215

CHAPTER 82: WHAT TO EXPECT FROM MASSAGE

International Therapy Examination Council (ITEC), James House, Oakelbrook Mill, Newent, Glos GL18 1HD. Tel: 0531 821875

CHAPTER 83: WHAT TO EXPECT FROM MUSIC THERAPY

The British Society for Music Therapy, 69 Avondale Avenue, East Barnet, Herts EN4 8NB. Tel: 081 368 8879

Association of Professional Music Therapists, The Meadow, 68 Pierce Lane, Cambridge, CB1 5DL. Tel: 0223 880377

The Council for Music in Hospitals, c/o Sylvia Lindsay, 340 Lower Road, Little Bookham, Surrey KT23 4EF

CHAPTER 84: WHAT TO EXPECT FROM NATUROPATHY

British Naturopathic and Osteopathic Association, Frazer House, 6 Netherall Gardens, London NW3 5RR. Tel: 071 435 8728

General Council and Register of Naturopaths: as above

British College of Naturopathy and Osteopathy, address as above. Tel: 071 435 7830

CHAPTER 85: WHAT TO EXPECT FROM ORTHOMOLECULAR THERAPY

International Institute of Vitamin and Mineral Therapists, 3 Ryde Mews, Binstead Road, Ryde, Isle of Wight PO33

CHAPTER 86: WHAT TO EXPECT FROM OSTEOPATHY

The General Council and Register of Osteopaths, 21 Suffolk Street, London SWl 4HG. Tel: 071 839 2060

The British Naturopathic and Osteopathic Association, Frazer House, 6 Netherhall Gardens, London NW3 5RR. Tel: 071 435 7830

The British School of Osteopathy, Littlejohn House, 1-4 Suffolk Street, London SW1Y 4HG. Tel: 071 930 9254.

CHAPTER 87: WHAT TO EXPECT FROM POLARITY THERAPY

Polarity Therapy Association, 48 Devonshire Buildings, Bath, Avon BA2 4SU. Tel: 0225 26327

CHAPTER 88: WHAT TO EXPECT FROM RADIONICS

Radionics Association, 16a North Bar, Banbury, Oxon. Tel: 0442 43333

British Society of Dowsers, Sycamore Cottage, Hastingleigh, Ashford, Kent TN25 5HW. Tel: 023375 253

Radionic Treatment of Animals, Sycamore Farm, Chadlington, Oxford OX7 3NZ

CHAPTER 89: WHAT TO EXPECT FROM REBIRTHING

British Rebirth Society and Breathe, Secretary, 18a Great Percy Street, London WC1X 9QP. Tel: 071 833 0791

Holistic Rebirthing Institute, 22 Shirlock Road, London NW3 2HS

CHAPTER 90: WHAT TO EXPECT FROM REFLEXOLOGY

The British Reflexology Association, Monks Orchard, Whitbourne, Worcestershire WR6 5RB. Tel: 0886 21207. For information and a list of practitioners send a cheque for £1.50 and SAE

International Association of Reflexology (UK), 28 Hollyfield Avenue, London N11 3BY. Tel: 081 368 0865

International Institute of Reflexology, 32 Coppetts Road, Muswell Hill, London N10 1JY. Tel: 081 444 6354

CHAPTER 91: WHAT TO EXPECT FROM REICHIAN THERAPY

Energy Stream (Post Reichian Therapy Association), 12 St Ann's Avenue, Leeds, Yorks LS4. Tel: 0532 785601

CHAPTER 92: WHAT TO EXPECT FROM ROLFING

Jennie Crewdson, 14 Phoenix House, 110 Charing Cross Road, London WC2H 0JN. Tel: 071 240 7454

Harvey Burns, 80 Clifton Hill, St John's Wood, London NW8. Tel: 071 328 9026

Anna Oren, 7 Glendale, Clifton, Bristol BS8 7PN. Tel: 0272 264917

Prue Rankin-Smith, 61 Grantham Road, Chiswick, London W4 2RT. Tel: 071 994 8544

CHAPTER 93: WHAT TO EXPECT FROM SHIATSU

To find a practitioner in your area, send SAE to: The Secretary, The Shiatsu Society, Tel: 0737 767 896

CHAPTER 94: WHAT TO EXPECT FROM YOGA

British Wheel of Yoga, 80 Leckhampton Road, Cheltenham, Gloucestershire, or J. Parry, 6 Orchard Rise, Shirley, CR0 7QY. Tel: 081 777 1748

British Yoga Federation, Aquarian House, Glyn Ceiriog, Llangollen, Clwyd. Tel: 069172 564

Friends of Yoga Society (FRYOG), Piriskey, 5 Weston Crescent, Old Sawley, Long Eaton, Nottingham, Notts NG10 3BS. Tel: 0602 735435

Iyengar Yoga Institute, 233a Randolph Avenue, London W9 1NL. Tel: 071 624 3080

Scottish Yoga Association, 4 Afton Place, Edinburgh, Scotland EH5 3RB

Yoga For Health Foundation, Ickwell Bury, Ickwell Green, Biggleswade, Beds. Tel: 0767 27271

CHAPTER 95: SMART MOVES: HOW TO TAKE THE HEARTACHE OUT OF MOVING HOUSE

The Society for the Protection of Ancient Buildings, 37 Spital Square, London E1 6DY. Tel: 071 377 1644

The Georgian Group, 37 Spital Square, London E1 6DY. Tel: 071 377 1722

The Victorian Society, 1 Priory Gardens, London W4 1TT. Tel: 081 994 1019

Buying abroad: Expert advice can be found in *Buying A House in France*, by Vivienne Menkes-Ivry, Simon and Schuster, £5.95

The International Property Owners' Organisation. Tel: 081 995 1331 or 061 946 0858

Chambre de Commerce Francaise de Grande-Bretagne Ltd., Knightsbridge House, 2nd fl, 197 Knightsbridge, London SW7 1RB. Tel: 071 225 5250.

Anglo-French Property Services, 42 Bedford Row, London WC1R 4LL

Royal Institute of Chartered Surveyors, 12 Gt. George St, Parliament Sq, London SW1P 3AD. Tel: 071 222 7000

Royal Institute of Chartered Surveyors Information Centre, Surveyor Court, Westwood Way, Coventry CV4 8JE. Tel: 0203 694757.

Royal Institute of Chartered Surveyors Scotland. Tel: 031 225 7078.

CHAPTER 96: DO YOU SINCERELY WANT TO BE RURAL?

The National Small Woods Association, Red House, Hill Lane, Great Barr, Birmingham B43 6LE

John Clegg and Company, Chesham, Bucks, is an estate agent specializing in small woods.

Crofters Commission, 4-6 Castle Wynd, Inverness IV2 3EQ

Ecology Building Society, 18 Station Road, Cross Hills, Keighley, West Yorkshire BD20 8TB. Tel: 0532 635933

CHAPTER 98: HOW TO SET UP YOUR SMALLHOLDING

On legal matters, start with The Law Society, 113 Chancery Lane, London WC2A lPL. Tel: 071 242 1222.

For information on VAT law, contact HM Customs and Excise, New Kings Beam House, 22 Upper Ground, London SE1 9PJ. Tel: 071 620 1313.

For advice about insurance contact The National Farmers Union, Agriculture House, 25-31 Knightsbridge, London SWlX 7NJ. Tel: 071 235 5077

Small Firms Advisory Service: dial 100 and ask for Freephone Enterprise

Small Firms Service, Department of Employment, 11 Belgrave Road, London SW1. Tel: 071 828 6231

Agricultural Development Advisory Service, Ministry of Agriculture, Fisheries and Food, Great Westminster House, Horseferry Road, London SW1P 2AB. Tel: 071 216 6311

Rural Development Commission, 11 Cowley Street, London SW1P 3NA. Tel: 071 222 9134

Agricultural Mortgage Corporation Ltd., Bucklersbury House, 3 Queen Victoria Street, London EC4N 8DU. Tel: 071 236 5252

CHAPTER 99: HOW YOU CAN SET UP AND RUN A SELF-RELIANT URBAN HOMESTEAD

Low-energy lightbulbs are manufactured by Wotan and Phillips.

London Ecology Centre, 21 Endell Street, London WC2H 9BJ. Tel: 071 379 8208

Centre for Alternative Technology, Llwyngwern Quarry, Machynlleth, Powys, SY20. Tel: 0654 702400.

Composting Non-flush Toilets: Contact the Centre for Alternative Technology (above) for details of the Clivus Multrum and the Bio-Loo, which can also handle kitchen waste, and the Toa-Throne, Ecolet and Bio-Let. All models use electricity and require careful maintenance.

Friends of the Earth, 26-28 Underwood St, London N1 7JQ. Tel: 071 490 1555.

CHAPTER 100: DIGGING IN: THE ADVANTAGES OF LIVING UNDERGROUND

Royal Institute of British Architects (RIBA), 66 Portland Place, London W1N 4AD. Tel: 071 580 5533.

Architects with special experience of underground homes: The Arthur Quarmby Partnership, 83 Fitzwilliam Street, Huddersfield HD1 5LG. Tel: 0484 536553

Consider approaching for help with finance: Ecology Building Society, 18 Station Road, Cross Hills, Keighley, West Yorkshire BD20 8TB. Tel: 0532 635933

Books: *Earth Sheltered Residential Design Manual,* Dr Raymond Sterling of the Underground Space Center, University of Minnesota, published by Van Nostrand Reinhold Co. Also from the Underground Space Center: *Earth Sheltered Housing Design,* (2nd ed)

Underground Homes: An Alternative Lifestyle, by Ray G Scott, TAB Books Inc 1981 ISBN 0-8306-9626-1(USA)

How to Build Your Own Underground Home, by Ray G Scott, TAB Books Inc (USA)

The Underground House Book, by Stu Campbell, Garden Way Publishing 1980 ISBN 088266-167-1 (USA)

An Architect's Sketchbook of Underground Buildings: Drawings and Photographs, by Malcolm Wells, Raven Rocks Press 1990 (USA)

CHAPTER 101: FENG SHUI: THE ART OF LIVING IN HARMONY WITH NATURE

Michael Hall, 89 Windmill Avenue, Wokingham, Berks

CHAPTER 102: THE BUNKER HUNTER'S COMPANION: ONE HUNDRED BEST WAYS TO IMPROVE YOUR HOME WITHOUT MOVING

British Decorators Federation (Decorating) 6 Haywra St, Harrogate, North Yorks HGl 5BL. Tel: 0423 57473

National Federation of Roofing Contractors, 24 Weymouth St, London W1N 3FA. Tel: 071 436 0387

Federation of Master Builders, 33 John St, London WC1. Tel: 071 242 7583

Glass and Glazing Federation, 6 Mount Row, London W1. Tel: 071 409 0545

National Association of Plumbing, Heating and Mechanical Services Contractors, 164 Powis Street, London SE18 6NL. Tel: 081 855 4715

To recycle aluminium contact: The Aluminium Can Recycling Association (ACRA), 1 Mex House, 52 Blucher Street, Birmingham Bl lQU. Tel: 021 633 4656

Anne Riding, Save-A-Can Manager, PO Box 18, Ebbw Vale, Gwent NP3 6YL. Tel: 0495 350818

British Plastics Federation, 5 Belgrave Square, London SW1X 8PD. Tel: 071 235 9483

Advertising Standards Authority, Brook House, 2-16 Torrington Place, London WC1E 7HN. Tel: 071 580 5555

The Consumers' Association, 2 Marylebone Road, London NW1 4DF. Tel: 071 486 5544

Committee of Advertising Practice, Brook House, 2-16 Torrington Place, London WC1E 7HN. Tel: 071 580 5555

Office of Fair Trading, Room 500, Chancery House, Chancery Lane, London WC2A 1SP. Tel: 071 242 2858 ext 293

CHAPTER 103: THE BLAZING TRUTH ABOUT YOUR HOME LIGHTING

For additional information about retinopathy of prematurity write to Peter Aleff at 2097 Cottonwood Drive, Vineland, NJ 08360, USA

CHAPTER 104: WHAT COLOUR CAN DO TO YOUR MENTAL STATE

International Association of Colour Therapists, Brook House, Avening, Gloucestershire. Tel: 0453 832150

International Association of Colour Healers, 33 St Leonard's Court, East Sheen, London SW14 7NG

Universal Colour Healers Research Foundation, 47 Pinewood Grove, Iver Heath, Iver, Bucks SL0 0QN

CHAPTER 105: SOMETHING'S IN THE AIR: IONIZERS AND AIR PURIFIERS

Friends of the Earth, 26-28 Underwood St., London N1 7JQ. Tel: 071 490 1555

Mountain Breeze Ionizers, 6 Priorswood Place, Skelmersdale, Lancs, WN8 9QB. Tel: 0695 21155

Foliage for Clean Air Council. Tel: (USA) 703-534-5268

CHAPTER 106: HOW TO TURN YOUR GARDEN INTO A NATURE RESERVE

Henry Doubleday Research Association, National Centre for Organic Gardening, Ryton-on-Dunsmore, Coventry CV8 3LG. Tel: 0203-303517. The HDRA Catalogue includes lists of cottage and wild flower seeds, gardening supplies, books and leaflets

Nature Conservancy Council, Northminster House, Peterborough, Cambs. PE1 1UA. Tel: 0733 40345. Advice, information and published material

Royal Society for Nature Conservation, The Green, Nettleham, Lincoln LN2 2NR. Advice, information and published material

Royal Society for the Protection of Birds, The Lodge, Sandy, Beds. Tel: 0767 680551. Advice, information and published material

London Wildlife Trust, 80 York Way, London N1 9AG. Tel: 071 278 6612. Advice, information and published material

The Soil Association, 86-88 Colston Street, Bristol BS1 5BB. Tel: 0272 290661. For advice, information and published material on companion planting, organic gardening and pesticide use

Forestry Commission Research Station, Alice Holt Lodge, Wrecclesham, Farnham, Surrey GU10 4LH. Suppliers of trees and tree seeds

The Woodland Trust, Autumn Park, Dysart Road, Grantham, Lincolnshire NG31 6LL. Tel: 0476 74297. For information and schemes promoting the protection of woodland

Suffolk Herbs Ltd, Sawyer's Farm, Little Cornard, Sudbury, Suffolk CO10 0NY. For seeds and seed mixes

The Cottage Garden Society, Old Hall Cottage, Pump Lane, Churton, Chester CH3 6LR. For seeds and plants

The Bat Project, Paignton Zoo, Paignton, Devon TQ4 7EU. Tel: 0803 521064. For advice, information and published material. They also have the name and number for a local contact and details of constructing and/or purchasing bat boxes

British Hedgehog Preservation Society, Knowbury House, Knowbury, Ludlow, Shropshire. For advice, information and published material on hedgehogs and hibernation boxes

CHAPTER 107: BEING NICER TO MOTHER NATURE: A GENTLER WAY WITH PESTS

The Soil Association, 86-88 Colston Street, Bristol BS1 5BB. Tel: 0272 290661.

Ask for their leaflet *How Does Your Garden Grow?* which lists and analyses 75 active ingredients used in garden pest control products. This association will help with queries regarding conservation, companion planting, composting, organic gardening and will supply a list of pesticides passed by the Organic Standards Committee

OXFAM, 274 Banbury Road, Oxford. Tel: 0865 56777. They supply citronella soap and other natural repellent products.

The Bat Project, Paignton Zoo, Paignton, Devon TQ4 7EU. Tel: 0803 521064. For advice, information and published material. They also have the name and number for a local contact and details of constructing and/or purchasing bat boxes

British Hedgehog Preservation Society, Knowbury House, Knowbury, Ludlow, Shropshire. For advice, information and published material on hedgehogs and hibernation boxes

Royal Horticultural Society, 80 Vincent Square, London SW1P 2PE. Tel: 071 834 4333. Ask for their list of companies specializing in insect predators

Natural Pest Control, Watermead Road, Yapton, Barnham, Bognor, Sussex PO22 0BQ. Tel: 0243 553250. This company supplies predators for insects infesting greenhouses: aphids, whitefly, red spider mite and mealy bug

Spider catcher and bat box from: Innovations Ltd, Euroway Business Park, Swindon, Wiltshire SN5 8SN. Tel: 0793 610870

British Pest Control Association, 3 St James Court, Friar Gate, Derby, DEl 1ZU. Tel: 0332 294288

CHAPTER 108: GROWING AND KEEPING GOOD NEIGHBOURS

National Association of Local Voluntary Service Councils (CVSNA), 26 Bedford Square, London WClB 3HU. Tel: 071 636 4066

Nacro Safe Neighbourhoods Advisory Service, Cranmer House, 2nd Floor, 39 Brixton Road, London SW9 6DZ. Tel: 071 735 0744

The Neighbourhood Initiatives Foundation, Chapel House, 7 Gravel Leasowe, Lightmoor, Telford, Shropshire TF4 3QL. Tel: 0952 590902. Supports initiatives for neighbourhood renewal. It puts groups in contact with each other and provides resources for start-up, advice on funding and dealing with bureaucracy.

The National Federation of Community Organisations, 8-9 Upper Street, Islington, London Nl 0PQ. Tel: 071 226 0189. Represents the interests of all neighbourhood groups and community associations and encourages further development.

The Adult Education Research Centre, Block B, Nottingham University, NG7 2RD. Tel: 0602 484848 ext 3699 (morning only)

CHAPTER 109: WHAT YOU CAN DO ABOUT A NOISE NUISANCE

Noise Abatement Society, PO Box 8, Bromley, Kent BR2 0UH

Obtain official codes of practice from: Department of the Environment Publications Store, Building 3, Victoria Road, Ruislip, Middlesex HA4 0NX

Department of Transport Central Enquiries Unit. Tel: 071 276 0800

For complaints about noise from aircraft taking off and landing at Heathrow, Gatwick and Stansted, 'phone 071 212 7172/3. Also The Department of Transport (CAP5 Division), 2 Marsham Street, London SW1P 3EB

Complaints about military aircraft should be made to the Ministry of Defence, DS8a, Main Building, Whitehall, London SW1A 2HB, who will also consider claims for compensation

CHAPTER 110: THE HARMLESS HOUSE – YOUR CARDINAL CHECKLIST FOR SAFETY

The Royal Society for the Prevention of Accidents (ROSPA), Cannon House, The Priory, Queensway, Birmingham B4 6BS Tel: 021 200 2461

CHAPTER 111: YOUR SUPERHOME'S ABSOLUTELY ESSENTIAL SURVIVAL INSTRUCTIONS

Electrical Contractors' Association, ESCA House, 34 Palace Court, London W2 4HY. Tel: 071 229 1266

National Association of Plumbing, Heating and Mechanical Services Contractors, 6 Gate Street, London WC2A 3HX. Tel: 071 405 2678/9

Confederation for the Registration of Gas Installers, St Martin's House, 140 Tottenham Court Road, London WlP 9LN. Tel: 071 387 9185

National Federation of Roofing Contractors, 24 Weymouth Street, London W1N 3FA. Tel: 071 637 5215

Master Locksmiths Association, 13 Parkfield Road, Northolt, Middlesex, UB5 5NN. Tel: 081 845 1676

Federation of Master Builders, 14 Great James Street, London WC1N 3DP. Tel: 071 242 7583

Royal Society for the Prevention of Accidents (ROSPA), Cannon House, The Priory, Queensway, Birmingham B4 6BS. Tel: 021 200 2461

CHAPTER 112: HOW TO BE A MEAN-STREETS SURVIVOR!

Transport 2000, Walkden House, 10 Melton Street, London NW1 2EJ. Tel: 071 388 8386

Association of London Authorities, 36 Old Queen Street, London SW1H 9JF. Tel: 071 222 4979

Capital Transport Campaign, 308 Gray's Inn Road, London WC1X 8DP. Tel: 071 833 4022

Environmental Transport Association, 15A George Street, Croydon, Surrey CR0 1LA

London Cycling Campaign, Tress House, 3/7 Stamford Street, London SE1 9NT. Tel: 071 928 7220

London Housing Unit, Bedford House, 125-133 Camden High Street, London NW1 5DD. Tel: 071 284 3147

Shelter, 88 Old Street, London EC1V 9HU. Tel: 071 253 0202

Housing Corporation, 149 Tottenham Court Road, London W1P OBN. Tel: 071 387 9466 (For information on housing co-ops)

London Ecology Unit, Bedford House, 125 Camden High Street, London NW1 5DD. Tel: 071 267 7944

National Society for Clean Air, 136 North Street, Brighton BN1 1RG

Read *Cohousing – a contemporary approach to housing ourselves*, by Kathryn McCamant and Charles Durrett, Ten Speed Press, 1989

CHAPTER 113: KEEPING YOUR NEAREST AND DEAREST SAFE ON THE STREETS

Both of these companies supply videos on how to avoid risk of attack:

Cygnet Films, Bilton Centre Studios, Coronation Road, High Wycombe, Buckinghamshire. Tel: 0494 450541

NACAB Vision, 115/123 Pentonville Road, London N1 9LZ.

CHAPTER 114: HOW YOU SHOULD HANDLE AN OBSCENE PHONE CALL

British Telecom Public Affairs. Tel: 071 356 6304

Victim Support. Tel: 071 735 9166

OFTEL. Tel: 071 822 1644

CHAPTER 115: HOW TO SET UP AND RUN A NEIGHBOURHOOD WATCH SCHEME

Association of British Insurers (ABI), Aldermary House, Queen Street, London ED4N 1TT. Tel: 071 248 4477

CHAPTER 116: WHAT TO DO AFTER A BURGLARY

Victim Support, Cranmer House, 39 Brixton Road, London SW9 6DZ. Tel: 071 735 9166

Victim Support London, Beauchamp Lodge, 2 Warwick Crescent, London W2 6NE. Tel: 071 289 0906

CHAPTER 117: THE TWELVE VITAL RULES OF FIRE SAFETY

Fire Protection Association, 140 Aldersgate Street, London EClA 4HY. Tel: 071 606 3757

CHAPTER 119: SOME THOUGHTS ON DEATH AND DYING

The Department of Social Security (DSS) runs a free telephone information service on 0800 666555

National Council for Carers and Their Elderly Dependents, 29 Chilworth Mews, London W2 3RG. Also c/o Mrs H.M. Mcquire, 9 Bertie Road, Cumnor, Oxford OX2 9PS. Tel: 0865 862122

Association of Carers, c/o Mrs J. Oliver, Medway House, Balfour Road, Rochester, Kent ME4 6QU

CRUSE – National Association for the Widowed, Cruse House, 126 Sheen Road, Richmond, Surrey TW9 lUR. Tel: 081 940 4818

National Association of Widows, Voluntary Services Centre, Chell Road, Stafford, Staffs ST16 2QA

Widows Advisory Service, Chell,Chell Road, Stafford, Staffs ST16 2QA

Samaritans, 17 Uxbridge Road, Slough, Berks. SL1 1SN

The Compassionate Friends, 6 Denmark Street, Bristol BS1 5DQ. Tel: 0272 292778. For bereaved parents

The British Humanist Association, 14 Lambs Conduit Pass, London WClR 4RH. Tel: 071 430 0908

The Voluntary Euthanasia Society, 13 Prince of Wales Terrace, London W8 5PG. Tel: 071 937 7770

The Hospice Information Service, St Christopher's Hospice, 51 Lawrie Park Road, Sydenham SE26 6DZ. Tel: 081 778 9252. Information on hospice-style care in this country and abroad. A full directory is available on receipt of a large (A5) SAE with two first-class stamps

Near-death experiences: Light Beyond Newsletter, Honey Pot Inc., PO Box UNIROK, Okauchee Lake, Wisconsin 53069, USA

Information about cryonic suspension from: Alcor UK, 18 Pottsmarsh Estate, Eastbourne Road, Westham, Sussex. Tel: 0323 460 257

CHAPTER 120: WHAT TO DO IF YOU ARE THE VICTIM OF A VIOLENT CRIME

The Criminal Injuries Compensation Board, 19 Alfred Place, London WClE 7EA. Tel: 071 636 9501

Rape Crisis Centres. Ring to find your nearest centre. Tel: 071 837 1600. In Scotland Tel: 031 556 9437

National Association of Victims Support Schemes, Cranmer House, 39 Brixton Road, London SW9 6DZ. Tel: 071 735 9166

CHAPTER 121: WHAT TO DO WHEN YOU THINK YOUR CHILD IS TAKING DRUGS

Standing Conference on Drug Abuse (SCODA), 1/4 Hatton Place, Hatton Garden, London ECIN 8ND. Tel: 071 430 2341

Dial Freefone 100 and ask for Freefone Drugs Problems. A recording gives information of drugs projects in the counties of southern England and a separate number for information about projects in Wales.

Organisation for Parents Under Stress (OPUS) is an umbrella organization for various parent groups offering support to parents throughout the country. They have a helpline, Tel: 0449 677707 which is manned by parents from 6pm throughout the night until 9am.

Families Anonymous, 310 Finchley Road, London NW3 7AG. Tel: 071 731 8060

Narcotics Anonymous. Tel: 071 351 6794

Release Emergency Service, 169 Commercial Street, London E1 6BW. Tel: 071 603 8654

For an excellent, impartial survey of all commonly encountered 'recreational' drugs, their hazards and effects, read the standard reference work on the subject: *Street Drugs*, by Andrew Tyler, New English Library 1986

CHAPTER 123: DEALING WITH DEPRESSION: NOT A DISEASE, BUT A HEALING PROCESS

Depressives Associated, PO Box 5, Castletown, Portland DT5 1BQ

The Manic Depression Fellowship Ltd, 13 Rosslyn Road, Twickenham TW1 2AR. Tel: 081 892 2811

CHAPTER 125: SEX PROBLEMS AND SEX THERAPY

Relate, National Marriage Guidance, Herbert Gray College, Little Church Street, Rugby CV21 3AP. Tel: 0788 73241

The British Counselling Association, 37a Sheep Street, Rugby, Warwickshire CV21 3BX. Tel: 0788 78328

CHAPTER 126: BECOMING A PERSON OF POWER

Phobics Society, 4 Cheltenham Road, Chorley cum Hardy, Manchester, Lancs M21 1QN. Tel: 061 881 1937

Phobics Trust, 51 Northwood Avenue, Purley, Surrey CR2 2ER

Phobic Research Campaign, 10 Silverknowles Bank, Edinburgh, Scotland EH4 5PB

Phobias Confidential, 1 Clovelly Road, London W5. Tel: 081 567 0262

Phobic Action, 547 High Road, London E11 4PB. Tel: 081 558 3463

School Phobic Helpline. Tel: 0302 833596, Monday-Friday 3pm-5pm. For parents of children suffering from school phobia.

CHAPTER 127: MANAGING YOUR RELATIONSHIPS

Relate, National Marriage Guidance, Herbert Gray College, Little Church Street, Rugby CV21 3AP. Tel: 0788 73241

Transaction, 8 Hereford Square, London SW7 4TT. Tel: 071 373 2192

Association for Group and Individual Psychotherapy, 1 Fairbridge Road, London N19 3EW. Tel: 071 272 7013

Association of Humanistic Psychology in Great Britain, 12 Southcote Road, London N19 5BJ. Tel: 071 607 7852

Concessions Register of the Natural Health Service, 36 Broadway Market, London E8 4QJ. Tel: 071 254 1158. Send SAE for a list of qualified therapists who offer concessions to the unemployed and low-waged.

British Association for Counselling, 37a Sheep Street, Rugby, Warwickshire CV21 3BX. Tel: 0788 578328. BAC Information Office has information about counsellors or counselling agencies in your area. Send SAE

Institute of Marital Studies, Tavistock Centre, 120 Belsize Lane, London NW3 5BA. Tel: 071 435 7111

Family Welfare Association, 501-505 Kingsland Rd, London E8 4AU. Tel: 071 254 6251. FWA has 12 area offices around the country

Archway – Support for Lonely People, c/o Paul Hawgood, 9 Green Ridges, Oxford, OX3 9PL. Tel: 0865 60650

National Council for the Divorced and Separated, 13 High St, Little Shelford, Cambridge. Tel: 0623 648297

CHAPTER 128: THE FRONTIERS OF THE NEW FAMILY

EPOCH – End Physical Punishment of Children, PO Box 962, London N22 4UX

National Society for the Prevention of Cruelty to Children, 67 Saffron Hill, London EC1N 8RS. Tel: 071 242 1626

Royal Scottish Society for the Prevention of Cruelty to Children, 41 Polwarth Terrace, Edinburgh. Tel: 031 337 8539

National Child Protection Line. Freephone 0800 181188 (24 hours)

British Agencies for Adoption and Fostering, 11 Southwark Street, London SE1 1RQ. Tel: 071 407 8800. Also called Families Forever, 11 Southwark Street, London SE1 1RQ. Tel: 071 407 8800

Education Otherwise, 25 Common Lane, Hemingford Abbott, Cambs PE18 9AN. Tel: 0480 63130

Peter Davies, Open School, Foxhole, Dartington, Devon TQ9 6EB. Tel: 0803 866542

National Council of One Parent Families, 255 Kentish Town Road, London NW5 2LX. Tel: 071 267 1361

Scottish Council for Single Parents, 13 Gayfield Square, Edinburgh, Scotland EH1 3NX

Childline. Tel: 0800 1111

Incest Crisis Line. Tel: 081 422 5100 or 081 890 4732

Mothers of Abused Children. Tel: 06973 31432

National Society for the Prevention of Cruelty to Children, 67 Saffron Hill, London EC1N 8RS. Tel: 071 242 1626

Royal Scottish Society for the Prevention of Cruelty to Children, 41 Polwarth Terrace, Edinburgh. Tel: 031 337 8539

FOOTNOTES

1 *The Washington Post* 11 March 1990
2 *New Scientist* 21 January 1989
3 Association of London Chief Environmental Health Officers, 1987
4 *The Times* 23 October 1987
5 *Which?* February 1989
6 *Today* 26 Janaury 1988
7 "Effect of vitamin and mineral supplementation on intelligence of a sample of schoolchildren." Benton D, Roberts G *The Lancet* 23 Jan 1988, 1 (8578) p140–3
8 "Vitamin/mineral supplementation and nonverbal intelligence," *The Lancet* 20 Feb 1988, 1 (8582) p407–9
9 *Today* 26 January 1988
10 "Can children's intelligence be increased by vitamin and mineral supplements?" Naismith DJ, Nelson M, Burley VJ, Gatenby SJ *The Lancet* 6 Aug 1988, 2 (8606) p335
11 "Effect of vitamin and mineral supplementation on verbal and non-verbal reasoning of schoolchildren," Crombie IK, Todman J, McNeill G, Florey CD, Menzies I, Kennedy RA *The Lancet* 31 Mar 1990, 335 (8692) p744–7
12 "Vitamin/mineral supplementation and intelligence," Benton D, Buts JP *The Lancet* 12 May 1990, 335 (8698) p1158–60
13 *Pure, White and Deadly*, John Yudkin, Penguin Books 1986
14 *The Independent* 18 February 1991
15 *The Independent on Sunday* 24 February 1991
16 *The Independent* 18 February 1991
17 "Irradiated food plans 'unworkable'" *Daily Telegraph* 3 Sept 1990
18 UPI 3 June 1983
19 "Ecogenetics of Parkinson's disease: prevalence and environmental aspects in rural areas." Barbeau A, Roy M, Bernier G, Campanella G, Paris S *Can J Neurol Sci* Feb 1987, 14 (1) p36–41
20 *The Independent* 18 July 1989
21 UPI 7 September 1989
22 *The Guardian* 1 February 1990
23 UPI 7 September 1989
24 UPI 7 September 1989
25 *Gluttons for punishment*, James Erlichman, Penguin 1985 and *World In Action*, Granada Television 17 Dec 1984
26 "The nitrate story–no end in sight," Vogtmann H, Biedermann R, Department of Agriculture, University of Kassel, Witzenhausen, West Germany. *Nutr Health* 1985, 3 (4) p217–39
27 *Redbook* May 1989, v173, n1, p116(5)
28 UPI 21 November 1983
29 *Proceedings of the National Academy of Sciences*, 1989, v86, p6377
30 *How to live longer and feel better*, Linus Pauling, Avon Books, New York 1987
31 *Better Nutrition* April 1990, v52, n4, p8(2)
32 Denham Harman, MD, PhD, Professor of Medicine and biochemistry at the University of Nebraska College of Medicine, quoted in *Men's Health* Spring 1989, v4, n1, p36(4)
33 "Immunological enhancement by fat-soluble vitamins, minerals, and trace metals: a factor in cancer prevention," Watson RR *Cancer Detect Prev* 1986, 9 (1–2) p67–77
34 Gerhard Schrauzer, PhD, of the University of California cited in *Better Nutrition* Nov 1989, v51, n11, p14(2)
35 *Redbook* April 1989, v172, n6, p96(5)
36 "The cholesterol/saturated-fat index: an indication of the hypercholesterolaemic and atherogenic potential of food," Connor SL, Gustafson JR, Artaud-Wild SM, Flavell DP, Classick-Kohn CJ, Hatcher LF, Connor WE *The Lancet* 31 May 1986, 1 (8492) p1229–32
37 "Paleolithic Nutrition: A consideration of its nature and current implications," Eaton SB, Konner MN, *N Engl J Med* v312, n5, pp283–9
38 "The effect of vegetarian diets on plasma lipid and platelet levels," Fisher M, Levine PH, Weiner B, Ockene IS, Johnson B, Johnson MH, Natale AM, Vaudreuil CH, Hoogasian J *Arch Intern Med* June 1986, 146 (6) p1193–7
39 "Diet, lipoproteins, and the progression of coronary atherosclerosis. The Leiden Intervention Trial," Source: Arntzenius AC, Kromhout D, Barth JD, Reiber JH, Bruschke AV, Buis B, van Gent CM, Kempen-Voogd N, Strikwerda S, van der Velde EA *N Engl J Med* 28 Mar 1985, 312 (13) p805–11
40 "Epidemiologic studies of diet and cancer." Willett WC *Med Oncol Tumor Pharmacother*" 1990, 7 (2–3) p93–7
41 "Does a vegetarian diet reduce the occurrence of diabetes?" *Am J Public Health* May 1985, 75 (5) pp507–12,
42 "Vegetarian lifestyle and bone mineral density," Marsh AG, Sanchez TV, Michelsen O, Chaffee FL, Fagal SM *Am J Clin Nutr* Sep 1988, 48 (3 Suppl) p837–41
43 "The correlates of blood pressure in Seventh-day adventist (Sda) and non-Sda adolescents," Kuczmarski, Robert John (Dr PH 1985 The University of North Carolina

at Chapel Hill). v46/11-B p3790 *Dissertation Abstracts International* 905018
44 *Animal Liberation*, Professor Peter Singer, Avon Books, New York 1975
45 *Nutrition Research Newsletter* May 1989, v8, n5, p56(1)
46 "Randomised trial of fish oil for prevention of restenosis after coronary angioplasty," Reis GJ, Boucher TM, Sipperly ME, Silverman DI, McCabe CH, Baim DS, Sacks FM, Grossman W, Pasternak RC *The Lancet* 22 Jul 1989, 2 (8656) p177–81
47 "Cardiovascular deaths among Alaskan natives, 1980–86," Middaugh, John P *Am J of Public Health* March 1990, v80, n3, p282(4)
48 "Increased incidence of epistaxis in adolescents with familial hypercholesterolemia treated with fish oil," Clarke JTR, Cullen-Dean G, Regelink E, Chan L, Rose V *Journal of Pediatrics* Jan 1990, v116, n1, p139(3)
49 *Men's Health* July 1989, v5, n7, p4(3)
50 *The Edell Health Letter* March 1989, v8, n3, p3(1)
51 *Chlorophyll Magic From Living Plant Life*, Dr Bernard Jensen, 1973
52 *Macrobiotics, The Way of Healing*, Georges Ohsawa, Georges Ohsawa Macrobiotic Foundation 1981
53 *The Independent* 29 March 1990
54 *Journal of Behaviour Therapy and Experimental Psychiatry* 1978, 9 (3): 227–233
55 *The Times* 27 January 1988
56 *Med Hypotheses*, July 1984, 14 (3)
57 *Daily Consumer News*, 30 June 1986
58 *Acta Derm Venereol* 1984, 64 (1)
59 The work of Dr Alan Ebringer, Department of Rheumatology, Middlesex Hospital and Immunologist at King's College, London
60 "Fasting and Vegan Diet in Rheumatoid Arthritis," Skoldstam, Lars, *Scand J Rheumatology* 1986, 15: 219–223
61 Wayne State University College of Medicine as reported in *Better Nutrition* March 1990, v52, n3, p9(3)
62 *The Nightshades and Health*, Norman Childers & GM Russo, Horticulture Publications, Somerville, New Jersey 1973
63 Raympiid Shatin, MD, Alfred Hospital, Melbourne, Florida, as reported in *Bestways* September 1989, v17, n9, p42(2)
64 "Yucca plant saponin in the management of arthritis." Bingham R, Bellew BA, Bellew JG *J Applied Nutr*, 1975, 27, p45–50
65 *The Lancet* 24 August 1990
66 Various studies including work by Professor Hans Eysenck and Dr Ronald Grossarth-Maticek, Institute of Psychiatry, London; Dr David Spiegel, Stanford University, USA
67 *The Causes of Cancer*, R Doll & R Peto, Oxford Medical Publications 1981
68 Interview: Kenneth K Carroll, PhD, Professor of Biochemistry, University of Western Ontario, *Canada Redbook* April 1989, v172, n6, p96(5)
69 *The Washington Post* and *Los Angeles Times* 1 August 1989
70 Michael P Osborne, MD, of Memorial Sloan-Kettering Cancer Center Breast Service, in conjunction with researchers at Rockefeller University, New York, and Rutgers University, New Jersey
71 Peter Greenwald, MD, Division of Cancer Prevention and Control, National Cancer Institute, USA
72 National Advisory Committee on Nutrition Education (NACNE) Report 1983 and Committee on Medical Aspects of Food Policy (COMA) Report 1984
73 Physicians' Health Study, begun 1982; Dr Charles Hennekens, Harvard Medical School and Brigham and Women's Hospital, Boston National Cancer Institute, Cancer Research Laboratory, Bethesda, Maryland, USA; Regina Ziegler, PhD, Environmental Epidemiology Department
74 "Can vitamins help prevent cancer?" *Consumer Reports* May 1983, v48, n5, p243–5
75 *Redbook* April 1989, v172, n6, p96(5)
76 "Good diet 'curbs cancer risk'" *The Independent* 3 October 1989
77 Gerhard Schrauzer, PhD, of the University of California cited in *Better Nutrition* Nov 1989, v51, n11, p14(2)
78 *Redbook* April 1989, v172, n6, p96(5)
79 "Advances in the role of minerals in immunobiology," Spallholz JE, Stewart JR, Center for Food and Nutrition, Texas Tech University, Lubbock 79409. *Biol Trace Elem Res* Mar 1989, 19 (3) p129–51
80 *Archives of Environmental Health* September/October 1976
81 "Selenium Deficiency and Increased Risk of Lung Cancer," Knekt, P. et al. Abstract of paper read at the Fourth International Symposium on Selenium in Biology and Medicine, Tubingen, West Germany, July 1988
82 "Selenium Deficiency and Lethal Skin Cancer," Reinhold, U, et al. Abstract of paper read at the Fourth International Symposium on Selenium in Biology and Medicine, Tubingen, West Germany, July 1988
83 *Nutrition Almanac*, Nutrition Search, Inc, McGraw-Hill Company
84 *The Calcium Connection*, Cedric Garland, PhD, and Frank Garland, PhD, Simon &

Schuster 1989; C Garland is Director of the Cancer Center Epidemiology Program, University of California, San Diego

85 American Cancer Society, nutritional guidelines, *Health* June 1984, v16, p9(1)

86 *Probiotics*, Leon Chaitow ND, DO and Natasha Trenev, Thorsons 1990

87 "The consumption of seaweed as a protective factor in the etiology of breast cancer," Teas J, *Med Hypotheses* 1981 7 (5), p601–13

88 "Can vitamins help cancer?" *Consumer Reports* May 1983, v48, n5, p243–45

89 "Can the macrobiotic diet cure cancer?", *Total Health* October 1989, v11, n5, p18(4)

90 *Total Health* October 1989, v11, n5, p18(4)

91 "Effects of an oats fibre tablet and wheat bran in healthy volunteers," Vorster HH, Lotter AP, Odendaal I *S Afr Med J* 29 March 1986

92 "Hypocholesterolemic effects of oat-bran or bean intake for hypercholesterolemic men," Anderson JW, Story L, Sieling B, Chen WJ, Petro MS, Story J *Am J Clin Nutr* December 1984

93 Delthia Ricks; UPI 17 March 1988

94 "Dietary fiber content of selected foods," Anderson JW, Bridges SR *Am J Clin Nutr* March 1988.

95 "Hypocholesterolemic effects of oat and bean products," Anderson JW, Gustafson NJ *Am J Clin Nutr* September 1988

96 *The Times* 8 February 1988

97 "Cholestyramine plus pectin in treatment of patients with familial hypercholesterolemia," Schwandt P, Richter WO, Weisweiler P, Neureuther G *Atherosclerosis* September 1982

98 "Natural hypocholesterolemic agent: pectin plus ascorbic acid," Ginter E, Kubec FJ, Vozar J, Bobek P *Int J Vitam Nutr Res* 1979

99 "Cholesterol-lowering effects of psyllium hydrophilic mucilloid for hypercholesterolemic men," Anderson JW, Zettwoch N, Feldman T, Tietyen-Clark J, Oeltgen P, Bishop CW *Arch Intern Med* February 1988

100 Influence of a psyllium-based fibre preparation on faecal and serum parameters," Burton R, Manninen V *Acta Med Scand* [Suppl] 1982

101 "Anaphylaxis following psyllium ingestion," Zaloga GP, Hierlwimmer UR, Engler RJ *J Allergy Clin Immunol* July 1984

102 "Anaphylactic shock due to ingestion of psyllium laxative," Suhonen R, Kantola I, Bjorksten F *Allergy* July 1983

103 UPI 1 March 1990

104 UPI 1 March 1990

105 "Vitamin C as a preventive medicine against common colds in children," Ludvigsson J, Hansson LO, Tibbling G *Scand J Infect Dis* 1977, 9 (2) p91–8

106 "Large scale studies with vitamin C," Anderson TW *Acta Vitaminol Enzymol* 1977, 31 (1–5) p43–50

107 "Reduction in duration of common colds by zinc gluconate lozenges in a double-blind study," Eby GA, Davis DR, Halcomb WW *Antimicrob Agents Chemother* Jan 1984, 25 (1) p20–4

108 "Role of sugars in human neutrophilic phagocytosis," Sanchez A, Reeser JL, Lau HS, Yahiku PY, Willard RE, McMillan PJ, Cho SY, Magie AR, Register UD *Am J Clin Nutr* Nov 1973, 26 (11) p1180–4

109 National Advisory Committee on Nutrition Education, *Proposals for nutritional guidelines for health education in Britain*, The Health Education Council September 1983

110 *Introducing Diabetes*, British Diabetic Association

111 *Diabetes in the United Kingdom, 1988*, British Diabetic Association

112 *Diabetes in the United Kingdom, 1988*, British Diabetic Association

113 "Preventing Insulin Dependent Diabetes Mellitus: the environmental challenge," Diabetes Epidemiology Research International, *BMJ* (Clinical Research) 22 August 1987, 295(6596), p479–81

114 "Nutritional Recommendations and Principles for Individuals With Diabetes Mellitus: 1986," American Diabetes Association *Diabetes Care*, v10, n1, Jan–Feb 1987

115 "Does A Vegetarian Diet Reduce the Occurrence of Diabetes?" Snowdon DA, Phillips RL *American Journal of Public Health* May 1985, v75, n5

116 Ibid

117 "Coffee consumption as trigger for insulin dependent diabetes mellitus in childhood," Tuomilehto, J et al. Department of Epidemiology, National Public Health Institute, Helsinki, Finland; *BMJ* 10 March 1990, 300(6725), pp642–3

118 "[Dermatomycoses and an antifungal diet]" Haurmykosen und Antipilzdiat, Putzier, E, *Wien Med Wochenschr* (Austria) 31 Aug 1989, 139 (15–16) p379–80

119 Sir James Black quoted in *The Independent* 22 October 1988

120 Ibid & John J Voorhees, MD, Department of Dermatology, University of Michigan Medical School, Ann Arbor, Michigan, USA, reported in *Archives of Dermatology* and *Better Nutrition for Today's Living* June 1990, v52, n6, p22–3

121 Donald O Rudin, MD, *The Omega-3 Phenomenon* and *Better Nutrition for Today's Living* June 1990, v52, n6, p22–3

122 *Better Nutrition for Today's Living* June 1990, v52, n6, pp22–3

123 "The Mechanism of Folate Deficiency in Psoriasis," L Fry, et al. *British Journal of Dermatology* 1971, 84:539–44

124 "Influence of maternal diet during lactation and use of formula feeds on development of atopic eczema in high risk infants," Chandra, Ranjit Kumar, Puri, Shakuntla, Hamed, Azza. *BMJ* 22 July 1989, v298, n6693, p228(3)

125 "A fasting and vegetarian diet treatment trial on chronic inflammatory disorders," Lithell H, et al. *Vessby B Acta Derm Venereol* (Stockh) 1983, 63 (5), pp397–403

126 Dr Kari Poilolainen et al. National Public Health Institute, Helsinki, as reported in the *B M J* and *The Independent* 23 March 1990

127 *B M J* July 1985

128 *Los Angeles Times* 18 July 1989

129 *HeartCorps*, December 1989, v2, n3, p67(4)

130 *HeartCorps*, December 1989, v2, n3, p67(4)

131 "Relation of moderate alcohol consumption and risk of systemic hypertension in women," Witteman, Jacqueline CM, Willett, Walter C, Stampfer, Meir J, Colditz, Graham A, Kok, Frans J, Sacks, Frank M, Speizer, Frank E, Rosner, Bernard, Hennekens, Charles H *American Journal of Cardiology* 1 March 1990, v65, n9, p633(5)

132 *JAMA*, 11 April 1990

133 "A vegan regimen with reduced medication in the treatment of hypertension," Lindahl O, Lindwall L, Spangberg A, Stenram A, Ockerman PA *Br J Nutr* Jul 1984, 52 (1) p11–20

134 "Blood-pressure-lowering effect of a vegetarian diet: controlled trial in normotensive subjects," Rouse IL, Armstrong BK, Beilen LJ, Vandongen R, *The Lancet*, 1 Jan 1983

135 "Randomised blind controlled trial of a high fibre, low fat and low sodium dietary regimen in mild essential hypertension," Dodson PM, Stephenson J, Dodson LJ, Kurnik D, Kritzinger EE, Taylor KG, Fletcher RF *J Hum Hypertens* June 1989, 3 (3), p197–202

136 "Consumption of olive oil, butter, and vegetable oils and coronary heart disease risk factors," Trevisan, Maurizio, Krogh, Vittorio, Freudenheim, Jo, Blake, Alma, Muti, Paola, Panico, Salvatore, Farinaro, Eduardo, Mancini, Mario, Menotti, Alessandro, Ricci, Giorgio *JAMA* 2 Feb 1990, v263, n5, p688(5)

137 "Nutritional aspects of hypertension," Seedat YK, *S Afr Med J* (South Africa) 18 Feb 1989, 75 (4) p175–7

138 *Better Nutrition* July 1990, v52, n7, p14(2)

139 "Serum calcium and salt restriction in the diet of patients with essential arterial hypertension," Uza G, Vlaicu R, Institute of Hygiene and Public Health Medical Clinic no. 1, Cluj-Napoca, Romania. *Med Interne* Apr-Jun 1989, 27 (2) p93–7

140 *Medical World News* 26 Feb 1990, v31, n4, p22(2)

141 "Selenium and High Blood Pressure," The Cleveland Clinic March 1976

142 "Role of life-style and dietary habits in risk of cancer among Seventh-Day Adventists," Roland L Phillips, *Cancer Research* November 1975, 35, 3513–3522

143 "Role of sugars in human neutrophilic phagocytosis," Sanchez A, Reeser JL, Lau HS, Yahiku PY, Willard RE, McMillan PJ, Cho SY, Magie AR, Register UD *Am J Clin Nutr* Nov 1973, 26 (11) pp1180–4

144 "Alkohol og infeksjoner," Morland B, Morland H Norges allmennvitenskapelige forskningsr. ANG. ad, Oslo. *Tidsskr Nor Laegeforen* 10 Feb 1990, 110 (4) p490–3. "Neutrophil elastase activity and superoxide production are diminished in neutrophils of alcoholics," Sachs CW, Christensen RH, Pratt PC, Lynn WS Department of Pathology, Duke University School of Medicine, Durham, North Carolina 27710. *Am Rev Respir Dis*, May 1990, 141 (5 Pt 1) p1249–55

145 "Human neutrophils are not severely injured in conditions mimicking social drinking," Corberand JX, Laharrague PF, Fillola G Central Laboratory of Haematology, CHU Rangueil, Toulouse, France. *Alcohol Clin Exp Res* Aug 1989, 13 (4) p542–6

146 "Role of sugars in human neutrophilic phagocytosis," Sanchez A, Reeser JL, Lau HS, Yahiku PY, Willard RE, McMillan PJ, Cho SY, Magie AR, Register UD *Am J Clin Nutr*, Nov 1973, 26 (11) p1180–4

147 "Vitamin B_6 deficiency and carcinogenesis," Reynolds RD US Department of Agriculture, Beltsville Human Nutrition Research Center, Maryland 20705. *Adv Exp Med Biol* 1986, 206 p339–47

148 "Suppression of tumor growth and enhancement of immune status with high levels of dietary vitamin B_6 in BALB/c mice," Gridley DS, Stickney DR, Nutter RL, Slater JM, Shultz TD *J Natl Cancer Inst* May 1987, 78 (5) p951–9

149 "Vitamin B_6 revisited. Evidence of subclinical deficiencies in various segments of the population and possible consequences thereof," Serfontein WJ, De Villiers LS, Ubbink J, Pitout MJ *S Afr Med J* 22 Sep 1984, 66 (12) p437–41

150 "Pyridoxine supplementation: effect on lymphocyte responses in elderly persons," Talbott MC, Miller LT, Kerkvliet NI Department of Foods and Nutrition, Oregon State University, Corvallis 97331. *Am J Clin Nutr* Oct 1987, 46 (4) p659–64
151 American Hospital Formulary Service, American Society of Hospital Pharmacists 1990
152 *Redbook* Janaury 1990, v174, n3, p96(2)
153 "Sensory neuropathy from pyridoxine abuse: a new megavitamin syndrome," Schaumburg H, Kaplan J, Windebank A et al. *N Engl J Med* 1983, 309:445–8; "Sensory neuropathy from pyridoxine abuse," Schaumburg H *N Engl J Med* 1984, 310:197–8; "Pyridoxine toxicity: report of a case," Vasile A, Goldberg R, Kornberg B *J Am Osteopath Assoc* 1984; 83:790–1
154 "Vitamin E and immune functions," Bendich A, Clinical Nutrition, Hoffmann La Roche Inc., Nutley, NJ 07110 *Basic Life Sci* 1988, 49 p615–20
155 "Vitamin E and immune functions," Bendich A, Clinical Nutrition, Hoffmann La Roche Inc., Nutley, NJ 07110. *Basic Life Sci* 1988, 49 p615–20
156 *Redbook* Janaury 1990, v174, n3, p96(2)
157 American Hospital Formulary Service, American Society of Hospital Pharmacists 1990
158 *Basic Life Sci* 1988, 49 p615–20
159 "Learning more about viruses," Berger, Stuart, MD *New York Post* 9 May 1989
160 "The effect of ascorbic acid deficiency on leukocyte phagocytosis and killing of actinomyces viscosus," Goldschmidt MC, Masin WJ, Brown LR, Wyde PR Dental Science Institute, University of Texas Health Science Center, Houston 77225. *Int J Vitam Nutr Res* 1988, 58 (3) p326–34
161 "Vitamin C as a preventive medicine against common colds in children," Ludvigsson J, Hansson LO, Tibbling G *Scand J Infect Dis* 1977, 9 (2) p91–8
162 "Large scale studies with vitamin C," Anderson TW *Acta Vitaminol Enzymol* 1977, 31 (1–5) p43–50
163 *Better Nutrition* April 1989, v51, n4, p16(3)
164 *How to live longer and feel better*, Linus Pauling, Avon Books, New York 1987
165 "Immunostimulatory effects of beta-carotene on T-cell activation markers and NK cells in HIV infected patients," Watson RR, Garewal HS, Ampel NM, Prabhala RH, Allen V, Dols C, Hicks MJ University of Arizona, Tucson, Arizona, USA. *Int Conf AIDS* 4–9 Jun 1989, 5 p663
166 "Nutrition and immune responses," Chandra RK *Can J Physiol Pharmacol* Mar 1983, 61 (3) p290–4
167 *Nutrition Reports International* 1988 17:157–163
168 "Prophylaxis and treatment of rhinovirus colds with zinc gluconate lozenges," Al-Nakib W, Higgins PG, Barrow I, Batstone G, Tyrrell DA MRC Common Cold Unit, Harvard Hospital, Salisbury, Wiltshire, UK. *J Antimicrob Chemother* Dec 1987, 20 (6) p893–901
169 *Better Nutrition* January 1989, v51, n1, p10(4)
170 Drs John Martin, Colorado State University, and Julian E Spallholz, Long Beach, California Veterans Administration Hospital, cited in *Better Nutrition* Nov 1989, v51, n11, p14(2)
171 Gerhard Schrauzer, PhD, of the University of California, cited in *Better Nutrition* Nov 1989, v51, n11, p14(2)
172 *Redbook* April 1989, v172, n6, p96(5)
173 "Macrophage activation and induction of macrophage cytotoxicity by purified polysaccharide fractions from the plant echinacae purpurea," Stimpel, M. et al. *Infection Immunity* 1984, 46, p845–9
174 *Potter's New Cyclopedia of Botanical Drugs and Preparations*, RC Wren, The CW Daniel Company Ltd, 1982
175 "Activation of Peritoneal macrophages by berined-type alkaloids in terms of induction of cytostatic activity," Kumazawa, Y, et al, *Int J Immunopharmac* 1984, 6, p587–92
176 *Potter's New Cyclopedia of Botanical Drugs and Preparations*, RC Wren, The CW Daniel Company Ltd, 1982
177 "Interferon induction by glycyrrhiz and glycyrrhetinic acid in mice," Abe N et al. *Microbial Immunol* 1982, 26, p535–9
178 "Antiviral activity of glycyrrhizic acid," Pompeii, R et al. *Experentia* 1980, 36, p304–5
179 "Antimicrobial agents from higher plants. Antimicrobial isoflavonoids from glycyrrhiza glabra L var. typica," Mitscher, L et al. *J Nat Products* 1980, 43, p259–69
180 *Potter's New Cyclopedia of Botanical Drugs and Preparations*, RC Wren, The CW Daniel Company Ltd, 1982
181 *Today's Living* September 1989, v20, n9, p5(6)
182 Cited in *Better Nutrition* January 1989, v51, n1, p10(4)
183 "Garlic as an antimicrobial and immune modulator in AIDS," Abdullah T, Kirkpatrick DV, Williams L, Carter J, Akbar Research Foundation, Panama City, Florida, USA, *Int Conf AIDS* 4–9 Jun 1989, 5 p466
184 "Green tea cuts cancerous growths" *New Scientist* 12 November 1987
185 "Natural Therapies for AIDS," Badgley

LE, MD *Townsend Letter for Doctors* October 1988.
186 "Milk intolerance in children with persistent sleeplessness: a prospective double-blind crossover evaluation," Kahn A et al. Pediatric Sleep Unit, University Children's Hospital, Free University of Brussels, Belgium *Pediatrics* Oct 1989, 84(4) p595–603; "Sleep characteristics in milk-intolerant infants," Kahn A et al. *Sleep* (US) June 1988, 11(3) p291–7; "Difficulty in initiating and maintaining sleep associated with cow's milk allergy in infants," Kahn A et al. *Sleep* (US) April 1987, 10(2) p116–21
187 "Experts link diet supplement to painful blood disorder" *The Washington Post* 25 November 1989
188 "Is migraine food allergy? A double-blind controlled trial of oligoantigenic diet treatment," Egger J, Carter CM, Wilson J, Turner MW, Soothill JF *The Lancet* 15 Oct 1983, 2 (8355) p865–9
189 *Living* April 1990, v21, n4, p14(3)
190 "Efficacy of feverfew as prophylactic treatment of migraine," Johnson ES, Kadam NP, Hylands DM, Hylands PJ *BMJ* [Clin Res] 31 Aug 1985, 291 (6495) p569–73
191 "Randomised double-blind placebo-controlled trial of feverfew in migraine prevention," Murphy JJ, Heptinstall S, Mitchell JR Department of Medicine, University Hospital, Nottingham. *The Lancet* 23 Jul 1988, 2 (8604) p189–92
192 "Antiplatelet effect of capsaicin," Wang JP et al. *Thrombosis Research* 1984, p497–507
193 Dr John McDougall, *Vegetarian Times* June 1989, n142 p60(3)
194 *American Journal of Medicine* 1950, 220:421
195 "Multiple sclerosis: twenty years on low fat diet," Swank RL *Arch Neurol* Nov 1970, 23 (5) p460–74
196 *The Multiple Sclerosis Diet Book*, Swank RL, Pullen MH Doubleday, Garden City, NY 1977
197 *The Edell Health Letter* May 1989, v8, n5, p6(1)
198 "Low-fat diet may cut deaths from MS," Celia Hall *The Independent* 6 July 1990
199 "Effect of low saturated fat diet in early and late cases of multiple sclerosis," Swank RL, Dugan BB *The Lancet* 7 July 1990, v336, n8706, p37(3)
200 *The Lancet*, 7 July 1990, v336, n8706, p25(2)
201 Dr John McDougall, *Vegetarian Times* June 1989, n142 p60(3)
202 National Osteoporosis Society Newsletter no 1
203 *The Independent* 23 October 1990
204 National Osteoporosis Society leaflet no 2
205 John Studd, Consultant Gynaecologist, King's College and Dulwich Hospitals, Vice-Chairman of the National Osteoporosis Society
206 *The Independent* 23 October 1990
207 "Postmenopausal osteoporosis: its clinical features," Albright F, Smith PH, Richardson AM *JAMA* 1941, 116:2465–74.
208 "Estrogen replacement therapy for the prevention of osteoporosis," Lufkin EG, Ory SJ, *American Family Physician* Sept 1989, v40, n3, p205(7)
209 "Estrogens and endometrial cancer in a retirement community," Mack TM, Pike MC, Henderson BE et al. *N Engl J Med* 1976, 294:1262–7
210 "A risk-benefit assessment of estrogen therapy in postmenopausal women," Cust MP, Gangar KF, Hillard TC, Whitehead MI Academic Department of Obstetrics and Gynaecology, King's College School of Medicine and Dentistry, London, England. *Drug Saf* Sep-Oct 1990, 5 (5) p345–58
211 "Hormone-replacement therapy and the risk of breast cancer," Hulka BS Department of Epidemiology, University of North Carolina, Chapel Hill. *CA* Sep-Oct 1990, 40 (5) p289–96
212 "Estrogen replacement therapy for the prevention of osteoporosis," Lufkin EG, Ory SJ, *American Family Physician* Sept 1989, v40, n3, p205(7)
213 "Effects of nitrogen, phosphorus, and caffeine on calcium balance in women," Heaney RP, Recker RR *J Lab Clin Med* Jan 1982, 99 (1) p46–55
214 *What everyone needs to know about osteoporosis*, The National Osteoporosis Society
215 Research Advances in Osteoporosis, Conference by the National Osteoporosis Foundation, the National Institutes of Health, and the American Society of Bone and Mineral Research, Arlington, Virginia, USA, February 1990
216 "Osteoporosis, calcium requirement, and factors causing calcium loss," Spencer H, Kramer L *Clin Geriatr Med* May 1987, 3 (2) p389–402
217 "Vegetarian lifestyle and bone mineral density," Marsh AG, Sanchez TV, Michelsen O, Chaffee FL, Fagal SM Department of Home Economics, Andrews University, Berrien Springs, MI 49104. *Am J Clin Nutr* Sep 1988, 48 (3 Suppl) p837–41
218 "Relationship of animal protein-rich diet to kidney stone formation and calcium metabolism," Breslau NA, Brinkley L, Hill KD, Pak CY Center in Mineral Metabolism and Clinical Research, Department of Internal Medicine, Dallas, Texas. *J Clin Endocrinol Metab* Jan 1988, 66 (1) p140–6

219 "Effect of dietary boron on mineral, estrogen, and testosterone metabolism in postmenopausal women," Nielsen FH, Hunt CD, Mullen LM, Hunt JR United States Department of Agriculture, Grand Forks Human Nutrition Research Center, North Dakota 58202. *FASEB J* Nov 1987, 1 (5) p394–7
220 "Osteoporosis strategies for prevention," White JE, Family Nurse Practitioner Program, University of Pittsburgh School of Nursing. *Nurse Pract,* 1986, 11(9) 36–46, 50
221 American Health Foundation, *Medical World News* 1979
222 *The Washington Post* 2 November 1990
223 *Evolutionary Biology of Ageing* Oxford University Press 1991
224 *JAMA* August 1988
225 Committee on Medical Aspects of Food Policy, Report of the Panel on *Diet in Relation to Cardiovascular Disease* 1984
226 Report by the Coronary Prevention Group 26 May 1987
227 *The Guardian* 24 July 1984
228 *Essence* April 1990, v20, n12, p26(2)
229 *Financial Times* 29 October 1988
230 Dr Lars Ekeland of the University of North Carolina at Chapel Hill *N Engl J Med.* 15 Nov 1988
231 *Women's Health Today,* Office of Health Economics 23 Nov 1987
232 Dr Lars Ekeland of the University of North Carolina at Chapel Hill *N Engl J Med.* 15 Nov 1988
233 National Cancer Research Institute, Tokyo
234 *The Economist* 7 July 1990
235 *The Times* 29 November 1988.
236 Dr Mary McGraw, Southmead Hospital, Bristol *Observer* 15 January 1989
237 *New Scientist* 21 January 1989
238 *New Scientist* 21 January 1989
239 *New Scientist* 3 March 1988
240 *New Scientist* 3 March 1988
241 *The Independent* 23 May 1990
242 *The Independent* 23 May 1990
243 "Hirnleistungsstorungen–Behandlung mit Ginkgo-biloba-Extrakt. Zeitpunkt des Wirkungseintrits in einer Doppelblindstudie mit 60 stationaren Patienten," Eckmann F *Fortschr Med* 10 Oct 1990, 108 (29) p557–60
244 "Einfluss von Ginkgo biloba-Extrakt auf neurophysiologische und psychometrische Messergebnisse bei Patienten mit hirnorganischem Psychosyndrom. Eine Doppelblindstudie gegen Plazebo," Munster/Westf. *Arzneimittelforschung* Aug 1989, 39 (8) p918–22
245 "Effects of Ginkgo biloba constituents related to protection against brain damage caused by hypoxia," Oberpichler H, Beck T, Abdel-Rahman MM, Bielenberg GW, Krieglstein J, *Pharmacol Res Commun* May, 1988, 20 (5) p349–68
246 "Ginkgo biloba extract facilitates recovery from penetrating brain injury," Attella MJ, Hoffman SW, Stasio MJ, Stein DG *Exp Neurol* Jul 1989, 105 (1) p62–71
247 "Effets sur l'activite fonctionnelle cerebrale de l'extrait de Ginkgo biloba. Bilan d'etudes cliniques et experimentales," Pidoux B, *Presse Med* 25 Sep 1986, 15 (31) p1588–91
248 "Traitement des troubles du vieillissement cerebral par l'extrait de Ginkgo biloba. Etude longitudinale multicentrique a double insu face au placebo," Taillandier J, Ammar A, Rabourdin JP, Ribeyre JP, Pichon J, Niddam S, Pierart H *Presse Med* 25 Sep 1986, 15 (31) p1583–7
249 "Traitement des troubles de l'equilibre par l'extrait de Ginkgo biloba. Etude multicentrique a double insu face au placebo," Haguenauer JP, Cantenot F, Koskas H, Pierart H *Presse Med* 25 Sep 1986, 15 (31) p1569–72
250 "Psycho-pharmacologie clinique de l'extrait de Ginkgo biloba," Warburton DM *Presse Med* 25 Sep 1986, 15 (31) p1595–604
251 *Gut* 30 (1989), 1201–1205
252 *Nutrition Health Review* Fall 1989, n52, p4(1)
253 *Nutrition Health Review* Fall 1989, n52, p4(1)
254 Associated Press 2 September 88
255 *The Independent* 11 May 1990
256 "Erythroleukaemia in two infant chimpanzees fed milk from cows naturally infected with the Bovine C-type Virus," McClure HH, Keeling ME, Custer RP, Marshak RR, Abt DA, Ferrer JF *Cancer Research,* 34: 2745–2757
257 "Induction of Syncytia by the Bovine C-type Leukaemia Virus," Diglio CA, Ferrer JF *Cancer Research,* 36:1056–1067
258 *Oncogenic Viruses,* Gross, L, 2nd ed., Pergamon Press, New York 1970. "Presence of particles with the morphology of viruses of the avian leukosis complex in meningeal tumours induced in dogs by Rous sarcoma virus," Robotti GF *Virology,* 24:686. "Avian tumour viruses," Vogt PK *Adv. Virus Res,* 7:293
259 *New Scientist* 5 November 1987
260 "Epidemiology of butchers' warts," Jab-Lonska S, Obalek S, GoLebiowska A, Favre M, Orth G *Arch Dermatol Res* 1988, 280 Suppl pS24–8
261 "Food-born viruses and malignant hemopoietic diseases," Lemon HM *Bact. Rev.,* 28:490–492
262 "Leukaemia in humans and animals in the light of epidemiological studies with refer-

ence to problems of its prevention," Aleksandrowicz J *Acta Med*, Polona, 9:217–230
263 "Leukaemia in Olmsted county, Minnesota, 1965–1974," Linos A, Kyle RA, Elveback LR, Kurland LT, *Mayo Clin. Proc.*, 53:714–718
264 "Cancer mortality among white males in the meat industry," Johnson, Fischman, Genevieve, Matanoski, Diamond *Jnl of Occupational Medicine* v28 n1, Jan 1986
265 *Scientific American* January 1989, v260, n1, p68(8)
266 *The Observer* 20 July 1986
267 *The Guardian* 20 September 1986
268 "Cooking up a storm," Linda Gamlin *New Scientist* 8 July 1989
269 "Cooking up a storm," Linda Gamlin *New Scientist* 8 July 1989
270 *US News & World Report* 20 February 1989, v106, n7, p77(2)
271 *US News & World Report,* 20 February 1989, v106, n7, p77(2)
272 *The Guardian* 8 January 1987
273 *Patient Care* 15 August 1989, v23, n13, p94(10)
274 *Patient Care* 15 August 1989, v23, n13, p94(10)
275 *FDA Consumer* February 1989, v23, n1, p10(5)
276 *JAMA* 21 October 1988
277 "Controlled trial of oligoantigenic treatment in the hyperkinetic syndrome," Egger J, Carter CM, Graham PJ, Gumley D, Soothill JF *The Lancet* 9 Mar 1985, 1 (8428) p540–5
278 "The Northern California diet-behavior program: An empirical examination of 3,000 incarcerated juveniles in Stanislaus County Juvenile Hall," Schoenthaler SJ *International Journal of Biosocial Research* 1983, v5(2), p99–106
279 "Types of offenses which can be reduced in an institutional setting using nutritional intervention: A preliminary empirical evaluation," Schoenthaler, SJ, Doraz WE *International Journal for Biosocial Research* 1983, v4(2), p74–84
280 "'Yuppie 'Flu' Turns Out to Be Real" *Los Angeles Times* 24 January 1991
281 *The Washington Post* 27 November 1990
282 *Patient Care* 15 November 1987, v21, n18, p79(4)
283 *Better Nutrition for Today's Living* May 1990, v52, n5, p20(4)
284 *Better Nutrition for Today's Living* May 1990, v52, n5, p20(4)
285 UPI 19 December 1990
286 *The Independent* 30 April 1991
287 *The Atlantic,* September 1987, v260, p56(16)
288 *Holistic Medicine* March-April 1990, p8(2)
289 *Chronic Fatigue Syndrome: The Hidden Epidemic,* Jesse Stoff and Charles Pellegrino, Random House, 1988
290 *East West* January 1989, v19, n1, p44(8)
291 *East West* January 1989, v19, n1, p44(8)
292 *New Scientist* 29 September 1990
293 "Oral contraceptive use and breast cancer risk in young women: UK National Case-Control Study Group," *The Lancet* 6 May 1989, 1 (8645) p973–82
294 UPI 28 February 1990
295 *The Independent* 7 August 1989
296 *FDA Consumer* March 1987, v21, p26(3)
297 British National Formulary n16
298 *FDA Consumer* March 1987, v21, p26(3)
299 *FDA Consumer* March 1987, v21, p26(3)
300 *FDA Consumer* March 1987, v21, p26(3)
301 *Computerworld* 17 December 1990, p96
302 "Home births in England and Wales, 1979: perinatal mortality according to intended place of delivery," Campbell R, Davies IM, Macfarlane A, Beral V, *BMJ* [Clin Res] 22 Sep 1984, 289 (6447) p721–4
303 "Having babies at home: is it safe? Is it ethical?" Hoff GA, Schneiderman LJ Department of Obstetrics and Gynecology, University of Utah Medical Center, Hastings. *Cent Rep* Dec 1985, 15 (6) p19–27
304 "Five year prospective survey of risk of booking for a home birth in Essex," Shearer JM, *BMJ* [Clin Res], 23 Nov 1985, 291 (6507) p1478–80
305 "Home birth and hospital deliveries: a comparison of the perceived painfulness of parturition," Morse JM, Park C. *Res Nurs Health* Jun 1988, 11 (3) p175–81
306 "The hazards of forceps: the viewpoint of the pediatrician and the obstetrician," Claris O, Audra P, Mellier G, Putet G, Salle B *Rev Fr Gynecol Obstet* Oct 1990, 85 (10) pp549–51
307 *Postnatal Infection: A survey Conducted by the National Childbirth Trust,* National Childbirth Trust 1988
308 "Vacuum extraction and forceps delivery in a district hospital," Carter J, Gudgeon CW *Aust N Z J Obstet Gynaecol,* May 1987, 27 (2) p117–19
309 *The New York Times* 28 July 1989
310 *The New York Times* 28 July 1989
311 UPI 26 July 1989
312 "Babies Mean Business," Edward Baer *New Internationalist* April 1982
313 Professor RK Anand, statement to the press 4th Oct 1988
314 "Effect of breast-feeding on antibody response to conjugate vaccine," Pabst HF, Spady DW *The Lancet* 4 Aug 1990, v336, n8710, p269(2)
315 "Protection of breast-fed infants against Campylobacter diarrhoea by antibodies in human milk," Ruiz-Palacios GM, Calva JJ,

Pickering LK, Lopez-Vidal Y, Volkow P, Pezzarossi H, West, SM, *Journal of Pediatrics* May 1990, v116, n5, p707(7)
316 *Mothering* Spring, 1990, n55, p70(2)
317 *The Doctor's People Newsletter* July 1989, v2, n7, p6(3)
318 *The Times* 6 March 1987
319 *The Times* 6 March 1987
320 *Am J Obstet Gynecol*1989, 161:1228
321 *Vegetarian Times* March 1990
322 "Pyridoxine (Vitamin B_6) and the Premenstrual Syndrome: A randomized crossover trial," H Doll et al. *J Royal College of General Practitioners* Sept 1989, 39(326): 364–368
323 "Sensory neuropathy from pyridoxine abuse: a new megavitamin syndrome," Schaumburg H, Kaplan J, Windebank A et al. *N Engl J Med* 1983, 309:445–8; "Sensory neuropathy from pyridoxine abuse," Schaumburg H *N Engl J Med* 1984, 310:197–8; "Pyridoxine toxicity: report of a case," Vasile A, Goldberg R, Kornberg B *J Am Osteopath Assoc* 1984, 83:790–1
324 *Nutrition Research Newsletter* February 1989, v8, n2, p16(2)
325 *Vegetarian Times* April 1990
326 *Nutrition Action Healthletter* May 1990, v17, n4, p1(4)
327 *Fertil Steril* 1987, 47:402
328 *British National Formulary Number 13* British Medical Association & The Pharmaceutical Society of Great Britain 1987
329 *British National Formulary Number 13* British Medical Association & The Pharmaceutical Society of Great Britain 1987
330 *British National Formulary Number 13* British Medical Association & The Pharmaceutical Society of Great Britain 1987
331 *Non-prescription Drugs*, Alain Li Wan Po, Blackwell Scientific Publications 1982
332 *Federal Register* v45, n103, p356-59
333 *The Lancet* 12 January 1980, pp60–1
334 *The Lancet* 1979, 2: 1367
335 *The Lancet* 1972, 2: 492
336 *JAMA* 1981, 245:1346–1347
337 *The Lancet* 1979, 2:1110–1111
338 *Ann Emerg Med* June 1982, 11:311–315
339 *Federal Register*
340 *Non-prescription Drugs*, Alain Li Wan Po, Blackwell Scientific Publications 1982 p374/5
341 *The Washington Post* 21 April 1987
342 *Philadelphia Inquirer* 19 September 1988
343 *The Health Scandal*, Dr Vernon Coleman, Sidgwick & Jackson 1988
344 *The Washington Post* 16 August 1987
345 "Clinical diagnosis: a post-mortem assessment of accuracy in the 1980s," Mercer J, Talbot IC *Postgraduate Medical Journal* August 1985, 61 (718) p713–16
346 *The Washington Post* 16 August 1987
347 "Report in Occupational Health & Safety," cited by Dr Edward Pinckney in *The Washington Post* 16 August 1987
348 *The Washington Post* 16 August 1987
349 *The American Journal of Roentgenology*, cited in *The Washington Post* 16 Aug 1987
350 *American Family Physician*, cited in *The Washington Post* 16 August 1987
351 *British National Formulary*, published by the British Medical Association and The Pharmaceutical Society of Great Britain
352 *The Health Scandal*, Vernon Coleman, Sidgwick & Jackson 1988
353 *JAMA* 21 July 1988, cited in *Facts on File*, 28 Oct 1988
354 *The Health Scandal*, Vernon Coleman, Sidgwick & Jackson 1988
355 *Sunday Correspondent* 26 November 1989
356 *Today* 13 July 1988
357 "Therapeutical trials with antimicrobial agents and cultured cecal microflora in Salmonella infantis infections in chickens," Seuna E, Nurmi E *Poultry Science* Sept 1979, v58 (5), p1171–1174
358 "Use of competitive exclusion in prevention of salmonellae and other enteropathogenic bacteria infections in poultry," Nurmi E, *Proceedings of the International Symposium on Salmonella*, New Orleans, Louisiana, USA, 19–20 July 1984, p64–71
359 "Probiotics in man and animals," Fuller R *J Appl Bacteriol* May 1989, 66 (5) p365–78
360 "Yoghurt with Bifidobacterium longum reduces erythromycin-induced gastrointestinal effects," Colombel JF, Cortot A, Neut C, Romond C, *The Lancet* 4 July 1987, 2 (8549) p43
361 "Successful treatment of relapsing Clostridium difficile colitis with Lactobacillus GG," Gorbach SL, Chang TW, Goldin B *The Lancet* 26 Dec 1987, 2 (8574) p1519
362 *Prevention* August 1989, v41, n8, p47(5)
363 "N-Nitroso Compounds and childhood brain tumors: A case-control study," Preston-Martin S, Yu MC, Benton B, Henderson BE, *Cancer Research* December 1982, v42, 5240-5245
364 *Prevention* August 1989, v41, n8, p47(5)
365 *Probiotics*, Leon Chaitow ND, DO and Natasha Trenev, Thorsons 1990
366 UPI 6 May 1985
367 *The Washington Post* 23 January 1990
368 *The Washington Post* 23 January 1990
369 *New Scientist* 7 July 1990
370 *Chicago Tribune* 24 June 1990
371 "Human exposures to volatile halogenated organic chemicals in indoor and outdoor air," *Environ Health Perspect* Oct 1985, 62 p313–18

372 *Chicago Tribune* 24 June 1990
373 *New Scientist* 27 January 1990
374 *Popular Science* October 1989, v235, n4, p78(3)
375 *The Curse of Icarus*, FS Kahn, Routledge 1990
376 "Galactic cosmic radiation exposure and associated health risks for air carrier crew members," Friedberg W, Faulkner DN, Snyder L, Darden EB Jr, O'Brien K *Aviat Space Environ Med* Nov 1989, 60 (11) p1104–8
377 *The Curse of Icarus*, FS Kahn, Routledge 1990
378 *Computerworld* 17 December 1990, p96
379 *Technology Review* October 1987, v90, n7, p52(8)
380 *Technology Review* October 1987, v90, n7, p52(8)
381 "Electrical wiring configurations and childhood cancer," Wertheimer N, Leeper E *Am J Epidemiol* Mar 1979, 109 (3) p273–84
382 "Adult cancer related to electrical wires near the home," Wertheimer N, Leeper E *Int J Epidemiol* Dec 1982, 11 (4) p345–55
383 "Possible effects of electric blankets and heated waterbeds on fetal development," Wertheimer N, Leeper E *Bioelectromagnetics* 1986, 7 (1) p13–22
384 "Mortality from leukemia in workers exposed to electrical and magnetic fields," Milham S Jr *N Engl J Med* 22 Jul 1982, 307 (4) p249
385 *Technology Review* October 1987, v90, n7, p52(8)
386 "Leukemia and occupational exposure to electromagnetic fields: review of epidemiologic surveys," Savitz DA, Calle EE *J Occup Med* Jan, 1987, 29 (1) p47–51
387 "Case-control study of childhood cancer and exposure to 60-Hz magnetic fields," Savitz DA, Wachtel H, Barnes FA, John EM, Tvrdik JG *Am J Epidemiol* Jul 1988, 128 (1) p21–38
388 Environmental Protection Agency Working Review Draft, *Evaluation of the potential carcinogenicity of electromagnetic fields* June 1990
389 "The risk of miscarriage and birth defects among women who use visual display terminals during pregnancy," Goldhaber MK, Polen MR, Hiatt RA *Am J Ind Med* 1988, 13 (6) p695–706
390 *The Times* 10 February 1987
391 *IEE News*, Issue No.48, 4 October 1990, p4
392 "Are Electric Cookers And Ranges A Magnetic-Field Health Hazard?" Dr Stuart A Kingsley 2 January 1991
393 *Woman's Day* 22 May 1990, p126(2)
394 *New Scientist* 19 May 1990
395 *New Scientist* 19 May 1990
396 Statement by the French Ministry of Agriculture 6 May 1986, quoted in *Health Guide for the Nuclear Age*, by Peter Bunyard, Roxby General Books Ltd 1988
397 Public Citizen Health Research Group, *Philadelphia Inquirer* 19 Sept 1988
398 *Alternative Therapy*, British Medical Association 1986
399 *Report on the BMA Board of Science Working Party on Alternative Therapy*, The British Holistic Medical Association July 1986. One of its first criticisms concerned the BMA's own working party, which, the BHMA said, was not discussed by the full council of the BMA, did not keep to its remit, lacked members with experience of primary health care or complementary medicine, and produced a report which failed to meet accepted scientific standards
400 *J Pharm* 1981, 227:387–92, quoted in *Drugs & Therapeutics Bulletin*, 15 Dec 1986, v24, n25
401 "Adverse Reactions to Herbal Medicines," *Adverse Drug Reaction Bulletin* Oct 1983
402 "Comfrey: Risk and Benefit," *Journal of Food & Nutrition* 1981, v38 (4), p176
403 *Health or Hoax?*, Arnold E Bender (Elvedon Press, 1985). Professor Bender's book should serve as a salutory warning to all those who, through greed or ignorance, make unsubstantiated claims on behalf of the so-called 'natural' products they pass off on an unsuspecting public. Bender's style is ploddingly dogmatic, and he frequently seems to be closed-minded when it comes to admitting the efficacy of anything that smacks of the unconventional. Nevertheless, the burgeoning 'alternative' health field needs its critics – just as much as the orthodox health industries do
404 *Drugs & Therapeutics Bulletin* 15 December 1986, v24, n25
405 "Adverse Reactions to Herbal Medicines," *Adverse Drug Reaction Bulletin* Oct 1983
406 *Drugs & Therapeutics Bulletin* 15 December 1986, v24, n25; *Health or Hoax?*, Arnold E Bender, Elvedon Press 1985; "Adverse Rections to Herbal Medicines," *Adverse Drug Reaction Bulletin* Oct 1983
407 "Adverse Reactions to Herbal Medicines," *Adverse Drug Reaction Bulletin* Oct 1983
408 Ibid
409 Ibid and *Drugs & Therapeutics Bulletin* 15 December 1986, v24, n25
410 *Health or Hoax?* by Arnold E. Bender, Elvedon Press 1985; "Adverse Reactions to Herbal Medicines," *Adverse Drug Reaction Bulletin* Oct 1983
411 *Drugs & Therapeutics Bulletin* 15 December 1986, v24 n25

412 "Is homoeopathy a placebo response? Controlled trial of homoeopathic potency, with pollen in hayfever as model," *The Lancet* 18 Oct 1986, 2 (8512) p881-6
413 *New Scientist* 27 August 1987
414 Said to the mother of one of the authors (PC)
415 *East West* November 1989, v19, n11, p50(5)
416 *East West* January 1989, v19, n1, p44(8)
417 *In Health* May-June 1990, v4, n3, p78(7)
418 *Los Angeles Times* 29 December 1987
419 *Los Angeles Times* 21 August 1988
420 "Antineoplastic properties of Maharishi-4 against DMBA-induced mammary tumors in rats," Sharma HM, Dwivedi C, Satter BC, Gudehithlu KP, Abou-Issa H, Malarkey W, Tejwani GA, *Pharmacol Biochem Behav* Apr 1990, 35 (4) p767-73
421 "Effect of the Indian gooseberry (amla) on serum cholesterol levels in men aged 35-55 years," Jacob A, Pandey M, Kapoor S, Saroja R, *Eur J Clin Nutr* Nov 1988, 42 (11) p939-44
422 *Los Angeles Times* 19 May 1989
423 "Low back pain of mechanical origin: randomised comparison of chiropractic and hospital outpatient treatment," Meade TW, Dyer S, Browne W, Townsend J, Frank AO *BMJ* 2 Jun 1990, 300 (6737) p1431-7
424 New Zealand Government Commission of Inquiry Into Chiropractic 1979
425 *The British Chiropractic Association Handbook* 1987/88
426 Joint working party of the National Radiological Protection Board and the Royal College of Radiologists, *New Scientist* 8 Sept 1990
427 *Proposals for nutritional guidelines for health education in Britain*, The Health Education Council, National Advisory Committee on Nutrition Education, Sept 1983
428 *Health* June 1984, v16, p15(3)
429 *A Cancer Therapy – Results of Fifty Cases*, Max Gerson MD p7, Gerson Institute, P.O. Box 430 Bonita California 92002
430 *A Cancer Therapy – Results of Fifty Cases*, Max Gerson MD
431 "A medical application of the Ling association-induction hypothesis: the high potassium, low sodium diet of the Gerson cancer therapy," Cope FW *Physiol Chem Phys* 1978, 10 (5) p465-8
432 "Aldosterone And The Gerson Diet – A Speculation," McCarty MF, *Med Hypotheses* 1981, 7(5):591-597
433 "A medical application of the Ling association-induction hypothesis: the high potassium, low sodium diet of the Gerson cancer therapy," Cope FW, *Physiol Chem Phys* 1978, 10(5):465-468
434 "The possibility of influencing tumor growth by diet," Plohberger R, *Krebsgeschehen* 1978, 10(6):149-151
435 Conversation with authors 8 May 1991
436 Conversation with authors 8 May 1991
437 Conversation with authors 8 May 1991
438 *The Independent* 3 October 1989
439 *The Washington Post* 28 April 1987
440 *The Power to heal*, Deavid Harvey, The Aquarian Press 1983
441 *The Independent* 30 December 1989
442 "Patients' perceptions of music during surgery," Stevens K *J Adv Nurs* Sep 1990, 15 (9) p1045-51
443 "[Emotional-volitional training in the combined treatment of patients with rheumatoid arthritis] Emotsional'no-volevaia trenirovka v kompleksnom lechnii bol'nykh revmatoidnym artritom," Siniachenko VV, Leshchenko GIa, Melekhin VD *Ter Arkh* 1990, 62 (1) p58–62
444 "[Music for rheumatism – a historical overview] Musik gegen Rheuma – Ein historischer Uberblick," Evers S *Z Rheumatol* May-Jun 1990, 49 (3) p119–24
445 "Effects of relaxation and music therapy on patients in a coronary care unit with presumptive acute myocardial infarction," Guzzetta C E *Heart and Lung* Nov 1989, v18, n6, p609(8)
446 "Integrating music in breathing training and relaxation: II. Applications," Fried R *Biofeedback Self Regul* Jun 1990, 15 (2) p171-7
447 "Opening doors for the child 'inside'," Grimm DL, Pefley PT *Pediatr Nurs* Jul-Aug 1990, 16 (4) p368-9
448 "[Advances in dental psychology] Fortschritte der Dentalpsychologie," Kreyer G *Z Stomatol* May 1989, 86 (3) p123-30
449 "The effects of music therapy on a group of profoundly mentally handicapped adults", Oldfield A, Adams M *J Ment Defic Res* Apr 1990, 34 (Pt 2) p107-25
450 "[Coping with illness in the early phase of severe neurologic diseases. A contribution of music therapy to psychological management in selected neurologic disease pictures] Krankheitsverarbeitung in der Fruhphase schwerer neurologischer Erkrankungen. Ein Beitrag der Musiktherapie zur psychischen Betreuung bei ausgewahlten neurologischen Krankheitsbildern," Jochims S *Psychother Psychosom Med Psychol* Mar-Apr 1990, 40 (3-4) p115-22
451 "Music therapy may help control cancer pain," Kerkvliet GJ *J Natl Cancer Inst* 7 Mar 1990, 82 (5) p350-2
452 "Singing helps Alzheimer's patients and their care-takers," Millard KA, Olderog,

Smith JM *The Brown University Long-term Care Letter* Oct 1989, v1, n9, p6(1)
453 UPI 17 July 1984
454 *How to live longer and feel better,* Linus Pauling, Avon Books 1986
455 *How to live longer and feel better,* Linus Pauling, Avon Books 1986
456 "The great minerals gold mine," Annabel Ferriman, *The Observer* 22 May 1988
457 *The Diets of British Schoolchildren,* Department of Health Report on Health and Social Subjects no 36
458 *On the State of the Public Health For The Year 1989,* HMSO
459 *Nutrition and Health in Old Age,* Department of Health and Social Security Report on Health and Social Subjects no 16
460 *Marketing* 9 May 1991
461 American Hospital Formulary Service Drug Information 1990
462 *How to live longer and feel better,* Linus Pauling, Avon Books 1986
463 *How to live longer and feel better,* Linus Pauling, Avon Books 1986
464 "Vitamin C and the common cold: a double-blind trial," Anderson TW, Reid DB, Beaton GH *Can Med Assoc J* 23 Sep 1972
465 "Health problems and vitamin C in Canadian Northern Military Operations," Sabiston BH, Radomski NW Defence and Civil Institute of Environmental Medicine Report No 74-R-1012
466 "Vitamin C in high doses in the treatment of the common cold," Asfora J; *Re-evaluation of Vitamin C,* ed. Hanck A, Ritzel G, Hans Huber, Bern
467 "Vitamins for the prevention of colds," Cowan DW, Diehl HS, Baker AB, *JAMA* 1942, 143:421-424
468 "Vitamin C prophylaxis in marine recruits," Pitt HA, Costrini AM *JAMA* 2 Mar 1979, 241 (9) p908-11
469 "Vitamin C, Titrating to bowel tolerance, anascorbemia and acute induced scurvy," Cathcart RF *Med Hypotheses* 7:1359-1376
470 "An open trial of high-dosage antioxidants in early Parkinson's disease," Fahn S *Am J Clin Nutr* Jan 1991, 53 (1 Suppl) p380S-382S
471 "A possible role for vitamins C and E in cataract prevention," Robertson JM, Donner AP, Trevithick JR *Am J Clin Nutr* Jan 1991, 53 (1 Suppl) p346S-351S
472 "[Radioprotective effect of ascorbic acid on oral structures in patients with cancer of the head and neck] Efecto radioprotector del acido ascorbico sobre estructuras orales en pacientes con cancer de cabeza y cuello.," Garcia-Alejo HR, Martin de Miguel MJ, Seoane LJM, Romero MMA, Esparza GGC, *Av Odontoestomatol* Sep 1989, 5 (7) p469-72
473 "[Humoral and cellular indices of non-specific resistance in viral hepatitis A and ascorbic acid] Gumoral'nye i kletochnye pokazateli nespetsificheskoi rezistentnosti pri virusnom gepatite A i askorbinovaia kislota," Vasil'ev VS, Komar VI, Kisel' NI *Ter Arkh* 1989, 61 (11) p44-6
474 "[Prevention of postoperative complications in patients with stomach cancer using an antioxidant complex] Profilaktika posleoperatsionnykh oslozhneniio u bol'nykh rakom zheludka antioksidantnym kompleksom," Sukolinskii VN, Morozkina TS *Vopr Onkol* 1989, 35 (10) p1242-5
475 "The role of ascorbic acid in carcinogenesis," Glatthaar BE, Hornig DH, Moser U *Adv Exp Med Biol* 1986, 206 p357-77
476 "The vitamin C treatment of allergy and the normally unprimed state of antibodies," Cathcart RF *Med Hypotheses* Nov 1986, 21 (3) p307-21
477 American Hospital Formulary Service, American Society of Hospital Pharmacists 1991
478 American Hospital Formulary Service, American Society of Hospital Pharmacists 1991
479 "High dietary intakes of vitamin E and cellular immune function," Moriguchi S, Kobayashi N, Kishino Y *J Nutr* Sep 1990, 120 (9) p1096-102
480 "Vitamin E and immune functions," Bendich A *Basic Life Sci* 1988, 49 p615-20
481 "Vitamin E: introduction to biochemistry and health benefits," Packer L, Landvik S *Ann N Y Acad Sci* 1989, 570 p1-6
482 "The role of vitamin E in immune response and disease resistance," Tengerdy RP *Ann N Y Acad Sci* 1990, 587 p24-33
483 "Effects of elevated d-alpha(RRR)-tocopherol dosage in man," Kitagawa M, Mino M *J Nutr Sci Vitaminol* Apr 1989, 35 (2) p133-42
484 "Vitamin therapy in the absence of obvious deficiency. What is the evidence?" Ovesen L *Drugs* Feb 1984, 27 (2) p148-70
485 "Vitamin A, Vitamin E, and the Risk of Cervical Intraepithelial Neoplasia," J Cuzick et al. *British J Cancer* Oct 1990, 62(4):651-652
486 "Vitamin E and cancer prevention," Knekt P, Aromaa A, Maatela J, Aaran R-K, Nikkari T, Hakama M, Hakulinen T, Peto R, Teppo L *Am J Clinical Nutrition* Jan 1991, v53, n1, p283S(4)
487 American Hospital Formulary Service, American Society of Hospital Pharmacists 1991
488 "Safety of high-dose vitamin A. Randomized trial on lung cancer chemoprevention," Pastorino U, Chiesa G, Infante M,

Soresi E, Clerici M, Valente M, Belloni PA, Ravasi G *Oncology*, 1991, 48 (2) p131-7

489 "Remission of precancerous lesions in the oral cavity of tobacco chewers and maintenance of the protective effect of beta-carotene or vitamin A," Stich HF, Mathew B, Sankaranarayanan R, Nair MK *Am J Clin Nutr* Jan 1991, 53 (1 Suppl) p298S-304S

490 "Reduction of leukemia cell growth in a patient with acute promyelocytic leukemia treated by retinol palmitate", Tsutani H, Iwasaki H, Kawai Y, Tanaka T, Ueda T, Uchida M, Nakamura T *Leuk Res* 1990, 14 (7) p595-600

491 "Vitamin A and lung cancer," Willett WC *Nutr Rev* May 1990, 48 (5) p201-11

492 *The Times* 22 October 1990

493 American Hospital Formulary Service, American Society of Hospital Pharmacists 1990

494 "Can nutritional supplements help mentally retarded children? An exploratory study," Harrell RF, Capp RH, Davis DR, Peerless J, Ravitz LR *Proc Natl Acad Sci USA* Jan 1981, 78 (1) p574-8

495 "Vitamin therapy and children with Down's syndrome: a review of research," Pruess JB, Fewell RR, Bennett FC *Except Child* Jan 1989, 55 (4) p336-41

496 "The effects of multivitamins and minerals on children with Down's syndrome," Bidder RT, Gray P, Newcombe RG, Evans BK, Hughes M *Dev Med Child Neurol* Aug 1989, 31 (4) p532-7

497 *How to live longer and feel better*, Linus Pauling, Avon Books 1986

498 "Down's syndrome: nutritional intervention," Reading CM *Nutr Health*, 1984, 3 (1-2) p91-111

499 "Nutritional aspects of Down's syndrome with special reference to the nervous system," Sylvester PE *Br J Psychiatry*, Aug 1984, 145 p115-20

500 "[Studies on the state of vitamins B_1, B_2 and B_6 in Down's syndrome] Untersuchungen zum Status von Vitamin B_1, B_2 und B_6 beim Down-Syndrom," Schmid F, Christeller S, Rehm W *Fortschr Med*, 11 Sep 1975, 93 (25) p1170-2

501 "Controversies in the treatment of autistic children: vitamin and drug therapy," Rimland B *J Child Neurol* 1988 (3 Suppl) pS68-72

502 *How to live longer and feel better*, Linus Pauling, Avon Books 1986

503 ARCHON – Weirdbase BBS St Louis, MO 1-314-741-2231

504 ARCHON – Weirdbase BBS St Louis, MO 1-314-741-2231

505 "Effect of yoga breathing exercises (pranayama) on airway reactivity in subjects with asthma," Singh V, Wisniewski A, Britton J, Tattersfield A *The Lancet* 9 June 1990, v335, n8702, p1381(3)

506 *New Scientist* 21 January 1988

507 *The Washington Post* 15 November 1988

508 *General Household Survey* 1987, Office of Population Censuses and Surveys

509 *An Architects Sketchbook of Underground Buildings: Drawings and Photographs*, Malcolm Wells, Raven Rocks Press 1990 (USA)

510 *Los Angeles Times* 12 October 1988

511 *Social Trends 20*, Central Statistical Office

512 *The Lancet* 7 August 1982, 2 (8293)

513 *J Cancer Res Clin Oncol* 1986, 112 (2)

514 *People's Medical Society Newsletter* August 1988

515 Superintendent Peter Bennett, West Yorkshire Police Projects Unit, Huddersfield, West Yorkshire; Paul E Boccumini, Director of Clinical Services, San Bernardino County Probation Department, San Bernardino, California

516 *Impact on Human Health of Air Pollution in Europe*, World Health Organization, July 1990

517 *New Scientist* 23 February 1991

518 "Impact of effects of acid precipitation on toxicity of metals," Nordberg GF, Goyer RA, Clarkson TW, *Environ Health Perspect* Nov 1985, 63 p169-80

519 UPI 8 February 1988

520 *Vegetarian Times* September 1990

521 "Making insect repellents safe," Curtis CF *The Lancet* 29 Oct 1988

522 *The Independent* 30 March 1990

523 Building Research Establishment survey. Press release from The Noise Abatement Society

524 *Psychology Today* June 1973

525 *Journal of Occupational Medicine* August 1990

526 Natl Inst Health Consensus Dev Conf *Consensus Statement* 22–24 Jan 1990

527 *Psychoneuroendocrinology* 1990, 15 (1)

528 *Psychol Med* May 1990, 20 (2)

529 *J Otolaryngol Suppl* Apr 1990, 19 (1)

530 *Defence Standard* 05/74/Issue 1

531 *Road Accidents Great Britain* 1989; *The Casualty Report*, HMSO 1990

532 *Social Trends 20* Central Statistical Office

533 *Road Accidents Great Britain* 1989; *The Casualty Report*, HMSO 1990

534 Raw data in *Road Accidents Great Britain* 1989; *The Casualty Report*, HMSO 1990, processed to form percentages of accidents per day

535 *Business Horizons* July-August 1990, v33, n4, p31(7)

536 *Ebony* May 1989, v44, n7, p96(3)

537 *National Review* 14 October 1988, v40, n20, p38(3)

538 *Psychology Today* September 1988, v22, n9, p14(3)
539 *The Atlantic* July 1987, v259, p96(2)
540 Gallup Poll 15 November 1990, Roper Center for Public Opinion Research
541 *Many Lives, Many Masters*, Brian L. Weiss, S&S 1988
542 *Many Lives, Many Masters*, Brian L. Weiss, S&S 1988
543 "Hypnotically recalled prebirth experiences: Life before life," *Psychic* 1977, 7(6):8-13
544 "An unusual case of hypnotic regression with some unexplained contents," Tarazi, *Journal of the American Society for Psychical Research* Oct 1990, v84(4) 309-344
545 *Julius Caesar*, II.ii.30
546 *Comparative Mortality from Drugs of Addiction*, BMA 1986
547 *Comparative Mortality from Drugs of Addiction*, BMA 1986
548 *Social Trends 20*, Central Statistical Office
549 *Street Drugs*, Andrew Tyler, New English Library 1986
550 *The Economist* 16 June 1990
551 *U S News & World Report* 20 January 1986, v100, p55(1)
552 *U S News & World Report* 20 January 1986, v100, p55(1)
553 *World Population Prospects*, United Nations Department of International Economic and Social Affairs, New York 1989 : Table II: 17-B
554 "The Extent of Physical Punishment in the UK," John and Elizabeth Newson *Approach*, 1989
555 *Children are People Too*, Peter Newell, Bedford Square Press
556 "The Extent of Physical Punishment in the UK," John and Elizabeth Newson *Approach*, 1989
557 *Psychology Today* June 1989, v23, n6, p16(1)

INDEX

~